The
Musician's Guide
to Acoustics

The Musician's Guide to Acoustics

Murray Campbell and Clive Greated

SCHIRMER BOOKS

A Division of Macmillan, Inc.

NEW YORK

Schirmer Books
A Division of Macmillan, Inc.
866 Third Avenue, New York, N.Y. 10022

First published in Great Britain by
J.M. Dent & Sons Ltd.
Aldine House
33 Welbeck Street
London W1M 8LX

Library of Congress Catalog Card Number. 87-4732

Printed in the United States of America

printing number
1   2   3   4   5   6   7   8   9   10

Library of Congress Cataloging-in-Publication Data

Campbell, Murray
  The musicians' guide to acoustics.

  1. Music—Acoustics and physics. I. Greated,
Clive A., 1940-   .   II. Title.
ML3805.C24 1987   781'.1   87-4732
ISBN 0-02-870161-5

Contents

Acknowledgments

A book covering as wide a field as this must rely heavily on the work of others. Here we pay a general tribute to the labours of our colleagues in the field of musical acoustics; when we have quoted from their published results, we have acknowledged this by giving a reference to the source of the quotation. Most of the references are to scientific journals and textbooks, and their inclusion serves an additional purpose by allowing those of our readers with a suitable mathematical background to use this book as an introduction to the research literature of the subject.

Figures 1.5, 1.6, 1.7, 1.11, 1.15, 1.17, 2.1, 2.21, 3.6, 3.12, 3.20, 3.27, 3.54, 3.55, 3.58, 3.59, 3.60, 3.61, 3.62, 3.63, 3.66, 6.5, 6.10, 6.15, 7.12, 7.16, 8.7, 8.21, 8.22, 8.27, 9.9, 9.13, 9.14, 9.15, 9.16, 9.17, 9.18, 9.19, 9.26, 9.29, 9.31, 9.34, 9.43, 9.46, 9.49, 9.52, 9.59, 9.61, 9.62, 9.69, 9.76, 9.92, 9.93, 9.101, 9.102, 9.103, 10.29, 10.37, 10.38, 10.41, 10.42, 13.2, 13.5, 13.14, 14.9 and 14.12 are based on measurements carried out by the authors in the acoustics laboratories at Edinburgh University Physics Department. Several generations of students contributed to the development of the apparatus used in these measurements, and we wish to thank especially James Follan, James Forsyth, Anne McDowall, Eric Middleton, Judith Barker, John Sharpe and Richard Stewart. The measurements on flutes shown in Figures 8.18, 8.19, 8.20, 8.24, 8.25 and 8.26 were performed by our research colleagues at Edinburgh, Eric Lucey. In experiments on professional flute technique we were fortunate in obtaining the co-operation of David Nicholson.

We are grateful to Bernard Richardson and Richard Smith for permission to reproduce the interference holograms shown in Figures 6.14 and 9.104 respectively, to Norman Haacke for supplying the photographs of the glottis shown in Figure 12.3, and to Bösendorfer for the illustration of a grand piano in Figure 7.11. The photographs of early keyboard instruments in Figures 7.1, 7.2 and 7.5 were supplied by Dr Grant O'Brien, Curator of the Russell Collection of Early Keyboard Instruments at Edinburgh University.

The remainder of the photographs reproduced in the book were taken by Peter Tuffy, whose patience and skill were invaluable. We are grateful to Dr O'Brien for permission to photograph details of instruments in the Russell Collection, and for his practical assistance and helpful comments. Andrew Shivas kindly lent examples from his extensive collection of percussion instruments for study and photography, and we are also grateful to John Barnes, Ian Dougal, William and Anne Giles and Simon Carlyle for the loan of instruments. Most of the instruments illustrated are in the Edinburgh University Collection of Historic Instruments, whose Honorary Curator, Arnold Myers, devoted much effort to assisting our choice. We are also indebted to Mr Myers for many illuminating discussions, especially on the subject of brass instruments. John Bowsher and John Webb also commented helpfully on parts of Chapter 9.

We wish to thank the following publishers for permission to reproduce copyright material in the respective figures:
Boosey and Hawkes: Figs. 7.13, 9.67, 9.70, 9.98, 10.13.
Breitkopf and Haertel: Fig. 2.26.
Dover Publications: Fig. 9.79.
Editions Durand S.A., Paris/United Music Publishers Ltd.: Fig. 3.26.
Eulenburg: Fig. 1.1 and 3.51.
Faber Music Ltd, London, on behalf of J. Curwen and Sons Ltd.:
Fig. 9.85.
Universal Edition Vienna (Alfred A. Kalmus Ltd.): Figs. 2.9, 3.44, 3.45, 9.90 and 12.17.

In the major task of preparing the typescript of the book we were extremely fortunate in obtaining the services of Mrs Alvis Ingram, whose skill and dedication were matched only by her unfailing good humour.

Finally we must record an enormous debt of gratitude to our wives and families, who have coped valiantly with the domestic disruptions inevitable in a project of this magnitude, and have offered constant support and encouragement.

Introduction

The sound of applause dies away, and the audience in the concert hall waits in expectant silence. The pianist seats himself at the instrument; the conductor's score is open at the first page of Beethoven's Piano Concerto No.5. As the dramatic piano arpeggios well up out of a majestic sustained orchestral chord, the genius of the composer, the technical and interpretative skills of the performers and the rapt attention of the listeners combine once again to weave that magic spell we call music.

Immune to the spell, a curious visitor from outer space sits unobtrusively at the back of the hall observing this fascinating human activity. Focusing his superior vision on the orchestral players in turn, he notes that the majority are scraping tensed horsehair back and forth over metal wires attached to wooden boxes of various sizes. Others are blowing air into or over tubes of wood or metal; one is hammering a plastic sheet stretched on a metal hemisphere. The soloist is operating a complicated system of wooden levers whose purpose is not immediately apparent. The mêlée is controlled, it seems, by hand signals from the conductor. Consulting the dials on a little black box which he is holding, the visitor detects small but very rapid fluctuations in the pressure of the air in the hall. These fluctuations have no obvious pattern; he dismisses the speculation that they are perhaps connected with the purpose of the ceremony, which remains obscure to him.

Our extraterrestrial observer has, of course, missed the point. Underlying the somewhat fanciful talk of 'magic spells' is the truth that the communication of a human experience is at the heart of music. An observer who is incapable of sharing the experience is liable to be led seriously astray in any attempt to investigate the processes involved in playing or listening to music. Occasionally some earthbound scientists have also fallen into this trap.

Nevertheless, the sublime aspect of music is inextricably bound to the

1

mundane and practical business of producing the right noises at the right time – and as soon as that is said, a host of questions tempt the curious musician. Why do certain noises have a sharply defined pitch, while others lack this quality? Why do certain sounds blend together euphoniously while others are strongly discordant? Why does one violin produce a gloriously rich tone while another, superficially identical, is obstinately unresponsive?

This curiosity is the motivation of the science of musical acoustics, which is simply an attempt to investigate such questions in a careful and systematic way. Fortunately, many notable scientists have also been musicians, and in the hundred and twenty-five years which have elapsed since Hermann von Helmholtz wrote the first great treatise on musical acoustics, *On the Sensations of Tone*, much has been learned about the ways in which musical sounds are created by instruments and interpreted by the human ear. In recent years the pace of discovery has been acceler-ated by the application of new scientific techniques, including the use of lasers and computers. Physicists, physiologists and psychologists have all contributed to the growing body of knowledge.

It is the conviction of the authors that the results of these investigations should be more widely known among musicians. Although this book has grown out of some fifteen years' experience of lecturing on musical acoustics to first year students in the Music Degree Course at Edinburgh University, it is intended to be of value to all those with some musical background who feel the need for a clearer understanding of the practical basis of their art. While reasonable familiarity with musical notation and terminology is taken for granted, only the most elementary school mathe-matics is assumed.

We start by discussing the nature of sound. This, after all, is the very fabric of music, and it is important to clarify our ideas on this topic before proceeding further. Sound is only of musical significance when perceived by the human ear; in Chapter 2 we look at the present understanding of the way in which the ear responds to musical sounds. In this field many questions remain unanswered; nevertheless, enough is known to shed a fascinating light on several aspects of musical experience.

The scientific analysis of a complex orchestral sound, which our extra-terrestrial investigator was attempting, is indeed a daunting task. We turn in Chapter 3 to consider a more tractable case – a single note. A musician describes a note of fixed duration in terms of three basic properties: pitch, loudness and timbre. We investigate how each of these properties is related to scientifically measurable features of the sound. In Chapter 4 we extend our discussion to deal with some important interactions which occur when two or more notes are played simultaneously; this brings in the ideas of consonant and dissonant intervals, scales and temperaments which underlie one of the musician's most crucial tasks: playing in tune.

2

The rest of the book is concerned with the means by which musical sounds are generated. Some of the general principles common to all musical instruments are outlined in Chapter 5. In Chapters 6 to 11 we survey the traditional classes of orchestral instruments – strings, woodwind, brass and percussion – and the more common keyboard instruments. In each case, we attempt to relate the acoustical features of the instrument to the way in which it is used in practical music making.

The historical development of the modern instrument is also examined from an acoustical point of view. In the last few years musicians have turned increasingly to period instruments and reproductions in the quest for more authentic performances of pre-nineteenth century music; it is thus of practical interest to look at the acoustical differences between, say, the oboe of Mozart's time and the present-day orchestral instrument. Some instruments, such as the cornett and the crumhorn, which have been revived for the performance of renaissance music, have no counterpart in the modern orchestral world, and deserve an acoustical description in their own right.

In Chapter 12 we turn to that most personal and expressive of musical instruments, the human voice. Chapter 13 offers a brief glimpse of the rapidly developing field of electronic and computer-generated music. Finally, in Chapter 14, we touch on the acoustics of what we can regard as the final stage of any instrument: the environment – whether concert hall, café, studio or public park – in which the music is performed.

In his excellent and witty study of orchestral practice, *Anatomy of the Orchestra*, Norman Del Mar discusses the different ways in which a horn player can achieve a muted sound by inserting his hand into the bell of the instrument. The effect of these muting techniques on the pitch of the note has been the source of a long-running controversy among horn players. Del Mar warns against 'getting bogged down in mathematical acoustics and the technicalities of what is happening to the column of air in the tube...'; such questions, he feels, are 'best forgotten by the practical man of the orchestra' (Del Mar 1983, p.245).

One can sympathise with the predicament of the conductor trying to deal with a barrack-room acoustician in his horn section. However, it is the firm belief of the authors that it is possible to steer a middle course between the bog of incomprehensible technicalities and the slippery slope of unsupported generalisations. A clear grasp of a few fundamental acoustical principles is all that is required to understand what happens when a horn is hand-stopped; the same applies to many similar questions of technique and practice. It is the aim of this book to present these acoustical principles in such a way that they can be both understood and used by the instrumental teacher and pupil, the composer and orchestrator, the musically educated listener – and by the practical man (and woman) of the orchestra.

3

1

The creation and transmission of musical sounds

In the first paragraph of the Introduction we described the start of a performance of Beethoven's 'Emperor' Concerto. We identified the process of communicating between performers and listeners as the musical heart of the matter. Let us now return to the concert hall to examine this process, taking the point of view of a musician equipped with a lively curiosity and some useful scientific tools of investigation.

The process can be conveniently divided into three stages: the creation of sound by the performer, its transmission from performer to listener, and its reception by the listener. We shall discuss the first two stages in the present chapter; the third stage will be the subject of Chapter 2.

SOURCES OF MUSICAL SOUNDS

The first downbeat from the conductor galvanises the orchestra into a range of activities, instructions for which are contained in the players' parts and in the musical score which the conductor follows (Fig. 1.1). In each case the instructions tell the player to set some part of his instrument into motion. For example, the timpanist drives the membrane stretched across one of his timpani downwards by a sharp blow, while the cellist pulls his bottom string sideways by bowing it. In fact, the essential feature of every source of sound is some component in motion: without motion there can be no sound. The particular type of motion which generates sound in practically all musical instruments is described as *vibratory motion*: that is to say, motion in which the object vibrates from side to side about the position which it occupies when at rest. The point on the drumskin which is struck by the stick cannot continue to move downwards indefinitely; after a while, its natural elasticity or springiness brings it to

CONCERTO No.5

Fig. 1.1. The first page of the score of Beethoven's Concerto No.5 for piano and orchestra.

rest, and it rebounds upwards. When it reaches the height at which it lay before the stroke, it overshoots because of its upward momentum. Eventually it comes to rest, and starts to move downwards again. When it reaches its original position we say it has completed one *cycle* of vibration. But now it overshoots because of its downward momentum, and thus continues the alternation of upward and downward motion which we call vibration.

Although the motion of the drumskin is too rapid for the eye to follow, the vibration can be seen as a blurring of marks on the skin. A fortissimo $E_2^\flat$ (using the pitch-labelling scheme described on p.73) causes the bottom string of the cello to vibrate so strongly that its thickness appears to increase by several millimetres. Similar vibrations can be found in all the instruments listed in Fig. 1.1, although in some cases the motion is not immediately obvious to the eye. The first note of the piano arpeggios generates a noticeable blurring of the $E_2^\flat$ strings, whereas the string motion caused by the striking of the last note of the quoted passage (G_6) is too small to be visible. In the case of a wind instrument, the vibrating object which is the source of sound is the column of air contained by the instrument; the vibrations of this air column are of course invisible.

6

Measuring vibrations

To understand how a musical instrument works we clearly need to be able to examine and measure its vibrations. Many scientific techniques have been devised for studying vibrating objects. One of the simplest methods uses an infra-red emitting device of the type used in burglar alarm systems. A beam of infra-red radiation is shone on to the vibrating object; radiation reflected by the object is picked up by a detector mounted close to the source (Fig. 1.2).

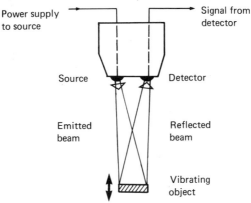

Fig. 1.2. Infra-red emitter and detector used to monitor vibrations.

When the system is correctly adjusted, the electrical signal generated by the detector is proportional to the amount of reflected radiation it receives, which in turn varies with the distance of the reflecting object. Thus if the object is vibrating, the electrical signal will rise and fall as the object approaches and recedes.

The use of this system is illustrated in Fig. 1.3, which shows how the

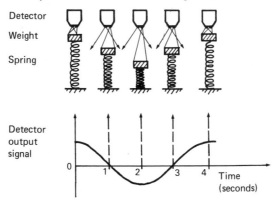

Fig. 1.3. The position detector signal from a weight oscillating on a spring. Vertical lines are spaced at one second intervals.

7

electrical signal changes with time for a simple case in which a weight supported on a spring bobs slowly up and down below the detector. We start a clock just as the weight reaches its highest point; it is then nearest the detector, and the electrical signal is therefore large. As the weight falls it gets further away from the detector, and the signal drops. After 2 seconds it reaches its lowest point, furthest from the detector; the signal then has its lowest value. The weight then starts to bounce back, and after a further 2 seconds again reaches its highest point, as does the signal from the detector. In fact, the variation of the electrical signal with time simply mirrors the motion of the weight.

The principal advantage of using this type of system is that very small movements give rise to measurable signals which can be amplified and displayed using electronic techniques. We have already seen, however, that the vibrations of musical instruments are too rapid for the eye to follow directly. To study the details of the motion of the drumskin or the cello string it is useful to feed the output of our electrical detector to another piece of equipment which has been of inestimable value in the study of sound and vibration: the oscilloscope.

The oscilloscope

As its name suggests, the oscilloscope is designed to display oscillating signals. A beam of electrons is used to create a bright spot on the screen of a tube similar to that in a television set. This spot can be deflected vertically by applying an electrical signal to the input. Simultaneously, the 'time-base' can be used to move the spot from left to right at a constant speed; this has the effect of drawing out the pattern of vibration on the screen.

An understanding of the operation of the oscilloscope can be assisted by imitating it with a pen and a piece of paper. If the pen is scribbled up and down without altering the horizontal position of the hand, a vertical line is drawn on the paper (Fig. 1.4(a)); a similar line appears on the oscilloscope

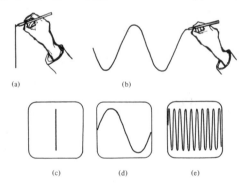

Fig. 1.4. (a) and (b): lines drawn by hand.
(c), (d) and (e): oscilloscope traces.

8

screen with the timebase switched off (Fig. 1.4(c)). If the hand is now moved steadily from left to right while continuing to scribble, a wave is drawn out on the paper (Fig. 1.4(b)).

The faster the hand moves, the more elongated is the pattern. Similarly, the speed of the timebase determines the nature of the picture produced on the screen. A typical oscilloscope screen is about 10 cm across; if the spot moves at a speed of 10 metres per second, for example, it will take 1/100th of a second to cross the screen. A signal oscillating 100 times every second will have just completed one up-and-down cycle in this time, and will appear on the screen as in Fig. 1.4(d). If the timebase is altered to make the spot travel at only 1 metre per second, it will now take 1/10th of a second to complete its journey across the screen. The signal will have completed 10 cycles of oscillation in this time, and will appear as in Fig. 1.4(e).

Vibrations of musical instruments

Examining the vibrations of musical instruments with the naked eye, we can see only a blur of motion. Let us study this blur through the scientific spectacles provided by the position detector and the oscilloscope.

In the first bar of Fig. 1.1 the cello plays a sustained fortissimo E♭. Placing our detector just above the bottom string of a cello while this note is being played we obtain a trace on the oscilloscope screen like that shown in Fig. 1.5. We call this the *displacement-time graph* for the vibration of the string, because the vertical axis represents the displacement of the string from its position of rest, while the horizontal axis represents the passage of time.

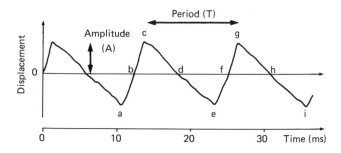

Fig. 1.5. Displacement-time curve for a cello C string playing E♭.

The most striking feature of this graph is its simplicity and regularity. The string is at its lowest point at a on the trace; it moves steadily upwards, passing through the point b at which it lay at rest before the note was played, until it reaches its highest point c. At that point it suddenly reverses direction, and starts to move steadily downwards. At point e it is as low as it was at a, and the motion again reverses. The line abcde

9

represents one complete *cycle* of up-and-down motion; the next cycle efghi is an almost exact repetition of abcde.

This type of string motion is called a *transverse vibration*, since a particular point on the string moves transversely (that is, at right angles to the string length). Normally the direction of transverse vibration of a bowed string is not perpendicular to the top plate, as we have assumed above, but this complication can be left to our detailed discussion of bowed string motion in Chapter 6. At present we shall merely treat Fig. 1.5 as an example of a graph representing a type of motion of fundamental importance in music: a *periodic vibration*.

Period and frequency

A vibration is called *periodic* if the motion repeats itself exactly after a time interval T, which we call the *period* of the vibration. The time taken to complete one up-and-down cycle of the cello string is represented in Fig. 1.5 by the horizontal distance between a and e. The next cycle takes a time represented by the distance between e and i, which is the same as that between a and e. Thus the up-and-down motion of the string is a periodic vibration, and its period T is measured by the distance a–e in Fig. 1.5. Since we know the horizontal speed of the spot which drew Fig. 1.5, we can mark out time intervals along the horizontal axis: a convenient time unit for vibrations of musical significance is the millisecond (1/1000 second), abbreviated ms. Observing that two cycles of the cello string vibration take just about 25 ms, we can see that the period is approximately $T = {}^{25}\!/_2$ ms = 12.5 ms. A careful measurement gives the value T = 12.8 ms.

Since the shape of the displacement-time graph is constant from cycle to cycle, we could equally well measure the period by the time between two successive high points (represented by the distance c–g), or between two successive upward crossings of the zero displacement line (represented by the distance b–f). In each case we would get the same result: T = 12.8 ms.

Musical vibrations are usually discussed in terms of frequency rather than period. The frequency (for which we shall use the symbol f) is the number of cycles of the vibration which are completed in one second. There is a straightforward relationship between period and frequency, which we can express by the equation

$$f = 1/T$$

All that this means is that if we write the period T as a fraction of a second, we get the frequency by turning the fraction upside down. For our example of the cello string, the period T is 12.8 ms, or ${}^{12.8}\!/_{1000}$ seconds. Turning this fraction upside down gives us ${}^{1000}\!/_{12.8}$, which is 78. Thus the cello string vibrates up and down 78 times every second. The accepted unit of frequency is the hertz (abbreviated Hz); the statement that the period of the string is 12.8 ms is therefore equivalent to the statement that its vibration frequency is 78 Hz.

We can also work this relationship backwards to find the period of a vibration if we know its frequency. A standard A tuning fork is labelled 440, which means that the frequency of vibration of its prongs is 440 Hz. Treating this as the fraction $^{440}/_1$, we can turn it upside down to find the period: $T = \frac{1}{440}$ seconds. Since there are 1000 milliseconds in one second, we can express this as $T = {}^{1000}/_{440}$ ms $= 2.3$ ms. So one back-and-forth wiggle of the tuning fork prong takes just over two thousandths of a second.

Tones and noises

The musical significance of periodic motion lies in the fact that only vibrations with a periodic character generate sounds with a strong sense of pitch. The rather vague phrase 'with a periodic character' is used advisedly; it would be too much to claim that only periodic vibrations generated pitched sounds. In fact, most musical sound generators are not strictly periodic vibrators. For example, Fig. 1.5 was obtained from a cello played in the laboratory, without vibrato. When the cello is played normally, a rocking motion of the finger stopping E♭ on the bottom string introduces a deliberate fluctuation in the period of the string vibration. Since the finger is rocking only a few times a second, while the string is vibrating with a frequency of 78 Hz, the effect of this 'vibrato' can only be detected after many cycles of string vibration; unless it is exaggerated, the ear registers it as a feature of the tone quality rather than as a variation of pitch. This type of vibration, which appears periodic over several cycles but shows fluctuations on a longer time scale, is called *quasi-periodic vibration*.

We can say, then, that periodic or quasi-periodic vibrations are associated with sounds of definite pitch, which we shall describe as *tones*. Objects which vibrate in a non-periodic way, with no definite and regular pattern of repetition, generate unpitched sounds: 'noises' rather than 'tones'. Such noises can be of considerable musical significance, of course – the clash of a cymbal is an example of an unpitched sound generated by non-periodic vibrations. But sounds of definite pitch are the building blocks of music, and periodic or quasi-periodic vibrators are therefore at the heart of most musical instruments.

Simple harmonic motion

If we place our position detector beside one prong of the tuning fork a second or two after it has been struck, we obtain a displacement-time graph of the shape illustrated in Fig. 1.4. This simple 'wave' shape is known as a *sine curve* in mathematics; it represents the simplest possible

11

type of periodic vibration, which goes by the quaint title of *simple harmonic motion*. The weight bobbing up and down on a spring, which we discussed earlier, was also performing simple harmonic motion (see Fig. 1.3). In general, musical instruments vibrate in a much more complicated way, and their displacement-time curves are correspondingly more complex. We shall see, however, that the idea of simple harmonic motion is of great help when we come to discuss these complex vibrations and the sounds which arise from them.

Amplitude

From the displacement-time graph we can measure not only the frequency of the vibration, but also its *amplitude*. Returning to our example of the cello string, we recall that Fig. 1.5 represents the up-and-down motion of a particular point on the string. The zero of displacement is taken as the position occupied by that point when the string is not vibrating: we call this the position of rest. The amplitude of the vibration is then defined as the maximum displacement from the position of rest. It is marked on Fig. 1.5 as the vertical distance between the zero line and the peak of the graph. It is perhaps worth noting that when the string is vibrating symmetrically, the total distance travelled from the highest point of the vibration to the lowest (which is the width of the blur seen by the naked eye) is *twice* the amplitude.

Steady state and transient

The measurement shown in Fig. 1.5 was made about one second after the note was first sounded. The displacement-time graph shows a steady pattern in which all the peaks are the same height above the zero line – that is, the amplitude is constant. However, if we look with our position detector at the string during the first tenth of a second after the bow is applied (Fig. 1.6 (a)), we see that the vibrations do not start immediately at full amplitude, but take several cycles to build up. The nature of this build-up will of course depend on the type of attack, which is one of the most important aspects of string technique. Our study of string vibrations must therefore include this *transient* part, when the amplitude is changing, as well as the *steady state* part, when the tone has stabilised and the amplitude is constant.

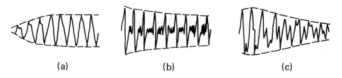

(a)   (b)   (c)

Fig. 1.6. Displacement-time curves for the first 100 ms of (a) cello string;
(b) piano string; (c) drumhead.

In many musical sounds there is no steady state part at all. In the first bar of Fig. 1.1 the cello and the drum each play an E^b, as does the piano at the beginning of the second bar. The cello note is sustained by continuous bowing; the other notes die away, that of the drum more rapidly than that of the piano. Looking at the piano string and the drumhead with our position detector, we find corresponding patterns of vibration: during the first tenth of a second the amplitude of the piano string has decreased to about 80% of its original value (Fig. 1.6 (b)), whereas the drumhead amplitude has dropped to less than 30% (Fig. 1.6 (c)).

Amplitude envelope

In each of the displacement-time graphs of Fig. 1.6 we have drawn a broken line which just touches each peak of the vibration curve; another broken line touches each trough. These two lines define the *amplitude envelope* of the vibration. When we focus our attention on the amplitude envelope we are looking at the way in which the vibration grows and decays, rather than at the details of the motion in each cycle. This overall pattern of growth or decay is an important characteristic of a particular instrument's vibrations: the amplitude envelopes of the cello, piano and drum shown in Fig. 1.6 are strikingly different.

Of course, the graphs in Fig. 1.6 cover only the first tenth of a second of each note. If we wish to see how the amplitude changes on a longer time scale, we can slow down the oscilloscope spot so that it takes longer to complete one traverse of the screen. Fig. 1.7 shows results obtained with the spot's horizontal speed reduced by a factor of 50, so that the time taken for each traverse is increased from one tenth of a second to 5 seconds. The wiggles of the individual vibration cycles can no longer be distinguished: the spot acts like a paintbrush, filling in the space between the two lines of the amplitude envelope.

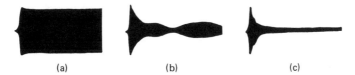

(a)   (b)   (c)

Fig. 1.7. Amplitude envelopes measured during the first 5 s of (a) sustained cello string vibration; (b) piano string vibration; (c) drumhead vibration.

On this timescale, we see the cello string vibrations (Fig. 1.7 (a)) rising very quickly to their steady value. For this measurement the note was played without vibrato and prolonged for more than five seconds; after the initial transient the amplitude envelope is composed of two horizontal lines. In contrast, the drumhead vibrations (Fig. 1.7 (c)) decay very rapidly

13

during the first quarter of a second; after this the rate of decay slows down, and vibrations can still be detected for several seconds after the stroke.

The amplitude envelope of the piano string (Fig. 1.7(b)) shows an interesting type of motion. When the key is depressed and the hammer strikes the string, the vibrations reach their peak amplitude almost instantaneously; for the next half-second the amplitude drops rapidly. For a further two seconds the vibrations continue to decay, although less rapidly than at first. But then we find something unexpected: when they look as though they have died away to nothing, the vibrations start to grow again. The amplitude envelope swells out for a further second or so, and just at the end of our five second trace it is starting to diminish once more. This observation is a good example of how details of a musical instrument's behaviour can be studied using scientific techniques. In Chapter 7 we shall see that measurements like that illustrated in Fig. 1.7 (b) can deepen our understanding of how the piano produces its characteristic sound.

Phase

A steady state vibration such as we found on the cello string in Fig. 1.5 can be described by a sketch of one cycle of the displacement-time graph and measurements of the amplitude and period. For example, Fig. 1.8 shows a particular point on the cello string vibrating with an amplitude of 2 millimetres and a period of 12.9 milliseconds; since it is a steady state vibration the complete displacement-time graph is simply obtained by repeating the given shape along the horizontal axis.

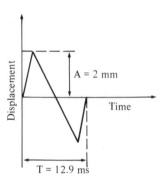

Fig. 1.8. Displacement-time curve for one cycle of a cello string vibration with amplitude 2 mm and period 12.9 ms.

In the first bar of the 'Emperor' Concerto, which is the musical context of our present discussions, the entire cello section of the orchestra (consisting of perhaps ten instruments) is instructed to play the same fortissimo $E_2^\flat$. In theory, at least, we would expect to find the same displacement-time graph whichever instrument we examined. No matter how well-drilled the section, however, the individual players can never synchronise exactly the start of the note – there will be an inevitable spread of at least a few tens of milliseconds in the times of attack. If we remember that one whole cycle lasts less than 13 milliseconds, we shall recognise that even if the ten cello strings were eventually vibrating with exactly the same amplitude and period, it could only be by a remote coincidence that they were all rising and falling in step with one another. To enable us to discuss the degree to which different vibrators are out of step we need one more concept: the *phase* of the vibration.

The musical round provides a good illustration of the significance of phase. In a straightforward round such as 'London's burning' (Fig. 1.9

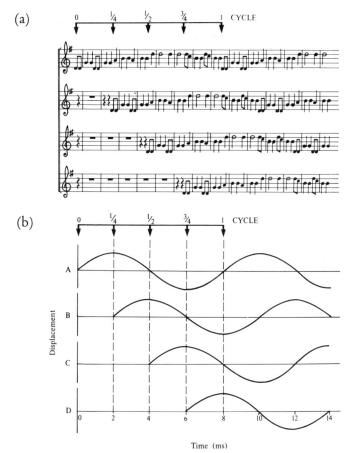

Fig. 1.9 (a). The round 'London's burning'.

Fig. 1.9 (b). Displacement-time curves for four out-of-phase vibrators.

15

(a)), each voice has exactly the same 8-bar melody, repeated indefinitely. If all four parts started simultaneously – that is, started 'in phase' – we would simply have a unison rendition of the melody. But in fact the second part enters two bars after the first, the third two bars after the second, and the fourth two bars after the third. If we call the 8-bar melody one cycle, we can say that there is a 'phase difference' of a quarter of a cycle between the successive entries of the parts. We can also say that the first and third parts are 'out of phase' by half a cycle.

Similarly, although on a much shorter time scale, we see in Fig. 1.9 (b) the displacement-time curves for four different vibrators. To simplify the diagram, we have shown each vibrator performing simple harmonic motion, with the same amplitude. The period of each vibrator is 8 ms – that is, after 8 ms the pattern of each vibration repeats itself exactly. One vibrator (which we call A) starts first; the next (B) starts 2 ms later; the other two (C and D) follow after delays of 4 and 6 ms respectively. The analogy with the round is obvious – one cycle of the vibration lasts 8 ms, and there is a phase difference of a quarter of cycle between A and B, B and C, or C and D.

The comparison of A and C is particularly interesting. These two vibrators are exactly half a cycle out of phase. When A is at its lowest point, C is at its highest, and conversely; A and C have zero displacement at the same instant, but while one is travelling downwards the other is travelling upwards. In fact, the motion of C is just a mirror image of A.

Of course, if we compare the vibrations of two instruments playing the same note, we are unlikely to find them out of phase by exactly a quarter or half a cycle. The two cellos whose vibrations are illustrated in Fig. 1.10, for example, have a phase difference of 2 ms; since the period is 13 ms, this corresponds to $\frac{2}{13}$ths of a cycle. In cases like this it is useful to consider one cycle of vibration to be divided into 360° (like a circle). A phase difference of half a cycle can then be described as $\frac{1}{2} \times 360° = 180°$; and our two cellos are out of phase by $\frac{2}{13} \times 360° = 55°$.

In practice, only electronic instruments maintain fixed phase differences over long time intervals. The small fluctuations of pitch which are an inherent feature of every humanly generated note give rise to constantly shifting phase relationships among the instruments in a section. It is for this reason that ten cellos playing in unison have a different quality of sound from an amplified solo cello; this is known as the 'chorus effect' and is discussed further in Chapter 3.

Analysis of complex vibrations

Much of our discussion so far has concentrated on the smooth back-and-fore vibration known as simple harmonic motion, for which the displacement-time curve is a sine curve (Figs 1.3, 1.4 and 1.9). Our first look at the

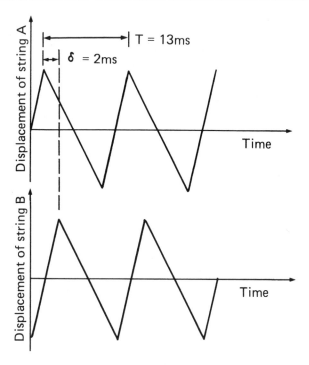

Fig. 1.10. Displacement-time curves for two out-of-phase cello strings.

vibrations in real musical instruments (Figs 1.5 and 1.6) revealed that the displacement-time curves for these vibrations had in general much more complicated shapes. Even in the case of the steady state part of the cello note (Fig. 1.5), the curve shows sharp peaks and dips rather than the rounded form of the sine curve. If we place our position detector above the belly of the cello instead of above the string, we find an even more complicated curve; although it repeats its pattern with the same period as the string vibration, there are many more back-and-fore wiggles within each period (Fig. 1.11).

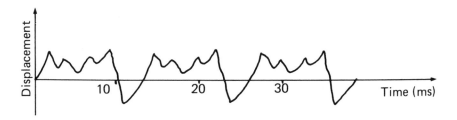

Fig. 1.11. Vibration pattern for a point on the belly of a cello playing $E^\flat_2$.

When we come to examine the musical significance of such complex vibrations, we shall find it helpful to make use of an idea first put forward by the French mathematician Fourier in 1822. He realised that any curve that repeats itself periodically, however complicated its shape, is equivalent to a set of sine curves added together. To find which combination of sine curves corresponds to a particular complex curve, we first measure the frequency with which it repeats. For the curve in Fig. 1.5, for example, we found that the repetition period was T = 12.8 ms, corresponding to a repetition frequency f = 78 Hz. We call this the *fundamental frequency* of the complex curve.

Fourier's remarkable result is that the complex curve is equivalent to a sine curve with the fundamental frequency, plus another sine curve with exactly twice the fundamental frequency, plus a third curve with just three times the fundamental frequency...and so on. If the complex curve contains many wiggles and sharp peaks, a very large number of components may be necessary; but each component will be a sine curve with a frequency equal to a whole number times the fundamental frequency.

Fig. 1.12 shows an example of a not very complex curve (a) analysed into its *Fourier components*. In this case only two components are necessary: a sine curve with the fundamental frequency (b) and another sine curve with twice the fundamental frequency (c). In general we have to find out the amplitude of each component sine curve, and also the phases of the different components. In the example we have chosen, the amplitude of the second component is half that of the first.

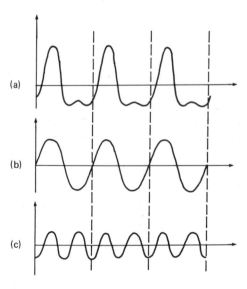

Fig. 1.12. Analysis of complex curve (a) into two component sine curves (b) and (c).

The effect of the relative phase of the components is shown by the comparison of Figs 1.12 and 1.13. In Fig. 1.13 (a) we have a curve whose shape is notably different from that of Fig. 1.12 (a); however, the two components into which it can be analysed (1.13 (b) and (c)) have the same frequencies and amplitudes as the corresponding components in Fig. 1.12. The only difference is that in Fig. 1.12 the two components peak at the same time, whereas in Fig. 1.13 the second component (c) is passing through zero as the first (b) peaks.

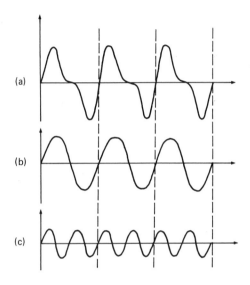

Fig. 1.13. Analysis of complex curve (a) into two component sine curves (b) and (c).

The harmonic spectrum

In many cases the musical effect of a complex vibration depends almost entirely on the amplitudes of the Fourier components, and hardly at all on their phases. If a loudspeaker were vibrating with the displacement-time curve shown by Fig. 1.12 (a), we would hear a certain sound; if the pattern changed to that of Fig. 1.13 (a) we would not notice any difference in the nature of the sound. If the relative proportion of the two components changed significantly, however, we would immediately be aware of a change in the sound quality. (See, however, Chapter 3, p.145.)

For this reason it is often adequate to describe a complex vibration by recording only the amplitudes of the Fourier components. The successive components have frequencies of 1,2,3,4... times the fundamental frequency; they are known as the 1st, 2nd, 3rd, 4th... *harmonics*. Thus the 1st harmonic is the component whose frequency is the fundamental repeti-

19

tion frequency, the 2nd harmonic has twice the fundamental frequency, and so on.

The customary way of representing the strengths of the different harmonics is in the form of a *harmonic spectrum*. This is a set of vertical bars, labelled by the appropriate harmonic numbers increasing from left to right. The height of each bar is proportional to the amplitude of the corresponding harmonic. Fig. 1.14 shows the harmonic spectrum obtained by analysing either of the vibrations illustrated by Figs 1.12 (a) and 1.13 (a).

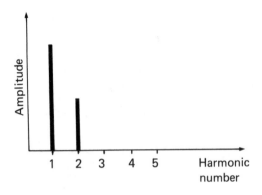

Fig. 1.14. Harmonic spectrum corresponding to either of the vibration patterns in Figs 1.12 (a) and 1.13 (a).

The displacement-time curve for the cello string (Fig. 1.5) was obtained by feeding the electrical signal from the position detector into an oscilloscope. If instead we feed the signal into a *frequency analyser* we see on its screen a picture of the corresponding harmonic spectrum (Fig. 1.15). This shows that there are four significant harmonics in the signal. We can interpret this as implying that the complex vibration of the cello string is equivalent to four simultaneous simple harmonic vibrations, each with a frequency and amplitude corresponding to one of the harmonic components. (In fact there are also several higher harmonics of low amplitude, which have been omitted from Fig. 1.15 to simplify the discussion.)

The significance of this point of view will become evident when we take up the detailed study of string vibration in Chapter 6. At this stage we shall simply note that string players use the term 'harmonic' in a way which is not exactly equivalent to our definition, although the two usages are closely related. When a cello player is faced with the notation of Fig. 1.16 (a), he interprets the small circle above the note D_4 as an instruction to play it as a 'natural harmonic'. He bows the open D string which normally produces a note of pitch D_3 (Fig. 1.16 (b)), while touching the string lightly at its mid point. This raises the pitch by an octave, and gives a characteristically 'thin' quality. We shall see in Chapter 6 that what the player is in fact doing is to damp out with his finger all the odd numbered harmonic components of the string's vibration, including the fundamental. Only the second, fourth and other even numbered harmonics are present in the harmonic spectrum (Fig. 1.17); the ear interprets the corresponding sound as having a pitch an octave higher than that of the open string played normally.

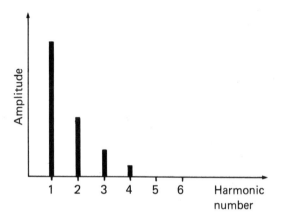

Fig. 1.15. Harmonic spectrum of the cello string vibration shown in Fig. 1.5.

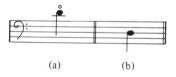

(a)   (b)

Fig. 1.16. (a) Natural harmonic on cello D string; (b) pitch of open string played normally.

Frequency analysis of non-periodic sounds

When we come to examine the behaviour of musical instruments in which sound is generated by plucking or striking (Chapters 6, 7 and 8), we will see that the resulting vibrations are not usually exactly periodic. It is still possible to analyse a non-periodic vibration into component sinusoidal vibrations, but the frequencies of the components will no longer be whole-number multiples of a fundamental. The components cannot then be described as "harmonics"; instead we can use the more general term *partials*, which carries no implication about the frequency ratios.

The harmonic spectrum is likewise replaced by a more general *frequency spectrum*. In some cases (e.g. the piano string) the frequencies of the partials deviate only slightly from a harmonic series, and the frequency spectrum will closely resemble a harmonic spectrum. Many percussion instruments, on the other hand, are characterised by a large number of closely spaced inharmonic partials, giving a much denser frequency spectrum (e.g. Fig.10.34).

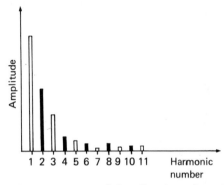

Fig. 1.17. Harmonic spectrum of the vibration of a point on a bowed cello open D string. When the string is touched lightly at its mid-point, only the even harmonics (shown as solid bars) remain undamped.

TRANSMISSION OF SOUND

So far, our scientific investigation of the performance of Beethoven's 'Emperor' Concerto has been confined to the concert platform. We have taken a close look at several of the instruments in action, and have seen that the rapid vibrations of their component parts are the essential source of the musical sound. We have also seen how to measure and describe vibrations; in later chapters we shall use these ideas to discuss why the different orchestral instruments have developed their present forms, and why they produce their characteristic sounds.

We now turn our attention to the next stage in the process of musical communication between performer and listener. How is it that the vibration of a cello string or a kettledrum membrane on the platform generates a response in someone seated at the back of the hall? It is common knowledge that the sound is transmitted in the form of a wave through the air between the instrument and the ear of the listener. An understanding of the nature of wave motion is thus important in discussing the acoustics of concert halls (Chapter 14); it is also an important aspect of the sound production of musical instruments (Chapter 5).

Sound waves in air

Let us start by considering what happens to the air just above the membrane of the kettledrum. It is useful to imagine this air divided into invisible horizontal layers, as in Fig. 1.18. We have seen that, after it has been struck, the membrane vibrates up and down (see Fig. 1.6 (c)). When it is rising, the layer of air in contact with it will also be forced upwards. This layer cannot rise freely, however, since it is obstructed by the layers of air above it; it is squeezed and compressed between the membrane and the higher layers. After a short time it is able to expand again by squeezing and compressing the next layer up; in turn, this layer relieves the pressure on it by compressing the layer above it; and so a pulse of compression travels upwards from the drumhead through the surrounding air.

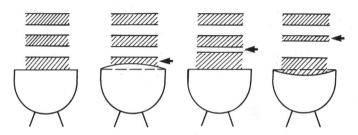

Fig. 1.18. A compression pulse travelling upwards from a kettledrum membrane. Alternate layers of air are shown hatched and unhatched; the compressed layer is shown by an arrow.

Meanwhile, the membrane will be falling again. The air just above it now has a larger volume to fill, so it expands into it. Consequently, the pressure drops below its normal atmospheric value. The air in the next layer up, finding a reduced pressure from below, also expands downwards; and thus a pulse of expansion follows the pulse of compression outwards from the drumhead.

As the membrane vibrates up and down, a regular train of pulses, alternating compression and expansion, is generated in the air. We call this pulse train a *sound wave* – the analogy with ripples generated by a stone thrown into a pool of water was already glimpsed by the Roman architect Vitruvius (Vitruvius 1960, pp.138–139). Indeed, sound waves can travel through liquids and solids as well as through air, and it is now possible to listen to music while swimming underwater in certain pools. However, we shall concentrate here on the more traditional musical environment, and limit our discussion to sound waves in air.

Longitudinal wave motion

If we examine a small segment of the air in the path of a sound wave, we find that it vibrates backwards and forwards along the direction of the wave. This type of motion is known as *longitudinal wave motion*. In Chapter 5 we shall come across another type of wave motion, in which the particles of the medium transmitting the wave vibrate in a direction perpendicular to the direction of the wave; this is known as *transverse wave motion*. Strings and membranes can carry both transverse and longitudinal waves, but only longitudinal waves can travel through air.

Since air is an invisible gas, it is a little difficult to illustrate the motion involved in the transmission of a sound wave. Some of the important features can perhaps be seen more clearly in the analogy shown in Fig. 1.19. Here we have a long line of people standing side by side and holding hands. To start with they are all upright and the same distance apart, as in line 1 of the diagram. The person on the extreme left of the line, whom we call A, starts to sway from side to side; lines 2 to 6 of Fig. 1.19 are pictures separated by equal time intervals, showing how the rocking of A gradually affects the rest of the line.

Fig. 1.19. Six successive views of a line of people, illustrating the progress of a longitudinal 'rocking wave'.

In line 2, A is leaning far to the right (as we see him). Reacting to the pressure, his neighbour B has also started to move rightwards; the rest of the line from C onwards is as yet unaware of the disturbance. In line 3 the pressure from B has pushed C over, and D is also moving to the right. Meanwhile A has pushed himself upright again; having reached his rightward extreme, B is also returning towards the vertical. By line 4 the rightwards push has been transmitted to E and F; A has now rocked over to the left, and C has come back to the vertical. Lines 5 and 6 show the disturbance reaching H and I, and then J and K, while A returns to the vertical and starts another cycle of rocking.

Although the disturbance generated by the swaying of A is clearly travelling from left to right along the line, each person is merely rocking from side to side about a fixed position. Similarly, there is no net flow of air in the direction of travel of a sound wave. If we could mark a small segment of the air and follow its motion, we would see that the position about which it was oscillating was just the position it occupied before the wave arrived, and at which it would come to rest when the wave died away.

We have illustrated in Fig. 1.19 the simplest type of wave motion, in which the displacement-time curve for each element of the medium transmitting the wave (each person in the line, or each layer of air) is a sine curve. Such a wave is called a *sine wave*. A sine wave in air corresponds to the rather featureless sound known as a *pure tone*. More complicated disturbances, such as that generated by the vibration of the body of a cello (Fig. 1.11), propagate through the air in the same way, although for any segment of the air, the displacement-time curve (known as the *waveform*) is correspondingly more complex; the corresponding sound is described as a *complex tone*.

Displacement-position diagrams

Fig. 1.20 (a) shows how our line of people looks after A has completed two cycles of rocking motion. We have assumed that the line continues indefinitely to the right; the wave has now reached beyond Q, and all the people in the drawing are rocking from side to side.

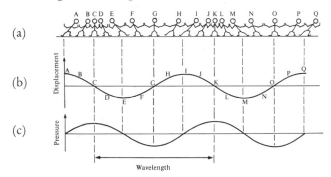

Fig. 1.20. (a) A further stage in the progress of the 'rocking wave'; (b) displacement-position and (c) pressure – position curves for the corresponding longitudinal sound wave in air.

Looking along the line, we can see a repeating pattern in the displacements. A has his maximum displacement to the right, C is vertical, E has his maximum displacement to the left, and G is again vertical. This sequence is exactly repeated with I, K, M and O. If we looked at the line a short time later, we would find that the entire pattern had moved to the right along the line.

In Fig. 1.20 (b) we have drawn a *displacement-position* diagram for the heads of our rocking figures. In this diagram the horizontal axis represents the position of the oscillating object before the wave arrived – here this corresponds to a point directly above the person's feet, which stay firmly on the ground throughout. The vertical axis represents the displacement from this equilibrium point. We have taken the displacement to be positive when the head moves to our right, and negative when it moves to our left. Thus A and I are represented by points at the maximum height above the horizontal axis, since their heads have the maximum displacement to the right; C and G are represented by points on the horizontal axis since their heads are in the equilibrium positions (above their feet). The point representing E is at the maximum depth below the axis since E's head is as far to the left of his feet as it can go.

Wavelength

When we draw a smooth line through these points it becomes clear why the term 'wave motion' is used: the displacement position curve has the characteristic wave shape. Exactly the same curve can represent the displacement of the air as a sound wave travels from left to right. Points A and I, which are at successive crests of the wave, represent segments of air with the maximum forward displacement. The distance separating these successive crests is known as the *wavelength*, usually symbolised by the Greek letter λ (lambda). If we looked at the displacement-position curve a short time later, we might find that the crests had moved on to points B and J, but they would still be the same distance λ apart.

Pressure in a sound wave

Looking again at Fig. 1.20 (a), we can see that, at the instant represented by that diagram, the wave has had the effect of squeezing the three heads B, C and D close together. On the other hand, the three heads F, G and H are much further apart than they were in the absence of the wave. In the corresponding case of a sound wave, the layer of air in the vicinity of C will be squeezed by the layers on either side, and the pressure will be higher than normal. Air will be sucked away from G by the retreat of the layers on either side, and the pressure will therefore drop below normal.

We have illustrated this variation of pressure with position in Fig. 1.20 (c). It is interesting to note that the maximum of pressure does not coincide with the maximum displacement; on the contrary, both maximum and minimum pressures occur at positions where the displacement is zero. Since the human ear responds to pressure variations, as do most microphones, it is often preferable to talk about the pressure changes caused by a sound wave rather than the displacement of the air.

The speed of sound

Fig. 1.19 illustrates how a rocking motion is gradually communicated along a line of people. If we know the distance separating the people and the time separating each picture, we can work out the speed at which the disturbance travels. For example, let us assume that the people are 1 metre apart, and the pictures are taken at intervals of 1 second. Since the disturbance involves two more people with each successive picture, it must be travelling at a speed of 2 metres per second. The speed is called the *wave velocity*.

A sound wave also has a characteristic velocity, which depends on the properties of the air. For dry air at a normal room temperature of 20°C, sound travels at a speed of 343 metres per second. To get a feel for the musical significance of this number, let us work out how long it will take for a sound created on the concert platform to travel to a listener at the back of the hall. Symbolising the distance by d, the time taken by t and the speed of sound by c, we have the relationship

$$c = d/t \; ;$$

this just states that the speed is equal to the distance travelled divided by the time taken. Rearranging this relationship gives

$$t = d/c \; .$$

If the distance d from instrument to listener is 50 metres, the time delay between creation and reception of the sound will be

$$t = 50/343 \simeq 0.15 \text{ seconds.}$$

This delay is just about one seventh of a second. In the second bar of the Beethoven piano concerto which we are using as our musical reference point (Fig. 1.1), the duration of each semiquaver is around one seventh of a second in a typical performance; the listener in the back stalls will therefore hear this passage one note behind the performer. Of course, he will be unaware of this delay, since every sound in the performance suffers the same time lag.

Such time lags can cause serious musical problems, however, when performers are for any reason widely separated. In the antiphonal choral works of Gabrieli, or in Stockhausen's 'Gruppen' with its multiple orchestras, the performers must judge their entries so as to produce the desired effect for the audience: their own perceptions will inevitably be different. For this reason alone, such works require a conductor (or even several conductors).

Temperature effects

Every player of a wind instrument knows that his instrument must be 'warmed up' in order to play in tune. The reason for this, which will be fully explored in Chapter 8, can be traced back to the fact that the speed of sound in air varies with the temperature. Fig. 1.21 shows that the speed of sound in dry air drops from 343 ms⁻¹ at 20°C to 331 ms⁻¹ at 0°C. This may seem a relatively small change, but it can have drastic musical consequences, since it corresponds to a pitch shift of more than half a semitone in a wind instrument. If an organ is tuned at 20°C, the organist dropping in for a practice on a freezing winter night will find his instrument playing very flat.

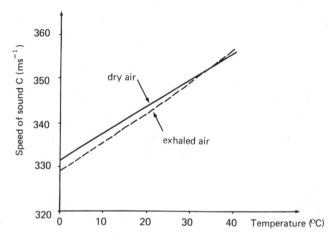

Fig. 1.21. Variation of the speed of sound with temperature.
Solid line: dry air (Weast 1974, p. E 54)
Dashed line: exhaled air (Nederveen 1969, pp. 17–18).

Orchestral wind instruments, unlike the organ, are filled not with dry air but with the exhaled breath of the player. This contains significant amounts of water vapour and carbon dioxide (and also, on occasions, other more alcoholic vapours which we shall ignore). These have only a small effect on the speed of sound in the instrument, as can be seen in Fig. 1.21. Of more significance is the fact that the player's breath emerges at a temperature of around 35°C. The air cools down as it passes through the instrument, but under normal playing conditions has an average temperature around 25°C. When discussing the behaviour of the air inside a wind instrument we should therefore use the value of the speed of sound for exhaled breath at 25°, which is 346 ms⁻¹.

Wavelength, frequency and speed

When we come to consider sound waves confined inside a wind instrument in Chapter 5, we shall see that the notes generated by the instrument can be most easily discussed in terms of their wavelengths. On the other hand, we shall find in Chapter 3 that the pitch of each note depends directly on the frequency of vibration of the enclosed air. It is therefore useful to be able to find the wavelength of a sound wave if we know its vibration frequency, or to find its frequency when we already know its wavelength. We shall now derive a simple relationship which enables us to do this.

If we look back to Fig. 1.19 and compare line 2 with line 6, we see that figure A has just completed one cycle of rocking motion in the time between these two pictures. In other words, lines 2 and 6 are separated by a time interval equal to the period of A's rocking motion, which we shall again symbolise by T. In that time the wave has travelled along the line from B to J – a distance which we earlier identified as the wavelength λ. If, as we assumed previously, the people are originally 1 metre apart and the lines are separated by time intervals of 1 second, the wavelength λ will be 8 metres and the period T will be 4 seconds. The wave will thus have travelled a distance of 8 m in 4 s, and its speed will be $\frac{8}{4} = 2$ ms^{-1}.

More generally, the speed of a sound wave can always be obtained by dividing the wavelength by the period:

$$c = \lambda/T.$$

Since we already showed (p. 10) that the frequency of vibration f is simply related to the period T by

$$f = 1/T$$

we can combine these two relationships to give $c = \lambda f$. For musical purposes it is useful to rearrange this equation in one of the following two forms:

$$\lambda = c/f$$

$$f = c/\lambda.$$

Thus we find the frequency by dividing the speed by the wavelength; alternatively, we can find the wavelength by dividing the speed by the frequency.

For example, we saw earlier that the first note played by each cello in Fig. 1.1, E♭, corresponded to a frequency f = 78 Hz. The sound wave radiated by the instrument must have the same frequency; what will be its wavelength? Using the relationship $\lambda = c/f$, we find

$$\lambda = 343/78 \simeq 4.4 \text{ m.}$$

The successive pressure crests in the sound wave travelling from the cello to the listener are more than 4 metres apart.

Reflection

We must pause at this point to discuss briefly some features of sound waves which have important musical consequences. First let us return to examine the sound wave which is radiated by the kettledrum. Fig. 1.18 is over-simplified, suggesting that the sound wave travels straight upwards; in fact, waves radiate out to the sides as well, as indicated in Fig. 1.22.

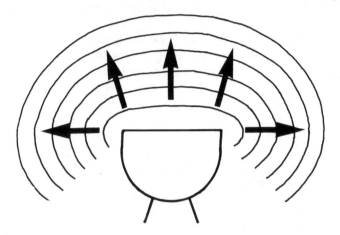

Fig. 1.22. Wavefronts radiating from the vibrating membrane of a kettledrum.

Nevertheless, the greater part of the sound energy emerges in the form of a wave travelling towards the roof. This energy is not wasted; when the wave reaches the roof, most of it is reflected back to the hall.

In this respect a sound wave behaves much like a beam of light (which is a different type of wave) striking a mirror. If the roof is horizontal, the wave will be reflected back downwards. It is frequently the case in concert halls that the roof above the platform has a slope, as shown in Fig. 1.23. In this case the wave will be reflected outwards towards the audience to an extent determined by the slope of the roof.

A sound wave can be reflected not only by a solid surface, but by any relatively abrupt change in its surroundings. When a wave travelling down a tube encounters a sharp bend, or reaches the open end of the tube, much of its energy may be reflected back up the tube; this is a vital factor in the working of wind instruments, as we shall see in Chapter 5.

Diffraction

Another important property of sound waves is their ability to bend round obstacles. If we go to a concert and find ourselves sitting behind a pillar, we can still hear the performers even though we cannot see them. This is partly because of sound waves which reach us indirectly after several reflections, but partly because the wave which travels directly towards us

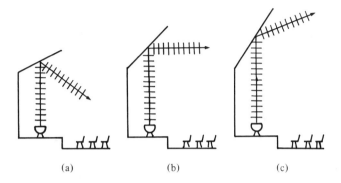

Fig. 1.23. Effect of a reflecting surface above concert platform.
(a) Reflector at 27° to horizontal: sound reflected downwards.
(b) Reflector at 45° to horizontal: sound reflected horizontally.
(c) Reflector at 56° to horizontal: sound reflected upwards.

can bend or *diffract* round the pillar. Fig. 1.24 (a) illustrates how this happens. We imagine ourselves looking down on a solid rectangular pillar while a sound wave approaches from the left. The presence of the wave is shown by the series of parallel straight lines, and the depth of shading indicates the strength of the sound. Immediately behind the pillar is an area of 'sound shadow': a listener here would receive very little diffracted sound. But if he backed off to the right, still keeping directly behind the pillar, he would find the strength of the sound increasing. In effect, the sound waves lap around either side of the pillar and join up again on the far side. By the time our listener reached the region at the right hand side of our diagram, he would be receiving a sound wave hardly affected by the presence of the pillar.

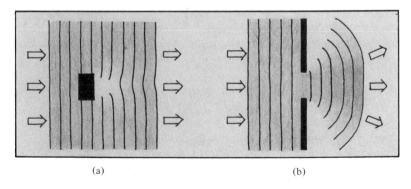

Fig. 1.24. Diffraction of sound by (a) a pillar (b) a door whose width is comparable with the wavelength of the sound wave.

31

In a similar way, when a sound wave passes through an aperture such as a door, it can bend round the sides of the door and spread out in the region beyond, as shown in Fig. 1.24 (b). The implications of this for the radiation of sound from wind instruments are taken up in Chapter 5.

Not all sound waves show diffraction to the same extent. A wave will only be significantly diffracted by an obstacle if the wavelength is larger than the width of the obstacle. When the wavelength is much smaller, we have the situation illustrated in Fig. 1.25 (a): the wave passes by without noticeably bending, and a soundless area stretches behind the pillar. Similarly, when a wave passes through an aperture much larger than its wavelength (Fig. 1.25 (b)) it does not bend significantly into the regions of sound shadow on either side.

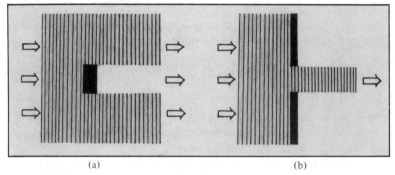

(a)   (b)

Fig. 1.25. For a pillar (a) or a door (b) whose width is much greater than the sound wavelength, diffraction is insignificant.

In fact, obstacles in a sound wave of sufficiently small wavelength cast shadows in just the same way that they do in a light beam. This is understandable: light is another type of wave, with an extremely small wavelength, and also shows diffraction effects with sufficiently small obstacles and apertures.

Longer wavelengths correspond to lower frequencies; and lower frequencies (as we shall see in Chapter 3) correspond to lower pitches. We therefore expect low pitched sounds to be diffracted more readily than high pitched sounds. This has an important musical consequence for the unfortunate listener seated behind a pillar. How well does he receive the sound waves that come directly from the orchestra when, for example, it plays the first chord of the 'Emperor' Concerto (Fig. 1.26)?

The lowest note in the chord, played by cellos and basses, radiates with a wavelength of 4.4 metres; if the pillar is 1 metre wide, the wave will diffract easily round it, since the wavelength is more than 4 times the width of the obstacle. On the other hand, the note played by the first flute has a wavelength of only 28 cm, little more than ¼ of the width of the pillar; this

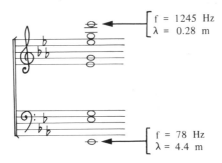

Fig. 1.26. Fundamental frequencies and wavelengths of the highest and lowest notes in the first chord of Beethoven's Piano Concerto No.5.

high pitched sound will not be strongly diffracted into the region behind the pillar. The direct sound reaching the listener will thus be deficient in its high pitch components – it will lack brilliance and edge, as if a treble tone control had been turned down.

Interference

In the discussion above we assumed implicitly that the sound wave radiated by one instrument would travel to the listener in exactly the same way whether or not it was accompanied by additional sound waves from all the other instruments in the orchestra. This assumption is justified: the separate sound waves do not interfere with one another in that sense.

The term *interference* is used in acoustics to describe some interesting effects which occur when the waves arrive at their destination – the ear of the listener, or perhaps a microphone recording the concert. For example, Fig. 1.27 shows a simple case in which two flautists are being recorded by an overhead microphone. The microphone turns the pressure fluctuations at its diaphragm into an electrical signal, so that by displaying this signal on an oscilloscope we can examine the variation of pressure with time at the position of the microphone (labelled M).

Fig. 1.28 (a) shows the oscilloscope trace obtained when flautist A plays the note two octaves above middle C, and flautist B remains silent. The pressure time curve is very close to a simple sine wave. Fig. 1.28 (b) shows the identical curve obtained when B plays the same note alone. When both instruments play together, the variation of pressure at the microphone due to A will be added to that due to B, and the outcome will depend on their relative phase. If they are exactly in phase – that is, if a peak of high pressure from A arrives simultaneously with a peak from B – the net effect will be a high pressure peak of twice the amplitude due to each flute

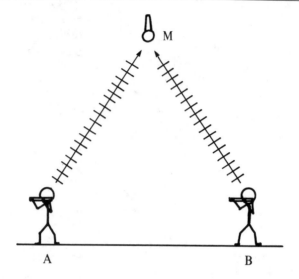

Fig. 1.27. Two flautists, A and B, equidistant from a microphone M.

separately. The low pressure troughs which follow will also arrive simultaneously, giving a double drop in the net pressure. This is an instance of *constructive interference*: the pressure-time curve for A and B together has the same form as that for A or B separately, but the amplitude is doubled.

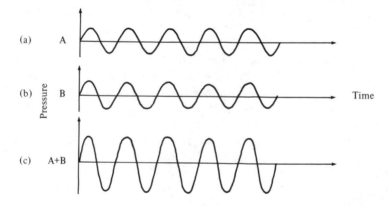

Fig. 1.28. Constructive interference due to the addition of two in-phase sine waves.

A more surprising result is obtained if the pressure fluctuations generated by the two flutes arrive at the microphone exactly 180° out of phase. This situation is illustrated by Fig. 1.29. As the wave from flute A tries to make the pressure rise, the wave from B is trying to make it drop; high pressure peaks of A arrive simultaneously with low pressure troughs from B, while troughs from A coincide with peaks from B. The net effect is that the two waves cancel each other out completely: although each flute is playing, the microphone records only silence.

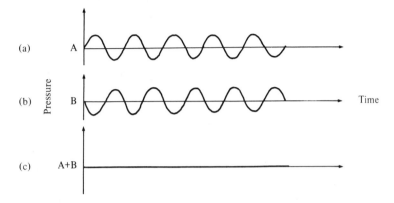

Fig. 1.29. Destructive interference due to the addition of two out-of-phase sine waves.

This extreme case of *destructive interference* rarely appears quite so starkly in realistic musical situations. For a start, we have ignored the sound which arrives after reflection from the walls of the room. Fig. 1.30 shows how a side wall reflects waves from A and B back to the micro-

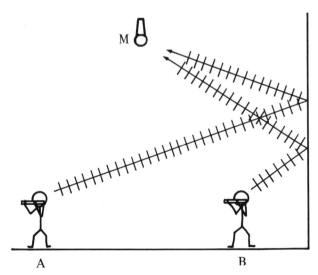

Fig. 1.30. Sound from flute A reaching the microphone after reflection by the side wall has travelled further than that from flute B.

phone; in this case the wave from A has to travel further than that from B. Thus even if a pressure peak leaves A at the same instant as a pressure dip from B, the peak will arrive at the microphone later than the dip and the two will not cancel completely. In fact, if the difference in the paths taken by the two waves is just half a wavelength, the peak from A will arrive at the same time as the subsequent peak from B, and the two waves will add constructively.

Another reason why we do not usually notice destructive interference in the sound of two instruments playing in unison is that the vibration patterns of musical sounds are normally more complicated than the simple sine waves of Fig. 1.28. When the flutes play middle C, for example, the pressure-time curves may have the appearance of Fig. 1.31 (a) and (b); even if these two disturbances arrive exactly 180° out of phase, they will not cancel completely, as is shown by Fig. 1.31 (c).

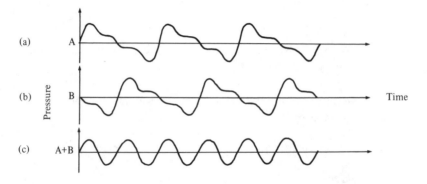

Fig. 1.31. (a) A complex periodic curve; (b) the same curve delayed in phase by 180°; (c) the sum of the two curves.

Beats

There is, however, one situation familiar to all musicians in which constructive and destructive interference are obvious (sometimes disastrously so). If two instruments play a slightly mistuned unison, a distinct throbbing or *beating* is heard in the sound. When the two notes are very close in pitch the rate of beating is slow; if they drift further apart the rate of beating increases.

Because the waves generated by the two instruments have slightly different frequencies, their relative phase at the ear of the listener is constantly changing. At the start of the time represented by Fig. 1.32, the two waves are in phase; the peak of A adds to the peak of B to produce a double amplitude peak, corresponding to a loud sound. After a few cycles it is clear that A is vibrating more rapidly than B; eventually it is half a cycle ahead, and a peak in A corresponds to a trough in B. At that point they are interfering destructively, and the sound has died away to nothing. But A goes on gaining on B, until it is one whole cycle ahead; the waves are again interfering constructively, and the sound has maximum loudness. This waxing and waning of the sound continues as A gains further cycles on B.

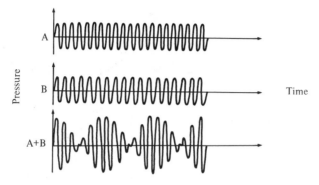

Fig. 1.32. Beats due to the addition of two sine waves with slightly different frequencies.

Listening for beats can be a useful guide when tuning instruments; it is a standard technique in piano tuning (see Chapter 7, p.252). By counting the number of beats per second, the frequency difference between two pure tones can be estimated. For example, consider two tones with frequencies of 100 and 103 Hz respectively; in one second the higher tone will have gone through three cycles more than the lower, generating three cycles of beating. In general, the number of beats per second is equal to the difference in frequency between the two component tones. Beating between complex tones is less straightforward to analyse, since many pairs of component pure tones can be beating simultaneously. This is the basis of Helmholtz's theory of dissonance (see Chapter 4).

The Doppler effect

There is one other property of sound waves in air which deserves a brief mention. We are all familiar with the way in which the pitch of a fire engine siren appears to drop as the engine races past. The reason for this effect, known as the *Doppler effect*, is illustrated in Fig. 1.33. When a source of sound is approaching the listener, the distance between pressure peaks (the wavelength) is reduced by the distance travelled by the source during the cycle between the peaks. The wave appears 'squashed up'. Since the speed of the wave is unaffected by the motion of the source, the reduction in wavelength must correspond to an increase in frequency: the pitch is raised. The reverse happens as the source recedes. The wave is 'stretched out'; the wavelength increases and the frequency and pitch drop.

For source speeds up to about 100 mph, the pitch change is proportional to the speed. The note of a fire engine passing at 60 mph changes by almost exactly a minor third.

The 'Leslie speaker', described in Chapter 13, makes use of the Doppler effect; apart from this example it is of little significance in musical life. It did, however, occur to one of the authors, who found himself trying to play jazz on a procession float travelling at around 20 mph, that an observant listener should notice the pitch of the 'Basin Street Blues' drop by a semitone as the band rolled by.

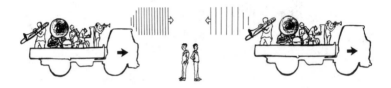

Fig. 1.33. The Doppler effect.

2

Hearing musical sounds

In Chapter 1 we saw that the player of a musical instrument creates sound by setting the instrument vibrating; the sound is then transmitted outwards in the form of a wave. What happens when the wave reaches the ear of a listener is the subject of the present chapter.

It is worth remarking on the complexity of the task faced by the human ear in a musical situation. In the first chord of the 'Emperor' Concerto seventy instruments may be playing simultaneously, at eight nominally different pitches. Sound waves generated by these instruments converge on the listener. The resulting pressure fluctuations are correspondingly complicated; looking at the output of a microphone on an oscilloscope (Fig. 2.1), it is difficult to see any pattern at all. Yet the ear immediately recognises the major chord, and can identify the separate contributions of many of the participating instruments. On the first beat of the second bar another instrument adds its contribution to the held chord; even a listener who could not see the platform, and had never before heard the piece, would know at once that the piano had entered.

Fig. 2.1. The electrical signal from a microphone recording the first five seconds of Beethoven's Piano Concerto No.5 (John Lill and the Scottish National Orchestra, conducted by Sir Alexander Gibson).

We do not yet fully understand how the ear performs such feats of detection. Most of the experiments on which our knowledge of the behaviour of the ear is based have been carried out with much simpler sounds and in laboratory conditions far removed from the ambience of the concert hall. In what follows we try to distil those aspects of the modern understanding of the human ear which offer insights into our response to musical sounds.

The structure of the human ear

When we talk of someone having big ears we are referring to the flaps of skin and cartilege which protrude from either side of the human head. Those parts of the human ear which are vital for our sense of hearing are, however, buried several centimetres inside the bone of the skull. This is a necessary protective measure, for, as we shall see, the ear is an extremely delicate and sensitive organ.

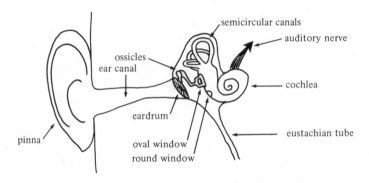

Fig. 2.2. Anatomical sketch of the human ear.

Fig. 2.2 is an anatomical sketch showing how the different parts of the ear are related. Most of the anatomical details can be ignored in our present discussion; Fig. 2.3 is a simplified diagram showing schematically the features which are important in understanding the musical response of the ear. Following the usual convention, we divide the ear into three sections: outer, middle and inner ears. We shall examine each section in turn, looking particularly at how it behaves when a musical sound is being received. Common English descriptive terms are used when available, with Latin equivalents in brackets.

THE OUTER EAR

The outer ear consists of the *pinna* – the external flap – and an almost cylindrical channel roughly 25 mm long and 7 mm in diameter, known as

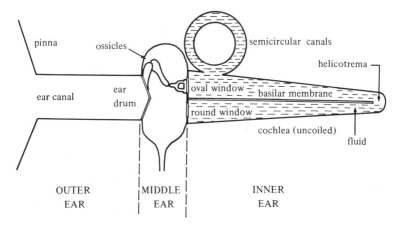

Fig. 2.3. Schematic diagram of the human ear.

the *ear canal* (*auditory meatus*). This channel is sealed at the inner end by the *eardrum* (*tympanic membrane*), which is a thin semitransparent membrane with the shape of a flattened cone. When a sound wave arrives at the outer ear, part of the wave is transmitted down the ear canal; the resulting pressure fluctuations force the eardrum into vibration. Behaving like a cylindrical tube closed at one end, the ear canal resonates at about 3800 Hz (see p.197), boosting the ear's response in this frequency range.

The elaborate shaping of the pinna suggests that it has some particular function to perform. It certainly acts as a funnel, collecting the sound energy arriving over a fairly large area and channelling it into the smaller area of the ear canal. Cupping a hand behind the ear increases the collecting area, and emphasises this effect.

Directional hearing

The pinna also plays a role in the ability of a listener to identify the direction from which a sound has come. It has been suggested (Batteau 1967) that this effect is partly due to the fact that waves reflected into the ear canal from different sections of the pinna will have travelled different distances. The brain may be able to analyse the corresponding time delays, which will vary with the direction of incidence of the wave (see Fig. 2.4). Experiments have shown (Butler 1975) that a listener's ability to judge the height of a sound source straight ahead is destroyed when the pinnae are flattened against the head.

If the sound source is not directly in front of the listener (or directly behind), the two ears will pick up different signals. This binaural disparity provides the dominant clues from which the brain recognises the position of the sound source in the horizontal plane (Jeffress 1975).

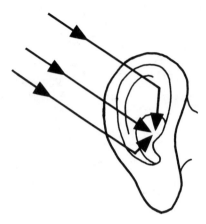

Fig. 2.4. Path differences between reflections from different parts of the pinna may contribute to the directional sense in hearing.

For low frequency sounds, the most significant clue is the time delay between the arrivals of a sound wave at the right and left ears of the listener. A wave approaching from the left will arrive first at the left pinna. If the wavelength is long enough, part of it will be diffracted round the head, arriving at the right pinna about 0.7 ms later. If the period of the sound wave is greater than this (that is, if its frequency is below about 1500 Hz), the delay will cause a phase difference of less than one cycle between ɩne signals in the two ears; the brain recognises in this difference a clue that the sound came from the left.

In the more common musical situation illustrated in Fig. 2.5, all of the players in the string quartet are in front of the listener. The sound from the cello, on the listener's right, still has a shorter journey to his right ear than to his left, while the sound from the first violin on the other side of the quartet will reach his left ear before his right. Using these clues, along with others based on small intensity differences, the brain constructs a spatially separated sound image: the listener can 'see' the positioning of the instruments with his ears, even when his eyes are shut.

THE MIDDLE EAR

Between the outer ear and the inner ear is a small air-filled cavity in the bone of the skull: this is the middle ear. Its outer boundary is formed almost entirely by the eardrum. On the other side of the cavity there are two small apertures in the bony wall dividing middle and inner ears; these are known (because of their shape) as the *oval window (fenestra ovalis)* and the *round window (fenestra rotunda)*.

Fig. 2.5. The stereophonic sound image of a string quartet.

Providing a link across the middle ear from eardrum to oval window is a lever system consisting of three small bones. These are known collectively as the *ossicles*, and are given the graphic (if somewhat imaginative) titles of the *hammer* (*malleus*), the *anvil* (*incus*) and the *stirrup* (*stapes*). We should not allow this cavalier use of the blacksmith's vocabulary to distort our sense of scale: the stirrup in the middle ear is only 3 mm high. Its footplate fits neatly into the oval window, with a flexible ligament providing a seal. A thin membrane also seals the round window.

The only way in which air can enter or leave the middle ear is through the eustachian tube, which connects it to the back of the throat. This passage serves to prevent a steady pressure difference building up between the middle ear and outside atmosphere. The sensation of discomfort or even pain resulting from a pressure difference across the eardrum is often experienced when descending in an aircraft, or driving rapidly downhill in a car. The pressure in the atmosphere increases with decreasing height; for a drop of 10 m it changes by about 1 part in 1000. This seems a tiny variation, but the ear is adapted to respond to the even tinier pressure fluctuations in sound waves, and perceives this increase in the steady pressure on the eardrum as a drastic overload. Fortunately it can be relieved by periodic swallowing, since this opens the normally closed eustachian tube and allows air to flow into the middle ear to equalise the pressures.

Transmission of sound through the middle ear

When a sound wave arrives at the eardrum, the pressure fluctuations set the membrane vibrating. The principal function of the middle ear mechanism is to transfer these vibrations to the oval window at the entrance to the inner ear. The hammer bone is firmly attached at one end to the inner surface of the eardrum, while its other end is fixed to the thick end of the anvil bone (Fig. 2.6). The stirrup bone is connected to the far end of the anvil by a flexible joint. Recent observations (Rhode 1978) suggest that in response to eardrum vibrations, the hammer and anvil pivot about their junction, causing the stirrup to move into and out of the oval window like a piston.

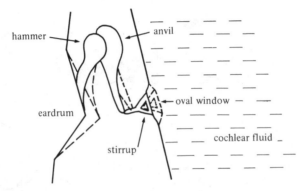

Fig. 2.6. Schematic diagram of middle ear mechanism.

In order to be able to hear very faint sounds, we need to transfer as much as possible of the sound energy in an incoming wave into the inner ear. The middle ear mechanism plays a vital role in improving the efficiency of this process. If the sound wave fell directly on the entrance to the inner ear, less than 1% of its energy would pass through; the rest would be reflected back out of the ear. Thanks to the intervention of the middle ear, about 50% of the sound energy is transmitted to the inner ear in the frequency range of greatest musical importance.

Impedance

To understand how the middle ear effects such a reduction in the reflected sound, we must think a little about how reflections occur. Let us consider first the situation represented by Fig. 2.7 (a): a sound wave approaches a solid wall, and is completely reflected. A pressure crest in the wave exerts a forward push on the wall, but because it is rigid it does not 'give'; no sound is transmitted to the far side. In contrast, Fig. 2.7 (b) represents a situation in which the wall is replaced by a layer of air. Of course, this layer of air is no different from the surrounding air, and the wave will pass through it without any reflection. The pressure crest will exert a forward push on the air 'wall', but unlike the solid wall it will 'give' in such a way as to transmit all the sound energy, and reflect none.

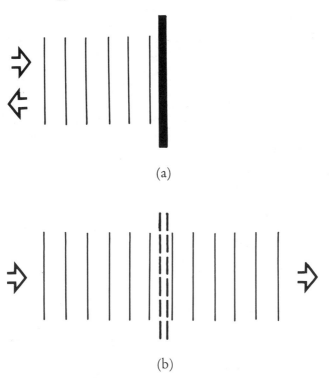

Fig. 2.7. A sound wave is reflected by a solid barrier (a), but passes freely through a layer of air of the same thickness (b).

The amount of 'give' in a barrier can be measured by observing the motion of the barrier when a sound wave of known pressure amplitude falls on it. If the pressure amplitude is P, and the barrier vibrates with maximum velocity V, its *specific acoustic impedance* z is defined as the ratio of P and V: $z = P/V$. An almost rigid barrier (like a wooden partition) vibrates very little for a given pressure amplitude; its specific acoustic impedance is therefore high. A membrane which flexes readily (like a drumskin) will vibrate much more strongly for the same pressure amplitude; it will have a much lower specific acoustic impedance.

The unit of specific acoustic impedance is the *rayl* (named after the nineteenth century scientist Lord Rayleigh). A 'wall' of air has a specific acoustic impedance of 415 rayls (Kinsler et al. 1982, p.111). Thus a barrier with z = 415 rayls will transmit a sound wave perfectly; the more its impedance differs from this value the greater will be the fraction of the sound energy reflected. The entrance to the inner ear shows a specific acoustic impedance of about 150,000 rayls (de Boer 1980, p.113). It would clearly be very inefficient to allow the sound wave to fall directly on this barrier. Instead it falls on the eardrum. The force exerted on the eardrum is equal to the pressure times the area; this force is transmitted through the ossicles to the oval window. Since the oval window has an area about one twenty-fifth of the vibrating area of the eardrum, the pressure on the oval window is increased by a factor of 25 over that on the eardrum. In addition, a lever action in the ossicles increases the pressure by another factor of roughly 2, while reducing the oval window velocity by the same factor. Thus the pressure at the oval window is about 50 times greater than that on the eardrum, while the velocity amplitude is halved (Fig. 2.8).

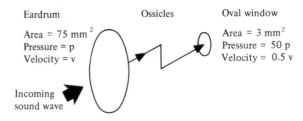

Fig. 2.8. Changes in pressure and velocity between eardrum and oval window, due to reduction in area and lever action of ossicles.

Remembering that the specific acoustic impedance is the ratio of pressure amplitude to velocity amplitude, we see that the impedance at the oval window is about 100 times that at the eardrum. Since the oval window impedance is around 150,000 rayls, the impedance at the eardrum is about $\frac{1}{100}$th of this, or 1500 rayls. This is still about three times the impedance of a layer of air, so that not all the sound energy is transmitted through the ossicles to the middle ear. About half the energy in the sound wave is reflected back up the ear canal for mid-range frequencies. For frequencies below a few hundred hertz, or above 10kHz, the impedance of the eardrum is considerably increased by factors related to the mass and stiffness of the middle ear mechanism. This increases the proportion of reflected sound. Some important musical consequences of this reflection are dealt with in our discussion of the response of the ear to different frequencies in Chapter 3.

The acoustic reflex

When a bright light flashes in our eyes we instinctively blink. A similar protective reaction, called the *acoustic reflex*, comes into play when a very loud sound is heard. A small muscle in the middle ear pulls the stirrup back from the oval window; this reduces the amount of sound energy transmitted to the delicate mechanism of the inner ear. Since this reduction is only significant for frequencies below about 1000 Hz, it has the effect of filtering out the low pitch components of a complex sound (Morgan and Dirks 1975).

Fig. 2.9. Excerpt from the 3rd movement of Tchaikovsky's Symphony No.6.

47

The sound levels required to activate the acoustic reflex are rarely encountered in live musical performances. It is conceivable, however, that the reflex plays some role in diminishing the effectiveness of the bass clef parts in very loud orchestral passages such as that quoted in Fig. 2.9. It will certainly be activated by the mind-blowing output of the average discotheque; it may be significant that the hearing loss suffered by listeners to loud rock music (see Chapter 3, p.137) occurs mainly at high frequencies, where the acoustic reflex affords no protection.

The reflex takes about a tenth of a second to come fully into play after the onset of a loud sound (Møller 1974). It thus cannot shield the ear from a sudden impulsive sound, such as a pistol shot, which can reach a dangerous level in a much shorter time.

THE INNER EAR

Beyond the middle ear is another cavity in the bone of the skull. This is the *inner ear*, also known as the *labyrinth*. As the latter title suggests, it is a complicated series of interconnecting passages and chambers, which are filled by watery fluid. One part of the structure, the *semi circular canals*, gives us our sense of balance; the other major part, the *cochlea*, is responsible for our sense of hearing.

The cochlea is a tube about 35 mm long, coiled up like the shell of a snail (see Fig. 2.2). There are roughly 2½ turns between the base of the spiral and the apex; the tube is about 2 mm in diameter at the base, and gradually tapers down towards the apex.

In this compact little structure the vibrations transmitted by the middle ear generate electrical signals which are sent down the auditory nerve to the brain. Ever since the cochlea was first clearly identified and described in the seventeenth century, a debate has raged over its function in the hearing process (Carterette 1978). This debate has centred on a topic of great importance to musicians: the ability of the ear to distinguish between sounds of different pitch.

Hearing chords

When we listen to a four-part chorale such as that which opens Tchaikovsky's overture 'Romeo and Juliet' (Fig. 2.10), our first impression is of a sequence of integrated chords. It is quite easy, however, to focus the attention on each of the four melodic strands in turn; this implies that we can distinguish the four separate pitches in each chord. In this case we are helped by the fact that different instrumental tone colours are employed. In the sforzando chord in the bar from Beethoven's 'Pathétique' piano sonata quoted in Fig. 2.11, we are deprived of this assistance; nevertheless it is possible by concentrated listening to repeated playing of this chord to hear each of the eight pitches distinctly.

Fig. 2.10. Opening of Tchaikovsky's Fantasy Overture 'Romeo and Juliet' (actual pitch).

Does the analysis of a chord into its component pitches take place in the inner ear? Or does the cochlea act simply like a telephone receiver, converting the vibrations of the oval window into an equivalent electrical oscillation which is then transmitted down the auditory nerve for analysis by the brain? To answer these questions we would like to be able to examine how the inner ear reacts when a musical sound is received.

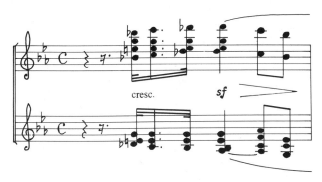

Fig. 2.11. Excerpt from Beethoven's Sonata Pathétique, Op. 13.

Because of the inaccessibility and sensitivity of the cochlea, it is very difficult to obtain such information from living human listeners; most of the experiments on which our present limited understanding is based have been carried out on the ears of people who have recently died, or on anaesthetised animals. By direct microscopic examination through small holes bored into the bony wall of the cochlea scientists have studied the movements which take place inside (Békésy 1960). The insertion of very delicate electrodes has permitted measurements of the electrical signals which are generated by the arrival of different musical sounds (Russell and Sellick 1977). Vibrations which are too small to be seen even in a microscope have been revealed by investigations using the 'Mössbauer technique', in which motion is detected by examining the radiation from a minute radioactive source implanted in the inner ear (Johnston and Boyle 1967).

As a result of these experiments we now know that the inner ear is indeed responsible for many of the musically important features of our hearing ability. In particular, at least some of our pitch discrimination takes place in the cochlea. It is therefore worth trying to understand a little of what goes on inside this amazing little spiral.

Structure of the cochlea

Fig. 2.12 shows a simplified cross-section of the cochlear tube. It is divided into three sections by two membranes which run practically the entire length of the tube. The *upper gallery (scala vestibuli)* is divided from the *cochlear duct (scala media)* by the very thin and flexible *Reissner's membrane*; separating the cochlear duct from the *lower gallery (scala tympani)* is the more substantial *basilar membrane*. Only at the apex of the spiral are the upper and lower galleries connected, through a hole called the *helicotrema*.

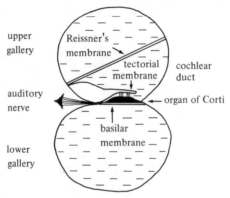

Fig. 2.12. Cross-section of cochlea.

The upper surface of the basilar membrane carries an array of hair cells which forms the *organ of Corti*. Leading out of the organ of Corti are about 30,000 nerve fibres, distributed more or less uniformly along the basilar membrane; these are the cables which carry the electrical signals to the brain. In order to understand how these electrical signals arise we must look at the motion of the basilar membrane when a sound is heard.

Motion of the basilar membrane

Consider first the sequence of events caused by a single handclap near the ear. A pressure pulse arrives at the eardrum, and exerts an inward force on it. This force, multiplied by the middle ear mechanism, is transmitted to the stirrup footplate, pushing it through the oval window into the upper gallery of the cochlea (Fig. 2.13). The liquid in the upper gallery is almost incompressible, and the incursion of the stirrup footplate occurs too rapidly for the displaced fluid to escape through the helicotrema. Something has to give – and what gives is the flexible basilar membrane, bulging downwards at the end nearest the oval window. Of course, this displaces the fluid in the lower gallery, but the membrane covering the round window bulges outwards to accommodate it.

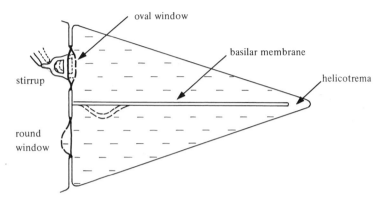

Fig. 2.13. Arrival of a pressure pulse at the oval window.

The tips of the hairs which emerge from the hair cells in the organ of Corti are embedded in the *tectorial membrane*, which lies above the organ. When the basilar membrane flexes, the tectorial membrane slides across it; this bends the hairs, causing the cells to 'fire' – that is, to send out electrical impulses. These impulses are picked up by the nerve fibres in the vicinity and communicated through them to the brain.

The bulge, which appears first near the oval window, travels rapidly along the basilar membrane towards the helicotrema. As it passes, the hair cells in the displaced section fire, and the nerve fibres from that section convey a corresponding signal to the brain.

Let us now consider what happens when we hear a continuous pure tone, causing the eardrum to vibrate with simple harmonic motion. The stirrup footplate is driven alternately into and out of the oval window; we would expect to find a sequence of alternately downward and upward bulges travelling along the basilar membrane. This expectation is indeed borne out. There is, however, a remarkable feature about these bulges, first discovered by the careful and ingenious studies of Georg von Békésy (1960): as they travel away from the oval window they grow in height until they reach a certain position on the basilar membrane, after which they diminish rapidly and disappear.

This motion of the basilar membrane is illustrated by the six successive cross-sections sketched in Fig. 2.14, showing how it flexes when a tone of frequency about 1000 Hz is being heard. In sketch (a) a broad upward bulge (indicated by an arrow) can be seen near the oval window end of the membrane. In sketches (b), (c) and (d) we see it travelling along the membrane towards the helicotrema, increasing in height and narrowing in width as it goes. In sketch (e) it has reached its maximum height, at a distance of about 20 mm from the oval window; it continues to travel, but within another 2 mm or so has shrunk almost to vanishing point (sketch (f)). The same pattern is seen with the downward bulge which follows it along the membrane.

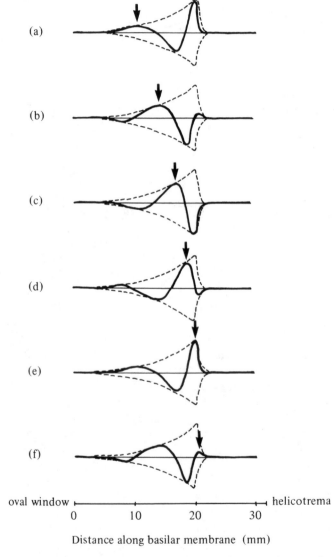

Fig. 2.14. Successive cross-sections of the basilar membrane, showing the progress of a travelling wave.

basilar membrane. The version of the theory which we have outlined above is an oversimplification, of course: a single pure tone excites hair cells not just under the peak of the amplitude envelope, but over the entire width of the envelope. The first observations of basilar membrane vibrations by Bekesy showed rather broad amplitude envelopes (Fig. 2.17 (a)), and it was difficult to see how this mechanism could account for the known frequency discriminating ability of the ear (Nordmark 1978). However, in recent years it has become possible to perform measurements in conditions much closer to those of normal hearing (Rhode 1978; Sellick et al. 1982); such measurements have implied an extremely sharp peak on the amplitude envelope, with a correspondingly precipitous cut-off beyond the peak (Fig. 2.17 (b)). It now seems that a place theory may be able to explain our ability to distinguish between two successive tones whose frequencies are only slightly different, by assuming that the brain focuses attention either on the part of the basilar membrane generating the maximum signal (the peak of the amplitude envelope) or on the part where the signal is changing most rapidly with position (the cut-off) (Evans 1975, p.92).

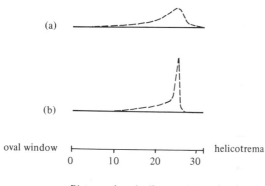

Fig. 2.17. (a) The broad amplitude envelope observed by Békésy.
(b) The much sharper type of envelope implied by more recent measurements.

Signals in the auditory nerve

It is possible, by inserting a tiny electrode into the auditory nerve, to pick up the electrical signals travelling along a single nerve fibre from the cochlea to the brain (Tasaki 1954). The signal takes the form of a series of voltage spikes; each spike corresponds to the firing of a hair cell connected to the nerve fibre.

If we examine a fibre coming from the region of the cochlea near the helicotrema, we find a response only to pure tones with frequencies below a few hundred hertz (see Fig. 2.15). A typical signal is shown in Fig. 2.18 (a). At first glance, the voltage spikes appear to be separated by random time intervals. But if we compare Fig. 2.18 (a) with Fig. 2.18 (g), which shows the vibration of the basilar membrane at the point in question, we see that the hair cells tend to fire when the membrane is near the top of its vibration cycle. Not every cycle fires a given hair cell; sometimes several cycles pass without a spike appearing on the nerve fibre.

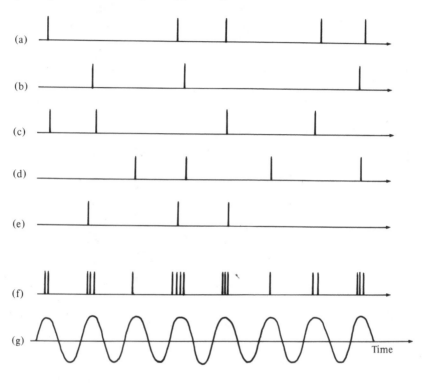

Fig. 2.18. (a)–(e) Electrical pulses on five different nerve fibres activated by the pure tone whose vibration curve is shown in (g). The sum of the signals on all five fibres is shown in (f).

If we look at another nerve fibre which is connected to the same region of the basilar membrane, we find a similar pattern of spikes (Fig. 2.18 (b)). Again the spikes occur near the top of the membrane vibration cycle; some cycles generate spikes in both fibres, others in only one fibre, while some cycles pass without a spike appearing in either fibre. Fig. 2.18 (c)–(e) shows the signal in three other fibres from the same part of the membrane. In Fig. 2.18 (f) the signals from all five fibres are added together. In this combined signal there is at least one spike, and sometimes several spikes, marking the peak of each vibration cycle.

These observations suggest that the brain may not need to rely solely on the place of origin of the signals in order to determine the frequency of a tone. According to the *volley* theory (Wever 1949), the brain combines the signals from a large bundle of nerve fibres; at every peak of the vibration cycle a 'volley' of spikes travels down this bundle. Thus if the brain has an internal clock it can estimate the number of volleys arriving per second, and hence the frequency of the tone.

There are other ways in which the brain could make use of the timing information in the nerve fibre signals. It has been suggested that the time intervals between successive pairs of spikes on a single nerve fibre (inter-spike intervals, or ISIs) may be measured and recorded by the brain (Whitfield 1978; Ohgushi 1983). From an analysis of a sufficient number of ISIs the period of the tone can be deduced. For example, the ISIs in Fig. 2.18 (a) are very nearly $3T$, T, $2T$ and T. This does not prove that the period of the tone being heard is T: it is possible that the period is $T/2$, or another submultiple of T. But if the period were $T/2$ we should expect to find ISIs of not only $T/2$ but also $3T/2$, $5T/2$, etc. Their absence from the signal in Fig. 2.18 (a) is suspicious; if none appeared after a few more spikes had been recorded, the brain might reasonably conclude that the period was indeed T.

Much ink has been spilled in battles between proponents of place theories and temporal theories (i.e. theories emphasising the use of the timing information in nerve signals). Although these battles are still being fought, many scientists have come to believe that both types of information are probably used in frequency discrimination.

Critical bands

Thus far we have been discussing the ability of the ear to distinguish between two pure tones of almost equal frequency when the two tones are heard separately. But what happens when two or more pure tones of different frequency arrive at the ear simultaneously? This is the normal musical experience: we shall see in Chapter 3 that all musical sounds, however complicated, can be considered as combinations of pure tones.

Let us take the case presented in Fig. 2.19 (a). Two tones with frequencies of 523 Hz and 1046 Hz are heard simultaneously; each tone will generate a pattern of vibration on the basilar membrane. The amplitude envelopes for these two vibrations are shown in the diagram (for simplicity, only the upper halves of the envelopes are drawn). The shaded area indicates the overlap of the two envelopes; because the tones are an octave apart, the area of overlap is small. This means that the excitation of the hair cells due to one tone will be almost unaffected by the presence of the other tone.

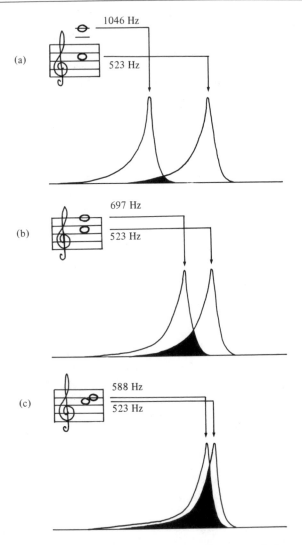

Fig. 2.19. As the interval between two tones decreases, their amplitude envelopes on the basilar membrane overlap to an increasing extent.

The situation changes when the frequency separation of the tones is reduced. In Fig. 2.19 (b) the upper tone is only a fourth above the lower; the area of overlap has grown. A significant number of hair cells will now be responding to both signals. When the separation is reduced to a tone (Fig. 2.19 (c)) the amplitude envelopes overlap almost completely, implying a strong interaction between the two sounds.

When two pure tones are so close in frequency that there is a large overlap in their amplitude envelopes on the basilar membrane, we say that their frequencies lie within one *critical band*. The concept of the critical band has been of great importance in the development of modern theories of hearing, and critical bandwidths have been defined and measured in a variety of sophisticated ways (Fletcher 1940; Zwicker et al. 1957; Plomp 1976). For our purposes we need only the essential idea: if two tones are separated in frequency by much more than one critical band they fire two largely separate sets of hair cells on the basilar membrane; if the two tones lie well within one critical band they fire almost the same set of hair cells.

The dependence of the critical bandwidth upon frequency is shown by curve (a) in Fig. 2.20. For tones with frequencies below 500 Hz the critical

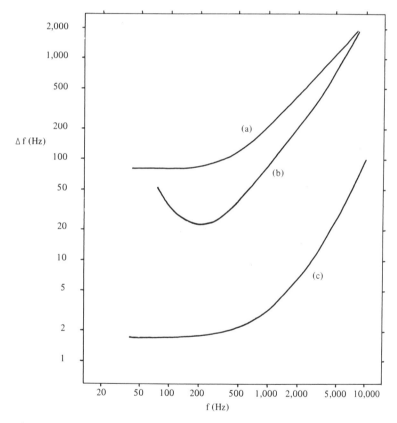

Fig. 2.20. (a) Critical bandwidth. From Zwicker et al. (1957), p.556, Fig. 12.
(b) Minimum frequency separation for which two simultaneous pure tones can still be distinguished. From Plomp (1964), p.1634, Fig. 10.
(c) Minimum detectable sudden change in the frequency of a pure tone. Calculated from Eqn. 4 in Nelson et al. (1983), for SL = 80 dB.

bandwidth is almost constant, at around 100 Hz; as the frequency of a tone is increased above 500 Hz the critical bandwidth also increases. Over most of the audible frequency range the critical bandwidth corresponds to a distance of about 1.3 mm along the basilar membrane: this gives us a rough idea of the effective width of the amplitude envelope.

To find whether two tones lie within one critical band, we first find the centre frequency (that is, the frequency mid-way between the two tones). From curve (a) in Fig. 2.20 we obtain the critical bandwidth at the centre frequency; if the frequency separation of the two tones is less than this bandwidth, they lie within a critical band. For example, the two tones in Fig. 2.19 (a) have frequencies of 523 Hz and 1046 Hz: the centre frequency is ½(523 + 1046) = 784.5 Hz, and the frequency separation is 1046–523 = 523 Hz. This separation is much greater than the critical bandwidth, which at 784.5 Hz is about 150 Hz; the two tones are thus well outside a critical band. For the two tones in Fig. 2.19 (b), the centre frequency is 610 Hz. At this frequency the critical bandwidth is about 130 Hz; the separation of 174 Hz puts the two tones just outside one critical band. On the other hand, the two tones in Fig. 2.19 (c), with a frequency separation of only 65 Hz, are clearly well inside a critical band.

Roughness, beating and the intertone

The interaction of two tones within a critical band takes different forms, depending on the frequency separation. If we start with two tones separated by more than a critical band, and gradually reduce the frequency separation, the first evidence of interaction is a sense of roughness in the sound of the two tones. This roughness becomes more prominent as the frequencies get close, reaching a maximum at a separation of about a quarter of the critical bandwidth (Plomp 1976, p.69).

At this stage, a large number of hair cells in the region of the basilar membrane where the amplitude envelopes overlap will be responding to a signal which is the sum of the two pure tone vibrations. As we saw in

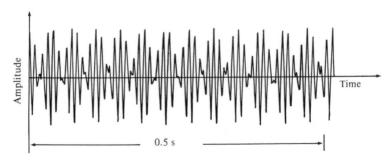

Fig. 2.21. Combination of two pure tones with frequencies 100 Hz and 125 Hz.

Chapter 1, two simple harmonic vibrations with a small frequency difference give rise to beats – periodic fluctuations in the amplitude of the
combined signal. Fig. 2.21 shows the combined signal due to two pure
tones with frequencies of 100 Hz and 125 Hz. These tones are separated
by 25 Hz, about a quarter of the critical bandwidth; as Fig. 2.21 shows, the
amplitude shows strong beats 25 times every second. This periodic 'tickling' of the basilar membrane seems to be responsible for the feeling of
roughness in the sound (Helmholtz 1863, p.255; Terhardt 1974(a)).

As the frequency separation of the tones is further reduced, the beating
continues, but the rate of beating slows down. The sensation of roughness
diminishes, and the beats are perceived as separate pulses in the sound. By
the time this stage is reached, we can no longer identify two separate tones;
instead we hear a single tone of intermediate pitch. The amplitude envelopes on the basilar membrane are now overlapping to such an extent that
the brain recognises only one peak instead of two.

Curve (b) in Fig. 2.20 shows the frequency separation below which two
simultaneous pure tones appear to merge into one. Under 200 Hz the
discriminating ability of the ear for simultaneous tones deteriorates
rapidly: two pure tones with frequencies 65 Hz and 98 Hz will be heard as
a single intertone with a frequency around 82 Hz (Fig. 2.22), although
they are separated by a pitch interval of a perfect fifth.

This is in strong contrast to the ear's ability to distinguish between two
tones which are heard one after the other, rather than together. Curve (c)
in Fig. 2.20 shows that below 500 Hz the average listener can tell the
difference between two successive tones whose frequencies are only 2 Hz
apart; this separation is only one fortieth of the critical bandwidth. Clearly
whatever technique is used by the brain to achieve this remarkable sensitivity is incapable of dealing with more than one tone at a time.

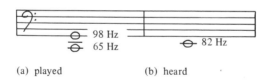

(a) played   (b) heard

Fig. 2.22. Two low pitch pure tones are heard as a single tone of intermediate pitch.

It should be emphasised that our discussion of the frequency discrimination of the ear applies so far only to pure tones. We shall see how the ear
judges the pitch and other properties of complex musical tones in Chapter
3; in Chapter 4 we shall make use of the ideas developed here to explore
the theory of the consonance and dissonance of musical intervals.

DISTORTION IN THE EAR

We have seen that the journey of a sound through the ear involves several different stages. The arrival of a sound wave at the outer ear generates pressure fluctuations which make the eardrum flex in and out; this motion causes vibration of the three ossicles in the middle ear, which in turn creates a vibration of the oval window in the cochlea. The resulting oscillation in the fluid filling the cochlea sends a travelling wave along the basilar membrane; the bending of the membrane fires the hair cells which communicate through the auditory nerve with the brain.

At some point in its journey, the sound signal suffers a curious transformation which has some interesting musical consequences. The signal becomes distorted in such a way that additional components, not present in the external sound wave, are added by the ear. These ear-generated sounds are passed on to the brain along with the original signal. Usually the level of distortion is so low that such additional sounds are not noticeable, but under certain circumstances they can be clearly distinguished as separate pitches. They also exert a more general influence over the way in which we respond to combinations of notes; the distortions generated by major and minor triads, for example, play a significant role in determining the contrasting 'feel' of these chords.

For many years the middle ear mechanism was held to be the culprit: it was thought that the movement of the stirrup in the oval window accurately followed the movement of the eardrum only for very quiet sounds, becoming increasingly inaccurate as the loudness of the sound increased (see, e.g., Helmholtz 1863, p.238; Stevens and Davis 1938, p.196). However, recent measurements have shown that the stirrup motion is a faithful copy of the eardrum vibration at all normal levels of loudness. On the other hand, the point on the basilar membrane at which the amplitude envelope peaks has been shown to behave in a non-linear way: as the stirrup vibration increases in amplitude, the membrane vibration does not increase in proportion (Rhode 1978; Sellick et al. 1982). It thus seems likely that the distortion effects in the ear originate on the basilar membrane.

Aural harmonics

One of the standard ways of testing an amplifier for distortion is to feed in a sine wave and examine the shape of the output signal. If the output is also a pure sine wave the amplifier is free from distortion. By varying the amplitude and frequency of the input sine wave it is possible to discover the limits beyond which distortion appears. Fig. 2.23 shows an example of such a test: for a low amplitude input signal (a) the output is a good sine wave (b), but a high amplitude input signal (c) gives a distorted output (d).

In Chapter 1 we saw that a periodic signal such as that represented by curve (d) in Fig. 2.23 was equivalent to a set of sine waves whose frequencies formed a harmonic series. Thus if we compare the harmonic spectra of input and output signals in Fig. 2.23, we see that the distortion of the wave shape at high amplitude has the effect of introducing harmonic components in the output which were not present in the input signal. If a sine wave with a frequency of 200 Hz is fed into our amplifier, we can find at the output not only an amplified 200 Hz signal, but also components with frequencies of 400 Hz, 600 Hz, 800 Hz, etc.

Measurements performed in the 1920s suggested that this kind of distortion was a significant feature of the performance of the ear (Fletcher 1930). For many years it was believed that a loud pure tone generated a

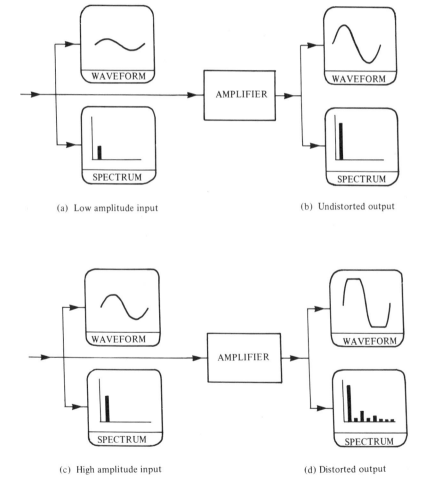

Fig. 2.23. Testing an amplifier for distortion.

series of *aural harmonics* – harmonics created in the ear – some of which were almost as loud as the original tone. It is now generally accepted that this belief was based on a misunderstanding of the early experiments. More recent measurements (Kuriyawaga and Kameoka 1966; Clack et al. 1972) have shown that, although the ear can introduce these distortion products, they are at such a low level in comparison with the original sound that they are of no musical significance.

Combination tones

A type of distortion much more important from the musical point of view arises when two or more pure tones are heard simultaneously. If the two tones are separated in frequency by more than a critical band, we do not experience the beating sensation described earlier, since each tone is activating a separate area of the basilar membrane. We may, however, hear some additional tones which disappear if either one of the original tones ceases to sound. These distortion products are called *combination tones*, since they depend for their existence on the combination of two externally generated tones.

The simple difference tone

The type of distortion which generates aural harmonics would also be expected to generate combination tones. If we hear two pure tones with frequencies f_1 and f_2 (f_2 being higher than f_1), we could anticipate hearing additional tones with frequencies $f_1 + f_2$ (the *sum tone*) and $f_2 - f_1$ (the *simple difference tone*) (Helmholtz 1863, pp.230, 621–623). Whether sum tones can actually be heard remains a matter of some controversy; certainly they are unlikely to be of musical significance. But the simple difference tone is quite a different case: in the right circumstances it is clearly audible (Plomp 1976, pp.28–30), and its musical importance in certain contexts is well established. Indeed, the discovery of the difference tone in the eighteenth century is generally ascribed to the German organist Sorge (1740) and the Italian violinist Tartini (1754).

The simple difference tone is only audible when the original tones are fairly loud, and separated by not much more than a perfect fifth. It is also more obvious if the original tones are high in pitch, since the difference tone can be several octaves below the tones which create it. In their upper register, the flute and the recorder produce sounds close in tone quality to pure tones; duets on these instruments provide good illustrations of difference tones. When the sequence of contracting intervals shown by the open notes in Fig. 2.24 is played by two recorders, the descending arpeggio shown by the black notes can be heard; by consulting the table of pitch and frequency on page 178 the reader can verify that these are the simple differences tones. If the sequence is repeated an octave higher the difference tones (also transposed up an octave) are even more obvious.

Fig. 2.24. Simple difference tones (black notes) generated by two pure tones (white notes).

The cubic difference tone

Anyone carrying out the exercise suggested in Fig. 2.24 will be struck by the discovery that the simple difference tones are by no means the only curious sounds to be heard. Indeed, another set of notes, this time a rising phrase (Fig. 2.25), is even more distinctly audible. These notes are *cubic difference tones*. The name is an historical accident, arising from a mistaken idea about the origin of the cubic difference tone. Its frequency is $2f_1 - f_2$, where f_1 is again the lower of the two original frequencies and f_2 the higher.

Fig. 2.25. Cubic difference tones (black notes) generated by two pure tones (white notes).

Comparing Figs 2.24 and 2.25 it can be seen that, while the simple difference tone frequency falls as the interval decreases, the cubic difference tone frequency rises. There is a more significant contrast between the behaviours of the two types of difference tone: while the simple difference tone becomes noticeable only for fairly loud sounds, the cubic difference tone is already audible when the original tones are at a low loudness level (Plomp 1976). Thus in many musical situations the cubic difference tone is the only significant distortion product.

An illustration of the way in which difference tones can affect our perception of music is provided by the excerpt from Sibelius's Symphony

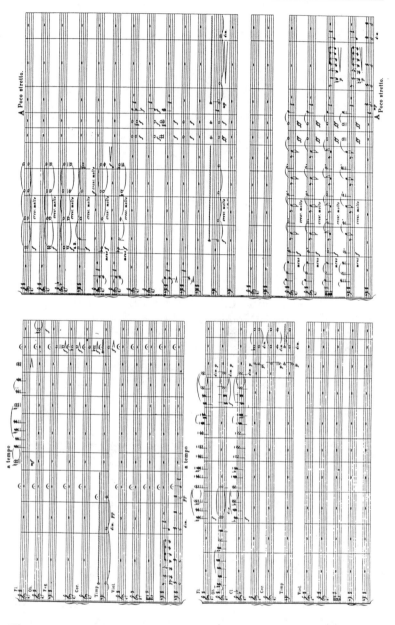

Fig. 2.26. Excerpt from the score of the last movement of Sibelius's Symphony No.1.

No.1 quoted in Fig. 2.26. The finale starts in E minor, and after fifteen bars (at A in the score) has modulated into B minor. The sense of key is maintained for six bars by the tremolando B on basses, reinforced by the timpani roll on B. This mysterious, low pitched rumble dies away; in dramatic contrast, two flutes enter, playing in thirds at a very high pitch. The simple and cubic difference tones generated in the listener's ears by the two flute tones are shown in Fig. 2.27.

The sense of remoteness and desolation engendered by the extreme upward leap in pitch, and by the use of two instruments which in this register create almost pure tones, is heightened by the harmonic implications of the difference tones. In the first three bars of Fig. 2.27, both simple and cubic tones return repeatedly to B♭ ; this is an abrupt transition from the B minor tonality previously established. In the last bar the difference tones are both Gs, forcing an interpretation of the flutes' B and D as part of a chord of G major. This is immediately contradicted by a forte chord of B minor from horns and bassoons.

Fig. 2.27. Difference tones generated by two flutes playing in thirds.

The audibility of combination tones in the example just quoted was brought home to one of the authors while he was participating in a performance of the Sibelius symphony. The passage is an ideal showcase for the phenomenon, since the two instruments are generating two closely spaced high pitched tones, and there are no lower pitched sounds to mask the difference tones. In more typical musical contexts, combination tones are much less prominent, although a practised ear may be able to identify them (Helmholtz 1863, p.328). The possible role of difference tones in either reinforcing or disturbing the harmonic sense of chords is touched on again in our discussion of major and minor triads in Chapter 4 (p.169).

3

Anatomy of a musical note

At the opening of the overture to Wagner's 'Rienzi' a solo trumpet plays a single note, starting pianissimo, swelling to forte and dying away. On the title page of Deryck Cooke's book *The Language of Music* (Cooke 1959) this brief extract is quoted as we have shown in Fig. 3.1, with an enigmatic question mark appended. The question which Cooke implies, and which his book courageously attempts to answer, is a very fundamental one: what did Wagner intend to convey to his audience by this note, and how does the audience understand it?

Fig. 3.1. The opening of the overture to Wagner's 'Rienzi'.

Such matters of musical aesthetics are well outside our remit here. Nevertheless, this quotation can well stand as the motto of the present chapter, if we accept that our question is a more mundane one: what are the factors which distinguish one single tone from any other that we might hear in a musical performance, and how can these factors be measured?

From the musical point of view, the distinguishing factors are immediately obvious; they are explicit in the musical notation. The pitch of the tone is given by the staff notation as the A above middle C, and its variation of loudness by the dynamic markings. The other distinctive feature is the timbre, or tone quality; this is basically determined by the instruction that the note should be played on a trumpet, although the manner of playing (molto sostenuto e maestoso) is also specified.

From the scientific point of view, this tone generates a vibration in the eardrum of the listener. We have seen how to measure and describe the frequency of such a vibration, and to record its amplitude envelope; we know also that the details of the vibration pattern can be represented either by a displacement-time diagram or (more economically) by a harmonic spectrum. In this chapter we examine the relationships that exist between these scientifically measurable quantities and the musical concepts of pitch, loudness and timbre.

PITCH

In Fig. 2.10 the first few bars of the score of Tchaikovsky's 'Romeo and Juliet' are reproduced. Pitch is indicated by staff notation, loudness by dynamic markings, and timbre by the scoring for clarinets and bassoons. We could play the same passage very quietly on the piano, or thunder it out on the organ; such violent changes in loudness and timbre would have no effect on the melodic or harmonic structure of the music. In this light, pitch appears as the most fundamental of the musical attributes of a tone. We shall therefore start by attempting to establish how the pitch of a tone depends on measurable properties of the corresponding vibration. In order to achieve this, we must have an agreed method of measuring and describing changes in pitch.

The subjective nature of pitch

The process of measurement involves comparison with a standard unit. For example, if we wish to measure the length of a rod, we place a ruler alongside it. The ruler is graduated in centimetres and millimetres; these graduations are fractions of the standard metre, the unit of length. The metre was originally defined in 1791 as 1/10,000,000 of the distance from the equator to the pole along the meridian line through Paris. Later an actual metal bar kept carefully in Paris was taken as the standard. In 1983 it was agreed that the metre should be defined as 'the length of the path travelled by light in vacuum during a time interval of 1/299,792,458 of a second' (Giacomo 1983). The important point is that these are all *objective* standards; they leave no scope for argument on the basis of an individual's 'feeling' for length.

The situation is quite different when we consider measurements of pitch intervals. Pitch is a *subjective* sensation, since it is the response of an individual to a particular type of sound vibration. There is no guarantee that two different individuals will respond in the same way to the same sound stimulus. Even when a pure tone of fixed frequency and amplitude

70

is presented alternately to the right and left ears of a single listener with normal hearing, the pitch sensation in the two ears can be up to half a semitone different (Burns 1982). This 'binaural diplacusis' can be much more severe for someone with impaired hearing. Later in this chapter we shall see that the pitch of a tone of fixed frequency depends to some extent on its amplitude. The magnitude and even the direction of this effect varies from individual to individual; if a group of people with normal hearing listen to a pure tone with a frequency of 440 Hz, some will hear the pitch rise as the loudness is increased, while others will hear it fall. We cannot appeal to an objective pitch standard to decide who is 'right': each individual has his own pitch sensation, which is right for him.

Octaves, semitones and cents

It is therefore remarkable that we can construct a scale of pitch intervals which commands almost universal agreement. The basic unit of this scale is the octave. Two pitches separated by an octave are recognised by most listeners as having a strong similarity; if a mixed choir is played the note A_4 and asked to sing it, the male voices will happily respond by singing one or even two octaves below (Fig. 3.2). The feeling that these widely separated pitches are somehow 'the same note' is reflected in the way we describe them by the same letter of the alphabet.

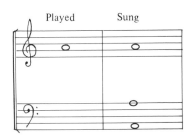

Fig. 3.2. Tones an octave apart are frequently accepted as different versions of 'the same note'.

We shall see later that the vibrations corresponding to two sounds an octave apart have some special properties, which help to explain the unique role of this interval. At this point we shall simply accept gratefully that we have an agreed basic unit of pitch.

We are on shakier ground when we try to agree on the size of a suitable subdivision of the octave. In the diatonic scale the octave is divided into tones and semitones, but the exact size of these intervals depends on the musical context (see Chapter 4). Most musicians would agree, however, that the chromatic scale of Fig. 3.3, played on an equally tempered keyboard, consisted of a succession of 12 equal pitch intervals. Since nearly all modern keyboard instruments are tuned (at least nominally) to equal temperament, it is convenient to accept the equally tempered (ET) semitone as a fact of musical life, and to use it as a subsidiary unit of pitch.

Fig. 3.3. An equally tempered chromatic scale divides the octave into twelve equal pitch intervals.

We shall frequently need to discuss pitch changes which are much smaller than a semitone. For this purpose we can consider the equally tempered semitone to be divided into one hundred *cents*. Since very few people can distinguish two pitches separated by less than a few cents, we do not require a smaller subdivision.

The relationships between the pitch units are thus:

100 cents = 1 ET semitone
1200 cents = 12 ET semitones = 1 octave.

Pitch notation

We have already made extensive use of *staff notation*, in which the pitch is indicated by the vertical positioning of the note-head on a reference frame of horizontal lines. This is the common language of nearly all musicians, and has developed over the centuries into a remarkably sophisticated system for describing the complex pitch variations of many simultaneous musical strands in an orchestral score (e.g. Fig. 1.1).

Staff notation has some drawbacks, however, as an accurate and consistent method of describing pitch. Because it developed from a system of notating modal plainchants, the intervals of pitch between successive horizontal lines are unequal: for example, the lowest two lines in the treble clef are separated by a minor third, whereas the lowest two in the bass clef are separated by a major third. The smallest interval which can normally be displayed is a semitone, although special symbols have been introduced in order to notate smaller intervals (Fig. 3.4).

Fig. 3.4. The major third between F and A divided into eight equal quarter-tones (Kagel 1962).

Occasionally we shall make use of a graphical pitch scale, in which intervals of a semitone are marked off on a vertical line. If the spacing of the lines of the great stave is distorted so that two lines a minor third apart have a separation only three quarters of the separation of those a major third apart, the stave can be fitted against such a graphical pitch scale (Fig. 3.5). This idea provides us with useful musical landmarks on the pitch graph (Young 1967). We should bear in mind, however, that the pitch of a tone can be represented by any point along the vertical graphical scale, whereas in normal staff notation a note is either 'on a line' or 'in a space'.

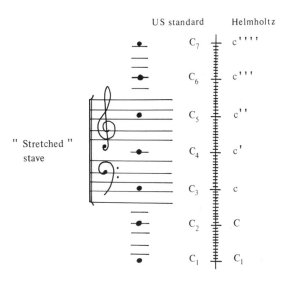

Fig. 3.5. Alternative methods for specifying pitch.

On the pitch scale of Fig. 3.5 we have marked the pitches of seven of the eight Cs on the piano keyboard. It is convenient to be able to identify the particular octave within which a note lies; two common methods of doing this are shown in Fig. 3.5. The rather cumbersome notation originally suggested by Helmholtz, using small and large letters, primes and subscripts, has now been superseded by a system proposed by Young (1939) and adopted by the USA Standards Institute (1960). In this system the lowest C on the piano is labelled C_1. The chromatic scale upwards is denoted by C_1, $C_1^{\#}$, D_1,...B_1, C_2, $C_2^{\#}$... and so on. Thus middle C becomes C_4 and the A of a 440 Hz tuning fork is A_4.

Working downwards from C_1 we have B_0, $B_0^{\flat}$, A...C_0. Do we then require negative subscripts? Fortunately not: the frequency corresponding to the pitch C_0 is 16 Hz, which is just about the lower limit of the sensitivity of the ear. The lowest pitch generated by the normal range of orchestral instruments is the $B_0^{\flat}$ bottom note of the contrabassoon. Even lower notes can be produced by very large organs, but these are generally described as being 'felt' rather than heard.

Factors affecting the pitch of a note

Having equipped ourselves with an agreed scale for measuring pitch intervals, and a suitable system of pitch notation, we can proceed to investigate the factors in a sound vibration which determine its pitch.

The loudness of the trumpet tone quoted in Fig. 3.1 varies over a wide range, from pianissimo to forte. Associated with the changes in loudness are changes in timbre – the tone quality is relatively pure and featureless at the pianissimo level, becoming harder and more brilliant as the loudness increases. The pitch, however, remains constant throughout the duration of the tone.

Let us compare these musical observations with the information about the sound which we can obtain using a microphone and an oscilloscope. The displacement-time curve for the microphone diaphragm, displayed on the screen of the oscilloscope, shows us how the eardrum of a listener vibrates when the sound wave generated by the trumpet falls upon it.

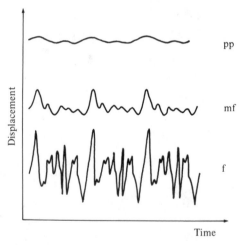

Fig. 3.6. The trumpet note of Fig. 3.1, measured at three dynamic levels.

Fig. 3.6 shows the vibration pattern for three different stages during the crescendo from pp to f. A comparison of the three displacement-time curves reveals that as the loudness increases, the amplitude of the vibration grows, and the waveform becomes less and less like a sine curve; the repetition period, and therefore the frequency, remains constant.

It thus appears that the pitch of the tone remains fixed so long as the repetition frequency does not change. In fact, the pitch is also affected to a small extent by variations in amplitude and waveform; we shall explore some interesting aspects of these topics later. For most practical musical purposes, however, we can assume that a fixed frequency corresponds to a definite pitch. It is on this basis that the standard of pitch is established by quoting its frequency: $A_4 = 440$ Hz.

Pitch and frequency

To investigate how pitch changes with frequency, we can use two electrical oscillators to generate pure tones of known frequency. Setting one oscillator to a fixed frequency of 440 Hz gives (by definition) the standard pitch of A_4. By adjusting the frequency of the second oscillator, we can tune the pitch of its tone to any desired interval relative to A_4. For example, when the variable oscillator is set to 880 Hz the pitch interval between the two tones is an octave; thus we establish that the pitch A_5 corresponds to a frequency of 880 Hz.

The complete result of such an experiment is shown in Fig. 3.7. The first thing to notice is that equal changes in frequency do not correspond to equal changes in pitch. To increase the pitch an octave from A_4 to A_5, as we saw above, the frequency must be increased from 440 Hz to 880 Hz, a difference of 440 Hz; but to make the octave leap from A_5 to A_6 we must increase the frequency from 880 Hz to 1760 Hz, a difference of 880 Hz.

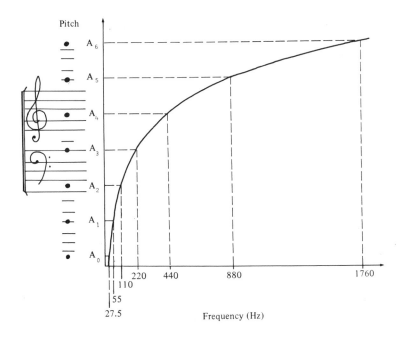

Fig. 3.7. The relationship between pitch and frequency.

On the other hand, when we look at *frequency ratios* we find a simple relationship. The frequency was doubled in the octave step from A_4 to A_5; it was doubled again in the step from A_5 to A_6. From a close inspection of the graph in Fig. 3.7 we can formulate a general rule: whenever the frequency is multiplied by 2, the pitch rises by an octave. Equally, to lower the pitch by an octave, the frequency must be divided by 2. That is, the octave is characterised by a frequency ratio of 2:1.

Frequency ratios of equally tempered intervals

Similar rules apply to other pitch intervals: each interval has its characteristic frequency ratio. For an ET semitone the frequency ratio is almost exactly 1.06:1; the frequency of $A_4^\#$ (on the equally tempered scale) is therefore $1.06 \times 440 = 466$ Hz. To find the frequency of B_4, an ET semitone above $A^\#$, we multiply by a further 1.06, obtaining $1.06 \times 1.06 \times 440 = 494$ Hz. Thus the frequency ratio corresponding to the (ET) tone $A_4 - B_4$ is $1.06 \times 1.06 = (1.06)^2 : 1 = 1.12:1$. This is an illustration of the general rule that when we add two pitch intervals we must *multiply* the corresponding frequency ratios.

Using this rule we can easily find the frequency ratios of other equally tempered intervals. For example, a major third contains 4 semitones; its frequency ratio is therefore $1.06 \times 1.06 \times 1.06 \times 1.06:1 = (1.06)^4 : 1 = 1.26:1$. The octave contains 12 ET semitones, and must therefore have a frequency ratio of $(1.06)^{12}:1$. Since we know that the frequency ratio for an octave is in fact 2:1, we can see that $(1.06)^{12} = 2$. We call 1.06 the 'twelfth root of 2', since 2 is obtained by multiplying 12 1.06s together (a more accurate value for the twelfth root of 2 is 1.05946, but 1.06 is close enough for most musical purposes).

Frequency ratios of just intonation intervals

We saw in Chapter 1 that a complex periodic vibration could be considered as a sum of simple harmonic components whose frequencies were members of the harmonic series. This implies that when we hear a complex musical tone with fundamental repetition frequency f, we are actually hearing a set of pure tones whose frequencies are members of the series f, 2f, 3f, 4f...etc.

Fig. 3.8 shows the pitches of the first six harmonics of a tone with fundamental frequency f = 110 Hz. The 1st and 2nd harmonics are separated by an octave (frequency ratio 2:1); the 2nd and 3rd by a perfect fifth (ratio 3:2); the 3rd and 4th by a perfect fourth (ratio 4:3); the 4th and 5th by a major third (ratio 5:4); and the 5th and 6th by a minor third (ratio 6:5). It is striking that these intervals, which are inherent in a single musical tone such as that described by Fig. 3.1, are the intervals which are normally considered to be musically consonant.

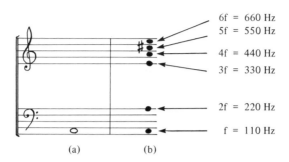

Fig. 3.8. The first six harmonics (b) of a musical tone with pitch A₂ (a).

Intervals corresponding to these simple whole-number frequency ratios are called *just intonation* (JI) intervals. The extent to which JI intervals are used in musical practice remains a matter of controversy. With the exception of the octave, they are not available on an equally tempered keyboard: the JI major third, for example, has a frequency ratio 5:4 = 1.25:1, whereas the ET major third has a frequency ratio 1.26:1 as we saw previously. It certainly seems likely that the simple ratios associated with just intonation reflect some fundamental principle underlying our decision to call certain intervals 'consonant'. We shall return to this topic in Chapter 4, where we shall see that the modern understanding of the behaviour of the ear goes at least some way towards establishing such a principle.

Calculating the size of pitch intervals

The ET major third, with a frequency ratio 1.26:1, is clearly a larger interval than the JI major third, with a frequency ratio 1.25:1. But how much larger? In order to answer this question we must know the size (in cents) of both intervals. The ET major third is 4 ET semitones, or 400 cents. Before we can calculate the size of the JI major third we must look briefly at the mathematical nature of the pitch-frequency relationship.

We have seen that equal pitch *intervals* correspond to equal frequency *ratios*, regardless of the absolute values of pitch and frequency. If a note has a frequency f, the note one octave above has a frequency 2f. A second octave step involves another doubling of frequency: the new frequency will be 2 × (2f) = 4f. For a further octave step, we multiply by a further factor of 2, so that the frequency rises to 2 × (4f) = 8f.

Using power notation, we can write $2 = 2^1$, $2 \times 2 = 2^2$, $2 \times 2 \times 2 = 2^3$, etc. In Table 3.1 the frequency ratios corresponding to multiple octave intervals are shown both as normal numbers and as powers of 2.

TABLE 3.1

Frequency ratios of multiple octave intervals

Pitch interval	Frequency ratio (f_2/f_1)	Power of 2 corresponding to f_2/f_1 $= \log_2 (f_2/f_1)$
1 octave	2	1
2 octaves	4	2
3 octaves	8	3
4 octaves	16	4

The power of 2 corresponding to a particular number is called the *logarithm (to base 2)* of that number. For example, $8 = 2 \times 2 \times 2 = 2^3$; 3 is thus the logarithm (to base 2) of 8, written $\log_2(8)$. From Table 3.1 it is immediately obvious that the size of a pitch interval is proportional not to the frequency ratio (f_2/f_1) but to the *logarithm* of the frequency ratio. In fact, we have the simple relationship:

$$\text{pitch interval (in octaves)} = \log_2(f_2/f_1).$$

Since there are 1200 cents in an octave, this is equivalent to:

$$\text{pitch interval (in cents)} = 1200 \log_2(f_2/f_1).$$

Although it might seem from the foregoing discussion that we could only find $\log_2(f_2/f_1)$ if f_2/f_1 was an exact power of 2, a more sophisticated treatment than that given here enables us to find the logarithm of any number. In practice, logarithms to base 10 (written $\log_{10}$) are normally used; the 'log' button on many pocket calculators gives $\log_{10}$ of the

TABLE 3.2

Frequency ratios and pitch intervals in cents.

Pitch interval	f_2/f_1	Size of interval (cents)
Octave	2	1200
Perfect 5th (JI)	$\frac{3}{2} = 1.5$	702
Perfect 5th (ET)	1.498	700
Perfect 4th (JI)	$\frac{4}{3} = 1.333$	498
Perfect 4th (ET)	1.335	500
Major 3rd (JI)	$\frac{5}{4} = 1.25$	386
Major 3rd (ET)	1.26	400
Minor 3rd (JI)	$\frac{6}{5} = 1.2$	316
Minor 3rd (ET)	1.189	300

number keyed into the calculator. Since $\log_2$ of any number is obtained from the corresponding $\log_{10}$ simply by multiplying by 3.322, it is easy to rewrite the formula for calculating pitch intervals in terms of logarithms to base 10:

$$\text{pitch interval (in cents)} = 1200 \log_2(f_2/f_1) = 1200 \times 3.322 \log_{10}(f_2/f_1)$$
$$= 3986 \log_{10}(f_2/f_1).$$

In Table 3.2 we show the sizes of several common musical intervals, in both just intonation and equal temperament, calculated from the above formula.

It is easier to judge the musical significance of small tuning discrepancies expressed as pitch intervals in cents rather than as frequency ratios. For example, we can see from Table 3.2 that the JI perfect fifth is only 2 cents (i.e. two hundredths of a semitone) wider than the ET perfect 5th; on the other hand, the JI major third is 14 cents (about one seventh of a semitone) narrower than the ET major third. Such calculations provide the basis for our discussion of scales and temperaments in Chapter 4.

Pitch and amplitude

The pitch provided by an A = 440 Hz tuning fork is usually accepted without question by musicians as an accurate and consistent standard to which instruments can be tuned. If we examine the sound generated by a tuning fork we find that after some initial high pitched components have died away we are left with a pure tone of constant frequency but steadily diminishing amplitude (Fig. 3.9). Can we be sure that the pitch does not change as the amplitude decreases?

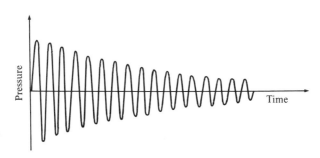

Fig. 3.9. The decaying sound radiated by a tuning fork (the rate of decay is normally much slower than that illustrated).

Unfortunately, for most listeners the pitch of a pure tone does depend on amplitude as well as on frequency. The nature and extent of the amplitude dependence varies very widely from person to person, but in general the pitch of a low frequency tone is heard to fall when the amplitude is increased. Fig. 3.10 shows the results of experiments carried out in the 1930s by Stevens (1935) and Snow (1936). It is remarkable that the listeners tested in this study found that the pitch of pure tones in the bass clef dropped by up to 4 semitones as the amplitude was increased from a level which gave a just audible tone up to a point where the sound was almost painfully loud. Pitches around C_7 were found to be almost

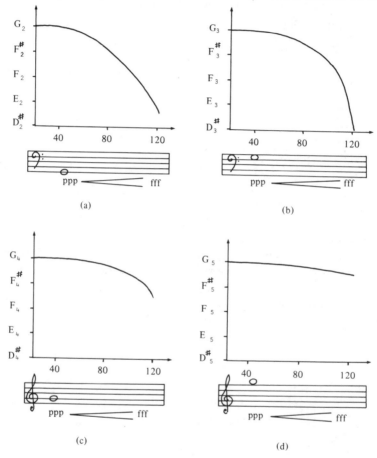

(a)

(b)

(c)

(d)

Fig. 3.10. (a) A pure tone of frequency 98 Hz has a pitch G_2 when heard ppp. As its loudness increases to fff, its apparent pitch can drop to below E_2.

(b), (c) and (d) show the corresponding variation of pitch with loudness found by Snow for pure tones with frequencies 196 Hz, 392 Hz and 784 Hz respectively. The curves shown are derived from Stevens and Davis (1939), p.74, Fig. 24.

Numbers along the horizontal axes are quantitative measurements of the loudness level in phons: the use of this loudness scale is explained later in the chapter.

independent of amplitude; above G_7 the pitch was observed to rise as amplitude increased.

At first these results appear to fly in the face of musical experience. We know that when we play Fig. 3.11 (a) on the piano we do not hear Fig. 3.11 (b); we hear a series of Gs at constant pitch. However, we saw in Chapter 1 that a piano string has a complex vibration pattern, and the sound radiated by a piano G_2 is far from being a pure tone (in the technical sense of having a sinusoidal waveform). Indeed, an isolated pure tone is rarely encountered in musical practice, and for the complex tones generated by most musical instruments the effect of amplitude on pitch seems to be insignificant (Lewis and Cowan 1939). We shall return shortly to consider how the ear interprets the pitch of complex tones; it is worth noting that if complex tones exhibited the same dependence of pitch on amplitude as do pure tones, the technical difficulty of low-pitch instruments would be fearsome, and an instrument like the 'piano-forte' would be in principle impossible.

Fig. 3.11. According to the measurements shown in Fig. 3.10, the phrase (a) played using pure tones of constant frequency would sound as phrase (b).

Several instruments generate almost pure tones in their highest register – the flute has already been quoted as an example. Fortunately such notes lie in the frequency region where pitch-amplitude effects are small. The tuning fork problem, with which we introduced this discussion, is a more serious case. If a tuning fork (A = 440 Hz) is struck loudly, most listeners can detect a drop in pitch as the prongs of the fork are brought up to within a few millimetres of the ear. When the fork is moved a few centimetres away the pitch rises again; the change can be a significant fraction of a semitone. Clearly an oboist must resist the temptation to hold a tuning fork too close to his ear while giving an A to the rest of the orchestra.

Pitch of complex tones

The trumpet note in Fig. 3.1 is not a pure tone – even at the pianissimo level its waveform is not a pure sine curve, and its complexity increases as the loudness grows (Fig. 3.6). A harmonic analysis of the sound at the fortissimo level shows that at least fifteen harmonic components are contributing significantly (Fig. 3.12(a)). A similar analysis of the note B_1^b played on the trombone shows that more than twenty components are present in this rich sound (Fig. 3.12(6)). In other words, when we hear the trombone play B_1^b, we are actually hearing more than twenty simultaneous pure tones. How is it, then, that we hear not twenty separate pitches, but only one?

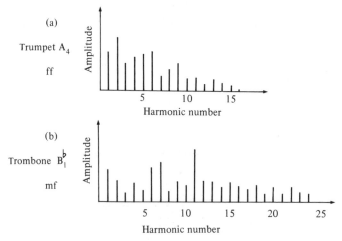

Fig. 3.12.   (a) Harmonic spectrum of the note A_4 played ff on the trumpet. (b) Harmonic spectrum of the note B_1^b played mf on the trombone.

If we listen carefully to a musical tone, we may in fact be able to hear some of the pure tone components in the sound. The brain can be persuaded to focus on a particular component if the expected pitch is sounded beforehand. For example, when the note C_3 is played on the piano, the second harmonic component has the pitch C_4; if C_4 is sounded quietly beforehand, as in Fig. 3.13, this pitch can be heard in the decaying

Fig. 3.13. An exercise in distinguishing individual harmonic components of a complex tone. When the white notes of the exercise are played on the piano, the black notes should be audible.

sound from the struck C_3. If G_4 is sounded beforehand, the third harmonic is more easily heard, since its pitch has been suggested to the brain. (The harmonics are often heard most clearly a few seconds after the note has been struck.)

The ability to distinguish the pure tone components of a complex tone varies from person to person. The seventeenth century musical theorist Marin Mersenne found it possible to hear the first seven members of the harmonic series distinctly; other investigators, perhaps blessed with more vivid imaginations, have claimed to be able to hear up to twenty-seven. Careful modern experiments have shown that harmonics above the eighth member of the series cannot be distinguished by the majority of listeners (Plomp 1964).

This limitation can be understood by returning to the idea of critical bands, introduced in our discussion of the ear in Chapter 2. If two harmonic components fall within one critical band they will be generating signals in the same region of the basilar membrane, and will be difficult to distinguish. In Fig. 2.20 the critical bandwidth was given in terms of frequency; in Fig. 3.14 the curve is redrawn in terms of pitch. For tones above C_5 the bandwidth is fairly constant at around 3 semitones, but as the pitch falls the bandwidth rapidly increases. For C_2 the bandwidth is about two octaves; all pure tones below C_2 fall within the same critical band, since all predominantly excite the same small region of the basilar membrane (near the helicotrema).

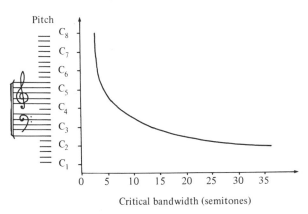

Fig. 3.14. Variation of critical bandwidth with pitch.

In Fig. 3.15 the pitches of the first twelve harmonics of C_3 are shown. For each harmonic, the width of the critical band is indicated by a vertical bar. Up to the 6th harmonic, the bars do not overlap; each harmonic is in a separate critical band, and should be distinguishable from its neighbours. Above the 6th harmonic the separation between adjacent harmonics is less than a minor third, which is the critical bandwidth in this region of pitch; the bars overlap, and the corresponding pitches become difficult to distinguish.

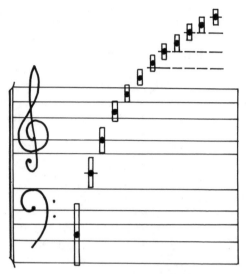

Fig. 3.15. The first twelve harmonics of C_3, shown as black circles on the stretched stave. The width of the critical band around each harmonic is indicated by a vertical bar.

Fusion of pure tone components

We have seen that the inner ear performs a partial frequency analysis of a complex musical tone, sending to the brain a distinct signal recording the presence of each of the first seven or eight harmonic components; in addition the brain receives signals from the part of the basilar membrane activated by the unresolved upper harmonics (Fig. 3.16). In normal musi-

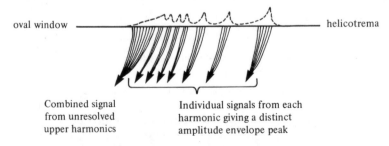

Fig. 3.16. Schematic diagram illustrating the signals sent to the brain when the basilar membrane is vibrating in response to a sound containing many harmonics.

cal listening we do not, however, perceive the lower harmonics separately; we hear only a single tone. This process by which the brain combines a previously analysed set of pure tones into a sound with only one pitch is known as *fusion*.

The pitch of a fused set of harmonics is essentially that of the fundamental (or 1st harmonic) of the series. If we record the sound of the note C_3, with the six harmonic components shown in Fig. 3.17 (a), and replay it through an amplifier with treble and bass controls, we can progressively remove the upper harmonics by turning down the treble control. The pitch of the tone remains constant even when all the harmonics except the first have been filtered out, leaving us with a pure tone of pitch C_3 (Fig. 3.17(b)). (We are ignoring for the moment the subtle effect discussed on p.93.)

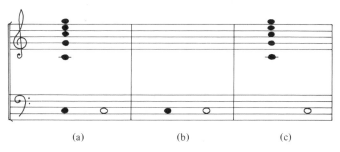

(a)   (b)   (c)

Fig. 3.17. (a) A set of six harmonics (black notes) gives a fused tone with
pitch C_3 (white note).
(b) When all harmonics but the first are removed, the pitch is
unchanged (white note).
(c) The set of harmonics from the second to the sixth (black
notes) is still perceived as having the pitch C_3 (white note).

We might be tempted to conclude from this experiment that the fundamental gives the pitch, while the upper harmonics merely add 'tone colour'. This simple theory can be shaken immediately by a further experiment. If we turn down the bass control of our amplifier, rather than the treble control, we can progressively remove the *lower* members of the harmonic series. When the fundamental has been filtered out completely, we still hear the pitch C_3, even though the lowest pure tone reaching our ears now has a pitch C_4, an octave higher (Fig. 3.17 (c)).

A set of pure tones fuse into a single pitch only if they are members of a harmonic series (or a close approximation). If the tones are not harmonically related, each tone is heard separately, and there is no definite feeling of pitch associated with the complete sound. Fletcher (1924) pointed out a unique feature of the harmonic series f, 2f, 3f ...: the frequency difference between adjacent members of the series is constant, and equal to f, the fundamental frequency. He suggested that the 'missing fundamental' in

Fig. 3.17 (c) was reintroduced by the ear as a unison set of difference tones. Fig. 3.18 illustrates this theory: the 2nd and 3rd harmonics (C_4 and G_4) give a difference tone C_3, as do the 3rd and 4th harmonics (G_4 and C_5); each succeeding pair of harmonics reinforces the difference tone with pitch C_3. Thus when we hear a set of upper harmonics, distortions in the ear add a *subjective fundamental*.

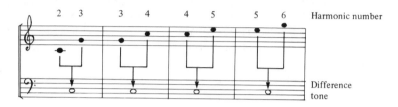

Fig. 3.18. Each pair of adjacent harmonics in Fig. 3.17 (a) (shown here by black notes) generates the same simple difference tone C_3 (shown by a white note).

The subjective fundamental is often clearly audible; however, in 1938 Schouten demonstrated that it is not responsible for the fact that a tone complex like Fig. 3.17 (c) is assigned a pitch lower than any of its component tones. He constructed a sound source which generated a set of upper harmonics, together with a fundamental component which had the same amplitude as the subjective fundamental but was 180° out of phase with it. The externally introduced fundamental therefore exactly cancelled the subjective fundamental; nevertheless, the pitch heard was still an octave below the lowest pure tone component present (the 2nd harmonic) (Schouten 1938). Similar results were later obtained when the subjective fundamental was masked by a band of noise (Licklider 1954; Patterson 1969).

Experiments with slightly inharmonic tone complexes

In 1956 de Boer reported the results of some experiments which provided a new insight into the way in which pitch is perceived (de Boer 1956; Plomp 1976, pp.118–120). In one of these experiments, listeners were played a complex tone consisting of five pure tone components with frequencies 600 Hz, 800 Hz, 1000 Hz, 1200 Hz and 1400 Hz. Since this is a harmonic series based on 200 Hz, with the first two components missing, the listeners heard a pitch corresponding to a 200 Hz tone (Fig. 3.19 (a)). They were then asked to compare the pitch of this tone with that of another set of five components, each shifted relative to the corresponding members of the first set by a constant frequency difference. In the example shown in Fig. 3.19 (b), this difference was 80 Hz, so that the second set consisted of pure tones with frequencies 680 Hz, 880 Hz, 1080 Hz, 1280 Hz and 1480 Hz. Although these frequencies were no longer members of an exact harmonic series, the deviation was small enough for the sound still to be heard as a fused tone. The pitch, however, had risen by nearly 200 cents, being matched by a single tone of around 220 Hz.

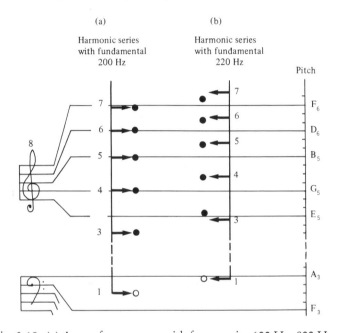

Fig. 3.19. (a) A set of pure tones with frequencies 600 Hz, 800 Hz, 1000 Hz, 1200 Hz, and 1400 Hz (black notes) is perceived as a single fused tone with frequency 200 Hz (white note).
(b) When each component has its frequency increased by 80 Hz, the set is no longer a harmonic series; the brain finds that a harmonic series with fundamental frequency 220 Hz (arrows) is a reasonable fit to the actual components, so hears the sound as a fused tone with frequency 220 Hz (white note).

The significance of this result is twofold. First, it provides another proof that difference tones are not the principal cause of the pitch of a tone complex like Fig. 3.19 (a). If they were, the pitch of the inharmonic complex Fig. 3.19 (b) would not be higher, since the frequency difference between successive members of this set is still 200 Hz. Second, the experiments of de Boer, together with many more recent experiments (de Boer 1976), suggest that the brain determines the pitch of a complex tone by searching for a harmonic pattern among the components separately resolved in the inner ear (Wightman 1973; Goldstein 1973; Terhardt 1974 (b)). For the set in Fig. 3.19 (a), an exact match is found to a harmonic series based on 200 Hz, and the perceived pitch is therefore the same as that of a pure 200 Hz tone. For the inharmonic set (b), the brain finds that a harmonic series based on 220 Hz provides the closest resemblance to the components provided; it considers the resemblance adequate, and therefore registers the sound as a complex tone with pitch equivalent to 220 Hz.

If the deviation from a true harmonic series is made much larger than that in Fig. 3.19 (b), the brain gives up the attempt to find a single matching set of harmonics. The components are then heard separately, rather than as a fused tone; several low pitches may also be heard, corresponding to possible (but ambiguous) harmonic matches.

Pitch as the recognition of a harmonic pattern

Our understanding of the ways in which the brain processes signals from the sensory organs is developing rapidly at present, and the pattern recognition theory of pitch is not yet universally accepted. It does, however, explain many features of musical sound which puzzled earlier generations of acousticians. We need no longer search for a 'missing fundamental' in the harmonic spectrum of a bassoon playing E_3 (Fig. 3.20): the brain recognises the pure tones analysed by the inner ear as the 2nd, 3rd and 4th members of a harmonic series based on E_3, and generates the sensation corresponding to that pitch. A combination tone of pitch E_3 will certainly be introduced by distortion in the ear, and may well be audible. If so, it will contribute one more piece of evidence which the brain can use in identifying the pitch of the bassoon note (Smoorenburg 1970;

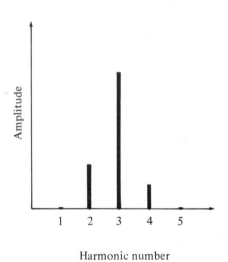

Fig. 3.20. Harmonic spectrum of the note E_3 played mf on the bassoon.

Plomp 1976, pp.122–124). But the three harmonics actually present in the sound reaching the ear provide sufficient evidence in any case that the pitch is E_3.

We observed earlier that two tones an octave apart are perceived as having a special relationship – as being, in a sense, 'the same note'. Some researchers have suggested that the sense of pitch associated with a tone has two different attributes: *tone height*, which simply measures how 'high' or 'low' the pitch is, and *chroma*, which is a quality shared by all notes described by a particular letter (Bachem 1950). Thus C_2 and C_3 are separated in tone height by an octave, but both have the same chroma – that associated with all Cs. The relationship between tone height and chroma is often illustrated by a *pitch spiral* (Fig. 3.21) (Drobish 1855; Revesz 1954; Shepard 1982).

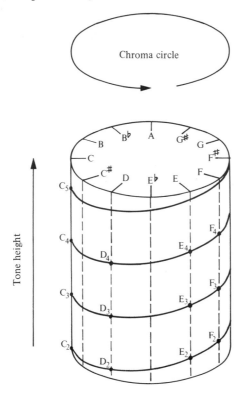

Fig. 3.21. Part of the pitch spiral.

In one interpretation of the pattern recognition theory of pitch, the brain searches for a distribution of peaks along the basilar membrane corresponding to a harmonic series of vibrations. On this basis, the fact that C_2 and C_3 evoke almost the same sensation can be readily understood.

In Fig. 3.22 the motion of the basilar membrane is illustrated schematically for the case in which a complex tone of pitch C_2 is being heard. The first seven harmonics excite separate peaks at positions indicated by horizontal bars; the higher harmonics are separated by less than a critical band, and their excitations merge into a continuously distributed disturbance stretching towards the oval window.

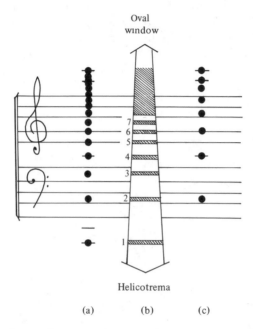

(a)   (b)   (c)

Fig. 3.22. A complex musical tone with pitch C_2 contains a set of harmonic components (a); each generates an amplitude peak on
the basilar membrane (b). To obtain the basilar membrane
pattern for the note C_3 (c), it is necessary only to remove the
odd numbered peaks in (b).

If the pitch of the tone heard changes from C_2 to C_3, no new parts of the basilar membrane will be excited. The 1st harmonic of C_3 generates a peak at the same position as the 2nd harmonic of C_2; the peak generated by the 2nd harmonic of C_3 is already present as the 4th harmonic of C_2. In other words, the excitation pattern for C_3 is contained *within* the excitation pattern for C_2. The fact that the pitch heard corresponds to C_3 rather than C_2 (or, for that matter, F_1 or C_1) implies that, having found various possible matching harmonic patterns, the brain selects the one with the highest fundamental frequency.

The discussion so far has concentrated on the signal sent to the brain by one ear. Normally, of course, both ears are active, providing information which is synthesised in the brain. That this central synthesis really occurs has been demonstrated by the experiments of Houtsma and Goldstein (1972). They showed that two adjacent upper harmonics were sufficient to establish the pitch of a tone in a musical context – for example, two pure tones with pitches B_5 and D_6 heard simultaneously in one ear were readily recognised as a single complex tone with pitch G_3. They then proceeded to show that this fusion still occurred even when one component was presented to the right ear and the other to the left. Clearly in the latter case each basilar membrane would have only a single amplitude peak; the addition of the signals, and the recognition of a harmonic pattern, must therefore occur further down the line, in the central nervous system.

For an instrument like the recorder, whose sound is close to a pure tone over much of its range, the evidence on which the brain must make its pitch match can be rather thin, and it is particularly easy to misjudge the octave in which the instrument is playing. This is especially the case when other sounds are present (for example, in ensemble playing). Indeed, in the sixteenth and seventeenth centuries it was customary to use a recorder in a group consisting otherwise of stringed instruments, playing the alto line an octave higher than the written part (Morley 1599; Praetorius 1619, p.21). David Munrow explained this practice by noting that to many people the recorder appears to be sounding an octave lower than is actually the case (Munrow 1976, p.53).

We have seen that our response to a musical sound can be divided into two stages:
(1) a partial frequency analysis of the sound vibration by the ear; and
(2) the interpretation by the brain of the signals sent to it by the ear through the auditory nerve.
The foregoing discussion has emphasised the importance of the second stage. Our ability to follow one part in a complex orchestral score depends to a large extent on the brain's ability to perceive a pattern even when supplied with incomplete evidence. Additional information is provided by the musical context, and by our knowledge of the score – in a sense, we hear what we expect to hear.

A striking illustration of the importance of context and expectation is offered by a recent experiment in which listeners were asked to judge the pitch of a complex tone consisting of a varying number of upper harmonics (Houtgast 1976). When the 5th, 6th and 7th harmonics of G_3 were present, most listeners could hear the pitch of the complex tone as G_3 (Fig. 3.23 (a)); this pitch sensation was still evident when only two harmonics were present (Fig. 3.23 (b)). When some background noise was added, the pitch sensation became much clearer. Indeed, with a noisy background, many listeners could hear the pitch G_3 even when the sound presented to them contained only one upper harmonic (Fig. 3.23 (c)).

At first sight it appears paradoxical that a single pure tone of pitch B_5 can evoke the sensation of a pitch G_3, more than two octaves below. It should be noted, however, that in this experiment the attention of the listeners had been focused previously on the pitch region around G_3 by a reference tone of that pitch. If, instead, the expectation of the pitch E_3 had been raised, the pure tone B_5 would have been heard (in a noisy background) as having the pitch E_3. It is significant that the brain is only willing to accept the evidence of a single harmonic in this way if there is reason to believe that other harmonics are being drowned by the background noise.

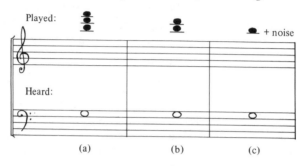

Fig. 3.23. The sensation of pitch G_3 (white note) can be evoked by three upper harmonics (a), or two upper harmonics (b). Even a single harmonic will suffice if background noise is present (c).

Dominant harmonics in pitch perception

Many musical sounds consist of sets of components which are slightly inharmonic. Important examples are the plucked and struck strings (e.g. harp and piano), discussed fully in Chapters 6 and 7. We saw in Fig. 3.19 (b) that the brain determines the pitch of such sounds by finding the best-matching harmonic series. In making this match the brain does not treat all the components present as having equal importance. Several experiments with electronically generated sounds have shown that there is a *dominance region* of frequency, roughly between 500 Hz and 2000 Hz; the pitch of a complex tone is determined principally by the components which lie within this dominance region (Plomp 1967; Ritsma 1967; Bilsen 1973).

The results of these experiments are summarised in Fig. 3.24. For notes in the bass clef, the 4th and 5th harmonics play the most significant role in establishing the pitch of a complex tone. At the top of the treble clef, the 2nd and 3rd harmonics are of greatest importance. Interestingly, it is only for tones at the upper extreme of the musical range (above C_7) that the 1st harmonic is the dominant factor in establishing the pitch.

Some modern 'pitch meters' operate on a complex tone by filtering out the upper frequency components and measuring the frequency of the fundamental. This can produce a misleading result with inharmonic tones. Consider, for example, a measurement of the note C_2 played on a piano. For reasons which will be discussed in Chapter 7, the 5th component of

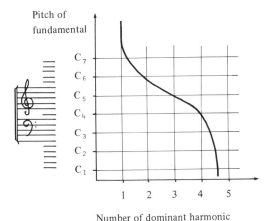

Fig. 3.24. The dominant harmonic in the perception of the pitch of a complex musical tone; based on Plomp (1976), p.117, Fig. 46.

this tone is likely to be around 10 cents sharper than a true 5th harmonic based on the fundamental vibration frequency of the string. Since the 5th harmonic is the dominant component, the pitch heard will be sharper than that registered by the meter.

Even with a sound whose components form an exact harmonic series, we cannot assume that the pitch corresponds exactly to that of a pure tone at the fundamental frequency. Experiments using sounds with a large number of high harmonic components have shown that such sounds are commonly perceived as having a pitch up to 30 cents flatter than that of the fundamental alone (Walliser 1969 (b); Terhardt 1971 (a)). This anomaly appears to be related to the fact that the pitch of one pure tone is altered by the addition of another pure tone at a different frequency (Terhardt and Fastl 1971). In general, the pitches appear to 'repel' one another: the lower tone drops in pitch, while the upper one rises. It has been suggested that this can be explained by shifts in the positions of the maxima on the basilar membrane (Plomp 1976, p.140).

For a complex tone consisting of several harmonics, we would expect this 'mutual repulsion' to shift the lower harmonics downwards and the upper harmonics upwards. Such effects have indeed been demonstrated for sounds with six harmonics, and fundamental frequencies below 400 Hz (Terhardt 1971(b)). The way in which the shifts of individual components affect the overall pitch associated with a complex tone is not yet clear, although it seems plausible that a large retinue of powerful high harmonics could depress the pitch of those lower harmonics which lie in the dominance region. Fortunately, such sounds have a very harsh timbre, and are rarely encountered in conventional musical practice; most sounds produced by orchestral instruments contain little energy above the 10th harmonic, and for such sounds pitch shifts associated with changes in harmonic spectrum can usually be ignored. They may, however, assume practical significance in electronic and computer-generated music (see Chapter 13).

Pitch discrimination

Like most human faculties, the ability to detect small changes in the pitch of a tone varies considerably from person to person. A keen musical ear is usually considered a vital attribute for a musician. We shall see in Chapter 4, however, that remarkably large variations in intonation occur in musical performances of the highest quality; these variations pass unnoticed by discerning audiences. Indeed, deliberate mistunings are an essential feature of the temperament of all keyboard instruments. It is therefore worth establishing at this point the limit below which pitch variations can be considered undetectable by the average listener.

In Chapter 2 we saw that for frequencies below 500 Hz a frequency difference of around 2 Hz was necessary for two pure tones to be reliably distinguished. Since a fixed pitch interval corresponds to a fixed frequency *ratio*, the pitch interval between 50 Hz and 52 Hz tones (frequency ratio 1.04:1) is much larger than that between 500 Hz and 502 Hz tones (frequency ratio 1.004:1), although both pairs of tones are only just distinguishable to the average ear. Thus although the *frequency* discriminating ability of the ear for pure tones remains roughly constant at low frequencies, *pitch* discrimination deteriorates dramatically at low pitches.

This deterioration is shown in curve (a) of Fig. 3.25, which is the frequency discrimination curve of Fig. 2.20 (c) redrawn in terms of pitch. Maximum sensitivity to small pitch changes is found between C_5 and C_8, where the pitch discrimination threshold is around 6 cents. In other words, if the semitone between C_6 and $C_6^{\#}$ (just above the treble clef) were divided into sixteen equal intervals, each of the seventeen notes spanning this semitone could be distinguished in pitch from its neighbours. In contrast, a tone of pitch C_2 (just below the bass clef) would have to change in pitch by half a semitone before the average ear became aware of any difference.

The pitch discrimination curve (a) in Fig. 3.25 was measured by experiments in which the pitch of a tone was changed from one steady value to another, with a short gap of silence between. Small pitch differences are more difficult to detect when the pitch is varied cyclically between upper and lower limits. Curve (b) in Fig. 3.25 was measured with the pitch fluctuating up and down four times every second; this is close to the frequency of musical vibrato. The span of the pitch fluctuation which was just detectable was about twice that shown in curve (a) for abrupt changes in pitch.

Curves (a) and (b) were both measured using fairly loud tones. Pitch discrimination is poorer for quiet tones: curve (c) shows that for a pianissimo tone the width of vibrato which is just noticeable as a variation in pitch is twice as great as that for a tone at the forte level.

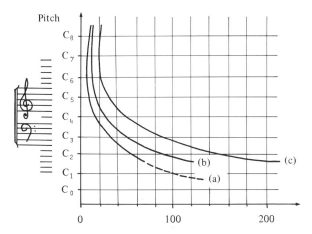

Minimum detectable pitch change (cents)

Fig. 3.25. The smallest pitch change which can just be detected in a pure
      tone by the average listener.
      (a) Abrupt change in loud tone; calculated from Eqn. 4. in
      Nelson et al. (1983), with SL = 80 dB.
      (b) Steady fluctuation in loud tone; based on Zwicker (1956),
      p.369, Fig. 6. SPL = 80 dB.
      (c) Steady fluctuation in quiet tone; based on Zwicker (1956),
      p.369, Fig. 6. LL = 30 phons.

The curves in Fig. 3.25 reveal an astonishing lack of pitch sensitivity at low pitches. According to curve (a), the average listener would be hard pressed to detect any change in pitch when a pure tone B_0 was followed by a pure tone C_1. Yet this interval is clearly recognisable as a semitone when it appears in a musical context – for example, in the contrabassoon solo which opens Ravel's Piano Concerto for the Left Hand (Fig. 3.26).

Contrabassoon
(sounding an
octave lower
than written)

Fig. 3.26. The opening contrabassoon solo from Ravel's Piano Concerto
      for the Left Hand.

The reason for this apparent discrepancy becomes clear when we recall that the pitch of a complex musical tone is determined, not by the fundamental component, but by those harmonics which lie in the 'dominance region'. When the contrabassoon plays the note C_1, it generates a sound rich in upper harmonics (Fig. 3.27); many of these harmonics lie in the region above C_5, where pitch sensitivity is greatest. Although a deviation of 20 cents would pass unnoticed in the fundamental, the same change in the eighth harmonic (C_4) would be easily detected, and the brain would be alerted to the change of pitch. For this reason, the pitch discrimination threshold for a sound rich in upper harmonics remains at around 10 cents down to the lowest musically significant pitch (Walliser 1969(c)).

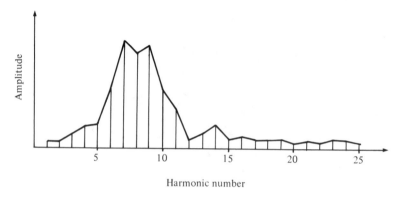

Fig. 3.27. Average spectrum envelope for a contrabassoon playing the note C_1.

Absolute pitch

One of the most fascinating aspects of pitch perception is the ability, possessed by a small minority of musicians, to generate or identify a specified pitch without access to a reference pitch. This ability is commonly described as 'perfect pitch', although the more meaningful term *absolute pitch* has come to be used by scientists studying the phenomenon.

In the light of our understanding of the behaviour of the inner ear, it is possible to speculate on how absolute pitch judgements might be made. A pure tone of frequency 440 Hz generates a maximum response at a particular place on the basilar membrane, and a bundle of nerve fibres from this place carries a signal to the brain. If the listener has learned at some stage to identify the stimulation of this bundle of nerve fibres with the name 'A_4' (or, indeed, any other name), then whenever the bundle is stimulated in the future the brain will respond with the corresponding name.

From this point of view it is surprising that so few people have this gift. The great majority of musicians possess only *relative pitch*: that is, the ability to generate or identify any pitch when supplied with a standard pitch as reference. Relative pitch is essentially interval recognition; given a standard A_4 from a tuning fork, the trained musician can recognise $C_6^{\#}$ as an octave plus a major third higher (whether or not such interval labels are consciously used). But after a time, or some distraction, the standard pitch is forgotten, and the ability to name pitches accurately disappears.

Is absolute pitch simply a good memory for a pitch standard? And if so, can the ability to memorise a standard pitch be developed with practice? These questions have occupied scientists and musicians for over a hundred years, and clear answers are still awaited (Stumpf 1883; Abraham 1901; Ward and Burns 1982). Many attempts have been made to 'learn' absolute pitch; while some improvements in pitch-naming ability have been reported (Meyer 1899; Gough 1922; Cuddy 1971), it has proved difficult to approach the level of performance of those who possess absolute pitch innately. However, in 1970 Paul Brady proved that it was possible to develop absolute pitch to a high degree by submitting himself to a learning programme using computer-generated tones (Brady 1970); subsequent tests showed that his pitch recognition was as accurate as that of natural possessors of absolute pitch (Carroll 1975). It has been suggested that the memory of a pitch standard is imprinted in natural possessors of absolute pitch in early childhood, and can only be learned subsequently with great difficulty (Copp 1916).

One interesting feature of absolute pitch recognition is that when errors are made they are often octave errors. That is, a tone of pitch C_5 is described as C_4, or C_6. This lends support to the idea that the brain recognises two aspects of pitch sensation – tone height and chroma (see Fig. 3.22). Absolute pitch is primarily an ability to recognise the chroma of a tone (i.e. whether it is a C, an $E^{\flat}$, or an A), and only secondarily an ability to place the tone within the correct octave.

Possessors of absolute pitch often perform more accurately when asked to name pitches played on the piano than when they are presented with pure tones. This may be because complex tones provide more material for the brain's 'pitch processor' to work on, or it may be because of clues associated with changes in timbre and other features of the sound of this particular instrument. Indeed, it has been suggested that the ability to name piano tones should be described as 'absolute piano' rather than 'absolute pitch' (Ward and Burns 1982, p.436).

Recently Gerald Balzano carried out tests on three people (including himself) who were capable of almost 100% accuracy in pitch naming (i.e. chroma identification) of piano tones (Balzano 1984). He found that they achieved levels of accuracy of between 84% and 95% with pure tones. In other words, the pitch was still correctly named about nine times out of ten. Balzano observed that most of the mistakes occurred in the lowest octave used in the test (A_2–$A_3^\flat$), and consisted of naming the pitch a semitone sharper than the correct value. At the other end of the pitch scale, he noticed a slight tendency to judge pitches above A_5 a semitone flat. These results suggest that the internal pitch scale used in making absolute pitch judgements is slightly 'stretched' relative to the standard pitch scale. A 440 Hz tone is recognised unambiguously as A_4; but a 110 Hz tone is perceived as a little too high for A_2, and is sometimes labelled $A_2^\sharp$. There is considerable evidence that relative pitch judgements, made by musicians without absolute pitch, also use a 'stretched' internal scale on which an octave between two successive tones corresponds to a frequency ratio slightly greater than 2:1 (Ward 1954; Terhardt 1971(b)).

The possession of absolute pitch is clearly of great advantage in many musical activities, such as the performance of modern vocal music with wide melodic leaps and an absence of tonal reference. However, it is not an unmixed blessing. Since the basic pitch reference seems to become established at an early age, a subsequent change in the pitch standard used in performance can cause distress to a performer who finds himself constantly obliged to play 'out of tune'. The violinist André Mangeot, who grew up in France with absolute pitch based on the standard continental European A of 435 Hz, relates that his first solo recital in England was ruined by his inability to adjust to an accompanying piano tuned to the 'Old Philharmonic' pitch of A = 452 Hz, nearly 70 cents higher (Mangeot 1953, p.14). The current practice of performing renaissance and baroque music at 'authentic' pitches, with As varying from 360 Hz to 510 Hz, must also cause some mind-boggling among possessors of absolute pitch.

There is also the opposite problem: although the external pitch standard remains fixed, the internal pitch reference may drift with time. In Chapter 2 we saw that the basilar membrane is stiffest at the end nearest the oval window, increasing in flexibility towards the helicotrema. A pure tone of pitch C_4 generates a wave on the basilar membrane which reaches maximum amplitude at a point determined by the stiffness of the membrane, stimulating a bundle of nerve fibres which (we have postulated) the possessor of absolute pitch has learned to identify with the name 'C_4'. If the elastic properties of the membrane change with age, the wave generated by this pitch will reach its peak amplitude at a different point on the membrane. A shift of around a quarter of a millimetre towards the oval window would cause the peak generated by the note C_4 to stimulate the bundle of nerve fibres previously associated with $C_4^\sharp$; the note C_4 would therefore be identified as '$C_4^\sharp$' (Fig. 3.28).

Philip Vernon has suggested this explanation of his own experience as a possessor of absolute pitch (Vernon 1977). At the age of 52 he began to notice a tendency to identify keys one semitone higher than they should be. After a time it became clear that his internal pitch scale had moved down by a semitone. This was particularly disconcerting to him, since he had come to identify particular keys with particular moods – the overture to Wagner's 'Die Meistersinger', in the appropriately 'strong and masculine' key of C major, was now perceived as being in C# major, which to Vernon had a 'lascivious and effeminate' character!

Fortunately the process continued, and by the time Vernon was 71 'Die Meistersinger' had drifted into the (presumably) sturdier key of D major. Several other possessors of absolute pitch have reported a similar drift in the internal standard. Of course, there is no reason why changes in the elasticity of the basilar membrane should be confined to possessors of absolute pitch. It may well be that most people in middle age hear music a semitone higher than they did as children; only those with absolute pitch would be aware of the change.

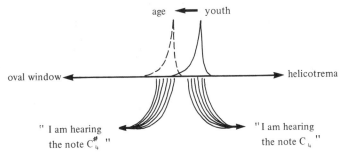

Fig. 3.28. A possible explanation of a shift in the internal scale of absolute pitch with age. The basilar membrane amplitude peak generated by a 262 Hz tone gradually drifts towards the oval window, but the labelling of the nerve fibre signals remains unaltered.

LOUDNESS

We have seen that musicians in general do not have an internal scale of absolute pitch; they do, however, possess a very keen sense of relative pitch. Although this subjective pitch sensation has been shown to vary to a small extent with changes in the amplitude and harmonic spectrum of a complex musical tone, it is determined almost entirely by just one feature of the vibration pattern of the tone: its fundamental repetition frequency.

We turn now to the second musical attribute of a sound – its loudness. We must recognise at once that the problem is not as clear-cut as in the case of pitch. From the musical point of view, loudness is expressed by dynamic markings (p,f, etc.), which are much less definite than the precise pitch specifications normally provided in a score. There is a corresponding lack of agreement as to just what does constitute 'f' rather than 'mf' in a given musical context; this reflects an inherent variability in our subjective loudness scale.

From the scientific point of view, too, loudness is a more troublesome quantity than pitch. In Fig. 3.6 we saw the pressure fluctuations corresponding to a trumpet tone at three different dynamic levels. A re-examination of these curves shows that greater loudness corresponds to greater amplitude in the pressure fluctuations. It is tempting to conclude that, just as pitch is basically determined by frequency, loudness is determined basically by pressure amplitude. If this were true, then a pure tone of constant pressure amplitude should have constant loudness regardless of its frequency. Unfortunately, experiment shows that this is far from being the case: the loudness of a pure tone depends strongly on its frequency as well as on its pressure amplitude. The shape of the vibration waveform also has a pronounced effect on loudness. A further complication arises from the fact that the loudness of one tone can be strongly modified by other tones sounded simultaneously, or shortly before.

In order to arrive at an understanding of how loudness can be measured and described in musically useful ways, we must start with the simplest case: a single pure tone of fixed frequency. Later we shall broaden our discussion to consider how the loudness of a pure tone changes with its frequency; then how the loudness is affected by the presence of another pure tone. Finally we can discuss the loudness of realistic musical sounds, with complex harmonic spectra.

Pressure and intensity in sound waves

Let us consider, then, the arrival of a sound wave corresponding to a pure tone of frequency 1000 Hz (1 kHz) at the ear. We choose this frequency (corresponding to a pitch 21 cents above B_5) because it is a standard frequency for acoustical tests, and has been used in many experiments in hearing.

When we listen to sound in a normal room, the waves reaching our ears come from many different directions (see p.525). We shall further simplify the discussion at this point by considering a single wave with constant amplitude (a 'plane wave' in the jargon of physics), travelling directly towards one ear.

When the sound wave arrives, pressure fluctuations at the eardrum generate vibrations which are transmitted through the middle ear and into the cochlea. While the tone continues to sound, energy is being extracted from the sound wave by this ear mechanism; some of the energy is being converted into electrical signals from which the brain derives its information about the sound. It is not surprising to find that the loudness perceived by the brain increases with the rate at which energy is absorbed by the ear.

How does the rate of energy absorption depend on the pressure amplitude? To understand this relationship we need to make use of the idea that when a force moves an object, it transfers energy to the object. The amount of energy transferred to the object is the product of the magnitude of the force (F) and the distance the object moves in the direction of the force (d):

$$\text{energy transferred} = Fd.$$

The rate at which energy is transferred is therefore the product of the force and the rate of motion (the velocity v):

$$\text{rate of energy transfer} = Fv.$$

If the eardrum has an area A, the force exerted on it by a pressure p is F = p A. (In all our discussions, it should be noted, p is the fluctuating part of the pressure caused by the sound wave; this fluctuation is superimposed on the much larger steady atmospheric pressure. In the present case the steady component on the outside of the eardrum is cancelled by the equal and opposite pressure on the inside, in the middle ear.) Hence the rate at which energy is transferred to the eardrum is R = pAv.

Since the sound being heard is a pure tone, the variation of p with time is sinusoidal (Fig.3.29(a)). The variation of v is also sinusoidal, but in general there is a phase difference between p and v. The most efficient transfer of energy occurs at frequencies around 4,000 Hz, where p and v are in phase. The two quantities are then simply proportional:

$$v = p/z,$$

where z is the specific acoustic impedance of the eardrum (see p.45). This expression for v can be substituted in the formula for the energy transfer rate:

$$R = pAv = pA(p/z) = p^2 \, A/z.$$

The fluctuating pressure p is alternately positive and negative (Fig. 3.29

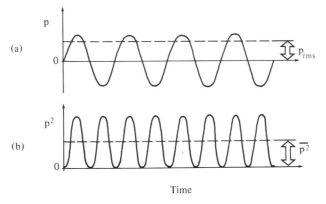

Fig. 3.29. (a) Variation of pressure with time in a pure tone sound wave.
(b) Variation of the square of the pressure with time.

(a)). Since the energy transfer rate depends on p^2 it is always positive, but does not have a steady value; it rises and falls between zero and its peak value twice every cycle (Fig. 3.29 (b)). A useful quantity is the average energy transfer rate, given by $\overline{p^2}$ A/z. Here $\overline{p^2}$ is the *mean square pressure*; this is simply the value of p_2 averaged over a complete cycle. The square root of $\overline{p^2}$ is known as the *root mean square pressure* or the *effective pressure*, and is usually written p_{rms} or p_e. For pure tones, p_{rms} is equal to the pressure amplitude divided by $\sqrt{2}$; for complex tones there is no such simple relationship.

The average energy transfer rate depends on the area and impedance of the eardrum. As we shall see shortly, the actual value of the pressure at the eardrum varies with the size and shape of the ear canal. Thus the amount of energy extracted from a given sound wave will vary from person to person. If the sound wave falls instead on an open window of area $1m^2$ (Fig. 3.30) placed perpendicular to the direction of travel of the wave, all the energy in this cross-section will pass through. The energy transfer rate through this standard area is a fixed and measurable property of the wave: it is called the *intensity* of the wave.

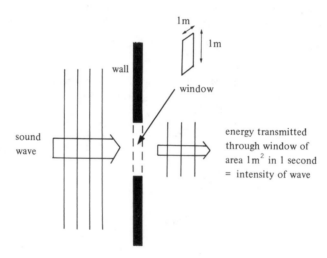

Fig. 3.30. Illustrating the definition of the intensity of a sound wave.

Bearing in mind that the specific acoustic impedance of a 'wall' of air is 415 rayls (p.46), we can see from the preceding discussion that the intensity of a wave of effective pressure p_e is given by

$$I = p_e^2 A/z \text{ with } A = 1m^2$$
$$z = 415 \text{ rayls}$$

$$= p_e^2/415.$$

In the international system of units now generally accepted in scientific work, energy is measured in joules (abbreviated J). The energy transfer rate can therefore be measured in joules per second (Js⁻¹); because energy transfer rates are important in many different fields, this unit has its own special name, the watt (W). The unit of intensity, which is the energy transferred per second by a sound wave across unit area, is thus the watt per square metre (Wm⁻²).

Sound power of musical instruments

The watt is familiar in everyday life as the unit of electrical power. A light bulb may be rated at 100W; this means that when switched on it will convert electrical energy into light and heat energy at a rate of 100 joules per second. An electric food mixer rated at 500 watts absorbs 500 joules of electrical energy every second. Some of this electrical energy is converted into mechanical energy, appearing as motion of the rotating blades which chop up the food. The mixer gets warm when it has been running for a time: this shows that some of the electrical energy is being converted into heat. And the fact that the mixer generates a fairly loud noise while it is running shows that electrical energy is being partly converted into a third form: sound energy.

The sound output of the mixer is of course an undesired by-product of its primary function, which is to chop up food; out of the total of 500 watts, perhaps only a tenth of a watt is converted into sound energy. Yet in terms of loudness this is quite a powerful source. We find a similar situation when we examine musical instruments as sources of sound energy. Only a small fraction of the energy expended by the player is radiated as a sound wave (Bouhuys 1965), and the *sound power* (sound energy radiated per second) is typically a small fraction of a watt even when the instrument is played at its loudest level.

Table 3.3 gives examples of the maximum sound power radiated by a

TABLE 3.3

Sound source	*Maximum sound power (watts)*
Orchestra (75 performers)	70
Flute	0.06
Clarinet	0.05
Horn	0.05
Trumpet	0.3
Trombone	6
Tuba	0.2
Bass drum	25
Double bass	0.16

symphony orchestra consisting of seventy-five performers, and by several of the individual instruments which it contains (Sivian et al. 1931).

Clearly the maximum sound power will depend on the performer, and on the particular instrument being played. The measurements in Table 3.3 must therefore be treated with caution; they are merely typical values for the instruments concerned. The most striking feature of the table is the enormous range of sound powers: the trombone radiates a hundred times as much sound energy per second as does the horn when both are playing fortissimo. Members of brass quintets, which customarily contain both horn and trombone, are familiar with the problem of maintaining a balance of loudness between the two instruments. We shall see shortly, however, that the way in which the ear responds to sound energy reduces the significance of these dramatic disparities in sound power.

Sound power and intensity

A typical trombone bell has a radius of about 0.1 m, and an area $A = \pi R^2 \simeq$ 0.03 m^2. Since the intensity of a sound wave is the power transmitted across unit area, we can obtain a rough estimate of the intensity at the bell by dividing the total radiated power (P) by the area of the bell. At maximum loudness $P \simeq 6$ W, and $I \simeq P/A$.

$$\simeq 6/0.03$$
$$\simeq 200 \ Wm^{-2}$$

Of course, it would be most unwise to place one's ear just in front of the bell of a trombone playing very loudly – this intensity is high enough to cause permanent damage to the ear (see p.137).

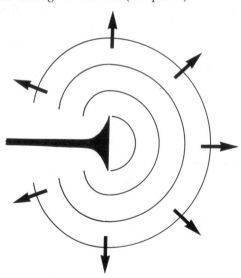

Fig. 3.31. Radiation of sound from a trombone bell.

Fortunately for the health of bassoonists, who find themselves sitting in front of the trombones in the standard orchestral layout, the intensity drops rapidly as the distance from the instrument increases. This happens because the sound wave does not simply radiate in a straight line forward from the instrument, but spreads out in all directions (see Fig. 3.31). Spreading is an inevitable consequence of diffraction; we saw in Chapter 1 that a wave passing through an aperture of width D suffers a large degree of diffraction if the wavelength λ is much bigger than D. The trombone is rarely called upon to play above C_5, with a wavelength of 0.7 m. Thus the wavelength is always at least three times the bell diameter, and diffraction is important. Indeed, at the lower end of the pitch range of the instrument, there is a negligible difference between the intensity of the sound radiated forwards and that radiated backwards (see Meyer (1978)).

A sound source radiating with equal intensity in all directions is called an *isotropic source*. For such an idealised source we can derive a simple relationship between the sound power (P) of the source and the intensity (I) at a given distance (R). Let us consider the source to be surrounded by an imaginary sphere of radius R, with a 'window' of area 1 m² marked out on the surface of the sphere (Fig. 3.32). The total area of the sphere is $4\pi R^2$, so that the area of the window is a fraction $1/4\pi R^2$ of the total area of the sphere. Every second, P joules of sound energy are emitted by the source; because sound energy does not build up inside the sphere, P joules must pass out through the surface of the sphere every second. Since this energy is uniformly spread out over the area of the sphere, the energy passing through the 1 m² window every second is P times $1/4\pi R^2$. But this is just the definition of the intensity of the sound wave reaching the window. Hence, for an isotropic source,

$$I = P/4\pi R^2.$$

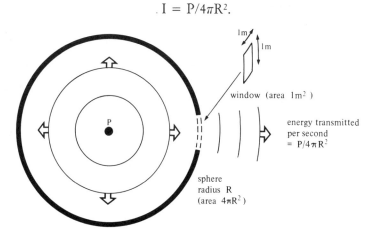

Fig. 3.32. The intensity at a distance R from an isotropic source radiating P watts of sound power is $I = P/4\pi R^2$.

As an illustration of the use of this formula, Fig. 3.33 shows how intensity varies with distance from an isotropic source of power 1 W. At a distance of 1 m, we find I from the formula by substituting P = 1, R = 1:

$I = 1/4\pi \simeq 0.08$ Wm^{-2}.

Since the intensity depends on $1/R^2$, doubling the distance causes the intensity to drop by a factor of 4; at 10 m the intensity is only 1/100th of its value at 1 m.

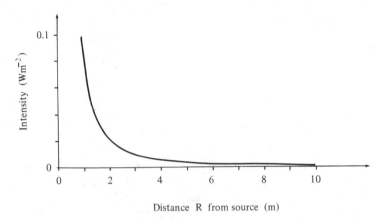

Fig. 3.33. Variation of intensity with distance from an isotropic source of sound power 1 W.

We must be cautious about using this formula to describe the behaviour of musical instruments in indoor settings. Apart from the fact that no real instrument behaves as an exactly isotropic source, we have ignored the effect of sound reflected from the walls of the room. We shall see in Chapter 14 that this 'reverberant' sound increases the intensity received by a listener from a sound source of given power, and reduces the rate at which it falls off with increasing distance from the source. Only in the open air, far from buildings and trees, can we expect our formula to apply, and even there reflections from the ground provide a complication. One of the nineteenth century pioneers of acoustical research, Professor Alfred Mayer, was driven to carry out some of his experiments 'in the middle of an open level field in the country on nights when the air was calm and noiseless' (Mayer 1876). Under these circumstances, a ticking clock placed on top of a post provided an acceptably isotropic source – although his experiments were periodically disturbed by the croaking of frogs, and the bark of a distant dog.

The musical dynamic scale

Intensity and pressure are objective properties of a sound wave, which can be measured using appropriate equipment. How are these objective properties related to the subjective sensation of loudness?

The loudness of musical sounds is usually prescribed by dynamic markings, ranging from pp (very quiet) to ff (very loud). This scale is often extended downwards to ppp (extremely quiet) and upwards to fff (extremely loud). Some composers have gone even further in specifying extremes of volume: in Fig. 2.9 we saw Tchaikovsky requiring ffff in the third movement of his 6th Symphony, and in the first movement of the same symphony (bar 160) the bassoon is (somewhat optimistically) asked to play a solo phrase pppppp.

If we take our standard 1000 Hz pure tone and ask musicians to rate its dynamic level at different intensities, we shall almost certainly find a considerable range of disagreement. Part of this disagreement will simply correspond to age differences – as we get older, we get deafer, and an intensity which sounded f at age 20 may only be mf at age 60. Most people with reasonably acute hearing find a 1000 Hz tone with an intensity of 0.01 Wm^{-2} extremely loud, so we might rate this fff on the musical dynamic scale. A reduction of the intensity by a factor of ten brings the tone roughly to the ff level; a further factor of ten to the f level; and so on. We thus arrive at the rough correspondence between intensity and musical dynamic level (for a single, isolated 1000 Hz tone) shown in Table 3.4.

TABLE 3.4

Musical dynamic level	Intensity (Wm^{-2})	IL (dB re 10^{-12} Wm^{-2})
fff	10^{-2}	100
ff	10^{-3}	90
f	10^{-4}	80
mf	10^{-5}	70
mp	10^{-6}	60
p	10^{-7}	50
pp	10^{-8}	40
ppp	10^{-9}	30

In Table 3.4 we have expressed intensities using the negative power convention, in which $10^{-3} = 1/10^3 = 1/1000 = 0.001$. This convention is very useful, since the high sensitivity of the ear means that very quiet sounds have extremely small intensities. From the Table we can see that a ppp tone has an intensity of only 10^{-9} Wm^{-2} (0.000000001 Wm^{-2}). The range of intensities is also remarkable: for a fff tone, the intensity is ten million times greater than for a ppp tone.

The fact that each of the conventional dynamic steps corresponds approximately to multiplying the intensity by a factor of 10 may remind us of the relationship between pitch and frequency: in that case, too, a standard musical step (the octave) corresponds to multiplication of the relevant physical variable (frequency) by a constant factor (2). Just as we found that the logarithm of the frequency ratio gave us a useful measurement of pitch interval, we shall find that the logarithm of the ratio of two intensities provides a valuable way of describing the difference in dynamic level.

The decibel

Table 3.4 shows that if a tone of intensity I_1 is one dynamic step louder than another of intensity I_2, the *intensity ratio* $I_1/I_2 = 10$. Thinking of 10 as 10^1, and recalling that $\log_{10}$ of a number is the power of 10 which corresponds to that number, we can see that in this case $\log_{10}(I_1/I_2) = 1$. If the tone of intensity I_1 is to dynamic steps above that of intensity I_2, then $I_1/I_2 = 10^2$ and $\log_{10}(I_1/I_2) = 2$. Thus the number of dynamic steps between the two tones is at least roughly equal to the logarithm (to base 10) of the intensity ratio.

If $\log_{10}(I_1/I_2) = 1$, the intensity ratio is said to be 1 bel (the unit is named after Alexander Bell, the inventor of the telephone). For more accurate measurements, this unit is subdivided into 10 *decibels*, abbreviated dB. Thus

$$\text{intensity ratio (in dB)} = 10\log_{10}I_1/I_2.$$

The intensity ratio corresponding to one step on the musical dynamic scale is therefore about 10 dB (for a pure tone at 1000 Hz).

Now that we have some idea of the relationship between intensity and musical dynamic level we can draw some interesting conclusions. If we have one instrument playing with a certain sound power and a second joins in, playing in unison with the first and radiating the same sound power, what will be the effect on the dynamic level? We must be careful here – the findings summarised in Table 3.4 relate only to pure tones at 1000 Hz. So let us consider two flutes playing a unison B_5; this has a frequency close to 1000 Hz, and in its upper register the flute has an almost pure tone. To avoid complications due to interference (p.33), we must also make the fairly realistic assumption that the phase difference between the two instruments is varying randomly.

If the listener is equidistant from the two instruments, he will receive the same intensity from each; thus the entry of the second flute will double the intensity. Since $\log_{10}(2) = 0.3$, the intensity increase can be expressed as $10\log_{10}(2) = 10 \times 0.3 = 3$dB. This is a fairly small increase in loudness – about a third of one dynamic step. To increase the loudness by a whole step (e.g. from mf to f), ten instruments would be required instead of one. A further step (from f to ff) would require one hundred instruments – assuming each played with constant sound power.

The result of this calculation agrees with musical experience. A choir of 300 is undoubtedly capable of producing a louder sound than a choir of 30, but the difference in volume is not as great as might be expected from the disparity in size. A hundred years ago it was customary to perform baroque choral masterpieces such as Handel's 'Messiah' or the Bach B minor Mass using enormous choruses, with orchestras to match. Recently the pendulum of musical fashion has swung back to favour a performing style using much smaller forces, in keeping with the normal musical practice of the baroque period. The result has been a gain in clarity and articulation, paid for by a remarkably small decrease in sheer loudness.

Open air performance

> Behold her, single in the field,
> Yon solitary Highland Lass!
> Reaping and singing by herself;
> Stop here, or gently pass!   (Wordsworth 1847)

A singer in the open air sounds quite different from the same performer indoors. A large part of this difference is related to the absence of reverberation, and to the associated rapid decrease of loudness with distance. If we can bring ourselves to treat Wordsworth's Highland Lass as an approximately isotropic sound source, we can assume that the intensity of her song would vary inversely with the square of the distance between her and the poet. Thus doubling the distance would reduce the intensity by a factor of 4; since $\log_{10}(4) = 0.6$, this corresponds to a drop of $10 \log_{10}(4) = 10 \times 0.6 = 6$ dB. The result is independent of the actual distances involved: the intensity at 10 m would be 6 dB below that at 5 m, while the intensity at 20 m would have dropped a further 6 dB.

Intensity level and sound pressure level

It is important to realise that decibels measure *ratios* rather than absolute quantities. A difference of 3 dB between two sounds tells us that one has twice the intensity of the other, and will sound a little louder; but it does not tell us whether both sounds are very loud, or very quiet.

In order to have an absolute logarithmic intensity scale, which we can relate directly to the musical dynamic scale in Table 3.4, we require a standard intensity which any other intensity can be compared to. (In the same way our relative pitch scale of octaves, semitones and cents was turned into an absolute scale by anchoring it to the standard pitch $A_4 = 440$ Hz.) The standard intensity chosen is $I_0 = 10^{-12}$ Wm^{-2}; this is slightly below the lowest intensity of a 1000 Hz tone which can just be heard under optimum listening conditions by someone with acute hearing.

We can now define the *intensity level* (abbreviated IL) of a sound by comparing its intensity I to the standard intensity I_0:

$$IL = 10 \log_{10} (I/I_0)$$

For example, a tone of intensity $I = 10^{-8}$ Wm^{-2} has 10,000 times the standard intensity, since

$$I/I_0 = 10^{-8}/10^{-12} = 1/10^8 \times 10^{12}/1 = 10^4.$$

Hence its intensity level is $IL = 10 \log_{10}(10^4) = 10 \times 4 = 40$ dB. Using this formula, the intensities in Table 3.4 have also been expressed as intensity levels.

For a uniform sound wave travelling in one direction (Fig. 3.30), or the spherical waves radiating from an isotropic source (Fig. 3.32), intensity and pressure are related by the expression derived on p.102:

$$I = p_e^2/415.$$

At the standard intensity $I_0 = 10^{-12}$ Wm^{-2}, the effective pressure is $p_0 = 2 \times 10^{-5}$ Pa (the unit of pressure is the *pascal*, abbreviated Pa). In the absence of a sound wave the air has a steady pressure of 10^5 Pa. It is truly remarkable that our ears can detect a sound corresponding to a change in atmospheric pressure of a few parts in ten thousand million.

Even more remarkable is the fact that, for this only just audible sound, the amplitude of vibration of the eardrum is about 10^{-11}m. This is less than a tenth of the diameter of the smallest atom. Until recently it was believed that the vibrations of the basilar membrane were of even smaller amplitude (Békésy 1960), and that the inner ear had some incredible way of sensing a motion of the membrane which was nowhere greater than one thousandth of an atomic diameter. The discovery of sharp, high peaks in the amplitude envelopes of quiet sounds has changed this picture: but even these peaks are still probably only about 10^{-10}m high for a just audible sound (Rhode 1978). Explaining this degree of sensitivity remains a major challenge to scientists studying the ear (Schroeder 1974).

Most microphones are sensitive to pressure rather than to intensity. Strictly speaking, measurements using such microphones should be quoted not as intensity levels but as *sound pressure levels*. The sound pressure level (SPL) of a tone with effective pressure p_e is defined as

$$SPL = 10 \log_{10} (p_e^2/p_0^2) = 20 \log_{10} (p_e/p_0)$$

with $p_0 = 2 \times 10^{-5}$ Pa. When a lot of reverberant sound is present, IL and SPL measurements can differ by several dB; for isotropic sources in the open they give identical values. For most musical purposes they can be used interchangeably, and from now on we shall ignore the difference.

Loudness and frequency: the threshold of audibility

If we know the intensity level of a 1000 Hz pure tone, Table 3.4 allows us to make a rough estimate of its loudness on the musical dynamic scale. When we alter the frequency of the tone while keeping the intensity level constant, the apparent loudness changes. This effect is illustrated in musical terms in Fig. 3.34, for a pure tone playing an arpeggio of G major from G_7 to G_0 at a constant intensity level of 60 dB. The tone sounds loudest at the highest pitch (corresponding to the highest G on the piano keyboard). The loudness falls by about one dynamic step as the pitch drops to G_5, rises slightly around G_4, then falls with increasing rapidity as the pitch descends through the bass clef region. Even under optimum listening conditions, the last note (G_0) would be completely inaudible.

Fig. 3.34. The loudness of a pure tone of constant intensity level 60 dB varies from mf at pitch G_7 to inaudibility at pitch G_0.

The threshold of audibility is the lowest intensity level at which a pure tone can be heard by a listener with acute hearing (Sivian and White 1933). Since we cannot hear G_0 at an IL of 60 dB, the threshold of audibility must be greater than 60 dB at 25 Hz. If the intensity is gradually raised, the acute listener will hear the 25 Hz tone at an IL of about 64 dB. From a large number of such experiments, the threshold intensity level has been measured over the complete range of audible frequencies, resulting in the curve furthest to the left in Fig. 3.35.

The threshold curve shows that the ear is most sensitive to pure tones with pitches around C_8, two octaves higher than the standard frequency of 1000 Hz. Indeed, between C_7 and E_8 the threshold intensity level is below 0dB. All this means is that the minimum audible intensity is smaller than the standard intensity $I_0 = 10^{-12}$ Wm^{-2}. At 1000 Hz the threshold IL is 4dB, showing that to be heard at this frequency a pure tone must have an intensity a little more than twice I_0.

The sensitivity of the ear falls off dramatically at low pitches, as we have already observed. The threshold at 25 Hz (64 dB) is 60 dB higher than that at 1000 Hz (4 dB): to hear a pure tone at pitch G_0, we require a million times greater intensity than at pitch C_6. The threshold curve does not continue below C_0 (16 Hz), because although pressure fluctuations of lower frequency can be detected at sufficiently high intensity, they do not give rise to a sensation of pitch.

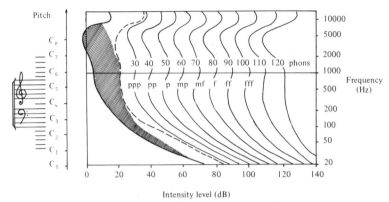

Fig. 3.35. Equal loudness contours, adapted from Robinson and Dadson (1956). The curve on the left represents the threshold of audibility for an acute listener. The dashed curve, representing the threshold for an average listener, and the shaded area, representing masking by typical concert hall background noise, are adapted from Fletcher (1953), pp.135–136.

At frequencies above 4000 Hz the threshold also rises. The highest frequency which can be heard is usually between 15,000 and 20,000 Hz. This limit decreases with the age of the listener, and many older people can hear nothing above 10,000 Hz. Fortunately, these very high frequencies are of little significance in music.

It should be emphasised that the solid threshold curve in Fig. 3.35 refers to listeners with acute hearing, tested in a soundproof laboratory from which distracting background noises have been carefully excluded. Only one person in a hundred has such sensitive hearing; if we invited all the members of a concert audience along to the laboratory and tested them, we would find quite a few with thresholds 30 dB or 40 dB higher. The dashed curve in Fig. 3.35 represents the intensity level at which half the audience would still hear the tone, while half would find it inaudible: this gives a more useful measure of the threshold for the average listener. Apart from an octave or so above C_7, this average threshold never falls below an IL of 20 dB.

In the concert hall we must also consider the effect of background noise. The movements of the audience, the operation of the ventilation system, the failure to exclude completely the hubbub of the world outside – all contribute to the creation of a minimum level of sound even when no instrument is playing. Although we are usually aware only of the occasional peaks caused by a cough, or the creak of a seat, the background noise has the effect of raising the threshold of audibility. This effect is illustrated in Fig. 3.35 by the shaded area. Pure tones in this area are above the laboratory-tested threshold for an acute ear, but would be inaudible in a concert hall with an average level of background noise.

From Fig. 3.35 we can see that there is no point in performing at intensity levels below 20 dB in a concert hall. The average listener would find all pure tone components up to C_7 in pitch inaudible because they fell below his (laboratory) threshold; even the most acute listeners would find these components drowned in the background noise.

Equal loudness contours: phons

Fig. 3.34 illustrated the way that the loudness of a pure tone of IL = 60 dB varied with pitch. Instead of keeping the intensity level constant, we can adjust the intensity so that at each frequency the loudness is the same.

Starting at 1000 Hz with an IL of 60 dB and steadily lowering the frequency, we find it necessary first to lower and then to raise the intensity in order to keep the loudness of the tone constant. At 440 Hz (A_4) an IL of 56 dB matches the loudness of the 1000 Hz tone at 60 dB; at 110 Hz (A_2) the loudness match is obtained with an IL of 66 dB.

This variation of IL with frequency for constant loudness is shown in Fig. 3.35 as an *equal loudness contour*. All the combinations of frequency and IL mentioned in the preceding paragraph lie on the same equal loudness contour, labelled '60 phons' in Fig. 3.35. The *phon* is the unit of *loudness level* (LL) (Barkhausen 1926): we say that a pure tone has a loudness level of 60 phons if it sounds as loud as a tone with IL = 60 dB at the standard frequency of 1000 Hz. Thus the equal loudness contour is in fact a line of constant loudness level.

From Table 3.4, we see that a 1000 Hz pure tone with IL = 60 dB has a loudness roughly corresponding to the dynamic marking 'mp'. But, by definition, a pure tone with loudness level LL = 60 phons matches this loudness at all frequencies. Thus a tone of any pitch with LL = 60 phons will sound 'mp'. Similarly a tone with LL = 90 phons will sound 'ff', regardless of its pitch. The intensity level (in dB) is an objective measure, telling us how much energy is being carried by the sound wave; the loudness level (in phons) is a subjective measure, telling us how loud the tone will sound.

Equal loudness contours are shown in Fig. 3.35 for loudness levels between 30 phons and 120 phons. The 120 phon contour is sometimes called the 'threshold of feeling', since sounds above this level tend to arouse a tickling sensation in the ear. At high frequencies, such sounds are literally 'painfully loud'.

If the ear were equally sensitive at all frequencies, the equal loudness contours in Fig. 3.35 would be vertical lines, corresponding to the lines of

113

equal intensity level. For a variety of reasons, including diffraction of the incoming sound wave around the head and resonances of the ear canal and eardrum, the curves actually show a series of wiggles at high pitches, and a steady swing towards higher intensities at low pitches. These deviations correspond to the variations of sensitivity that we have already noted.

The contours in Fig. 3.35 were measured under 'free field' conditions – the listener was placed in an anechoic room (p.545), facing the loudspeaker which was the source of sound. When instead the sound is presented via headphones, the diffracting effect of the head is removed; the contours then show a smoother variation, particularly at high frequencies (Fletcher and Munson 1933).

The dynamic range of the ear

An important feature of the ear's response to musical sound can be seen in Fig. 3.35. The contours corresponding to very quiet sounds bend much more strongly towards high intensities at low pitches than do the contours describing very loud sounds. The threshold of audibility is 60 dB higher at G_0 than at C_6, but the 100 phon (fff) equal loudness contour increases only by 22 dB between these two pitches. As a consequence, the contours are squeezed together at low pitches.

Thus although a low pitch tone needs a relatively high intensity level in order to be audible at all, a relatively small change in intensity level is required to raise it through the seven dynamic steps from 'ppp' to 'fff'. Fig. 3.36 shows how this change in IL, which is equal to the difference between the 100 phon and 30 phon equal loudness contours in Fig. 3.35, varies with

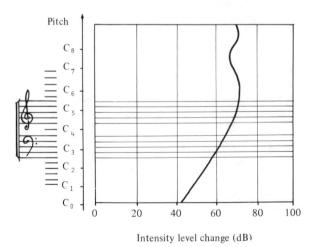

Fig. 3.36 The change in intensity level necessary to span the dynamic range from ppp (30 phons) to fff (100 phons).

pitch. A 70 dB range of intensity levels is required to span the complete range of musical dynamics with a pure tone of pitch C_6; at higher pitches a few dB less may suffice (65 dB at G_7); but at the pitch C_1, only 47 dB are necessary. The average width of each dynamic step, about 10 dB at C_6, is reduced to under 7 dB at C_1.

The contraction of the ear's dynamic range at low frequencies must be taken into account when electronic amplification of sound is used. An amplifier which boosts the intensity of all frequencies by the same number of dB will increase the loudness more at low pitches than at high; conversely, when the gain of the amplifier is reduced, the loudness of low pitches will diminish more rapidly than that of high pitches. If we are listening to Tchaikovsky's 6th Symphony on the record player at home, and the neighbours knock on the wall just as we are revelling in the ffffs of Fig. 2.9, we may be obliged to reduce them to mere mfs by turning down the gain of the amplifier – but we will then have to turn up the bass boost if we wish to retain the correct balance of loudness between the piccolo and the tuba.

A similar effect is evident when we listen to a band marching into the distance. In the open air, as we saw earlier, the intensity of a sound drops by about 6 dB for every doubling in distance between source and listener. Since this corresponds to a greater decrease in loudness for the low pitch tones radiated by the band than for those of higher pitch, the sound of the band becomes increasingly 'top heavy' as it gets further away. If Wordsworth's Highland Lass had been a Highland Lad, the poet would have heard the song die away more quickly as he wandered on his way.

The sone scale of loudness

We have seen that the loudness level scale agrees fairly well with the musical dynamic scale, in that successive steps on the scale of dynamics correspond to approximately equal changes of LL (10 phons). There is, however, another scale of subjective loudness in common use. It is based principally on a large number of laboratory tests in which people were asked to adjust the intensity of one pure tone until they judged it to be 'half the loudness' of another tone of the same pitch and fixed intensity. These tests showed that, despite large individual variations, there seemed to be a consensus that the loudness of a pure tone was halved when its loudness level dropped by 10 phons (Stevens 1936, 1955).

This means that the apparent loudness of a tone is not simply proportional to the loudness level (in phons). If it were, an 80 phon tone would be twice as loud as a 40 phon tone; the tests quoted above showed that a 50 phon tone sounded twice as loud as a 40 phon tone.

Stevens (1936) got round this difficulty by defining a new unit of loudness, the *sone*: this was arbitrarily chosen as the loudness of a 40 phon pure tone. A loudness of 2 sones is by definition twice as loud as 1 sone, and therefore corresponds to an LL of 50 phons. A loudness of 4 sones is likewise twice as loud as 2 sones, and is obtained by a further 10 phon step to an LL of 60 phons. The relationship between loudness level in phons and loudness in sones is shown in Fig. 3.37; Table 3.5 gives the sone equivalents of the musical dynamic scale.

TABLE 3.5

Loudness in sones	Musical dynamic level	Dynamic step size (sones)
0.5	ppp	
1	pp	0.5
2	p	1
4	mp	2
8	mf	4
16	f	8
32	ff	16
64	fff	32

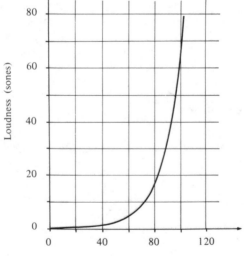

Fig. 3.37 Relationship between loudness in sones and loudness level in phons.

Clearly, equal steps on the sone scale do not correspond to equal steps in musical dynamic level: the difference between 'pp' and 'p' is 1 sone, while that between 'f' and 'ff' is 16 sones. What this really tells us is that 'loudness' and 'musical dynamic level' are two different things. On reflection, most musicians would probably agree that there is a sense in which the 'loudness gap' between 'f' and 'ff' is much larger than that between 'p' and 'pp'. Yet composers and performers have not felt the need to fill in this gap between 'f' and 'ff' with finer gradations of dynamic level. Thus – at least for isolated pure tones – the phon scale of loudness level is more directly related to musical practice than the sone scale.

There is an interesting parallel here with the subjective sensation of pitch. Using the same technique which established the sone scale of loudness, psychologists have constructed a *mel scale* of pitch by asking listeners to judge when one tone was 'half the pitch' of another (Stevens et al. 1937). Table 3.6 shows the mel equivalents of a range of pitches from C_3 to C_8.

TABLE 3.6

"Pitch" in mels	*Musical pitch*	*Octave size (mels)*
3,000	C_8	
1,950	C_7	1050
1,050	C_6	900
460	C_5	590
195	C_4	265
92	C_3	103

Once again, we can see immediately that the mel scale has no direct musical relevance, since the size of the octave measured on this scale varies widely over the musical range. Yet, as with the sone scale of loudness, the mel scale does tell us something about our perception of musical sound which is easily overlooked in our preoccupation with conventional musical notation. The mel scale measures an attribute of an interval which, although not equivalent to the musical pitch difference, is none the less part of our appreciation of that interval; and even musicians might be prepared to admit that, in terms of that attribute, two notes separated by an octave in the bass clef do sound 'closer together' than two notes an octave apart above the treble clef.

As far as actual numerical values are concerned, both sone and mel scales should be taken with a pinch of salt. Most people find it hard to judge when a tone is 'half as loud', or 'half as high', as another. Although the relationship between sones and phons given in Fig. 3.37 has been incorporated in an international standard for loudness measurements (ISO R131 – 1959), more recent tests by Warren (1977) have suggested that a doubling of loudness corresponds to a change of only 6 phons, rather than the 10 phons on which Fig. 3.37 was based. Since doubling the distance from an isotropic source gives a drop in LL of 6 dB, this result corresponds to the simple rule that, for a sound source in the open air, twice as loud = twice as close. Warren has proposed that our judgements of relative loudness are in fact based on a subconscious comparison with the remembered effect of relative distance from an open-air source. However, in the light of the discrepancies between loudness-halving tests, such theories must be considered tentative.

Loudness and nerve impulses

Our discussion so far has given us a way of relating the measured intensity (or pressure) in a sound wave to the equivalent level on the musical dynamic scale – so long as the sound is a pure tone. Complications arise when we turn to real musical sounds, which are nearly always mixtures of many pure tone components. It turns out that the contribution of each component tone to the overall loudness is affected by the presence of the other components. To understand why this is so, we must look briefly at how the brain receives information about the loudness of a sound.

In Chapter 2, we saw that vibration of the eardrum creates a wave motion on the basilar membrane, which in turn generates electrical impulses in the nerve fibres making up the auditory nerve. In Fig. 2.18, it was shown that the timing of these electrical impulses carries information about the frequency and phase of the sound vibration. Let us now examine the impulses on a single nerve fibre when it responds to sounds of different intensity level (Kiang et al. 1965).

Even in the absence of sound, a fibre occasionally fires, giving rise to 'spontaneous' impulses (Fig. 3.38 (a)). If we are examining one of the most sensitive fibres, we shall record an increase in the impulse rate once the sound level at the ear exceeds the threshold of audibility (Fig. 3.38 (b)). As the intensity level of the sound increases, the impulse rate also grows (Fig. 3.38 (c), (d) and (e)): this shows that the fibre fires more frequently as the basilar membrane vibrations become larger. However, a nerve fibre

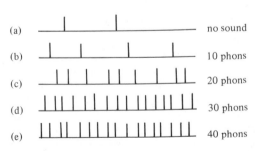

Fig. 3.38. Illustrating the nature of the oscilloscope trace recording the electrical impulses on a nerve fibre with low threshold. (a) Spontaneous activity; (b), (c) and (d) impulse rate increasing with increasing sound level; (e) fibre saturated.

118

requires a recovery time of about 3 ms between firings, and is therefore incapable of generating more than about 300 impulses per second. A normal fibre reaches this firing rate at a sound level around 40 dB above its threshold; it is then 'saturated', and a further increase in the loudness of the sound produces no change in the number of impulses per second on the fibre (Evans 1975, p.22).

It is important to note that the *size* of each nerve impulse is the same. Louder sounds do not generate bigger pulses: they do, however, generate more of them. It might therefore seem plausible that the brain estimates the loudness of a sound from the number of impulses per second carried by the nerve fibres. However, the saturation of each individual nerve fibre then poses a problem. The fibre we examined in Fig. 3.38 will send the same signal to the brain in response to a 40 dB tone as it does for a 120 dB tone; both are loud enough to generate the maximum possible firing rate. How is it that we are aware of changes in intensity level over a range of up to 120 dB when the signal on the nerve fibre changes only over a 40 dB range?

One answer to this question lies in the variation of threshold levels among nerve fibres. The normal nerve fibres which make up the bulk of the auditory nerve have thresholds which vary over a range of about 30 dB; thus although those with the lowest thresholds will behave as shown in Fig. 3.38, those with the highest thresholds will only start to respond at an IL of around 30 dB, and will saturate at an IL of 70 dB.

In addition, another set of nerve fibres has recently been discovered with properties quite different from those of the normal fibres (McGee et al. 1984). They respond individually over a much wider intensity range (up to 70 dB), and the range of thresholds is greater than 70 dB. Thus a bundle of these 'super-fibres' can convey loudness information to the brain over the entire 120 dB intensity span used in normal hearing. A picture of the hearing process is thus emerging in which the brain gathers information about the loudness of quiet sounds from the multitude of normal nerve fibres, but relies on the 'super-fibres' for information about loud sounds which saturate the normal fibres.

There is yet another way in which the brain may obtain information about the intensity of a tone from signals in the nerve fibres. For a low intensity pure tone, the amplitude of the basilar membrane vibration is only large enough to fire nerve fibres in a small region, under the peak of the amplitude envelope (Fig. 3.39 (a)). As the intensity increases, the peak of the envelope grows, but the envelope also broadens, especially towards the oval window end of the membrane (Fig. 3.39 (b)). Thus for loud sounds, the brain will receive additional nerve impulses from the fibres under this 'tail' of the envelope (Fletcher 1953, p.272). There is considerable disagreement at present over the extent to which these additional impulses contribute to the perceived loudness of the tone (Scharf 1978).

119

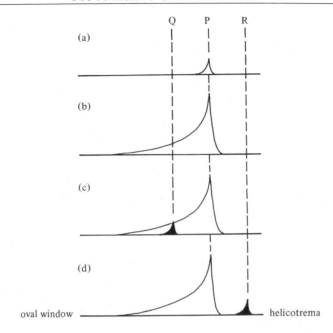

Fig. 3.39. Basilar membrane amplitude envelopes corresponding to (a) quiet 1000 Hz tone; (b) loud 1000 Hz tone; (c) loud 1000 Hz tone + quiet 2000 Hz tone; (d) loud 1000 Hz tone + quiet 500 Hz tone.

Masking

'Am I Too Loud?' The title of the accompanist Gerald Moore's autobiography (Moore 1962) epitomises one of the musician's greatest problems – that of achieving a good balance with other performers. This problem is more serious than at first sight appears. Take, for example, the four-part woodwind chorale at the beginning of Tchaikovsky's Fantasy Overture 'Romeo and Juliet' (Fig. 2.10). If the second bassoon were to make a crescendo in the third bar, instead of in the fourth bar as marked, the lowest part would become too prominent, and the effect of homogeneous chords would be lost. But listeners would not only hear the second bassoon becoming louder in the third bar – they would also hear the other three instruments becoming quieter. Indeed, if the second bassoon had a brainstorm and played 'ff' the other three instruments would be almost completely inaudible.

The apparent loudness of one sound is thus dependent on the loudness of other simultaneous sounds. This is true, not only for combinations of sounds from different instruments, as in Fig. 2.10, but also for the individual pure tone components of a single musical note. We cannot estimate the loudness of a complex tone simply by adding up the loudnesses of its

120

components. If we do that, we are liable to get a result which is too high, since we have ignored the fact that each component may reduce the effective loudness of its neighbours.

One sound is said to be *masked* by a second if the first is audible in the absence of the second, but inaudible when the second is present (Zwislocki 1978). In order to understand how masking can occur, we must call on our understanding of how nerve impulses are generated by sounds in the inner ear. Let us consider first the simplest situation, in which only two pure tones are heard together.

Figure 3.39 (b) indicates the shape of the amplitude envelope for a pure tone of frequency 1000 Hz and IL = 60 dB; the peak, about 25 mm from the oval window, is marked P. A second tone, an octave higher at 2000 Hz, will generate a peak 7 mm nearer the oval window at Q. But the nerve fibres at Q are already being stimulated to a considerable extent by the 1000 Hz tone; the brain will only become aware of the addition of the 2000 Hz tone if it recognises the separate contribution of this tone to the firing rate at Q.

Figure 2.18 showed that, even for a constant amplitude of membrane vibration, there is an inherent random fluctuation in the firing rate of nerve fibres. The brain 'smooths out' and ignores these fluctuations. If the amplitude of the 2000 Hz peak at Q is smaller than the height of the 1000 Hz tail at that point (Fig. 3.39 (c)), the change in the firing rate due to the 2000 Hz tone will be regarded by the brain as just another random fluctuation, and will be ignored (Green and Swets 1966). The 2000 Hz tone will thus be inaudible, because it is *masked* by the 1000 Hz tone.

Tones with frequencies less than 1000 Hz generate peaks further from the oval window than P. Since the amplitude envelope drops sharply in this direction, the 1000 Hz tone has little masking effect on tones of lower frequency. This is illustrated in Fig. 3.39 (d), for a tone an octave lower at 500 Hz. The peak of the amplitude envelope for this tone is at point R; since the nerve fibres here are unaffected by the 1000 Hz tone, there will be no masking.

Masked threshold

Masking is equivalent to a raising of the threshold of audibility (Wegel and Lane 1924). The masking effect of a 1000 Hz pure tone is shown in this way in Fig. 3.40. The dotted line shows the threshold in the absence of the tone; the solid curves show how the threshold is raised by various intensities of the tone. It should be emphasised that, like the curve for the unmasked threshold, these masking curves represent the typical properties of an 'average' ear; the measurements on which they are based show that the efficiency with which one sound masks another varies widely from person to person.

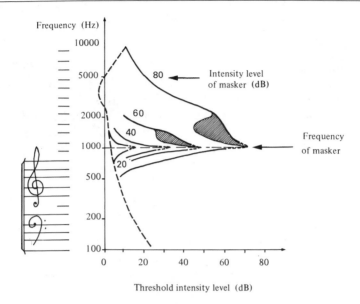

Fig. 3.40. Showing how the presence of a 1000 Hz tone at various intensity levels raises the threshold for the perception of other tones. The explanation of the shaded areas is given in the text. Based on measurements of Greenwood (1971), Zwicker (1975), and Zwicker and Jaroszewski (1982).

These curves confirm that a loud pure tone masks pitches higher than itself much more effectively than pitches below itself. The pitch of the 1000 Hz tone is close to C_6; if its loudness level is 80 phons, the threshold an octave higher at C_7 will be raised by over 50 dB. On the other hand, an octave below the masking tone, at C_5, the threshold is not significantly raised. This asymmetry disappears when the loudness of the masker is reduced to 40 phons, and in fact shows a slight (and as yet unexplained) reversal for very quiet maskers (Zwicker and Jaroszewski 1982): the 20 phon tone masker raises the threshold more for lower pitches than for higher. However, such very quiet sounds are of little musical significance, since they are usually themselves masked by background noise.

Two features of the threshold curves in Fig. 3.40 require further explanation. In the neighbourhood of the 1000 Hz masking tone, the curves are shown broken rather than solid. When the two tones are separated in frequency by less than about 50 Hz, measurement of the threshold is complicated by beating between the tones. This has the effect of drawing attention to the quieter sound, even though its average level would place it below the threshold. A similar effect occurs for tones corresponding to points in the shaded areas of Fig. 3.40. In this case, tones which would otherwise be inaudible can be detected because of the generation of a cubic difference tone. Recalling (p.65) that the cubic difference tone due to two tones with frequencies f_1 and f_2 has a frequency $2f_1 - f_2$, we can see that in the present case the difference tone will have a frequency $2000 - f_2$. Since f_2 is greater than 1000 Hz for tones in the shaded area, the cubic difference tone will be below 1000 Hz; it will thus remain audible, even when the primary tone (f_2) is masked. Special measuring techniques have been evolved to allow the straightforward masking effect to be separated from these complicating interactions (Egan and Hake 1950; Greenwood 1971).

Partial masking

The term 'masking', as we have used it so far, refers to the obliteration of one sound by another. Figure 3.40 shows us that a 1000 Hz tone at 80 dB IL raises the threshold at 2000 Hz to 55 dB IL: a 2000 Hz tone at 50 dB IL will therefore be completely inaudible, even though it would be heard distinctly if the 1000 Hz tone were stopped. If we raise the intensity of the 2000 Hz tone to above 55 dB IL, it will be heard, but its loudness will be reduced by the presence of the 1000 Hz tone: we then say that it is *partially masked* by the 1000 Hz tone.

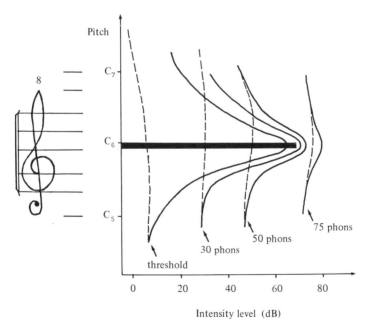

Fig. 3.41. The distorting effect on equal loudness contours of a narrow band of noise, intensity level 70 dB, centred on 1000 Hz. Solid bar: masking noise; dashed lines: undistorted contours; solid lines: distorted contours. Derived from Scharf (1978), p.216, Fig. 11.

Just as total masking is equivalent to a distortion of the threshold of audibility curve, partial masking can be represented as distortion of the equal loudness contours shown in Fig. 3.35. In Fig. 3.41 we show how the equal loudness contours are bent by a masking sound at 70 dB IL. The masking used in these measurements was not a pure tone, but a *narrow band noise* centred on 1000 Hz. This type of sound, which is equivalent to a large number of pure tones with frequencies clustered around 1000 Hz, is often used in experiments in hearing; it generates a similar masking effect to a single pure tone, but beats and difference tones are much less noticeable.

Fig 3.41 reveals an aspect of masking which is of considerable musical significance. In the frequency region shown, the undistorted equal loudness contours (dashed lines), which represent the behaviour of the ear in the absence of the masker, are close to being vertical lines of constant intensity level. The 70 dB IL masker raises the threshold by 60 dB in the vicinity of 1000 Hz; the 75 phon equal loudness contour, on the other hand, is raised by only 7 dB. The masker has the effect of squeezing the equal loudness contours together in the vicinity of its own frequency. Tones which are more intense than the masker suffer only a slight reduction in loudness.

As a practical musical example of these effects, let us consider two instruments playing the notes C_6 and D_6 (Fig. 3.42). As we have not yet

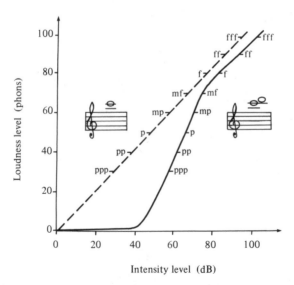

Fig. 3.42. The relationship between the intensity level and loudness level of a pure tone of pitch C_6 is shown with (solid curve) and without (dashed curve) another tone of pitch D_6 and IL 80 dB. Based on Chocholle and Greenbaum (1966).

discussed the masking properties of complex tones, we shall choose flutes, which generate almost pure tones in their upper register. The solid curve in Fig. 3.42 shows how the loudness level of the instrument playing C_6 depends on its intensity level, while the second instrument plays D_6 at a constant intensity level of 80 dB (corresponding to a musical dynamic marking 'f'). For comparison, the dashed line shows the relationship when the second instrument is silent.

The extent to which the C_6 is partially masked by the D_6 is shown by the horizontal distance between the dashed line and the solid curve. If the C_6 is played 'f', and the second player adds the D_6, the first player must increase the intensity level of his sound by about 5 dB to restore the C_6 to its original loudness. If the C_6 is played 'p', on the other hand, nearly 20 dB increase in intensity level will be required to compensate for the masking effect when the D_6 is added.

A much greater degree of control over the intensity of sound production is required of musicians playing in ensemble than when playing unaccompanied. We saw earlier that, for an unmasked tone, a single musical dynamic step corresponds to a change in intensity level of about 10 dB. Fig. 3.42 shows that, in the presence of the masking tone, the four dynamic steps between ppp and mf each require a change in intensity level of only 4 dB. It is thus difficult to maintain a quiet tone at a constant loudness when it is partially masked by a louder sound: relatively small variations in the amount of sound energy produced by the player have a magnified effect on the loudness.

Masking by complex tones

One of the principal problems of orchestration is that of ensuring that individual melodic strands remain audible in a complex musical texture. This is clearly a question of masking: but instead of two pure tones we now have many complex tones, each of which can exert a masking influence on all the others. In such a complicated situation, the only sure guide is experience. Nevertheless, our discussion of pure-tone masking does shed a little light on the difficulties faced by the practical orchestrator.

We saw that a pure tone masks most effectively tones which are higher in pitch than itself. For complex tones, this upward bias of masking is even more marked, since each of the harmonic components will make a contribution to the total masking effect. Figure 3.43 illustrates how the threshold is raised by a complex tone of pitch C_4, with a spectrum of ten harmonic components each having an intensity level of 70 dB. The pitch of each harmonic is indicated by a black note at the right of the figure. The first six harmonics give rise to distinct peaks in the threshold, whereas the higher harmonics (separated by less than a critical band) together give an additional broad peak.

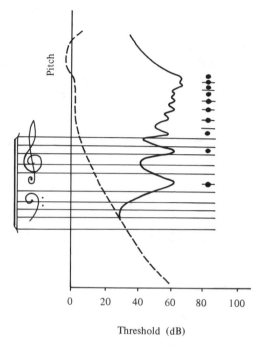

Fig. 3.43. Masking effect of a complex tone consisting of ten harmonic components, each at an intensity level of 70 dB. Based on Houtgast (1974), reproduced in Plomp (1976), p.14, Fig. 7.

Clearly, any tone higher in pitch than C_4 is liable to be totally or partially masked by this sound unless its intensity level is substantially above 70 dB. Of course, this masking sound has a rather artificial harmonic spectrum, but we shall see shortly that most orchestral instruments have fairly rich harmonic spectra when playing loudly in low and middle registers. It is therefore likely that the masking effect of a loud musical note will extend at least two octaves above its fundamental pitch.

From this consideration we can draw a rough rule of thumb for orchestrators: an instrument playing a melody can easily be drowned completely by an overloud accompaniment at *lower* pitch; it is unlikely to be drowned by an accompaniment at *higher* pitch, although its apparent timbre could be altered. Since the lower pitched brass instruments are among the most powerful in the orchestra (see Table 3.3), particular care is necessary when they are used in an accompanying role.

As an illustration of these points, we may consider two examples from Tchaikovsky's 6th Symphony. We have already seen that the composer exercised unusual care over questions of dynamic level in this work, using twelve separate dynamic steps from 'pppppp' to 'ffff' in the score. This care is evident in the markings of the example from the first movement in

Fig. 3.44. Here the melody, on violins and violas, is accompanied by pesante chords from the rest of the orchestra (excluding the 'heavy brass').

To avoid masking of the melody, the accompaniment is marked 'sempre p' while the violins and violas enter 'mf' and make a cresendo. At the climax of the melody (bar 5 of the example), the accompaniment swells to

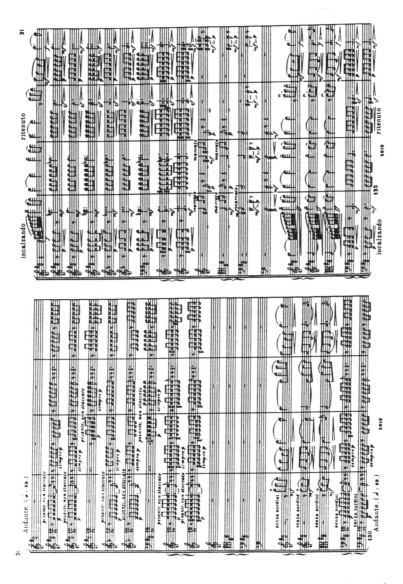

Fig. 3.44. Excerpt from the 1st movement of Tchaikovsky's 6th Symphony.

127

'mf'; the strings, however, are marked 'ff' at this point, and are supported by a flute playing 'f'.

This concern to keep the melody at a higher level than the accompaniment may be contrasted with our second example from the same movement (Fig. 3.45). Here the vital trombone motif is marked only 'ff', despite the fact that it enters against a held chord from woodwind and strings marked 'fff'. The point is that most of the sound energy in this chord is at pitches well above that of the trombones; even the bassoons and double

Fig. 3.45. Excerpt from the 1st movement of Tchaikovsky's 6th Symphony.

basses, whose fundamental F_2 is below the bass trombone and tuba, generate most of their volume in the fifth or sixth harmonics, some two octaves higher. Thus although the brilliance of the trombones will be reduced by masking of their upper harmonics, the weight of tone conveyed by the lower harmonics will be clearly audible in the orchestral texture, even at the 'ff' level. Indeed, if the trombones were to play 'fff', there would be a danger that they would mask the important descending counter-motif in the flutes and upper strings.

The masking power of the low pitch instruments is some compensation for the fact that they are condemned to generate much of their sound energy in a pitch region in which the ear is relatively insensitive. The addition of high trumpet parts to an orchestral score, as in Bach's 3rd Orchestral Suite, increases the brilliance of the sound without diminishing the effectiveness of the lower parts. On the other hand, one carefully chosen chord played with maximum volume on three trombones can reduce an entire orchestra to impotent miming. Richard Strauss doubtless had this in mind when he warned the young conductor: 'Never look encouragingly at the brass'.

Loudness of complex tones

We can now see that the relationship between the loudness of a complex tone and the intensities of its various harmonic components is complicated by the fact that each component masks all the other components to a greater or lesser extent (Fletcher and Munson 1937). Elaborate schemes have been devised to take account of masking when calculating loudness (Zwicker and Scharf 1965; Stevens 1972), but these need not concern us. It is, however, instructive to look briefly at two special types of complex tones whose loudness can be easily estimated.

First, let us consider a tone whose harmonics are separated by several critical bands. In this case we can assume that, at least for moderate loudness, there is negligible masking of one harmonic by another. The total loudness (in sones) will then simply be the sum of the loudnesses of the component tones (each expressed in sones). Take as an example the note A_5, with only the first and second harmonics present at an IL of 60 dB (Fig. 3.46): the separation of these harmonics is 880 Hz, about four times the critical bandwidth in this frequency range. Each component would separately have a loudness of 4 sones, and the complex tone will have a loudness of $4 + 4 = 8$ sones. From Fig. 3.37 we see that this corresponds to a loudness level of 70 phons.

Second, let us consider a complex tone with a small cluster of upper harmonics all lying within one critical band. In this case each component tone will be exciting more or less the same set of nerve fibres in the cochlea, and we can simply add the *intensities* together. The example illustrated in

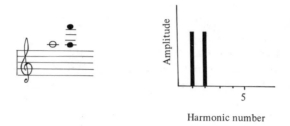

Fig. 3.46. A complex tone of pitch A_5 (white note), containing two harmonics (black notes) of equal intensity.

Fig. 3.47 is the note F_1 with only the 4th and 5th harmonics present: these have frequencies 175 Hz and 218 Hz, and therefore lie within one critical band (width about 100 Hz in this region). If each component again has an intensity level of 60 dB (corresponding to a loudness level of 60 phons), the total intensity in the critical band will be twice that due to each component separately; since doubling the intensity corresponds to an increase of 3 dB in the IL, the overall IL of the complex tone will be 63 dB (LL 63 phons).

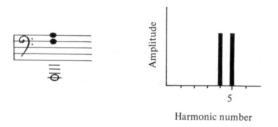

Fig. 3.47. A complex tone of pitch F_1 (white note), containing two harmonics (black notes) of equal intensity.

Comparing the two examples, we can see the effect of mutual masking of the components. If we start with only one component, then add another of equal intensity *within* a critical band, the loudness level increases by only 3 phons. If we add the second component *well outside* a critical band, the loudness level increases by 10 phons.

Sound level meters: the dB(A) scale

For many purposes it would be convenient to have a 'loudness meter' – that is, a device which would measure the objective parameters of the sound wave and give a reading corresponding to the subjective loudness of the sound. The practical realisation of such a device is complicated by three factors. First, most interesting sounds have spectra containing many pure tone components, and the response of the inner ear varies both with intensity and with frequency. Second, each component may mask other components, reducing their contribution to the loudness. Third, the signals sent to the brain are subjected to a sophisticated analysis in which the perceived loudness is affected by such factors as context and expectation.

We shall return shortly to the role of the brain in interpreting loudness information. The effects of frequency response and masking in the inner ear can be taken into account by measuring the intensity of each of the pure tone components in the sound, and making use of standardised equal loudness contours and masking curves. Such a loudness measurement requires elaborate and expensive equipment, and considerable calculation (Hassall and Zaveri 1979).

Relatively simple *sound level meters* are, however, available; these are small, portable instruments giving an almost instantaneous reading. The sound level meter contains a microphone which senses the pressure fluctuations in the sound wave, and a 'weighting network', which is an electrical circuit boosting some frequencies and cutting down others. The intention behind the weighting network is to make the meter respond to components of different frequency in roughly the same way that the ear does. For example, the ear is much less sensitive to a 100 Hz tone than to a 1000 Hz tone of the same intensity; the weighting network is chosen so that the 100 Hz tone is amplified much less than the 1000 Hz tone, and so contributes less to the total reading on the meter.

Because the equal loudness contours get less curved as the intensity increases (Fig. 3.35), three different weighting networks were originally chosen. For quiet sounds, the A-weighting network was used, giving a meter response roughly equivalent to the 40 phon equal loudness contour. For moderate loudnesses, the B-weighting network was chosen, with a response similar to the 70 phon contour; at high volumes the C-weighting network gave an almost constant amplification (Beranek 1949).

In practice, however, it has been found that the A-weighting network, whose frequency response is shown in Fig. 3.48, produces a measurement which correlates well with perceived loudness for many types of sound, even at high volume (Parkin 1965; Young and Peterson 1969). This is surprising, since for loud sounds A-weighting applies a much too strong attenuation to low frequencies. On the other hand, strong low pitch components of a sound exert a considerable masking effect on the higher components. Thus although the meter will undervalue the contribution of the low pitch components to the loudness, it will overvalue the contribution of the (masked) high pitch components; it seems that these effects to some extent cancel each other out.

Measurements performed with an A-weighted sound level meter are described as dB(A) readings. They provide a useful guide to the apparent loudness of sounds, although misleading results can be obtained for certain types of musical sound. For example, a pure tone of pitch C_4 (262 Hz) and IL 80 dB has a loudness level of 84 phons. However, the A-weighting curve of Fig. 3.48 shows that a 262 Hz tone is amplified by 9 dB less than the standard 1000 Hz tone. The sound level meter reading for the C_4 tone will therefore be only 71 dB(A), 15 dB lower than the reading for an equally loud C_6 tone.

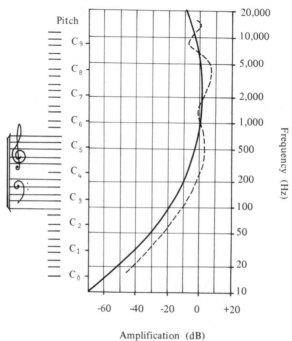

Fig. 3.48. The solid curve shows the relative amplification provided by an A-weighting network at different frequencies (Hassall and Zaveri 1979, p.53, Fig. 3.11). The dashed curve shows the equivalent response of the ear at 40 phons (from Fig. 3.35).

A single pure tone is, of course, an extreme case. The studies previously quoted showed that for urban traffic noise and aircraft noise, sounds with equal dB(A) levels had equal loudness levels according to the calculation scheme of Stevens, although the Stevens phon rating was typically 10 to 15 dB higher than the dB(A) rating. The situation is probably similar for orchestral music with a wide frequency range.

Sound levels in musical practice

Most of our discussion of loudness so far has referred to sounds heard in isolation, under laboratory conditions. When we return to the concert hall, we must remember that listening to music is a process in which the brain is involved in an elaborate set of comparisons and judgements. Thus although the perceived loudness of a particular note in an orchestral piece will, to a large extent, be determined by the factors we have previously discussed, it will also be affected by the expectation aroused by the context. In an extreme case, it is possible that a note from a familiar phrase may be 'heard' by the brain even though it has been omitted by the performer or completely masked by another sound (Deutsch 1982). Bearing this in mind, let us examine the loudness levels used in musical practice. Table 3.4 suggested intensity levels equivalent to the normal dynamic gradations, for a 1000 Hz pure tone. The 70 dB range of intensity levels required by this correspondence is beyond the capacity of all conventional musical instruments – to achieve it, a performer would have to vary his sound power output by a ratio of ten million to one. In any case, the necessity for keeping even the quietest sounds well above the level of background noise means that in practice intensity levels in live music rarely fall below 40 dB.

For most instruments, there is a minimum level of sound power production, below which it is impracticable to sustain a musical tone. The intensity level corresponding to this minimum power output will depend on the distance between performer and listener, and on the acoustical nature of the environment. If we place a sound level meter at a distance of about two metres from a violinist in a medium-sized domestic room, such as might be used for individual practice or rehearsal of chamber music (Fig. 3.49), we find that the average player cannot produce an acceptable continuous tone at a level below about 60 dB(A). The loudest acceptable sound gives a reading of around 95 dB(A). These limits are approximately constant over most of the usable pitch range, although fluctuations of

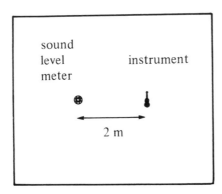

Fig. 3.49. Testing the sound pressure level generated in a domestic room by various musical instruments.

several decibels can occur from note to note (see Fig. 6.6). Trumpet players in the same test find it difficult to maintain a steady sound below about 70 dB(A), but can achieve over 100 dB(A) at full power.

In a concert hall, the same sound power will generate a considerably lower intensity level, but the difference (in dB) between highest and lowest levels will be similar to that obtained in a smaller room. Thus the solo violinist or trumpeter does not have the full dynamic range of Table 3.4 available; the dynamic levels must be chosen from within a restricted span of between 30 and 40 dB.

In fact, musicians usually choose an even more restricted dynamic range. Fig. 3.50 (a) illustrates the results of tests in which a number of amateur violinists experienced in orchestral playing were asked to perform a chromatic scale, as smoothly as possible, first at the 'pp' level and then at the 'ff' level. It was found that as a player ascended the scale, the intensity level did not remain constant, but rose and fell in an apparently erratic way. These fluctuations are related to the acoustical properties of the instrument, as will be shown in Chapter 6. The bands marked 'pp' and 'ff' in Fig. 3.50 (a) show the regions within which most of the corresponding tones were found.

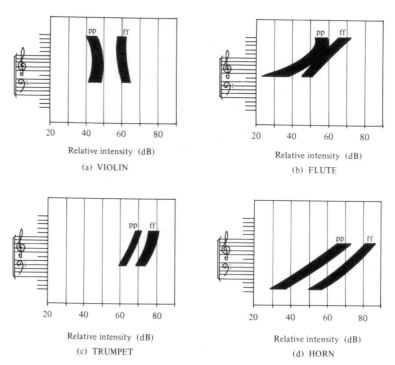

Fig. 3.50. Measurements of the dynamic ranges used by various instruments in orchestral music. Based on Clark and Luce (1965).

Two remarkable facts are evident from Fig. 3.50 (a). Variations in intensity level of around 5 dB occur even in scales which are accepted musically as being of uniform loudness; yet the average difference in IL between 'pp' and 'ff' at pitches around C_5 is only 15 dB. If the player wished to divide this dynamic range into the five steps pp-p-mp-mf-f-ff, each step would correspond to only 3 dB. This is less than the fluctuations in a scale at a constant dynamic marking. In other words, the player's intensity level would change more as he played a scale at a uniform 'mp' than it would if he deliberately raised the dynamic level to 'mf'.

Similarly compressed dynamic ranges were found for other orchestral instruments: the results for flute, trumpet and horn are shown in Fig. 3.50 (b), (c) and (d). It should be borne in mind when looking at these graphs that the players were asked for levels of pianissimo and fortissimo considered normal in orchestral performance. There are good practical reasons for a musician avoiding the extremes of the dynamic range of the instrument – pitch, loudness and timbre all tend to be more difficult to control at these extremes. In the orchestral context, a solo marked 'pp' is likely to be played at moderate volume to avoid the risk of its being masked by the accompaniment. The player will also wish to keep a little in reserve for the occasional pppp or ffff. It is clear, however, that musicians interpret dynamic markings in a flexible way which depends very much on the context and on the limitations of their instruments: it is impossible to find a direct correspondence between intensity levels in dB (or loudness levels in phons) and dynamic markings applicable to the performance of individual instruments.

For the overall sound of a large orchestra, the relationship between sound intensity and dynamic marking is more straightforward. For example, measurements carried out in the City Hall, Brunswick, during a performance of Bruckner's 9th Symphony by the Cleveland Orchestra under George Szell, showed that the opening string tremolo, marked pp (Fig. 3.51 (a)), generated an intensity level of 48 dB in the middle stalls; the corresponding reading during the fff tutti in bar 63 (Fig. 3.51 (b)) reached 99 dB (Winckel 1962). At the conductor's rostrum each level was 3 dB higher, whereas in the balcony both were reduced by 3 dB. The overall dynamic range of 51 dB between pp and fff is close to that suggested in Table 3.4. The desire for such a large range of dynamic contrasts was to a considerable extent responsible for the growth in size and diversity of the romantic orchestra in the nineteenth century.

The minimum perceptible change in loudness

We have seen that when a large orchestra makes a crescendo from mf to f, the intensity level rises by about 10 dB; when faced with the same dynamic markings, a solo performer may increase his sound power output by less

Fig. 3.51. Two excerpts from Bruckner's 9th Symphony.

than 3 dB. Will such a small increase in intensity level produce a noticeable increase in loudness? Laboratory measurements with pure tones have shown that, for very quiet sounds, the average ear can just detect a change in loudness when the intensity is increased by about 1.5 dB. For loud sounds, even smaller changes can be detected: an increase of only 0.5 dB in the intensity level gives a noticeable change in loudness (Jesteadt et al. 1977).

A change in IL of 3 dB should thus give a perfectly recognisable dynamic step. We are then faced with the difficulty that the performer, at least, is apparently oblivious to considerably larger fluctuations when playing a scale at constant dynamic level. The resolution of this paradox may lie in the brain's remarkable ability to process the information which it receives from the ears. Presented with a set of notes of varying intensity, the brain appears able to decide, partly on the basis of experience and expectation, whether the intensity variations are intended by the player or not. In the former case, it will register the corresponding changes in loudness; in the latter, it will smooth them out, and the listener will hear a uniform loudness.

We already saw an example of such sophisticated information processing in the brain's assessment of the pitch of complex tones. The failure to recognise the importance of this final stage in the perception of sound has resulted in several fruitless controversies between scientists and musicians. Nevertheless, it must be admitted that the task of the brain is made less onerous when the musician can make the dynamic steps greater than the variations within each level. One of the secrets of the virtuoso performer is the ability to command an unusually wide dynamic range on the instrument, thus giving greater scope for dynamic nuances (Patterson 1974).

Loud sounds and ear damage

It has been known for many years that prolonged exposure to loud sounds can lead to a reduction in hearing ability (Burns and Robinson 1970). Workers in noisy environments are obliged by law in most countries to wear some form of ear protection if the background noise exceeds a prescribed level. It has frequently been alleged that the sound levels experienced by devotees of discos and rock concerts are high enough to cause hearing damage. We have seen, however, that sound levels in the auditorium during the performance of a romantic symphony can approach 100 dB. Should a Bruckner fortissimo carry a government health warning?

The effects of loud sounds on the ear can be divided into two categories: temporary reductions in hearing ability, from which the ear eventually recovers, and permanent changes, which are related to the destruction of part of the inner ear mechanism. As with the other aspects of hearing which we have studied, susceptibility to damage from noise exposure varies widely from person to person. Nevertheless, several general principles can be deduced from the studies which have been performed in this field (Miller 1974).

The masking effect of a loud sound is equivalent to a raising of the threshold of audibility. When the sound ceases, the threshold does not immediately return to its normal level in the absence of sound; a *temporary threshold shift* (TTS) persists for periods ranging from a few minutes to several days, depending on the loudness of the sound.

Measurements of sound levels in discotheques and at live pop concerts have shown that average sound levels can exceed 110 dB, especially near loudspeakers (Flugrath 1969; Fearn 1975(a)). Fig. 3.52 shows the results of measurements of threshold shift carried out at different times after the participants had listened to an hour of continuous rock music at 110 dB. Curve (a) shows that, 2 minutes after the end of the performance, the threshold at 4kHz(C_8) was still 26 dB above its normal value, although the threshold at 1kHz(C_6) was raised by only 5 dB. Curve (b) shows that, after 30 minutes, there remained a shift of nearly 15 dB at 4000 Hz. Even after 90 minutes (curve (d)) the sensitivity of the ear to frequencies around 4000 Hz was still noticeably impaired.

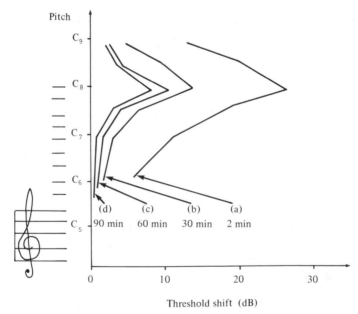

Fig. 3.52. Temporary threshold shift due to exposure to rock music at 110 dB IL for one hour. The measurement was made (a) 2 minutes, (b) 30 minutes, (c) 60 minutes and (d) 90 minutes after the music had stopped (Rintelmann et al. 1972).

138

The frequency spectrum of the music was analysed: a broad range of frequencies was present, with maximum intensity between 1000 Hz and 2000 Hz. The peak in the threshold shift curves at 4000 Hz is characteristic, not of the music, but of the ear. It appears that the part of the inner ear which responds to this frequency is most easily desensitised by loud sounds. Although the threshold shifts in Fig. 3.52 are only significant at pitches above C_6, we should remember that much of the essential character of a musical sound is conveyed by its upper harmonics; the intelligibility of speech or singing also depends on high frequency components. The ability to appreciate subtleties of tone colour can thus be reduced by immediately previous exposure to very loud sound – a point which should perhaps be borne in mind by composers and orchestrators.

If the loudness of the sound, or the length of the exposure, is increased beyond a certain limit, the threshold will never return to its previous level – a *permanent threshold shift* (PTS) will have occurred. Despite a great deal of research which has been carried out in many countries, it has proved difficult to establish safe limiting sound levels which can be guaranteed to produce no PTS (Kryter 1973). The damaging effect of a sound depends not only on its average intensity level and its duration, but also on many other factors such as its frequency spectrum, whether it contains occasional sharp peaks of loudness, and whether it is listened to continuously or intermittently. Nevertheless, several general rules have been incorporated in international standards of noise control (Hassall and Zaveri 1979, pp.62–66).

A-weighted sound level measurements are the basis of most noise standards. It is generally accepted that levels much below 80 dB(A) produce insignificant PTS even when heard continuously for long periods. In Britain, the USA and many other countries, a limit of 90 dB(A) has been set as the highest average level of background noise which is considered safe in an industrial environment. If someone is working in a factory where the noise level, averaged over a working day of 8 hours, exceeds 90 dB(A), the employer is legally obliged to provide ear protection; without it, the employee is likely to develop PTS over the course of time.

Few people listen to very loud music for 8 hours at a stretch; however, we have seen that sound levels in both classical and pop music performances are liable to exceed 90 dB(A) for shorter periods. In Britain, noise legislation has adopted an 'equal energy' principle – the maximum sound energy which the ear is allowed to receive during an 8 hour period is that which it would receive during the same period from a continuous sound with a steady level of 90 dB(A). Remembering that doubling the intensity of a sound is equivalent to raising its intensity level by 3 dB, we can see that the maximum permissible 'sound dose' would be received in 4 hours from a 93 dB(A) sound, 2 hours from a 96 dB(A) sound, and so on.

This trading of increased intensity for reduced time is shown by Fig.

3.53. Here the time during which the sound is heard has been shown on a logarithmic scale; this makes it easier to see the potentially damaging effects of very loud sounds lasting only a few minutes, which are of particular musical interest. We can see that a 100 dB(A) sound would have to be sustained for 50 minutes to exceed the limit – even on Bruckner's expansive time-scale, we do not find an hour of unremitting fortissimo! Averaged over the whole performance, the sound levels experienced by audiences at orchestral concerts range typically from 70 dB(A) to 90 dB(A), depending on the nature of the hall and the type of music being played (Fearn 1975 (b)). It therefore seems unlikely that performances of Wagner and Strauss will be banned on health grounds.

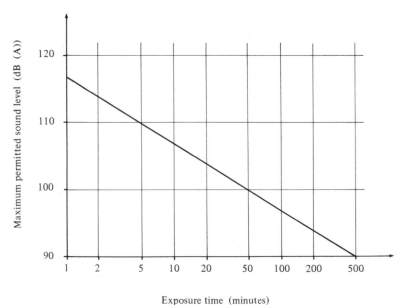

Exposure time (minutes)

Fig. 3.53. Showing the maximum number of minutes (in an 8 hour working day) during which exposure to sound levels exceeding 90 dB(A) is considered safe.

The evidence about pop music is less reassuring. Exposure to 110 dB(A) for only 5 minutes exceeds the British safety criterion; the evidence suggests that, of those who habitually frequent discotheques where music is played at this level, more than one in ten will suffer a significant permanent hearing loss (Whittle and Robinson 1974). It is clearly necessary for the music to be at a level well above the background noise from the audience, which can be over 80 dB(A) at a pop concert (Fearn 1975 (b)); an average level of 95 dB(A) satisfies this criterion, and is also within the safe limit for a performance lasting 2 hours. It is to be hoped that those performers who habitually operate at much higher sound levels will appreciate the damage they may be doing to their customers' hearing.

The growing popularity of listening to music through stereophonic earphones also poses a potential hearing risk. Equipment with a relatively modest electrical power rating can easily generate dangerously high sound levels. One test of popularly available stereo equipment found that a tape of 'acid rock' music played on a particular combination of tape player and earphones was capable of generating a level of 155 dB(A) (Wood and Lipscomb 1972). Fortunately, the test was performed using an 'artificial ear'; such a level would cause immediate and severe damage to a human ear.

We have discussed the effect of a musician's sound output on the hearing of listeners; what about the effect on the performer himself? The player is usually much closer to the source of sound than the audience; he may also spend several hours every day in practice. Is his 'sound dose' likely to exceed the safe limit?

Tests with a sound level meter held close to the ear of the player in a moderately reverberant practice room show that oboe, clarinet, trumpet and trombone generate just over 100 dB(A) when played fortissimo. The violin also generates about 100 dB(A) at the ear nearer the instrument; the other ear receives about 10 dB(A) less. It would thus require a pretty strenuous practice session with any of these instruments, equivalent to non-stop fortissimo playing for an hour, before the safe limit would be approached. The high register of the piccolo, on the other hand, can easily generate over 110 dB(A) at the player's ear; there is a significant risk that an hour every day spent practising fortissimo passages in this register could ultimately lead to a noticeable permanent threshold shift. This would be particularly unfortunate for a piccolo player, since PTS occurs predominantly above 1000 Hz (see Fig. 3.52), and accuracy of intonation on the piccolo depends on acute hearing ability in this frequency range.

TIMBRE

In the darkened opera house, a player concealed in the orchestra pit sounds a single note – the note of Fig. 3.1. It is immediately recognisable to most of the audience as the sound of a trumpet, even in the absence of visual clues or a knowledge of the scoring of 'Rienzi'. Even more remarkable is the ability, possessed by most experienced listeners to music, to identify an instrument when its voice is added to an already complex orchestral sound. For example, the entry of the first flute in bar 5 of Fig. 3.44 is readily recognised, even though violins and violas are doubling it in unison or octaves, and the remaining woodwind and horns are playing accompanying chords.

The characteristic quality of an instrument, which enables it to be identified in this way, is usually described as *timbre*. This term is used in various different shades of meaning, both in musical parlance and in acoustical discussions. The most restricted definition relates only to continuous, 'steady state' tones, with constant pitch and loudness; the timbre of a sound is then defined as that property which permits it to be distinguished from another sound of the same pitch and loudness (Helmholtz 1863, pp.27ff).

The analysis of steady state sounds makes a useful starting point for our discussion of timbre. Many experiments have demonstrated, however, that the transient features which occur when a musical instrument is first set into vibration play a crucial role in providing the brain with clues to help in the identification of the instrument (Stumpf 1926; George 1954; Berger 1964; Saldanha and Corso 1964; Grey and Moorer 1977). From the musical point of view, this means that the nature of the attack is an important feature of an instrument's characteristic sound. This is obvious, of course, in an instrument like the harp or piano, whose sound contains no steady state at all; the shape of the amplitude envelope has a strong effect on the perceived tone quality. A striking illustration of this is provided by playing a tape-recording of piano music backwards (Taylor 1966). The instrument is transformed into a leaky old harmonium, although only the order of presentation of the sounds has changed. The concept of timbre is frequently extended to include such time-varying aspects of the sound (Rasch and Plomp 1982).

An even broader use of the term is its occasional application to describe that combination of varying features which identifies a particular instrument at any pitch or loudness (Risset and Wessel 1982, p.26). For example, we noted earlier that as the loudness of the trumpet note in Fig. 3.1 increased, the tone quality of the sound also changed. Despite this, it remained recognisable as a trumpet – indeed, this change of tone quality with volume is one of the most characteristic features of a brass instrument (Risset and Mathews 1969).

In what follows, we shall use the term *timbre* in the second sense described above, including both steady state and transient features of a particular tone. The combination of acoustical variables which leads to the recognition of a specific instrument we shall describe as the *characteristic* of that instrument. Thus we can say that the trumpet characteristic includes a progressive variation of timbre with loudness.

Steady state waveforms

In Chapter 1 we saw that a steady state vibration could be completely described by its repetition frequency, its amplitude and its waveform. In the present chapter we have been able to relate the pitch of a sound primarily to its frequency, with amplitude and waveform playing almost insignificant roles. In contrast, the loudness of a sound has been shown to depend in a complicated way on all three factors. Let us now examine the vibration patterns corresponding to steady state sounds, of equal pitch and loudness, played on different instruments: from the musical point of view these sounds can differ only in timbre.

Fig. 3.54 (a) shows the vibration pattern for the note A_4 played on the open A string of a viola; Fig. 3.54 (d) shows the pattern for the same note, played with the same loudness (mp) on a tenor trombone. Each sound was recorded by a microphone placed about 0.5 m from the instrument, in a fairly reverberant room. Repetition period and frequency are the same for both patterns, and the amplitudes are roughly equal; the pronounced difference in timbre between the two sounds is clearly related principally to the striking difference in waveform. The rich, rather edgy sound of the open string corresponds to a waveform with many wiggles and sharp peaks, whereas the simpler, rounded sound of the trombone in its upper register is represented by a much more smoothly varying waveform.

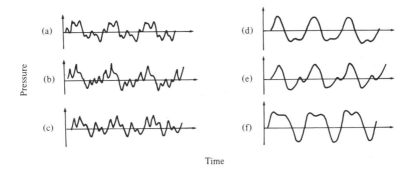

Fig. 3.54. Vibration patterns showing the variation of pressure with time in the sound wave corresponding to the note A_4 played on (a), (b) and (c) a viola (open string); (d), (e) and (f) a tenor trombone.

At first sight it appears that we can define any particular musical timbre simply by recording the corresponding waveform. It is certainly true that if we reproduce exactly the waveform of Fig. 3.54 (a), we shall recreate exactly the same open string timbre that we originally recorded. However, there are many other waveforms which will create an indistinguishable timbre. Figs. 3.54 (b) and (c) illustrate two further measurements of the sound of the open A_4 on the viola. The circumstances of recording were identical to that of Fig. 3.54 (a), and the timbre of the sound was not noticeably different in the three cases; the waveforms have the same general character, but are quite different in detail. A similar result was obtained when the trombone A_4 measurement was repeated (Fig. 3.54 (d),

(e) and (f)). Three notes with essentially the same timbre gave three different waveforms.

Harmonic spectra

In Chapter 1 we saw that a periodic vibration with a complex waveform could be analysed into a set of Fourier components whose frequencies made up a harmonic series; the relative amplitudes of the harmonic components could be represented by a harmonic spectrum. The detailed shape of a waveform depends on the relative phases of the harmonic components, as well as their amplitudes. However, changes in these relative phases create only small differences in timbre, which are normally of little musical significance (Schroeder 1975; Plomp 1976, pp.88–93). This insensitivity of the ear to changes in phase partly accounts for the fact that different waveforms can elicit the same sensation of timbre.

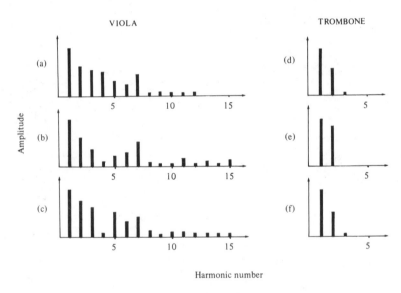

Fig. 3.55. Harmonic spectra corresponding to the waveforms of Fig. 3.54. (a), (b) and (c) viola A₄ (open string); (d), (e) and (f) tenor trombone A₄.

The harmonic spectra of the sounds whose waveforms are given in Fig. 3.54 are presented in Fig. 3.55. The two trombone tones represented by (d) and (f) in the two figures show the same harmonic spectra, with only 1st and 2nd harmonics significant. The reconstruction, or *resynthesis*, of the waveforms from their components is simple in this case, since only two sine waves have to be added together: the reconstruction process is illustrated in Fig. 3.56. In each case, the amplitude of the 2nd harmonic is just half that of the 1st harmonic; the phase relationship between the two components is different in the two cases, and this accounts for the difference between the waveforms.

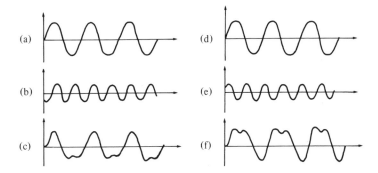

Fig. 3.56. Combining (a) and (b) with suitable phases gives (c), which is the resynthesis of the waveform in Fig. 3.54 (d). Altering the phase relationship between the two harmonics, (d) and (e) add together to give (f), the resynthesis of Fig. 3.54 (f).

It appears that the harmonic spectrum is a more economical way of representing the steady state timbre of a sound than the waveform, since a whole class of different waveforms with the same timbre can be represented by a single harmonic spectrum. Many textbooks do in fact quote 'typical harmonic spectra' to illustrate the steady state timbre of different instruments. Such information should not be taken too seriously, however. Quite apart from the fact that the timbre of a particular instrument may be different for each note within its compass, and will change with the dynamic level at which the note is played, we must recognise that different measured harmonic spectra can give rise to the same sense of timbre. This is illustrated by comparison of the spectra in Fig. 3.55 (d), (e) and (f): although the timbre of the three sounds was almost indistinguishable, the spectrum of (e) is noticeably different from that of (d) and (f), with a considerably stronger 2nd harmonic. Similar variations in the amplitudes of the harmonic components are seen in the spectra of the repeated viola notes (Fig. 3.55 (a), (b) and (c)).

Part of the variation in the measured spectra can be attributed to involuntary fluctuations in sound production by the player. The remainder will have arisen from small changes in the relative positions of instrument and microphone. Sound is not radiated uniformly in all directions by an instrument; the pattern of directionality is likely to be different for different harmonics (Meyer 1978). Thus one orientation of the instrument may favour the radiation of the 4th harmonic towards the microphone, whereas a different orientation may result in the 5th harmonic being radiated preferentially in this direction (Benade 1976, pp.482–483, 564–565).

Harmonic spectra in reverberant rooms

We must also remember that the sounds of Figs. 3.54 and 3.55 were recorded in a room with a considerable amount of reverberation. The sound reaching the microphone was thus a mixture of direct and reflected waves. The reflected sound has the effect of reducing the significance of the directional patterns discussed in the preceding paragraph, since a harmonic radiated preferentially away from the microphone can nevertheless return after several reflections from the walls.

There is, however, another aspect of reflected sound which increases the variability of harmonic spectra (Plomp and Steeneken 1973; Plomp 1976, pp.100–101). There are many possible paths that a sound can take between instrument and microphone in a reverberant room (see Fig. 3.57); each path will introduce a phase shift between direct and reflected waves which will depend on the path length and on the wavelength of the harmonic concerned. The amplitude of a particular harmonic measured by the microphone will therefore depend on exactly how all the reflected waves add to the direct wave.

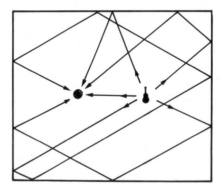

Fig. 3.57. Illustrating some of the many different paths along which sound travels from instrument to microphone in a reverberant room.

It can thus happen that for one arrangement of instrument and microphone in the room, many of the reflections of a particular harmonic will arrive at the microphone in phase with the direct sound. The separate contributions will add constructively, emphasising the contribution of this harmonic to the spectrum of the sound received by the microphone. Moving either the microphone or the instrument by a small distance (of the order of half a wavelength of the harmonic), we can find another arrangement in which a significant part of the direct sound is cancelled by destructive interference from out-of-phase reflections. The relevant harmonic will have a much smaller amplitude in the spectrum measured with this arrangement.

This argument applies not only to sound recorded by a microphone, but also to the sound arriving at the ear of a listener. If the listener moves around in a room while a performer plays a steady tone with uniform timbre, the harmonic spectrum of the sound received by each ear will be constantly changing. Not only that, but the spectra of the sounds received by the two ears will in general be different, since they are at different positions in the room (Benade 1976, pp.197–201).

The remarkable fact is that a listener moving his head from side to side in a concert hall is not aware of pronounced changes in timbre, although the amplitudes of individual harmonic components in the sound which he hears can be varying by more than a factor of two. On the contrary, a certain amount of head motion brings the timbre of a steady sound into clearer focus. Once again, the brain appears to be performing a subtle analysis of the information presented to it by the two ears. Differences between the harmonic spectra at the right and left ears are more likely to be related to the properties of the room than to the nature of the instrument generating the sound; when the head is held fixed, the average of the two spectra gives the best available characterisation of the instrument. If the head is allowed to move, the averaging process can be extended over all the spectra received by both ears during the motion of the head. Some of the effects of standing waves in the room are thereby averaged out, leaving a spectrum which is more characteristic of the instrument itself.

We should not be misled, therefore, into thinking that the differences between the harmonic spectra measured in Fig. 3.55 (a), (b) and (c) tell us anything significant about the timbre of the viola sound. Our best representation of the timbre in terms of a harmonic spectrum is obtained by averaging the three measured spectra. The average spectrum is shown in Fig. 3.58 (a); the corresponding average spectrum for the trombone A_4 is shown by Fig. 3.58 (b).

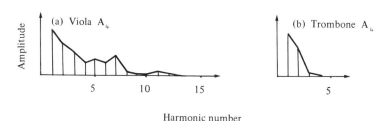

Fig. 3.58. Average spectrum envelopes for the sounds of Fig. 3.54: (a) viola A_4 (open string); (b) tenor trombone A_4.

From the preceding discussion, it should be clear that it is the general form of the average spectrum which is significant for the brain's assessment of timbre, rather than the detailed amplitudes of individual harmonics. To emphasise this general form, a line may be drawn connecting the upper ends of the vertical bars representing harmonic amplitudes; this line is called the *average spectrum envelope*. The envelopes are drawn in Fig. 3.58 to provide a clear picture of the relative importance of different regions of frequency in the harmonic spectra.

In interpreting these harmonic spectra, it should be borne in mind that vertical distance represents the amplitude of the pressure fluctuations corresponding to each component harmonic. The intensity of a particular harmonic is proportional to the square of the pressure amplitude; thus, if one harmonic has twice the amplitude of another, it will have four times the intensity. However, if we want to display the relative importance of each harmonic in the perceived sound, we must convert each harmonic amplitude into the corresponding loudness level (in phons), or loudness (in sones): the harmonic spectrum is then described as a *loudness spectrum*. Average loudness spectrum envelopes for the viola and trombone notes of Fig. 3.54 are shown in Fig. 3.59: in general outline they are similar to the amplitude spectrum envelopes of Fig. 3.58. The principal difference is that high numbered harmonics appear more prominently in the loudness spectra, reflecting the greater sensitivity of the ear to high frequencies.

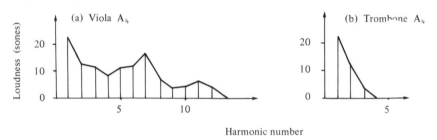

Fig. 3.59. Loudness spectrum envelopes for the sounds of Fig. 3.54: (a) viola A$_4$ (open string); (b) trombone A$_4$.

How many dimensions has timbre?

Pitch and loudness are both one-dimensional attributes of sound. This means that they each vary along a single scale: high–low in the case of pitch, loud–soft in the case of loudness. Provided that we have established a means of quantifying this scale, and an appropriate method of measurement, we can uniquely define either the pitch or the loudness of a steady state tone by a single number, representing its position on the corresponding scale.

Timbre, however, is a multi-dimensional attribute (Licklider 1951;

Plomp 1970). Two sounds can differ in timbre in a variety of ways, and musicians use a wide range of more or less colourful terms to describe these differences. For example, one sound might be judged 'dark' and another 'bright'; one might be judged 'smooth' and another 'rough'. These judgements relate to different aspects of the timbre: we might have a 'dark, smooth' sound, a 'dark, rough' sound, a 'bright, smooth' sound, or a 'bright, rough' sound.

If the scales 'dark–bright' and 'smooth–rough' were completely independent, and if these two factors were enough to specify completely a particular steady state timbre, we could conclude that timbre was two-dimensional. However, there are many other verbal scales in common use. In a comprehensive study of this question, Bismarck (1974 (a)) collated 69 possible pairs of terms which might be used to rate timbre. By eliminating pairs considered synonymous, or otherwise unsuitable, he reduced this number to 28, twelve of which are listed in Table 3.7.

TABLE 3.7

Some verbal scales used to rate timbre (after Bismarck)

fine	–	coarse
reserved	–	obtrusive
dark	–	bright
dull	–	sharp
soft	–	hard
smooth	–	rough
broad	–	narrow
wide	–	tight
clean	–	dirty
solid	–	hollow
compact	–	scattered
open	–	closed

We need not necessarily conclude that timbre has 28 dimensions; the 28 scales may not be independent. For example, a given degree of 'tightness' (as opposed to 'wideness') might always be equivalent to a fixed combination of 'closedness' and 'compactness'. If this were so, the timbre of any sound could be specified without making use of the 'tight–wide' scale.

Tests using sophisticated statistical methods have suggested that 3 or 4 scales should be enough to specify most steady-state musical timbres with a fair degree of accuracy (Bismarck 1974(a); Plomp 1976, Ch.6). Bismarck's work showed that one of the verbal scales in Table 3.7 was particularly significant: the 'dull–sharp' scale. When musicians were asked to judge the timbre of a large number of different sounds by assigning a number on a scale from 1 = 'very dull' to 7 = 'very sharp', consistent results were obtained. Comparison of sounds with the same 'sharpness' rating indicated that the remaining differences in timbre were relatively subtle. In principle, similar ratings on two or three other scales should be enough to pin down the residual differences; in practice verbal scales corresponding to these other dimensions have not been identified.

Measuring timbre: the tristimulus diagram

We saw earlier that the harmonic spectrum of a sound could alter significantly in detail without causing a noticeable change in the perceived timbre. If timbre is in fact a three-dimensional attribute, we should require only three numbers to specify a given timbre completely. Clearly the harmonic spectrum of a particular viola A_4 (cf. Fig. 3.55), with 15 numbers representing the amplitudes of 15 harmonic components, must contain a considerable amount of redundant information.

Various attempts have been made to find a satisfactory method of boiling down the information contained in a harmonic spectrum to yield a small set of numbers which would define the timbre (Plomp 1970; Bruijn 1978; Preis 1984; Padgham 1986). Usually these numbers have been chosen to summarise the general features of the spectrum envelope.

An interesting approach along these lines has recently been developed by Pollard and Jansson (1982 (a)), following an analogy with a long-established technique for defining colour in vision. The eye contains three different types of cone receptors, each type sensitive to a different part of the visible spectrum: one set responds predominantly to red light, another responds to green, while the third responds to blue. When light corresponding to a mixture of different wavelengths is received by the eye, the brain is able to judge the spectral distribution of the light by comparing the signals from the three types of receptor. A colour can therefore be defined by three numbers, representing the relative strengths of the components in the red, green and blue regions respectively. The success of this analysis is confirmed by colour television, in which red, green and blue pictures are presented together on the screen, and accepted as full colour by the brain.

The hearing mechanism is of course quite different from that of vision. Nevertheless, Pollard and Jansson have suggested that the salient properties of a spectrum envelope can likewise be reduced to three numbers, representing the effective loudness of three regions of the spectrum. The first region contains only the fundamental (the 1st harmonic); the second contains harmonics 2, 3 and 4; the third region contains all higher harmonics. The calculation of effective loudness in the second and third regions must take account of masking.

Let us call the loudness (in sones) of the fundamental component N_F, the combined loudness of the mid-range components (2nd, 3rd and 4th harmonics) N_M, and the combined loudness of the high components (all harmonics above the 4th) N_H. The total loudness will be $N = N_F + N_M + N_H$. The proportions of the loudness in each region will thus be given by the three fractions

$$f = N_F/N, \quad m = N_M/N, \quad \text{and} \quad h = N_H/N.$$

Since these must add up to 1, we need only specify two of them; we can obtain the third by subtracting the sum of the other two from 1.

If we choose to specify the fractions m and h, representing the relative strengths of mid-range and high-range components respectively, we can display the timbre of any steady state sound as a point on a *tristimulus diagram* (Fig. 3.60). On this diagram, horizontal distance represents the value of m and vertical distance the value of h. (In Pollard and Jansson's original suggestion, the vertical axis represented m, and the horizontal h; it seems more appropriate, however, that a sound dominated by high harmonics should be represented by a point near the top of the diagram.) Thus a pure tone, consisting only of the fundamental component, would have $f = 1, m = 0, h = 0$; it would be represented by a point at the origin. The trombone A_4, whose average loudness spectrum envelope was shown in Fig. 3.59 (b), had a fundamental of loudness 23 sones and a 2nd harmonic of 12 sones; higher harmonics could be neglected. Thus the total loudness was 35 sones, and the tristimulus fractions are

$$f = 23/35 = 0.66; \quad m = 12/35 = 0.34; \quad \text{and} \quad h = 0/35 = 0.$$

This gives a point one-third of the way along the horizontal axis in Fig. 3.60.

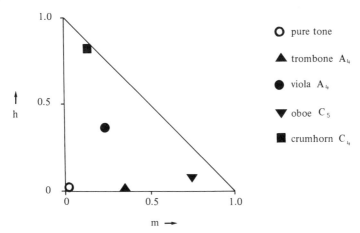

Fig. 3.60. Representation of various steady state timbres on the tristimulus diagram.

The loudness spectrum for the viola A_4 (Fig. 3.59 (a)) showed a strong fundamental, significant mid-range components and a powerful range of high harmonics; this balanced timbre appears as a point near the middle of the tristimulus triangle. The refined sound of an oboe C_5, with a predominance of mid-range harmonics (Fig. 3.61 (a)), places its timbre near the right hand corner of the triangle; in contrast, the cheerful buzz of the alto crumhorn C_4 has a spectrum completely dominated by high harmonics (Fig. 3.61 (b)), and its tristimulus representation is close to the top corner of the triangle.

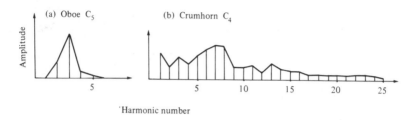

Fig. 3.61. Average spectrum envelopes for (a) oboe C_5; (b) alto crumhorn C_4.

The tristimulus diagram provides a useful way of encapsulating the measured properties of a sound in a way which can be closely related to the perceived timbre. We have illustrated its use in comparing and contrasting different steady state timbres; we shall see shortly that it also provides a useful method of displaying the changes which occur in the harmonic spectrum during the onset of a tone. It should be borne in mind, however, that since only two independent numbers are required to specify a point on the tristimulus diagram, only two of the three or more dimensions of timbre can be represented in this way. A point on the diagram may be a useful guide to timbre, but it cannot be a complete specification.

Formants

We saw in Fig. 3.58 (b) that the tone A_4 played on the trombone gave a spectrum envelope which was highest at the 1st harmonic, still quite high at the 2nd harmonic, but practically zero for the 3rd and higher harmonics. Can we consider this spectrum envelope shape to be a characteristic of trombone timbre? If so, we would expect to find the same envelope shape when we play other notes on the trombone.

What we actually find is shown by Fig. 3.62. For the note F_3 (played mp), the 3rd harmonic, insignificant in the A_4 spectrum, is the largest, and all harmonics up to the 5th make a sizeable contribution. For the note F_2, the first 10 harmonics are important, and even the 13th harmonic cannot be ignored. Clearly, whatever it is that enables us to recognise a trombone characteristic in these three sounds, it cannot be that they have the same spectral envelope shape.

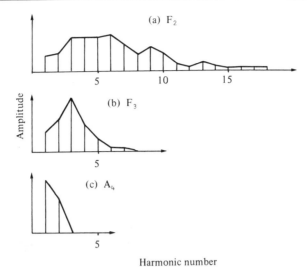

Fig. 3.62. Spectrum envelopes for three different trombone notes: (a) F_2; (b) F_3; (c) A_4.

There is, in fact, a unifying feature in the spectra of all three notes, which becomes evident when we display the envelopes, not in terms of the harmonic numbers, but in terms of the actual pitches of the components. This is done in Fig. 3.63: the pitch of each harmonic is marked on the stave by a black circle, and the amplitude by the displacement of the curve to the right.

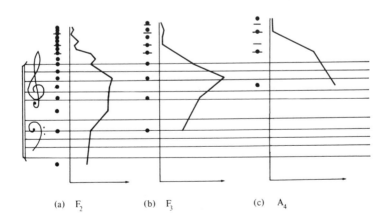

(a) F_2　　　　(b) F_3　　　　(c) A_4

Fig. 3.63. Average spectrum envelopes from Fig. 3.62, replotted on a pitch scale to show a formant around B_4.

We can now see that, for all the notes, the harmonic with the largest amplitude is the one closest to the pitch B_4 (frequency about 500 Hz). This feature is clearest for the note A_4 (where the relevant harmonic is the 1st) and F_3 (where it is the 3rd), but it is also noticeable in the spectrum of F_2, for which the envelope rises slowly up to the 6th harmonic (C_5) and diminishes rapidly for higher harmonics.

What we have identified in the trombone sound is a *formant* – a region of frequency (or pitch) in which the spectrum envelope is likely to have a peak. Our measurements show a broad formant, with a maximum at around 500 Hz. Formants have been observed in the spectra of many musical instruments (Sirker 1974; Meyer 1978), although their role in determining the characteristic of a particular instrument remains a matter of some debate.

The attribute of timbre which Bismarck describes as 'sharpness' is related to the existence of one or more formant regions in an instrument's sound. It has been found that sounds which are judged to have high 'sharpness' values have a concentration of sound energy in harmonics at high frequencies, whereas those with low 'sharpness' (i.e. 'very dull' sounds) have their most prominent harmonics at low frequencies (Bismarck 1974 (b)). Thus a sound with a fixed envelope shape would get 'sharper' in timbre as it got sharper in pitch, since the frequency of its most prominent harmonics would also rise. On the other hand, an instrument dominated by a formant would have a relatively constant 'sharpness', corresponding to the formant frequency: whatever the pitch of the fundamental (so long as it was below that of the formant), the most prominent harmonics would be around the formant frequency.

In one area of music, the crucial importance of formants is undisputed. The intelligibility of vowel sounds in singing, as in speech, is dependent on formant structures in the sounds (Fant 1970). To generate the vowel sound 'ee' as in 'feed', for example, a singer must adjust the opening of the lips and the position of the tongue in such a way as to amplify harmonics within three principal formant regions: one around 300 Hz, one around 2300 Hz and the third around 3000 Hz (Fig. 3.64 (a)). To change the vowel sound to 'oo' as in 'food', the second formant must be lowered to around 800 Hz, and the third to around 2500 Hz; the first formant remains close to 300 Hz (Fig. 3.64 (b)). The techniques used by singers to manipulate formants, and some of the musically significant consequences, will be discussed in Chapter 12.

Long-time-average-spectra

One of the goals of scientists working in the field of musical instrument acoustics is to devise a method of measuring timbre which is sufficiently meaningful and reliable to distinguish between instruments judged musically to be 'good' and those judged 'poor'. This turns out to be a surprisingly elusive goal: the factors which lead to an instrument being considered of high musical quality are not easy to pin down. It seems that the spacing and strength of formants are important features in determining the quality of members of the violin family, at least (see Chapter 6); the same may apply to other instrumental classes.

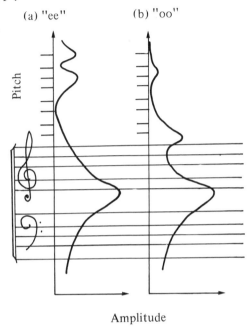

Fig. 3.64. Formants of the vowel sounds (a) 'ee'; (b) 'oo'.

We might hope, then, to obtain useful information about the tonal quality of a particular violin by identifying its formant structures. To do this, we must analyse the frequency spectra from a large number of different notes played on the instrument. In order to understand the necessity for a wide range of notes, consider the note G_3 played on an instrument with a single strong formant peak at 300 Hz. The first two harmonics of this note would lie on either side of the formant peak, at 196 Hz and 392 Hz respectively; they would probably have roughly the same amplitude. Since no harmonic existed at 300 Hz, there would be no way of telling from this measurement that a strong peak was located there. This information would be revealed by a measurement of the note D_4, whose first harmonic (300 Hz) would be strongly boosted by the formant.

A convenient way to carry out spectral measurements over a wide range of different notes on the instrument is to obtain a *long-time-average-*

spectrum (LTAS) (Jansson and Sundberg 1975; Jansson 1976; Sundberg and Jansson 1976). In this technique, the player is situated in a reverberation room, which is a chamber whose surfaces are designed to reflect sound strongly without emphasising particular frequencies more than others (see p.545). A series of scales, covering the complete playing range of the instrument, is recorded on tape. The microphone used in the recording is shielded from the direct sound of the instrument, so that directional patterns in the instrument's sound radiation do not distort the measurement: whatever the original direction of radiation, there is an equal probability that, after a sufficient number of reflections, the sound will arrive at the microphone.

The recorded sound is played back through a set of filters. Each filter is adjusted to let through only those frequency components which lie within a particular critical band. The average intensity level in each critical band is then calculated, the average being taken over the complete playing time; this average intensity level is then plotted against frequency or pitch to give the long-time-average-spectrum.

As an example of the use of the technique, we show in Fig. 3.65 LTAS curves, obtained by Gabrielsson and Jansson, for two groups of violins. The first group, whose LTAS is represented by the solid line in Fig. 3.65, consisted of eight violins which had been judged of high tonal quality by a

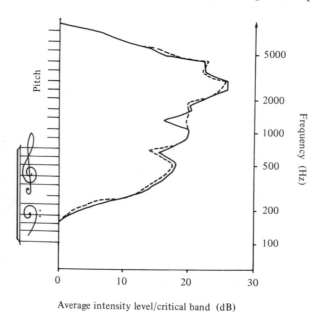

Average intensity level/critical band (dB)

Fig. 3.65. Long-time-average-spectra for a group of (a) high quality (solid curve), (b) inferior quality (dashed curve) violins. Adapted from Gabrielsson and Jansson (1979), p. 49, Fig. 2.

jury of professional violinists in the 1975 Instrument Exhibition of the Scandinavian Violin Maker Association. The second group consisted of seven violins which had also been submitted to the exhibition, and had been rated much inferior in tone quality by the same jury; the LTAS of this group is shown by the dashed line in Fig. 3.65.

The most striking feature of Fig. 3.65 is the similarity of the two curves. There is a broad peak around 500 Hz: we shall see in Chapter 6 that this is a formant due to the 'main wood resonance' of the violin. Other peaks are in evidence around 1000 Hz and 3000 Hz. The only obvious discrepancy between the two curves is the sharp dip in the solid curve around 1250 Hz, which is missing in the dashed curve. This suggests that strong radiation of components around this frequency (an octave above the open E string) is considered to be an undesirable feature in violin timbre. However, the overall similarity of the LTAS curves for violins which musicians judged to be markedly different casts some doubt on the prospect of making musically useful predictions of tonal quality on the basis of such measurements.

Transients

In Chapter 1 we examined the vibration pattern of a cello string during the first 100 ms after it had been set into motion by the action of the bow. Fig. 1.6 (a) showed that the vibration of the string did not start right away at full amplitude, but built up over the course of several periods of the vibration cycle. This build-up is known as the *onset transient* (or *attack transient*) of the vibration.

A similar feature is evident in the sound radiated by the cello. Indeed, all non-electronic musical instruments exhibit this type of transient behaviour at the beginning of a note. The upper curve in Fig. 3.66 shows the first 10 periods of the sound wave generated by an oboe playing G_4. For this note, of frequency 392 Hz, the length of one period is

$$T = 1/f = 1/392 \text{ s} = 2.55 \text{ ms};$$

the entire trace was thus recorded in about 25 ms. It will be seen that the amplitude has approached its full value by the end of the 6th period (i.e. after about 15 ms). It is also important to note that as the amplitude grows during the first few cycles, the waveform changes; this implies that the different harmonic components of the oboe sound are not all growing at the same rate.

Computers can now be programmed to generate sounds with any desired waveform or frequency spectrum. If we measure the height of the upper curve in Fig. 3.66 at each of a large number of closely spaced time intervals (i.e. we 'digitise' the curve), we can feed these numbers into a computer, and ask it to regenerate the sound. This is in fact the basis of the modern technique of digital recording, so we should not be surprised to find that the regenerated sound was a faithful copy of the original sound: the instrument would be easily recognised as an oboe.

If, however, we fed into the computer the digitised version of the lower curve in Fig. 3.66, which is the upper curve with its transient replaced by a sudden 'switch on', we should find it much more difficult to identify the sound as that of an oboe. Although the steady state waveform is the same in both cases, the sound represented by the lower curve has a characteristically 'artificial' quality; the removal of the onset transient has eliminated an important characteristic of the oboe sound.

Similar results are obtained when other instrumental sounds are computer synthesised: unless the steady state waveform is preceded by an appropriate onset transient, the synthesised timbre is a poor imitation of the original sound (Grey and Moorer 1977). This confirms earlier experiments in which onset transients were physically cut out of tape recordings of instrumental sounds (Berger 1964; Saldanha and Corso 1964). The decay transient, which occurs at the end of the note, is found to be much less important a feature of the characteristic timbre of an instrument.

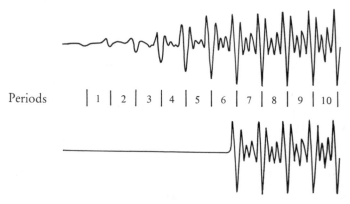

Periods

Fig. 3.66. The upper curve shows the pressure-time curve measured by a microphone during the first 10 periods of an oboe G_4. In the lower curve, the initial transient has been replaced with a sudden switch-on.

Spectral analysis of onset transients

A steady state periodic sound could be described by a harmonic spectrum, giving the (fixed) amplitude of each component. To describe the onset transient, we require an amplitude envelope for each component showing how it develops with time.

Fig. 3.67 illustrates the analysis of the first 60 ms of the sound of an organ Gedackt 8′ pipe playing the note C_4 (Pollard and Jansson 1982 (b)). The Gedackt pipe is a stopped wooden pipe (see Chapter 11); its spectrum therefore contains only the odd numbered members of the harmonic series. The sound was analysed by a set of filters, each of which selected components within one third of an octave (corresponding roughly to one critical band). Harmonics up to the 9th were picked out individually by this technique, and the change of amplitude of each harmonic with time was recorded. The 11th and 13th harmonics, falling within one critical band, gave a composite reading, as did the 15th and 17th; higher harmonics were not analysed.

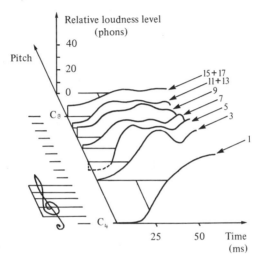

Fig. 3.67. Development of harmonic components during the onset transient of a C_4 Gedackt organ pipe. Adapted from Pollard and Jansson (1982 (b)), p.254, Fig. 4.

In Fig. 3.67 the results of the analysis are displayed in a three-dimensional diagram. In the horizontal plane, one axis represents time, while the other represents pitch. The vertical axis represents the relative loudness level of each component (in phons), measured relative to the average background level (which was about 40 phons). The diagram should be visualised as a set of receding 'pop-up' cutouts, each one representing an amplitude envelope.

Clearly, the components do not all rise at the same rate: this means that the spectrum is changing during the onset transient. Harmonics from the 7th upward are dominant at the start of the sound; after about 25 ms, the 3rd harmonic has grown a lot, and the 1st harmonic is starting to rise; by 50 ms, the 1st harmonic is the dominant feature of the spectrum.

Crucial factors in timbre characterisation

How much of the information contained in Fig. 3.67 is essential for the characterisation of this particular sound? The question is of considerable practical importance to the designers of electronic organs, who wish to recreate the sound of a pipe organ with the minimum amount of complicated circuitry or computer programming. Some light has recently been thrown on the matter by experiments in which sounds have been computer synthesised using various degrees of approximation, and listeners have been tested to see whether they could distinguish the approximations from the complete resynthesis (Risset and Wessel 1982). It appears that the detailed wiggles in the individual amplitude envelopes are relatively unimportant; so long as the general shape of each envelope is maintained, the curves can be ironed out without noticeably affecting the timbre.

Of potentially greater importance is the fact that real musical sounds are not strictly periodic: the components are not exact multiples of a fixed fundamental, but exhibit small fluctuations in pitch as time goes by. If these pitch variations are not reproduced, the sounds of some instruments (such as the soprano saxophone) cannot be adequately synthesised; on the other hand, they seem relatively insignificant for other instruments (such as the oboe) (Grey and Moorer 1977). Their importance in organ timbre has not been established, but in view of the mechanical nature of the sound production, a major effect seems unlikely.

At the very start of the sounds of some instruments, components are found which are far removed in pitch from any harmonic of the expected note. These inharmonic components usually have very low amplitudes, and disappear as the tone becomes established; nevertheless, they seem to be an important feature of the characteristic timbre of several instruments, including the bass clarinet, the alto saxophone and some organ pipes.

In an extensive survey of the factors affecting timbre recognition, Grey (1977) identified three attributes of crucial importance. One is the overall distribution of sound energy in the steady state frequency spectrum, which is closely related to the quality described previously as 'sharpness'. Another is the presence of low amplitude, high frequency sound (possibly inharmonic) at the start of the attack. The third is the extent to which the higher components in the onset transient are synchronised – that is to say, whether or not they rise simultaneously and at the same rate.

Transients on the tristimulus diagram

On the tristimulus diagram, the steady state harmonic spectrum is represented by a single point. At any instant during the development of the onset transient, the relative strengths of the different components can be represented by a point on the diagram; as the balance of fundamental, middle range and high range components changes with time, the point will trace out a line on the diagram. This provides a convenient method of summarising the important features of the spectral variation during the transient.

For example, Fig. 3.68 is the tristimulus diagram for the Gedackt C_4 sound whose evolution is illustrated in Fig. 3.67. The circles marked on the line indicate time intervals (in milliseconds) after the start of the tone. The preponderance of higher harmonics at the beginning of the sound (one of Grey's important factors) is shown clearly by the fact that the line starts well up towards the top (high range) corner of the triangle. The steady growth of the 3rd harmonic pulls the line towards the right hand (mid-range) corner for about 30 ms; after that, the fundamental starts to dominate, and the curve veers toward the bottom left corner.

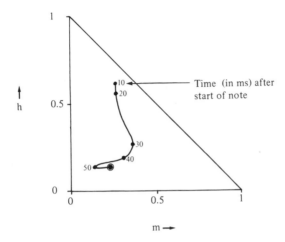

Fig. 3.68. A tristimulus diagram illustrating the evolution of the Gedackt C_4 organ pipe sound shown in Fig. 3.67. Adapted from Pollard and Jansson (1982 (a)), p.168, Fig. 6.

The example illustrates the power of the tristimulus method in abstracting important information from a mass of detail (compare Figs 3.67 and 3.68).

Vibrato

In 1938 Carl Seashore published his class study *Psychology of Music*, which included the results of a series of careful measurements of variations of pitch during vocal performance. It is worth reproducing part of one of his curves (Fig. 3.69), as it still has the power to shock musicians. The curve illustrates how the pitch of the singer Herald Stark's voice varied while he was singing the first four bars of the Bach-Gounod 'Ave Maria'. To emphasise the musical significance of the measurement, we have redrawn Seashore's curve against the 'distorted stave' we have used previously, in which equal semitone steps are represented by equal vertical distances.

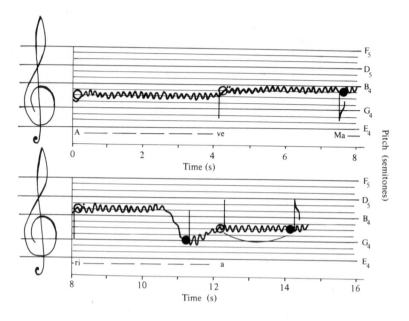

Fig. 3.69. Measured variation in pitch of a tenor voice singing the first four bars of 'Ave Maria' (Bach-Gounod). Adapted from Seashore (1938), p.35, Fig. 1.

The remarkable fact revealed by this curve is that even the first semibreve has no 'steady state': after the initial transient, with a characteristic 'scoop' up to the true pitch, the note continues to fluctuate in pitch, rising and falling in a regular way with a frequency of about 6 Hz. This would not surprise a musician, of course; it would indeed be surprising to hear this particular piece of music performed without such pitch modulation, known musically as *vibrato*. But it is perhaps a little disconcerting to find that the pitch is varying by as much as a semitone during the vibrato.

The extent to which vibrato is used by singers and instrumentalists is a matter of taste and performance practice. The curve in Fig. 3.69 represents a fairly full vibrato, but to most listeners it would be considered perfectly acceptable. The most interesting aspect from the point of view of our present discussion is that vibrato is not in general perceived as a variation in pitch (unless it is excessive), but rather as an enriching of the timbre of the sound.

Does this mean that the ear is incapable of following pitch variations of a semitone which occur 6 times every second? Clearly not – in a chromatic scale each note can be clearly heard at more than twice this rate. We saw in

Fig. 3.25, however, that pitch discrimination was less acute for slowly varying tones than for sudden pitch changes. It appears that, although the nerve cells in the ear can respond to changes which occur in only a few milliseconds, the brain's assessment of sounds whose properties are varying slowly and regularly is usually performed in a way which averages out fluctuations occurring faster than about 10 times a second. Although their vibrato is a little slower than this, the notes in Fig. 3.69 would be heard as steady in pitch by many listeners. If a recording of such a piece of music were slowed down to half speed, so that the vibrato rate was only about 3 Hz, the pitch fluctuation would become glaringly obvious.

Why do musicians use vibrato? The nature of the sound production mechanism of the voice, and of certain classes of instrument (notably bowed strings), makes a certain extent of pitch fluctuation inevitable; the deliberate imposition of vibrato partly conceals and partly regularises such fluctuation. It has also frequently been suggested that vibrato makes an instrumental sound more 'human' by giving it this characteristically vocal property; in the words of Seashore (1938), 'tenderness of tone results from awareness of organic trembling'.

Vibrato also modifies the timbre in a direct way, by altering the relationship between the fundamental repetition frequency and any formants which exist. In the third bar of Fig. 3.69, the note C_5 is sung with a vowel sound close to the 'ee' whose formant structure is shown in Fig. 3.64 (a). As the pitch fluctuates, the harmonic spectrum will be swept up and down; the formant frequencies, on the other hand, will remain fixed. The relative strengths of the different harmonics will therefore be modulated at the vibrato rate. A similar effect occurs due to resonances of the room in which the performance takes place. The complex formant structure in instruments of the violin family makes this spectral modulation an important feature of violin vibrato (Fletcher and Sanders 1967).

The chorus effect

In Chapter 1 it was pointed out that the timbre of a section of ten violins playing in unison is quite different from that of a solo violin. The primary reason for this difference, which is known as the *chorus effect*, is the fact that each of the ten instruments is an independent sound source; no two instruments will have exactly the same repetition frequency. There will thus be a constantly changing phase relationship between any given harmonic component produced by one instrument and the same component produced by each of the other members of the section. When only two instruments are playing in unison, a high degree of playing control is necessary in order to avoid an unpleasant beating sensation due to these phase differences; if each instrument uses a slightly different vibrato rate, the regularity of the beat pattern is broken up, and the effect is less prominent. With a section of ten instruments, the wide variety of different beating rates produces a 'shimmer' which is an important aspect of the chorus effect.

From the point of view of the frequency spectrum, the sound generated by a section of instruments, or a chorus of voices, does not correspond to a series of lines at harmonic frequencies, but rather to a series of peaks centred on the appropriate harmonics. A good orchestral string section, or a well-drilled choir, normally generates a sound with frequency peaks corresponding to a pitch spread of under 20 cents. On the other hand, one professional choir is reported as having a pitch spread of almost a full semitone on the lower notes (Meyer 1978, p.28). This is presumably due to the use of wide vibrato by the individual choir members, rather than to poor intonation; in any case, the generous brain interprets the sound as a musical tone with a definite, stable pitch and a rich choral timbre.

4

Playing in tune

In this chapter we consider the reasons why specific intervals and scales are used as the basis for musical composition in most Western music and also the significance of tuning variations in musical performance. We have already seen that pitch is essentially determined by frequency, although loudness also plays a minor role. The question is, why do certain combinations of frequencies sound more pleasing to the ear than others? This whole subject is one which is still quite unsettled and it is known that the answer as to whether a particular interval sounds consonant or dissonant to a listener is very much a question of musical training. However, in the Western world at least, certain intervals, namely the octave, perfect fifth, and major and minor thirds, are generally considered as consonant provided that the notes are tuned within certain limits. The German physicist Hermann von Helmholtz (1821–1894) put forward a theory which at least partly explains why this should be, and more recently his ideas have been confirmed by detailed psychophysical experiments (Plomp 1976).

CONSONANCE AND DISSONANCE

In Chapter 2 we analysed the way in which the ear registers two pure tones sounded simultaneously. We saw that as the separation between the tones is reduced below the critical bandwidth, a roughness in the sound becomes apparent which reaches a maximum at about one quarter of a critical bandwidth. For low notes in the region of 100 Hz (G_2) the roughness is a maximum at around 20 Hz separation, corresponding to three semitones, whereas for all notes above middle C maximum roughness occurs at a separation of approximately one semitone.

165

Helmholtz explained the concept of consonance and dissonance in terms of the roughness generated by beating. His theories are described in the momentous volume *Lehre von den Tonempfindungen als phys-iologische Grundlage für die Theorie der Musik* (1863; published in English in 1875 as *Sensations of Tone as a Physiological Basis for the Theory of Music*). He argued that when two notes are sounded simul-taneously on actual instruments, interference occurs not only between the fundamentals but also between the various harmonics which are present. The degree of dissonance is then determined by the extent to which roughness is generated from the beating between all the different har-monic components. Over the major part of the playing range a semitone separation is the one which creates the most roughness, with the tone coming next. The relative consonance or dissonance of different intervals can then be found by comparing the number of tone and semitone separations between the harmonic constituents of the two notes.

Fig. 4.1 shows six different selected intervals with their related harmon-ics: the tone and semitone separations between harmonics have been marked by single and double line arrows respectively. Only the first six harmonics have been included since these are sufficient to show the essential features of the intervals, although it is recognised that this is an oversimplification of most real situations. In the case of the octave all of the harmonics coincide so there are no clashes and the result is a perfectly smooth interval. In the case of the perfect fifth there are just two clashes of a tone, which create only a small degree of dissonance. At the other end of the range is the very dissonant augmented fourth with three semitone clashes and one tone clash. It can be seen that the more simple the frequency ratio between the two fundamentals, the less is the chance of the harmonics of one tone interfering with the harmonics of the other.

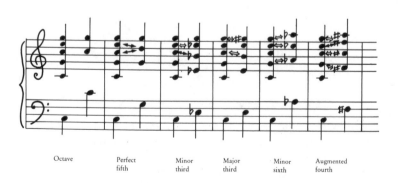

Octave	Perfect	Minor	Major	Minor	Augmented
	fifth	third	third	sixth	fourth

Fig. 4.1. Intervals and their related harmonics. Tone and semitone separations between harmonics are indicated by single and double line arrows respectively.

The degree of dissonance depends on the tonal quality and therefore the harmonic spectrum associated with the individual notes. In many cases the dissonance associated with a particular interval does not register because the particular clashing harmonics are either absent or of very low amplitude. Two flutes for example will generally play smoother sounding intervals than two oboes, which have very rich harmonic spectra. A clarinet has very weak even harmonics when playing in the lower register. The reason for this will be explained in Chapter 8. It can be seen that two clarinets can produce relatively smooth sounding major thirds in the low register since for this interval it is the fourth and sixth harmonics of the lower note which are primarily responsible for generating the dissonance.

We have so far discussed only the dissonance created by notes separated by simple frequency ratios. However, Helmholtz and other workers have extended these ideas to the dissonance created by two notes having a gradually varying separation. Fig. 4.2 shows how the dissonance changes as the separation of the two notes varies up to an octave. The data for the curves have been obtained from laboratory tests using a large number of subjects, but their general shapes are also confirmed by theoretical calculations using the same principles that we have already applied for the simple frequency ratios. Four curves are shown. The lowest is for two pure tones

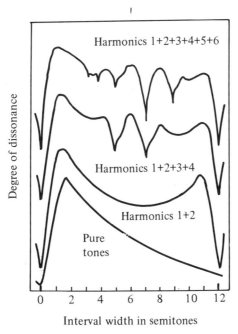

Fig. 4.2. Variation of tonal dissonance of a musical interval with the interval width and the harmonic content of the component tones. Adapted from Plomp (1976).

and the one above for tones containing only the fundamental and the second harmonic. Above this is for notes containing harmonics 1 to 4 and the top curve for notes formed from all the harmonics 1 to 6. A number of interesting inferences can be drawn from the graph. Firstly note that the dissonance increases with the number of harmonics as would be expected and also that there are large reductions in dissonance at intervals normally considered consonant, especially the octave, perfect fifth and perfect fourth. The sharpness of these dissonance valleys is important because it shows the effect of mistuning in the interval. It is seen that the octave and the fifth with their tuning ratios of 2:1 and 3:2 are characterised by relatively sharp valleys compared with the major and minor thirds with their tuning ratios of 5:4 and 6:5. This indicates that the octave and fifth are more sensitive to small deviations from the true tuning ratios than are the thirds. Note however that only the octave valleys are clearly defined for the tones with just the fundamental and second harmonics. It will be seen later in this chapter that the relatively greater importance of correct tuning in the octave and fifth has important implications in the aural effect of differently tempered scales.

Care must be exercised in interpreting Figs 4.1 and 4.2 and the scientific concept of consonance and dissonance as first put forward by Helmholtz. The roughness caused by beating at certain intervals is a basic property of the interval sensation, whereas the terms consonance and dissonance to the musician have a historical significance and are related to the context in which the intervals are played. The diminished fifth and minor seventh, for example, were generally considered to be dissonant intervals in the time of Palestrina and Lassus (Swindale 1962) but are used quite freely by contemporary composers. The acceptability of an interval to a musical ear is also dependent on the manner in which it is approached and quitted. Fig. 4.2 is derived from experiments in which untrained subjects were presented with isolated tone intervals. In this way the effects of musical training and context were deliberately avoided. The shapes of the curves define a purely sensory phenomenon and do not imply for example that a musician will consider a major seventh consisting of two pure tones in isolation to be consonant or that a non-musician would consider this interval to be consonant when heard in context. The terms tonal consonance and tonal dissonance, or alternatively sensory consonance and dissonance, are sometimes used to indicate that the sensory rather than the musical understanding is meant. It is interesting to note from Fig. 4.2 that for example the sensory dissonance produced by two flutes playing pure tones a minor second apart is less than that of two oboes, heavy in upper harmonics, playing a perfect fifth or even a unison.

Major and minor triads

Thus far we have discussed only the dissonance of pairs of tones. A musical triad contains three such pairs – for example, the major triad C_4 E_4 G_4 contains the major third C_4 E_4, the minor third E_4 G_4 and the perfect fifth C_4 G_4. Can we estimate the total dissonance of this triad by adding together the dissonances of a major third, a minor third and a perfect fifth?

Helmholtz (1863, p.326) pointed out a difficulty in this approach. The minor triad $C_4E_4^\flat G_4$ also contains a major third, a minor third and a perfect fifth; we should then expect it to have the same total dissonance as a major triad. This does not seem in accord with musical experience.

According to Helmholtz, the difference between the straightforward harmoniousness of the major triad and the more 'mysterious, obscure effect' of the minor triad arises from the influence of the combination tones generated in the two cases (see p.64). Fig. 4.3 (a) shows the pitches of the simple difference tones arising from a triad of pure tones C_4 E_4 G_4, and from its first and second inversions; these pitches are readily obtained using the pitch-frequency table on p.178. It will be seen that the difference tones reinforce the C major tonality of the triad. For the minor triad C_4 $E_4^\flat$ G_4, on the other hand, Fig. 4.3 (b) shows that the difference tones introduce a disturbing implication of $A^\flat$ major tonality in root position and first inversion, with the even more disruptive addition of a $B^\flat$ in the second inversion.

Fig. 4.3. Difference tones in (a) major and (b) minor triads. The interval at which the simple difference tone lies below the lower note for a given separation is as follows:

Separation:	5th	4th	maj 3rd	min 3rd	maj 6th	min 6th
Interval:	oct	12th	2 oct	2 oct + maj 3rd	5th	maj 6th

The musical reality of the difference tones in Fig. 4.3 is strikingly evident when the triads are played on three soprano recorders (an octave higher than written). Nevertheless, the significance of combination tones in harmony remains a matter of debate. Hindemith, for one, was in no doubt – 'an interval without combination tones would be an abstract concept, as bodiless as the ratio with which we express it mathematically' (Hindemith 1940).

169

ORIGIN OF SCALES

The processes by which scales have been conceived and adopted are numerous and not fully understood, but are closely related to those of speech inflections. Although in theory any number of pitches may be used as a basis for musical expression, in practice different cultures have adopted patterns made up of relatively few discrete pitches which they consistently employ. The origin of these schematic arrangements in Western civilisation is centred around the consonant intervals, particularly the octave, fifth and major and minor thirds. However, it will be seen later that it is impossible to devise a practical scale of fixed frequencies in which all of these intervals are true. In reality most instruments like the voice have a flexibility of tuning which allows the player to make small corrections and bring the most important intervals into tune. This does not apply to keyboard instruments, where the tuning is generally fixed, so that the pitches of the notes must inevitably be some form of compromise and the musician must be resigned to the fact that some intervals will not sound true.

The Pythagorean scale

Even in primitive cultures, the octave plays an important role in that the intervals between the notes of a scale generally repeat themselves at the octave. In these primitive cultures, however, and also to a certain extent in modern China, India, Turkey and Arabia, the interval relationships within the scale are not necessarily derived from considerations of consonance. This may be acceptable because their music is primarily monophonic. In Western civilisation there is a history of music developing polyphonically so that it is essential for scales to be based on consonant intervals in order that two or more parts may be played or sung simultaneously without undue dissonance. Even so, the Western Diatonic Scales may be traced back as far as the early Greeks and the Greek philosopher Pythagoras (6th century BC), before polyphonic music was established. From experiments on the subdivision of a string into segments, he recognised the fundamental nature of the octave and the perfect fifth and formulated a seven note scale based on these intervals (and the inversion of the perfect fifth, the perfect fourth). Starting for example on the note F_3 one can proceed up in fifths as follows to obtain all seven white notes on the piano: F_3 C_4 G_4 D_5 A_5 E_6 B_6. These notes form the scale of C major when F_3 is raised an octave, D_5 and A_5 are lowered an octave and E_6 and B_6 are lowered by two octaves, i.e. we have C_4 D_4 E_4 F_4 G_4 A_4 B_4. Alternatively, working entirely in terms of the two intervals of a fourth and a fifth one can derive the same scale without going outside the octave. Commencing on C_4, step up a fifth to G_4, down a fourth to D_4, up a fifth to A_4, down a fourth to E_4 etc. The frequency ratios and intervals in cents for the Pythagorean scale obtained in this way are shown in Fig. 4.4. Notice that the scale has only two intervals, the major tone (204 cents) and the Pythagorean semitone (90 cents), but the tone is greater than two semitones in width. All the intervals of a fourth and a fifth have their correct ratios according to the harmonic series, i.e. 4/3 and 3/2 respectively as one would expect, since this is the basis on which the scale has been derived. This can easily be checked in the interval D_4 to A_4 for example. The frequency ratio of these two notes is $27/16 \div 9/8$ which is identical to $3/2$.

Note	C_4	D_4	E_4	F_4	G_4	A_4	B_4	C_5
Frequency ratio to C_4	1	$\frac{9}{8}$	$\frac{81}{64}$	$\frac{4}{3}$	$\frac{3}{2}$	$\frac{27}{16}$	$\frac{243}{128}$	2
Nö. of cents above C_4	0	204	408	498	702	906	1,110	1,200
Intervals between adjacent notes in cents		204	204	90	204	204	204	90

Fig. 4.4. Pythagorean scale starting on C_4, the number of cents above C_4 and the interval between adjacent notes in the scale.

Circle of fifths

The successive intervals of perfect fifths used by Pythagoras can be displayed on a circle like the numbers on a clock face. It will be seen that the seven notes of the diatonic major scale can be extended by successively moving up in fifths until eventually all the black notes have been introduced and the circle is complete. The complete circle supplies the full chromatic scale (Fig. 4.5).

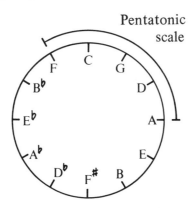

Fig. 4.5. The circle of fifths.

171

By stopping at different places on the circle we obtain various scales which have been used for polyphonic music in different cultures. For example, a segment of five notes such as F, C, G, D, A gives us the *tonal pentatonic scale* used in music from Scotland, Southern Asia and elsewhere. In its most common form it consists of all the black notes, i.e. the segment from F$^{\#}$ to B$^{\flat}$. 'Auld Lang Syne' for example can be played on only the black notes of the piano. This scale has been used extensively by modern composers, e.g. Kodály in his '24 Little Canons on the Black Notes'.

It might appear at first sight that the circle of fifths gives the complete answer to the problem of scale formation, but unfortunately this is not the case. From the harmonic series we know that the frequency ratio between any two adjacent notes in the circle should be 3/2 and there are 12 intervals, thus one complete circle will increase the frequency by $(3/2)^{12} =$ 129.75. It will be seen, however, that the final note should be exactly 7 octaves higher than the starting note, i.e. the frequency ratio corresponding to one complete circle should be $2^7 = 128$. The discrepancy is known as the *Pythagorean comma*. Thus

$$1 \text{ Pythagorean comma} = 129.75/128 = 1.014 \approx 23.5 \text{ cents}$$

The fact that it is impossible to derive a scale in which all the ratios are correct according to the harmonic series is a fundamental problem which has been tackled over the ages in many diverse ways by musicians, philosophers and mathematicians alike. Here we shall consider only the solutions which are of most relevance to the practising musician.

JUST DIATONIC SCALE

In addition to the difficulty which arises from the discrepancy in the formation of the circle of fifths, there is a further problem with the Pythagorean scale, namely that the thirds are badly mistuned. This can be seen for example in the interval C_4 to E_4. The frequency ratio of these two notes according to the harmonic series should be 5/4, which corresponds to 386 cents (p.78); it is in fact 81/64, i.e. 408 cents. Thus it is 22 cents too wide. This interval, which is just slightly smaller than a Pythagorean comma, is termed a *syntonic comma* and will arise later in our discussions on temperament. The minor third E_4 to G_4 is correspondingly too narrow by the same amount. Since the major triad is at the foundation of harmony in Western music, the Pythagorean scale has largely been discarded in favour of the *just diatonic scale*. This is based on the primary major triads and as such is generally considered as the basis for the formation of practical tuning systems, although it still does not overcome the problem of closing the circle of fifths. The frequencies of the notes in a root position major triad are given by the fourth, fifth and sixth harmonics in the series, i.e. the frequencies should be in the ratio 4:5:6. If the tonic is C_4, for example, then the ratios of E_4 and G_4 to C_4 should be 5/4 and 3/2 respectively. Fig. 4.6 shows how the C major scale may be formed from these frequency ratios. Firstly the C major tonic triad is formed with C_4 as the root. The other notes in the scale are then obtained by forming the two other major triads in the scale, i.e. chord IV (F major) and chord V (G major), maintaining the frequencies of the common notes, i.e. chord IV is formed with C_4 in the upper part and chord V with G_4 in the bass. Since the frequency ratio of 2:1 must be maintained for each octave interval it follows that the frequencies of F_4 and A_4 must be twice these of F_3 and A_3 respectively and similarly the frequency D_4 must be half that of D_5. The frequency ratios for the complete C major scale from C_4 to C_5 are shown in Fig. 4.7 together with the intervals in cents. The exact frequency ratios for the three major triads have been maintained. In fact all of the major and minor thirds are correct except D to F which is too narrow. Notice that there are three basic intervals, the *major tone* (204 cents labelled M), the *minor tone* (182 cents labelled m) and the diatonic semitone (112 cents labelled s). The difference between the major and minor tones is a *syntonic comma* equal to 22 cents. The minor third D to F and also the perfect fifth D to A are one syntonic comma too narrow, so the minor triad DFA, i.e. chord II, is out of tune.

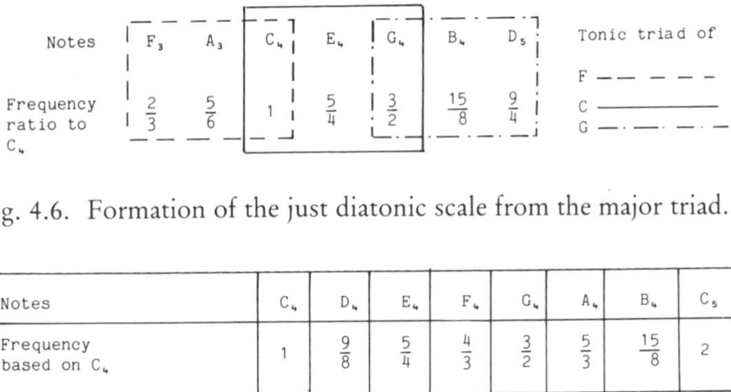

Notes	F_3	A_3	C_4	E_4	G_4	B_4	D_5	Tonic triad of
Frequency ratio to C_4	$\frac{2}{3}$	$\frac{5}{6}$	1	$\frac{5}{4}$	$\frac{3}{2}$	$\frac{15}{8}$	$\frac{9}{4}$	F — — — — — C ——————— G —·— ·· —·—

Fig. 4.6. Formation of the just diatonic scale from the major triad.

Notes	C_4	D_4	E_4	F_4	G_4	A_4	B_4	C_5
Frequency based on C_4	1	$\frac{9}{8}$	$\frac{5}{4}$	$\frac{4}{3}$	$\frac{3}{2}$	$\frac{5}{3}$	$\frac{15}{8}$	2
Number of cents above C_4	0	204	386	498	702	884	1088	1200
Intervals between adjacent notes in cents		204 M	182 m	112 s	204 M	182 m	204 M	112 s

Fig. 4.7. The basic frequencies and intervals for the just diatonic scale of C major with C_4 as the tonic.

Playing melodies and chords

In ensemble playing adherence to the just diatonic pitches ensures that harmonies based on the primary triads are true in a major key and also in some simple melodies based around these chords it is possible to make all intervals true. An example is in the opening of the Haydn Serenade shown in Fig. 4.8 (a). Problems arise, however, in playing chord II or melodies involving the minor third from the supertonic to the subdominant or the perfect fifth from the supertonic to the submediant, i.e. D to F or D to A in C major. This can be seen in the opening of the Handel Flute Sonata (Fig. 4.8 (b)), where the interval B♭ to G is a comma smaller than the natural minor third. This would normally be corrected by moving either the B♭ upwards or the G downwards at the expense of spoiling the two adjacent intervals. The two notes B♭ and G in this context are referred to as *mutable notes*.

It will be seen that it is impossible to devise a fixed scale in which all the perfect fifths and major and minor thirds are true. The pitches shown in Fig. 4.7 must therefore be altered by the musician as the context requires in order to maintain just intonation for the most important intervals (Wye 1982). These continuous corrections are gauged partly by the memory process and partly by the detection of beats. When two players are sounding notes simultaneously a rapid beating and roughness of the sound will be heard when intervals are mistuned. This will be eliminated by the experienced player, who can rapidly make fine tuning adjustments. In solo playing it may be that the player subconsciously registers beats between successive notes through the reverberation of the room. This would explain why tuning is easier in more reverberant rooms.

Haydn Serenade

(a)

1st Movement. Handel Flute Sonata in F

(b)

Fig. 4.8. Two example melodies. In (a) all of the intervals can be made true whereas in (b) mutable notes must be introduced.

The question of how best to tune intervals in both ensemble and solo playing is one which cannot be answered entirely by the just diatonic scale, partly because of the difficulties of mutable notes but also because of the problems associated with modulation, which will be dealt with in the next section. Some modern research (Ward 1970) has shown in fact that players sometimes tend towards Pythagorean tuning despite the relatively dissonant thirds. This is not too surprising when one considers that the fifths are more sensitive to small degrees of mistuning than the thirds, as was illustrated in Fig. 4.2. In the Pythagorean scale all the fifths are true whereas in the just diatonic scale the fifth between the supertonic and submediant is too narrow.

Modulation

We shall now consider the problems associated with introducing sharps and flats into the scale and modulating into different keys. Suppose using the just diatonic scale we wish to modulate from C major into the dominant. In the new key we want the intervals between adjacent notes to remain the same. The order is

$$M \ m \ s \ M \ m \ M \ s.$$

The positions of these notes on the two scales is seen in Fig. 4.9, where the lengths have been marked off in proportion to the pitch.

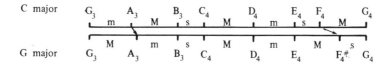

Fig. 4.9. Relative positions of the notes in the just diatonic scale for the keys of C major and G major.

Clearly a new note $F^{\#}$ needs to be added. The interval $F - F^{\#}$, which is the difference between a major tone and a diatonic semitone, is termed a *chromatic semitone*. Apart from this, all the notes of the old key can be used except for A_3, which should be a syntonic comma higher in G major. If we modulate further into D major then as well as a further note $C^{\#}$ being required, we would need to raise the E by a syntonic comma. In fact modulation into each new major key would require the addition of two new notes. The situation is similar if we wish to modulate into the minor keys. For example, modulation from C major to A minor would call for two new notes, a $G^{\#}$ and a new D a syntonic comma lower than in C major. Even putting aside the difficulties associated with mutable notes, it is seen that an impractical number of notes would be required on any instrument which was designed to play the just scale and would allow modulation between different frequencies. In fact keyboard instruments have been constructed to play in just intonation but the complexity of the keyboard is such that they have never found any degree of favour with musicians. One of the earlier and less ambitious was the keyboard devised by Salinas in the early 18th century. This had 24 notes to the octave which made it possible to play all the major triads in the cycle of fifths from G^b to $G^#$ and all the minor triads from E^b to $E^#$.

TEMPERED SCALES

On keyboard instruments the pitches of the notes cannot generally be altered in performance, i.e. mutable notes are not allowed. Because of this and also the difficulties associated with modulation, keyboard instruments are always tuned to a tempered scale, temperament being the term used to indicate a compromise scheme.

Mean tone temperament

The problems with the just diatonic scale just outlined arise because the scale has two different intervals for the tone. In mean tone temperament, which was introduced into Europe during the 17th century, this problem is overcome by introducing a new tone which, as the name implies, is equal to the mean or average of the major and minor tones in just intonation. Since a major tone plus a minor tone is equal to a major third, the mean tone is equal to half of a major third or 193 cents. Since the complete octave of 1200 cents is made up of 5 tones and two semitones, it follows that a mean tone semitone is equal to 117.5 cents. The complete mean tone scale is shown in Fig. 4.10.

Notes	C_4	D_4	E_4	F_4	G_4	A_4	B_4	C_4
Number of cents above C_4	0	193	386	503.5	696.5	889.5	1082.5	1200
Interval between adjacent notes in cents	193		193	117.5	193	193	193	117.5

Fig. 4.10. Mean tone temperament for the scale of C major.

Enharmonic notes

The mean tone scale resembles the Pythagorean sale in that it is made up of five equal tones and two equal semitones, the semitones not being equal in value to half a tone. The fact that two diatonic semitones do not add to give a tone gives rise to difficulties if one wishes to play in more than six major and three minor keys. This is because enharmonically equivalent notes will not have the same frequency.

As an example consider the key of A major in the mean tone temperament. This has $G^#$ as its leading note. The first key in the cycle of sharps and flats that contains the enharmonic equivalent A^b is E^b major. These two keys has the note D in common and, since the sequence of tones and semitones is T T S T T T S, the leading note $G^\#$ will be three tones above the subdominant D in the scale of A major. In the key of $E^\flat$ major, on the other hand, D is the leading note, so $A^\flat$ being the subdominant will be two tones plus two semitones higher. Thus $A^\flat$ will be sharper by 42 cents than its enharmonic equivalent $G^\#$ (since $2 \times 117.5 - 193 = 42$). This is almost half a semitone and is referred to as the *diesis*. The interval $C^\#$ to $A^\flat$ is then seen to be $695.5 + 42 = 738.5$ cents, since $C^\#$ to $G^\#$ is $3 \times 193 + 117.5 = 696.5$ cents. This is more than one third of a semitone wider than a perfect fifth, which is 702 cents. The interval is sometimes referred to as a *wolf fifth*. Keyboard instruments, particularly organs, have been built where separate keys are provided for a number of enharmonic equivalents, e.g. $G^\# A^\flat$ and $D^\# E^\flat$. An example is the organ that Handel presented to the Foundling Hospital. It can be seen that in the absence of additional enharmonic notes the mean tone system is restricted to not more than six major and three minor keys. For example, all the major keys through from $B^\flat$ major to A major could be played without encountering enharmonic notes. Introducing the further key of $E^\flat$ major would lead to the problem of having differently tuned notes $G^\#$ and $A^\flat$. In the minor mode the three corresponding keys which could be played are G, D and A. If one attempted to introduce the further key of E minor, for example, the enharmonic notes $D^\#$ and $E^\flat$ would arise.

Equal temperament

The ultimate compromise appears in equal temperament, where all tones are equal to 200 cents and all semitones to 100 cents, exactly half a tone. This is the only system which allows complete freedom of modulation. Its principal defect is that the thirds are badly mistuned, equal temperament major thirds being too wide by 14 cents and minor thirds being too narrow by 16 cents. However, from what we have already discussed about dissonance, this is not too serious a defect. Fig. 4.11 shows the equal temperament scale of C major.

Notes	C_4	D_4	E_4	F_4	G_4	A_4	B_4	C_5
Number of cents above C_4	0	200	400	500	700	900	1100	1200
Interval between adjacent notes in cents		200	200	100	200	200	200	100

Fig. 4.11. Equal temperament scale of C major.

177

We saw in Chapter 3 that in equal temperament the frequency ratio for each semitone is the same and equal to $2^{1/12} = 1.05946$ or approximately 1.06 since there are twelve semitones in the octave. Using this relationship, the frequencies of all the notes in the scale can easily be calculated relative to one fixed note, normally $A_4 = 440$ Hz (Backus 1977). A complete set is given in Fig. 4.12.

Octave	0	1	2	3	4	5	6	7	8
B	30.87	61.74	123.5	246.9	493.9	987.8	1976	3951	7902
A#	29.14	58.27	116.5	233.1	466.2	932.3	1865	3729	7459
A	27.50	55.00	110.0	220.0	440.0	880.0	1760	3520	7040
G#	25.96	51.91	103.8	207.7	415.3	830.6	1661	3322	6645
G	24.50	49.00	98.00	196.0	392.0	784.0	1568	3136	6272
F#	23.12	46.25	92.50	185.0	370.0	740.0	1480	2960	5920
F	21.83	43.65	87.31	174.6	349.2	698.5	1397	2794	5588
E	20.60	41.20	82.41	164.8	329.6	659.3	1319	2637	5274
D#	19.45	38.89	77.78	155.6	311.1	622.3	1245	2489	4978
D	18.35	36.71	73.42	146.8	293.7	587.3	1175	2349	4699
C#	17.32	34.65	69.30	138.6	277.2	554.4	1109	2217	4435
C	16.35	32.70	65.41	130.8	261.6	523.3	1047	2093	4186

Fig. 4.12. Table of frequencies for notes in the range C_0 to B_8 in the equal temperament scale based on $A_4 = 440$ Hz.

Comparison of scales

Fig. 4.13 gives a comparison of the different scales with the just diatonic scale as the base. Positive numbers indicate the sharpness of a note in cents compared to the just scale. Negative numbers indicate the number of cents flat.

In comparing different systems it is helpful to return to the circle of

Notes	C	D	E	F	G	A	B	C
Just Diatonic	0	0	0	0	0	0	0	0
Pythagorean	0	0	+22	0	0	+22	+22	0
Mean Tone	0	-11	0	+5.5	-5.5	+5.5	-5.5	0
Equal Temperament	0	-4	+14	+2	-2	+16	+12	0

Fig. 4.13. Comparison of scales with the just diatonic scale as base.

fifths. In the case of equal temperament each tone is of the same size and exactly equal to two semitones, so the circle of fifths will close (Fig. 4.14 (a)). In mean tone temperament there is only one size of tone and one size of semitone, so as a consequence there is only one size of fifth. However, this is 3.5 cents short of the fifth used in equal temperament, so the circle will fall short of closure by $12 \times 3.5 = 42$ cents (Fig. 4.14 (b)), giving rise to the wolf. In Pythagorean tuning the fifths are again equal, but 2 cents wider than in equal temperament, giving rise to an overlap in the circle of $12 \times 2 = 24$ cents (Fig. 4.14 (c)). We shall not attempt to draw a similar diagram for just intonation because the fifths have different sizes and mutable notes must be used.

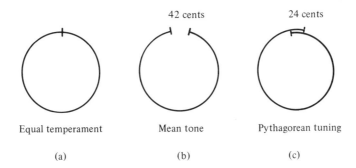

Equal temperament	Mean tone	Pythagorean tuning
(a)	(b)	(c)

Fig. 4.14. The circle of fifths showing (a) closure for equal temperament, (b) a gap for mean tone and (c) an overlap for Pythagorean tuning.

Regular temperaments

In the mean tone system the fifths are all equal and have been tempered by 5.5 cents, a quarter of a syntonic comma, in relation to the true fifth. For this reason the temperament is sometimes referred to as ¼ *comma mean tone.* This in fact is the only true mean tone temperament since the tone is derived from the mean of the major and minor tones used in just intonation. It is possible, however, to have other schemes where the tones and fifths both have fixed values. These are generally referred to as *regular temperaments* and are more loosely described as forms of mean tone tuning. An example is the ⅓ comma mean tone temperament devised by Salinas and shown in Fig. 4.15 (Barbour 1953).

C_4	D_4	E_4	F_4	G_4	A_4	B_4	C_5
0	190	379	505	695	884	1074	1200

Fig. 4.15. Salinas ⅓ comma mean tone temperament, showing the number of cents over C_4.

A number of other schemes similar to this are given in the book by Barbour. In nearly all of these the interval of the fifth is smaller than in equal temperament and larger than in true mean tone. Equal temperament is regular and can be referred to as 1/11 comma mean tone.

Circular temperaments

In the case of equal temperament one can think of the Pythagorean comma (which we shall take as equal to 24 cents for simplicity of arithmetic) as being equally distributed between the 12 fifths in the circle, each fifth being contracted from 702 to 700 cents. It is possible to distribute the Pythagorean comma in different ways between the 12 fifths and in the late 17th and 18th centuries a number of temperaments were employed making use of this device. They are known as *circular temperaments,* since for these the circle of fifths closes exactly. It is often said that Bach's 48 Preludes and Fugues were written to demonstrate the effectiveness of equal temperament. Recent research (Barnes 1979), however, has shown that he probably wrote them for a circular temperament similar to one devised by Werckmeister. In this temperament (known as Werckmeister III) the narrowing of the fifths is as follows:

Notes	$E^\flat$	$B^\flat$	F	C	G	D	A	E	B	$F^\sharp$	$C^\sharp$	$G^\sharp$	$E^\flat$
Narrowing in cents	0	0	0	6	6	6	0	0	6	0	0	0	

A circular temperament such as this eliminates the wolf and makes it possible to play in all keys on a 12 note keyboard, although some keys sound better than others. In order to see which keys sound best it is necessary to examine the size of the major thirds since these will be more out of tune than the fifths. The major third C–E, for example, is fixed by the four fifths C–G, G–D, D–A and A–E. If the fifths had all been correct then this third would have been 22 cents too wide as in the Pythagorean scale. In the Werckmeister III temperament it will be $22 - 3 \times 6 = 4$ cents too wide. Corresponding widths can be found for all the other thirds and are shown in Fig. 4.16. The 6 under the note C, for example, refers to the fifth C–G and the 4 to the third C–E.

Notes	E♭	B♭	F	C	G	D	A	E	B	F#	C#	G#
Narrowing of 5th in cents	0	0	0	6	6	6	0	0	6	0	0	0
Widening of major thirds in cents	16	10	4	4	10	10	16	16	16	22	22	22

Fig. 4.16. Narrowing of fifths, and widening of major thirds in the circular temperament devised by Werckmeister, known as Werckmeister III.

It can be seen that in this circular temperament the keys with few sharps or flats sound better than those with many, though the worst ones remain usable.

Characteristics of tempered scales

The equally tempered scale is now universally accepted for tuning pianos and other modern keyboard instruments, since this is the only temperament which allows the complete freedom of modulation demanded by modern music. Despite this, however, there is an increasing interest in and awareness of other systems, not least because of the feeling that music of earlier periods, particularly the baroque, should be played on authentic instruments of the period. It is the tuning of these instruments which is one of the essential features which give them their characteristic sound. Another reason for the increased interest is that the development of computer generated music allows one, at least in theory, to change the tuning of notes at will.

One of the characteristics of equal temperament is that all keys sound alike since the interval relationships between notes is unchanged in moving from one key to another. This is not the case with other temperaments and in fact many musicians over the ages have associated emotional characteristics with the different keys. Beethoven, for example, described the key of D♭ major as "majestic" and C major as "triumphant". There is still much debate as to whether the key does significantly influence the emotional quality of the music. In unequal temperament such differences could be associated with tuning discrepancies between keys. However, it seems that the majority of musicians can tell when a piece of familiar music is played in the "wrong" key on an equally tempered piano, even if the interval of transposition is as little as one semitone (Terhardt and Ward 1982). The nature of this ability, and its possible relationship to "key colour", requires further investigation.

It is only in recent times that equal temperament has found more or less universal favour. In the 19th century it found criticism amongst musicians and scientists alike. Helmholtz was amongst the fiercest critics. It appears that over the generations our ears have become atuned to accepting equal temperament just as they have to accepting the more dissonant harmonies of modern music.

5

Sound production in musical instruments

In this chapter we shall consider the basic physical principles by which sound is generated in different musical instruments. The range of instruments available to the musician is so vast that at first sight this might seem an insurmountable task. Nevertheless, many of these have similarities which enable us to group them together for the purpose of analysis. In this connection it will be helpful if we start by considering how instruments fit into the different classification groups.

CLASSIFICATION OF MUSICAL INSTRUMENTS

In the orchestra it is normal to divide the instruments into four classes, strings, woodwind, brass and percussion. This classification is convenient because it relates directly to the sound quality of the instruments and also the positions at which they are situated within the orchestra. However, it is not based on acoustical principles so it will not help us with a scientific understanding of how the different instruments work. For example, it does not take account of the fact that in both brass and woodwind the sound is generated by exciting a column of air within a tube. In this sense the sound production mechanism in a trumpet, for example, is similar to that of a clarinet. It is clear that there are many ways in which the instruments can be grouped and in fact many scholarly works have been devoted to this subject. The most generally accepted scientific classification is that of Curt Sachs (Sachs 1940). In his system, instruments are divided into five main groups, idiophones, membranophones, chordophones, aerophones and electrophones and within each group there are a number of subdivisions.

183

(1) Idiophones

These are instruments made of naturally sonorous material, not requiring any additional tension as do strings or drumskins. They are subdivided according to the method by which they are set into vibration as follows:

(a) Striking: There are two forms of striking. The idiophone may consist of one or several pieces of substance struck by a stick or similar device. Examples of this are the xylophone, marimba, gong, triangle and celesta (a small keyboard instrument with metal resonators). Alternatively there may be a pair of resonance elements which are struck together, e.g. in the cymbals, the castanets or the clappers.

The xylophone and marimba are part of the tuned percussion section of the orchestra.

(b) Plucking: The most common instrument of this type is the Jaw's harp, commonly misnamed the Jew's harp. This has a flexible tongue attached to a frame, usually metal. The tongue is plucked by a finger and resonated by the mouth, giving a clear but tiny sound almost inaudible to the listener. Another example is the zanza (or sansa), found commonly in Africa. This has sets of tongues plucked by the thumbs and resonated by a small box. The musical box is a form of mechanised zanza.

(c) Rubbing and Scraping: An interesting example of this class of instrument is the glass harmonica invented by the American Benjamin Franklin in about 1761. This developed from the idea of producing notes by rubbing a moistened finger round the rim of a wine glass. In the glass harmonica there are thirty or forty bowls of graded size whose centres are attached to a spindle which can be rotated using a pedal. The moving rims are touched by the player's fingers to set the bowls into vibration. In this way the player can produce either single note melodies or chords. In the late 18th century the instrument attracted a number of professional players and music was written for it by leading composers, including Mozart and Beethoven.

In addition to the glass harmonica there are many primitive instruments in this class. For details see Sachs (1940).

(d) Shaking: The instruments in this small group are essentially forms of rattles.

(e) Stamping: Here either the player stamps on the resonating member or the resonator is itself struck on the ground. This group of instruments is primarily of interest to anthropologists.

(2) Membranophones

In a membranophone the sound is produced by a vibrating membrane stretched over an opening. Virtually all membranophones can be referred to as drums, although there are exceptions, e.g. the mirlitons. Membranophones are primarily classed according to their method of excitation as follows:

(a) Striking: This is by far the largest class and includes the tympani and the kit drums, e.g. snare, bass drum, tom-tom and roto-tom.

(b) Friction: All the instruments in this class are referred to as friction drums. The hand is rarely rubbed directly on the membrane. Instead there is usually a cord, or alternatively a stick, which passes through a hole in the centre of the membrane or just touches it. This is rubbed by the resined fingers of the player, which sets the membrane into vibration.

(c) Blowing: Mirlitons are instruments having a vibrating membrane which the player blows on. A familar example is the kazoo.

(3) Chordophones

In the chordophones the sound is generated by a vibrating string usually attached to some form of resonator for amplification. The enormous range of instruments in this group is frequently reduced to four types, namely zithers, lutes, lyres and harps. In the zithers there is no neck, the strings being stretched between the two ends of the body. A lute, on the other hand, is composed of a body and a neck. The latter serves both as a handle and as a means of stretching the strings beyond the body. In the lyre the neck is replaced by a yoke, i.e. two arms projecting upwards and connected together by a crossbar, on to which one end of the strings is attached. In the harps the strings are vertical and in a plane perpendicular to the soundboard.

From the acoustics point of view it is most relevant to consider the classification according to the method of excitation as follows:

(a) Striking: Examples are the dulcimer, clavichord and piano.

(b) Plucking: The harp, mandoline, harpsichord and guitar are all plucked instruments.

(c) Bowing: The violin, viola, cello and double bass are the best-known of the bowed chordophones. An interesting example in this group is the tromba marina. This is similar in appearance to a very narrow cello but there is no finger board. Only harmonics are played, these being produced by the player touching the strings in different places.

(d) Rubbing: A well-known example of the rubbed chordophone is the hurdy-gurdy. This is a kind of mechanical violin which makes use of a rosined wheel, rotated by the player, instead of a bow. The strings are stopped by means of a set of keys and frequently there are unstopped strings which can be tuned to produce drone notes. The hurdy-gurdy is known to have existed before the year 1000. These early instruments were five or six feet in length and required two players. The 17th century instrument was about the size of a violin and was used primarily for folk music. This instrument should not be confused with the more recent street

185

organ which is similarly played by turning a crank and is often referred to as a hurdy-gurdy. Fig. 5.1 shows a hurdy-gurdy from the Edinburgh University collection.

(e) Wind-excited: The Aeolian harp is a form of harp where there is no player, the strings being set into vibration by the wind. These instruments were much in favour in the early 19th century for use in parks and on ruins of medieval castles.

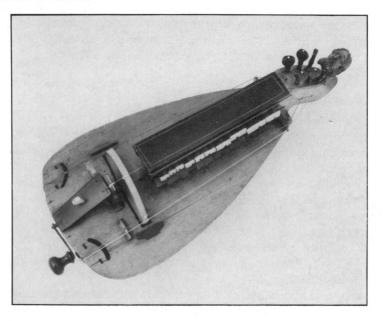

Fig. 5.1. Hurdy-gurdy by Colson (EUCHMI 287).

(4) Aerophones

Aerophones are all those instruments where the sound is produced by a vibrating column of air, i.e. the orchestral woodwind and brass instruments, together with the free aerophones where some mechanical part acts directly on the outer air. Subdivision is by the method of excitation as follows.

(a) Mechanical reed: Here there is a vibrating air column and a reed, e.g. the clarinet, saxophone, oboe and bagpipe.

(b) Air reed: These instruments are generally referred to as the flute family and include transverse flutes, recorders, pan pipes, ocarinas and whistles.

(c) Lip reed: This is primarily the brass section of the orchestra and includes the trumpet, trombone, horn and bugle.

Groups (a) and (b) contain the woodwind section of the orchestra.

An example of a free aerophone is the primitive *bull-roarer*, which is a thin piece of wood tied to a string which is whirled around the head in circles. The wood generates periodic oscillations in the air which give rise to a screaming sound.

(5) Electrophones

In electrophones the sound is produced by a vibrating loudspeaker driven by an amplifier. Subdivision is by the method of producing the input signal to the amplifier as follows.

(a) Acoustic: Here the instrument is capable of producing a sound independent of any electronic devices, but the vibrations are picked up by a microphone or similar detector and amplified electronically. The most common example is the acousto-electric guitar. Instruments in this group can be played without the electrical attachments.

(b) Vibrating member: Many electronic instruments rely on the mechanical vibrations of some member to produce the signal but do not have any acoustic amplification so they cannot be played satisfactorily without the electronic attachments. An example is the electric stage piano, which has tone bars similar to a celesta but with electric pick-ups. There are also electric pianos which use strings and electric pick-ups but do not have sound boards for acoustic amplification. The solid type of electric guitar and the bass guitar are in this group.

(c) Electronic: These instruments rely on electronic oscillators and other circuits to produce the signals, e.g. the electronic organ and the synthesizer. Computer generated music also comes into this category.

To sum up, we have seen that all the known musical instruments can be put into one of the five main groups and each group itself can be broken down into subdivisions. It should be remembered that a completely logical classification is impossible because instruments are artificial contrivances of man originating from many diverse sources. However, the groupings are helpful in the recognition of acoustic similarities between different instruments. In the following sections we shall outline the main acoustic principles underlying the operation of the various groups.

RESONANCE

The heart of a musical instrument is the *sound generator*. This is a device which vibrates and initiates the sound waves which travel through the air and eventually reach the ear, e.g. in a violin or piano the sound generator is the string. A sound generator can be excited in a number of different ways, e.g. in the case of a violin by bowing or plucking. The waves from the sound generator are frequently amplified and radiated by a *resonator*. In the case of a piano the resonator is the soundboard. The resonator also has an important effect on the tone quality of the instrument.

Standing waves

Systems such as strings fixed at both ends and air columns which have certain definite frequencies at which they will vibrate are known as resonant systems. Resonance occurs because disturbances are reflected, e.g. from the fixed end of a string, such that the wave at any position is actually the superposition of waves travelling in more than one direction.

Fig. 5.2 shows two progressive waves moving in opposite directions. It can be seen that there are certain positions, e.g. position N in the diagram, where the displacement of the superposition wave (wave 1 + wave 2) is zero. The displacement at this point will always remain zero since as the progressive waves move to new positions an increase in the displacement of wave 1 is matched by a corresponding decrease in wave 2. A point such as N is termed a *node* ('no' for no displacement). Mid-way between adjacent nodes are points of maximum displacement termed *antinodes*. Adjacent nodes are half a wavelength apart.

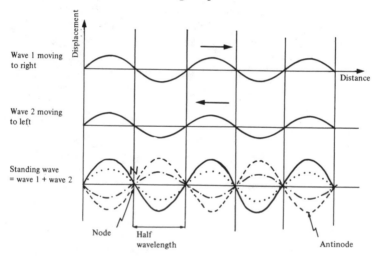

Fig. 5.2. The formation of a standing wave from the superposition of two progressive waves moving in opposite directions.

Response and damping

Resonant systems vary in their sharpness of response. Suppose we have a resonator (e.g. an air cavity) which resonates at a particular frequency f_R and we excite it with a tone of frequency f (e.g. by holding a tuning fork close to it). The amplification will be greatest when $f = f_R$ but there will also be some amplification when f is not equal to f_R. The range of frequencies to which the resonator responds determines the sharpness of its response. When the resonator is excited and then left to itself it will continue to vibrate, but the vibrations will gradually die away because of *damping*. The damping is caused by a loss of energy through friction, loss of sound energy etc. A system with low damping will continue to resonate for a long time and will have a narrow frequency response. A heavily damped resonator will have a broad frequency response. The reason for this can be seen by considering what happens when a system with broad frequency response is suddenly excited. Standing waves will be set up at many slightly different frequencies and corresponding wavelengths. These may all start together in phase but after a very short interval of time they will become out of phase and the waves will cancel, i.e. the sound will disappear.

Fig. 5.3 shows the ranges of frequency response for two different systems (a) lightly damped and (b) heavily damped. In case (a) the frequency response curve has a sharp peak and the oscillations die very slowly. In fact the time for the signal to die to half of its original amplitude is approximately equal to the reciprocal of the half-width of the resonance peak measured at a corresponding fraction of the peak height, since this is the time required for the interference cancelling effects first mentioned to take place. In case (b) the frequency response curve is much broader so the oscillations die very rapidly.

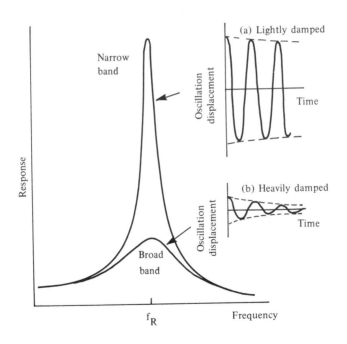

Fig. 5.3. Frequency response curves for (a) lightly and (b) heavily damped systems.

189

Formants

In many musical instruments the resonator is designed to have a fairly flat response over the audible range utilised by the instrument. This is the case with the soundboard of a piano; the ideal soundboard would have a flat response over the complete frequency range. A flat response is achieved by arranging that there are many overlapping resonances and that any dominant ones lie outside the range of operation. In practice the resonators on instruments such as the piano and violin have a response curve which shows a series of definite peaks and troughs, rather than being flat. The way in which the amplification varies with frequency is sometimes called the *formant* shape (p.154). In some instruments it is possible to define a definite formant shape which remains fixed for all notes, whilst in other instruments it is not. The formant shape determines the amplification of the upper harmonics as well as the fundamental. If for example the main amplification occurs in the region of the second harmonic for a particular low note, then when a note an octave higher is played the same formant peak would emphasise the fundamental.

IMPEDANCE AND COUPLING

We saw in Chapter 2 that any medium through which waves propagate will present an impedance or resistance to the driving force. Both air masses and mechanical elements have an impedance which is in effect the ratio of the applied force or pressure to the speed of the wave displacement. In a medium of high impedance a large force or pressure is required to produce a small displacement amplitude and vice versa in a medium of low impedance. In analysing the acoustics of most musical instruments it is important to understand how vibrations are transferred from one medium to another; e.g. in a violin the vibrations of the strings are transferred to the bridge and then on to the body of the instrument before the actual acoustic vibrations of the air are formed for transmission to the ear.

The rate at which vibrations are transferred from one medium to another depends on the relative magnitude of the impedances for the two media (Benade 1976). As an example which can be easily visualised, consider two lengths of string which are attached together at some point. Waves are produced in the first length of string using a vibrating mechanism and these travel along the string until they meet the join. If the second length of string is much heavier than the first it will act like a fixed end and nearly all of the incident wave energy will be reflected, only a small amount being passed on to the heavy string. A similar situation occurs if the first string is very heavy compared to the second, although in this case the reflected wave has a phase different to that in the former situation. In the case when both strings have similar mass per unit length, the join is not detected by the incident wave so all of the wave is transmitted to the second string. In this example the heavy string has a high impedance and the light string a low impedance. Thus when waves pass from one medium to another, maximum transmission occurs when the impedances are equal. Widely different impedances result in large wave reflections. Transmission of waves between two media of widely different impedance can be enhanced by the inclusion of an intermediate medium (p.44). Choosing the intermediate element to optimise wave transmission is referred to as impedance matching. The horn on a loudspeaker, for example, could be considered as an impedance matching element between the speaker and the surrounding atmosphere. This is analogous to the impedance matching transformer which is used to couple a loudspeaker or microphone to an amplifier.

When dealing with purely mechanical vibrations it is best to work in terms of forces rather than pressures. The ratio of force to velocity is then termed the *characteristic mechanical impedance* (Z_M), or mechanical impedance for short. The mechanical impedance of a long flexible string having mass per unit length m and tension T is

$$\text{string } Z_M = (mT)^{1/2}.$$

Frequently one is interested in the vibrations of a flat plate, e.g. a sound board. In this case it is not possible to give such a simple formula for the impedance because of the large number of parameters affecting its magnitude, but it is known that the mechanical impedance is proportional to the thickness squared.

In the case of the piano, to take a specific example, the impedance of the soundboard-bridge combination is very great compared with that of an individual string, so the vibrations of the string are almost unaffected by those of the soundboard. In this case the *coupling* is said to be weak (or loose). If the coupling between two resonant systems is strong, then each system will influence the vibrations of the other. In this situation beating occurs with the energy being fed periodically back and forth between the two systems. This can be observed if the two lowest strings on a guitar are tuned to the same note. When one string is plucked its vibrations will die, but at the same time the other string will begin to vibrate. The vibrations from the second string will in turn pass their energy back to the first string and so on. It is quite instructive to see the effect of gradually changing the tuning of one of the strings. When the pitches are very close there is maximum transfer of energy between the strings but the beat rate is very slow. As the frequencies are moved apart the energy transfer is reduced and the beat rate increases. The coupling is seen to be greatest when two vibrational modes have the same frequency. Strong coupling can have important consequences for the player, e.g. in the production of wolf notes on the viola. This will be discussed in Chapter 6.

WAVES ON A STRING

The sound generator in a chordophone is a tensioned string fixed at both ends and sometimes stopped by the player to shorten the *speaking length*, as in the case of the violin or clavichord (the speaking length is the effective length producing the note).

Speed of wave propagation

Suppose that we have a very long string, fix one end and move the other end up and down in a periodic motion. A progressive wave will then propagate down the string moving towards the fixed end. If we mark different positions on the string then these markers will move up and down in a direction perpendicular to the direction of propagation. For this reason waves on a string are said to be *transverse* in contrast to the longitudinal sound waves in a tube, which we shall be dealing with later.

The *wave velocity*, more correctly referred to as the *phase velocity*, is the speed with which the wave crests or troughs move along the string. This is dependent both on the tension T and the mass per unit length m. Using simple principles of mechanics it can be shown that the wave velocity is

$$c = (T/m)^{1/2}.$$

Normal modes of vibration

The wavelengths of standing waves which can be set up on a string are determined by the boundary conditions. Since the ends are fixed these must be nodes, i.e. positions of very high impedance (theoretically infinite impedance). Therefore for a string of length L we must have

$$L = n \lambda/2$$

where n is an integer, i.e. 1, 2, 3...etc. Hence the only possible wavelengths are $\lambda = 2L/n$. The corresponding frequencies of vibration are

$$f = nc/(2L)$$

The different vibrational patterns, known as the *normal modes*, are shown in Fig. 5.4. In the first or fundamental mode n = 1, so the frequency of vibration is $f_0 = c/2L$. The frequency in the 2nd mode is twice this value, i.e. c/L and so forth. This gives rise to a set of frequencies which form a complete harmonic series, a factor which makes the vibrating string one of the most useful means of producing musical sounds.

On an actual musical instrument one of the ends of the string is normally passed over a bridge or is attached in some way to a soundboard. The support will not have infinite impedance. If it had, then none of the energy of the string would be transmitted to the soundboard or resonator. The impedance must be such that sufficient energy is reflected in order to sustain the vibrations of the string, but sufficient is transmitted to produce a sound of adequate volume. The impedance that a soundboard presents to a string depends on the position of support, i.e. whether the string is attached near to a node or an antinode in the soundboard's vibrational pattern, and this varies with frequency. If the point of attachment is near a node, then the impedance it presents will be high, akin to a completely rigid fixing. The rate of transfer of energy to the soundboard will then be relatively small. Maximum energy transfer will occur if the fixing is near an antinode.

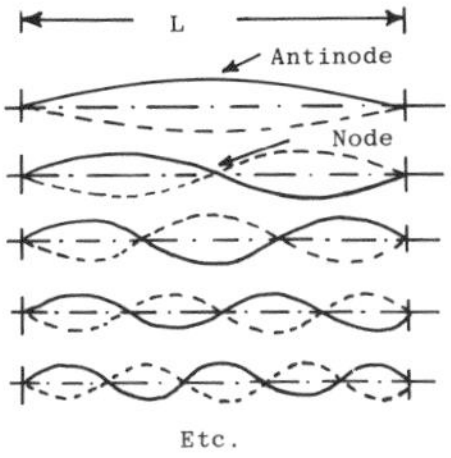

	Mode	Wavelength	Frequency	Note
	1st	$\lambda = 2L$	$f_0 = \dfrac{c}{2L}$	Fundamental
	2nd	$\lambda = L$	$2f_0$	Octave
	3rd	$\lambda = 2L/3$	$3f_0$	12th
	4th	$\lambda = L/2$	$4f_0$	2nd Octave
	5th	$\lambda = 2L/5$	$5f_0$	major 3rd in 3rd octave

Fig. 5.4. The first five normal modes of vibration of a string fixed at both ends. The solid and dotted lines indicate the positions of the string at opposite phase positions in the cycle. At intermediate phase positions the string lies somewhere between these two lines.

In terms of the string tension and mass per unit length the normal mode frequencies are

$$nf_0 = nc/2L = n(T/m)^{1/2}/2L$$

It is seen that halving the length will double the frequency, i.e. raise the pitch an octave. For a fixed string length this increase in pitch could be achieved either by increasing the tension by a factor of 4 or reducing the mass per unit length by a factor of 4. In order to achieve the low pitch of bass strings used on a piano or the G string on a violin, the mass per unit length is generally increased by wire winding. Strings used for the upper register are correspondingly light.

The above analysis assumes that the string is completely flexible, i.e. has no *stiffness* or resistance to bending. Stiffness tends to damp the higher modes as well as making their frequencies sharp. This point will be discussed further in Chapter 7.

Complex vibrations and superposition

Generally speaking, when a string is plucked, bowed or struck by a hammer it will not vibrate in one single mode since the energy is not supplied at a single frequency. Instead, the actual displacement along the string will be the superposition (i.e. the sum) of the displacements corresponding to a number of modes. For example, if only the first and second modes were present the displacement at a given instant of time might appear as shown in Fig. 5.5.

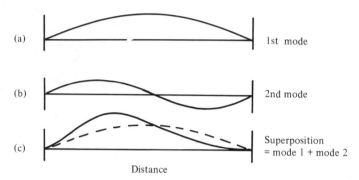

Fig. 5.5. Example of the superposition of two waves on a string. The complete displacement profile (c) results at a given instant of time from the superposition of two sinusoidal waveforms ((a) and (b)) of different wavelength.

It can be shown that any complex vibration of the string can be considered to be the superposition of a number of normal modes of vibration, although in some cases it may be necessary to sum a large number of modes in order to arrive at a particular vibrational pattern. Strictly speaking the superposition method can only be applied if the vibrations are small in amplitude, but this restriction is not of any great practical significance.

Each normal mode will radiate its own particular frequency of sound, the actual sound heard being the sum of a number of harmonics. This is registered by the ear as a single musical note, since the frequencies are in a harmonic series. The magnitudes of the harmonic components determine the tone quality of the note as described in Chapter 3 (p.144).

WAVES IN TUBES

Standing waves may be set up in the air column enclosed within a tube, in a similar manner to the waves on a string. In this case the waves are in the form of compressions and rarefactions moving down the tube, i.e. the waves are *longitudinal*, rather than transverse as in the case of the string. Associated with the pressure changes are to-and-fro movements of the air molecules in the direction of the tube axis, although the magnitude of these movements is very small, of the order 1 mm for the very loudest notes. The normal modes of vibration depend in this case on whether the tube ends are open or closed, as well as on the shape of the tube.

We saw earlier that in order that a standing wave can be set up there must be reflection, in this case from the end of the tube. It seems clear that waves will be reflected from a tube end that is closed, but it is not so obvious that reflection will take place in the case of an open end. The reason for the reflection is that waves are diffracted (i.e. bent) outwards when they reach the tube end, thus they suffer an abrupt change in conditions. This results in some of the wave energy being reflected, in order to maintain the standing wave, the remainder being transmitted to the ear. The amount of diffraction depends on the ratio of the wavelength λ to the bore diameter D as shown in Fig. 5.6. If this ratio is small then the sound wave is nearly all transmitted out of the tube, just as we saw that the wave in Fig. 1.25 (b) passes through a relatively large opening with only minimal disturbance. If the ratio λ/D is large then there will be very considerable diffraction and a large proportion of the sound energy will be reflected from the open end. This situation corresponds to waves passing through a small opening as shown in Fig. 1.24 (b). The bore diameter is chosen by the instrument designer to obtain a balance between these two.

The formation of standing waves can be explained in terms of *acoustic impedance*. In Chapter 2 we saw that the specific acoustic impedance was defined as the ratio of pressure fluctuation to particle velocity: $z = p/v$. For a wall of air z was equal to 415 rayls. In dealing with tubes it is most convenient to work in terms of the volume velocity (or discharge) U defined as the particle velocity times the tube area A. The acoustic impedance is then $Z = z/A = p/U$. For a tube of constant diameter, so long that reflection from the far end can be neglected, Z is constant and can be expressed in terms of the density ϱ and the bulk modulus of elasticity B. The expression is

$$Z = (B\varrho)^{1/2}/A.$$

The unit of acoustic impedance is the *acoustic ohm (Ω)*. When waves meet

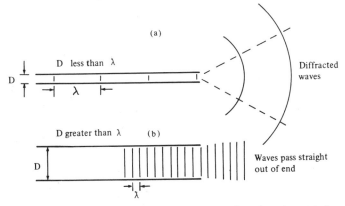

Fig. 5.6. The diffraction of waves at the end of a tube when (a) the ratio λ/D is large, (b) λ/D is small.

an open end they encouter a sudden change in impedance since the impedance outside is similar to that of a very wide tube and is therefore very small. This results in some of the wave energy being reflected and the remainder transmitted. The amount of reflection, however, is dependent on the wavelength to diameter ratio. The standing wave models to be described in the next section, which consider the open end of a tube to be a pressure node, are only approximations to the real situation. If the open end were a true pressure node then all of the sound energy would be reflected and there would be no sound tramsission.

Cylindrical tube open at both ends

In the case of a cylindrical tube open at both ends (referred to as an open tube) the pressure at each end must be atmospheric, i.e. the ends are pressure nodes. On the other hand the air particles are free to move in and out of the ends so that they will be displacement antinodes. The relationship between the pressure and the particle displacements can be seen in Fig. 5.7 for the fundamental mode of oscillation. At (a) the particles which have their mean position at the ends of the tube have moved inwards, causing a compression of the air within the tube. Thus the pressure varies from zero at the ends to a maximum at the centre of the tube. Particles at the centre of the tube will not move because they are compressed equally from either side. In fact the particle displacements become progressively smaller as one moves closer to the centre. At (b), a quarter of a cycle later, the particles have moved back to their equilibrium positions and there is no pressure variation along the tube. At (c), after a further ¼ cycle, the

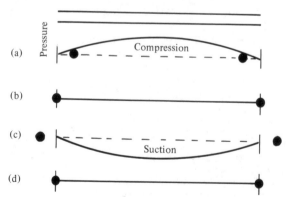

Fig. 5.7. Pressure variation with particle positions throughout a complete cycle in an open tube: (a) particles move inwards causing compression; (b) ¼ cycle later particles are in equilibrium positions; (c) after a further ¼ cycle particles have moved outwards causing suction; and (d) particles return to equilibrium positions.

particles have moved outwards causing a suction or negative pressure within the tube. At (d), after a third quarter cycle, the particles are back to their equilibrium position and then the complete cycle starts again.

Fig. 5.7 represents the oscillation in the lowest or fundamental mode, but higher modes also occur. These are shown in Fig. 5.8, where the separation between the curved lines, at a certain distance along the tube, represents the displacement amplitude at that position. In the fundamental mode the wavelength is $\lambda = 2L$ where L is the length of the tube, hence the frequency is $f_0 = c/2L$, c being the velocity of sound in air. In the second mode, i.e. the second harmonic, the frequency is $c/L = 2f_0$. In the third mode the frequency is $3f_0$ and so forth. Note that the frequencies form a complete harmonic series, i.e. fundamental, octave, 12th etc., as was the case with the string fixed at both ends.

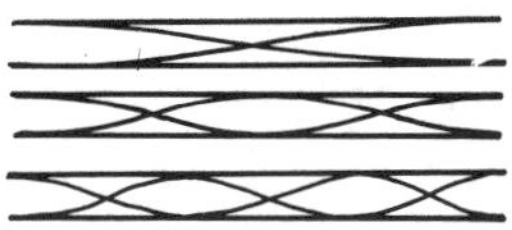

Mode	Wavelength	Frequency	Note
1st	$\lambda = 2L$	$f_0 = \dfrac{c}{2L}$	Fundamental
2nd	$\lambda = L$	$2f_0$	Octave
3rd	$\lambda = 2L/3$	$3f_0$	12th.

Fig. 5.8. First three modes of vibration for an open cylindrical tube.

Cylindrical tube closed at one end

In the case of a cylindrical tube closed at one end and open at the other (referred to as a closed tube) the closed end will be a displacement node, i.e. a pressure antinode, since no particle motions are possible at the closed boundary. The open end will be a pressure node (displacement antinode) as in the case of the tube open at both ends. The possible modes of vibration are shown in Fig. 5.9 where again the curved lines represent the particle displacements in their extreme positions. In this case there is always an odd number of quarter wavelengths within the tube with one quarter wavelength in the fundamental mode. The closed tube will therefore have a fundamental frequency f_0 which is one octave lower than the open tube. The complete range of sounding frequencies is f_0, $3f_0$, $5f_0$, $7f_0$ etc., i.e. only the odd harmonics are present.

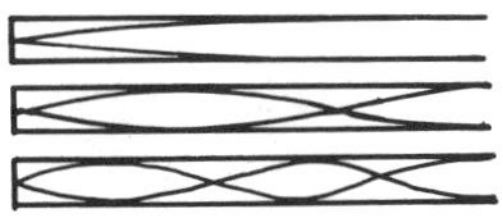

Mode	Wavelength	Frequency	Note
1st	$\lambda = 4L$	$f_0 = \dfrac{c}{4L}$	Fundamental
2nd	$\lambda = 4L/3$	$3f_0$	12th
3rd	$\lambda = 4L/5$	$5f_0$	Major 3rd in 3rd octave

Fig. 5.9. First three modes of vibration for a closed cylindrical tube.

Effects of side holes

In many of the instruments side holes are used to progressively shorten the sounding length so that a range of different notes can be played. If a side hole is sufficiently large, i.e. of a diameter comparable with that of the tube radius, then it becomes effectively equivalent to an open end and defines the position of a pressure node. Very tiny side holes, on the other hand, do not significantly affect the sounding length of the tube and are used in practice as speaker holes to assist in the initiation of higher modes of vibration. Holes of intermediate size make partial reductions in the speaking length L as indicated in Fig. 5.10.

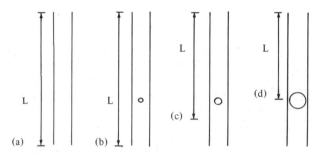

Fig. 5.10. Effect of a side hole on the speaking length L of a tube where the vibration is initiated from the upper end of the tube. (a) indicates the tube without side hole; (b) the side hole is so small that it has negligible effect; (c) an intermediate-size hole partially reduces L; (d) a large side hole acts as an open end.

In designing an instrument it is first necessary to consider how many holes are required in order to produce a scale. The player may blow the lowest note on the instrument by closing all the side holes. In the case of an open tube he can blow a note an octave higher by overblowing, i.e. blowing harder in order to initiate the second mode of vibration. Six holes in all will then be required in order to produce a major scale, as can be seen in Fig. 5.11. Here we have assumed that the tube sounds C_4 with all holes closed. Opening one hole then gives D_4, two holes gives E_4, etc. In the case of a closed tube the instrument will overblow the 12th, i.e. if it plays C_4 in its fundamental mode with all holes closed then it will overblow to G_5, so the same fingering cannot be used in the second octave as in the first. In this case it is seen that ten holes are required in order to play all the notes of the major scale in more than one octave.

Assuming that the side holes are large enough to act as open ends it can be seen that their spacing will gradually increase as the distance from the blowing end increases. If, for example, the sounding length for B_4 is L in Fig. 5.11 then the second hole must be placed at a distance $(1.06)^2 L =$

1.12L from the end to produce A_4 since A_4 is two semitones below B_4. The distance between the upper two holes is therefore 0.12L. D_4 on the other hand is nine semitones below B_4 so its hole should be $(1.06)^9 L$ from the end, i.e. 1.69L, and similarly the lowest hole will be $(1.06)^{11}L = 1.90L$ from the end. The spacing between the lowest two holes is therefore 0.21L, i.e. almost twice that between the upper two holes.

The six hole arrangement for playing the seven note scale is basic to all woodwind instruments and is referred to as the *basic scale*, although on some instruments the third note from the bottom is the minor third rather than the major third. The effect of a cross-fingering is much more complicated to calculate but is discussed by Nederveen (1969) and Brindley (1969). More details about the placing and size of tone holes will be given when discussing the flageolet in Chapter 8.

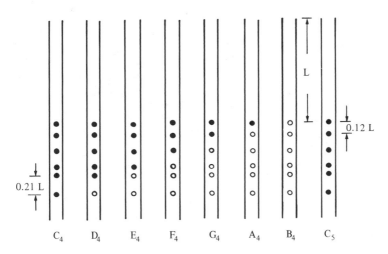

Fig. 5.11. Production of the scale of C major using an open tube with six holes. For C_4 and C_5 all the holes are closed. For D_4 only the lowest hole is open, etc. The distance between the lowest two holes is 0.21L.

End effects

In our analysis of cylindrical bore tubes we have assumed that the displacement antinode at an open end coincides exactly with the end of the tube, whereas in reality it lies a short distance outside. Theoretical calculation and experimental measurements have shown that the antinode is actually placed at a distance of approximately D/3 from the end where D is the tube diameter, as shown in Fig. 5.12. This makes the sounding length D/3 longer than the actual tube length for a closed tube and 2D/3 longer for an open tube.

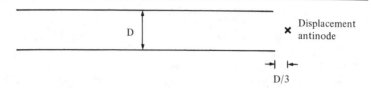

Fig. 5.12. Position of the displacement antinode at the open end of a cylindrical tube.

Conical tube

An important feature of the cylindrical tube is that for all the harmonics the frequency is inversely proportional to the sounding length. This means that when the tube is overblown the distances between the holes will be the same for each semitone or tone interval as they are in the fundamental mode. In fact for lowering the pitch by one semitone the sounding length should be increased by a factor 1.06 and this applies equally in the fundamental mode and when the tube is overblown. This means that the same set of holes can be used for notes in the different registers, a fundamental requirement for any practical instrument. It can be shown (Benade 1960 (a)) that there are a number of tube shapes for which this fundamental requirement is satisfied, these being known as Bessel horns after the 19th century German astronomer F.W. Bessel. However, the only Bessel horns of practical utility for musical instrument purposes are the cylinder and the cone (Fig. 5.13). It can be shown that a cone has the same vibration frequencies as an open tube of the same length, i.e. its fundamental frequency is the same and all of the harmonics are present. Strictly speaking, the length L should be the slant length, but in practice we are only interested in cones of very small angle, so this makes a negligible difference.

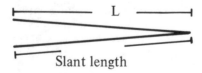

Slant length

Fig. 5.13. Conical tube. This has the same vibration frequencies as an open tube of the same length.

Warming up a wind instrument

We said in Chapter 1 that changes in air temperature can have a fairly dramatic effect on the pitch of a wind instrument. We are now in a position to look a little more carefully at what takes place.

The linear expansion rates for the solid materials from which wind instruments are made are extremely small. Silver, for example, has a linear expansion coefficient of 1.9×10^{-5} (per °C), which means that a strip of silver 1 cm in length will expand by 1.9×10^{-5} cm for 1°C rise in temperature. For, say, a 10°C rise in temperature, a concert flute, which has a length of 62 cm up to the embouchure hole, will expand by $10 \times 62 \times 1.9 \times 10^{-5}$ cm, which amounts to just over one tenth of a millimetre. For most practical purposes, then, the sounding length of the instrument may be assumed constant. Now, we have seen that for both open and closed ended tubes, with either cylindrical or conical bores, the frequencies of all the notes sounded are proportional to the velocity of sound in air and inversely proportional to the tube length. If the tube length is constant, then the frequency is just proportional to the speed of sound. Fig. 1.21 shows us that the speed of sound always rises with increasing temperature, so this will clearly be accompanied by a rise in pitch. Taking a 10°C temperature rise again as an example, the corresponding rise in velocity is seen to be 6.25ms^{-1}, i.e. the proportional rise in velocity is $6.25/340 \approx 2\%$. This represents a pitch increase of about one third of a semitone, since a 6% rise in pitch corresponds to one semitone. Notice that the pitch rise is independent of tube length and so will be the same for each note on the instrument.

The actual air temperature inside the instrument at any stage of the warming up process will depend on many factors and there will always be a variation along the tube length. Measurements on flutes have shown that when an instrument is fully warmed up the temperature near to the embouchure hole is typically 5°C higher than at the open end. The ease with which an instrument warms up depends to some extent on the thermal conductivity of the material. Heat travels rapidly through materials having a high thermal conductivity and conversely travels slowly if the conductivity is low. Silver has a very high thermal conductivity, which may be one of the contributing factors that make it so favoured for flute construction. In the case of the flute, many players speed the warming up process by blowing down the open end for a short while before playing.

6

Bowed and plucked stringed instruments

In this chapter we shall study the bowed and plucked members of the chordophone family. By far the most important group in this section is the violin family, so this will be considered first in some detail. The violin family originated in Italy during the Renaissance (1400–1600) alongside another similar group of instruments known as the viols. The violins did not evolve from the viols, but rather the two groups emerged from similar sources, the violins coming about a century later. In the early years the great composers wrote prolifically for both groups of instruments and there was keen rivalry between them. Gradually the violins, with their more powerful sound, found increasing favour amongst composers and virtuoso performers until eventually they reigned supreme for symphonic music.

THE VIOLIN

The term violin comes from the Italian *violino*, meaning little viola. It is not known exactly who invented the violin but the instrument was developed by the Cremona school of violin makers in Northern Italy, founded by Andrea Amati who died in 1580. Its construction was perfected over the 150 years following his death, by his pupils and descendants, particularly Antonio Stradivari and Giuseppe Guarneri. Perhaps the main reason for the dominant position of the violin in the modern orchestra is its extraordinary flexibility in producing tones of different quality, loudness and attack, surpassed only by the voice.

The main components of the violin are shown in Fig. 6.1. The instrument has four strings tuned to G_3, D_4, A_4 and E_5 stretched over the *nut* at one end and the *bridge* at the other, the distance between these being the *speaking length.* A range up to two octaves above the top-most open string can be achieved with good effect. This top string is normally of fine steel wire, although nylon or the more traditional twisted gut is sometimes used. Gut strings are only reliable under favourable conditions of temperature and humidity. Bottom strings are generally of gut overwound with fine wire (silver wire on the best strings) to increase the mass per unit length. This is required in order that the tension can be made large enough to produce a strong tone. The middle strings can be either of overwound gut or wire or just plain gut of different gauges.

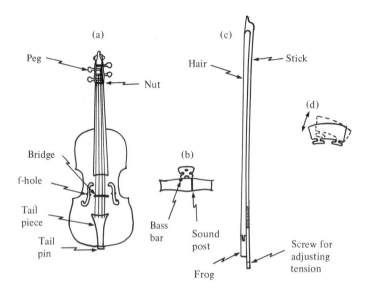

Fig. 6.1. The violin: (a) face on; (b) in cross-section; (c) the modern violin bow; (d) the rocking motion of the bridge, where the dashed lines indicate the extreme position and the arrows the direction of motion of the strings and the bass foot.

The body (or sound box) consists of a *front plate*, sometimes known as the belly, and a *back plate*, both arched outwards and joined by the supporting ribs (or sides). Traditionally the back plate and the sides are made of curly maple, the former being carved out either as a single piece or as two pieces joined together. Other woods such as sycamore or pear are sometimes used. The back plate varies in thickness from about six millimetres in the centre to two millimetres close to the edges, whereas the sides are only about one millimetre, thin enough to allow the wood strip to be bent round to the required shape. The top plate is generally of spruce and is in the form of two matching sections cut from the same log and joined lengthwise down the centre. Its thickness is between two and three millimetres. Cut in the top plate are two *F-holes* which affect the resonance characteristics of the contained air in a manner that will be explained later in this chapter.

The back plate and top plate are connected by the *sound post* which is almost below the bridge and the E string. This is made of spruce and is held in position by friction. It transmits vibrations between the plates, and its exact positioning and tightness of fit is crucial in the making of an instrument of a desired tone quality (Firth 1976 b), so much so that it is sometimes referred to as the soul of the instrument. Below the other side of the bridge, running longitudinally below the top plate, is the *bass bar*. This is also made of spruce and has the effect of distributing the pressure and increasing the speed at which vibrations are transmitted, its function being similar to that of the ribs on a piano soundboard. The bass bar can be seen in Fig. 6.2 (a), which is a photograph of a violin with the back plate removed.

Vibrations from the strings are transferred to the body of the instrument and the contained air by means of the bridge. This moves primarily in its own plane with a rocking motion, as indicated in Fig. 6.1 (d), the treble foot acting as fulcrum, since this is nearly over the sound post and is therefore essentially fixed in position (Cremer 1981; Hacklinger 1978).

The violin has altered somewhat since the heyday of violin making in the 17th and 18th centuries. The most commonly used pitch in this period was about a semitone lower than the standard pitch of today, but the rise in pitch has not been matched by a shortening in string length. In fact the neck of the violin has been lengthened by about half an inch, meaning that the strings are that much longer. Thus the string tensions on the modern violin are significantly higher, which has necessitated a heavier bass bar to support the increased force exerted by the bridge. The object of these changes has primarily been to increase the volume of sound in response to the requirements of the modern symphony orchestra. Many old instruments have had to be strengthened by the insertion of heavier bass bars and this has impaired their playing qualities.

The violin is now held universally between jaw and shoulder to the left side of the tail piece, for a right-handed player. The chin can also be placed to the right of the tail piece and this practice has often been in favour in the past. Fig. 6.1 (c) shows the components of the bow. This is strung with horse hair which is resined to improve the grip on the string. The stick on the modern bow bends inwards towards the hair in contrast to early bows where sticks bent outwards. This significantly affects the feel for the player, as can be seen by considering what happens when a force is applied to the hair. In playing, this force is brought into action when the bow is pressed against the string. Fig. 6.3 gives a schematic representation of how the two types of bow respond. We shall asssume for the sake of comparison that the force is applied in the centre of the hair and its magnitude is the

Fig. 6.2. The inside of (a) a violin (EUCHMI 351) and (b) a guitar by
Panormo (EUCHMI 2014).

same for both bows. With the old type of bow the curvature of the wood is
increased; the two points marked X move inwards and hence contribute to
the inward motion of the points marked Y which are attached to the hair.
With the modern type of bow, on the other hand, the points marked X
move outwards, which partly cancels the inward motion of the Y points.
This inward motion has the effect of slackening the hair, so the
displacement indicated by δ in Fig. 6.3 is much smaller for the modern
bow. Since the force required for a unit displacement is high for the

modern bow, the player feels it responding rather like a stiff spring despite its light construction. This makes it much better for producing strong attacks and articulations. A bow of the old type having the same spring stiffness would need to be made of thicker wood and would be much heavier.

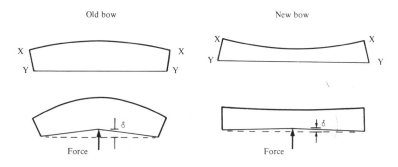

Fig. 6.3. Schematic representation of how the old and modern violin bows respond to the application of a force on the hair.

Acoustic characteristics

The quality of tone produced by a violin is primarily determined by the resonance characteristics of the wooden body and the contained air. These are coupled in a complex way; the resonant frequencies associated with the different modes are not harmonically related, as they are for the string, this being a consequence of the complex geometry of the instrument. Also the response characteristics of the various resonant peaks are very broad in contrast to the narrow resonance peaks associated with the strings, i.e. any individual mode will respond to a wide range of frequencies. In fact if the violin had no sound box it would produce only the tiniest of sounds, since the surface area of the vibrating strings is so small that they move only a very small amount of air by themselves. Practice violins have been made with no sound box, just a wooden frame, and the sound produced by these is virtually inaudible. Another interesting instrument which illustrates the acoustic principles is the *stroviol* (Fig. 6.4 (b)). Here there is a direct mechanical coupling between the bridge and a diaphragm rather similar to that in the old wind-up gramophones. As the string and bridge vibrate, the diaphragm is moved in and out producing the sound waves which are radiated through a horn. The volume, when the listener is directly in line with the horn, is quite loud but the quality is extremely poor, due mainly to the very limited response characteristics of the diaphragm and linkage system. The instrument was used in the early days of sound recording and is nowadays sometimes employed in folk groups.

Returning now to the violin, we shall first consider the resonance of the

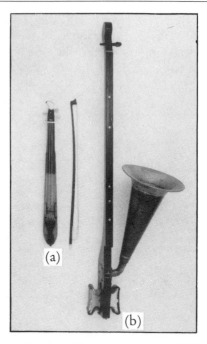

Fig. 6.4. Two unusual stringed instruments. From left to right; (a) the kit (EUCHMI 332) and (b) the stroviol (EUCHMI 1646).

air contained in the sound box. Air enclosed in any container with an opening will resonate at a certain frequency which can usually be determined at least approximately by blowing over the opening. A familiar example is when one blows over the top of a bottle. The violin air resonance frequency known as the *main air resonance* (MAR) can similarly be estimated by blowing over the f-holes. The manner in which the oscillations are sustained can be explained as follows. Suppose that at a certain instant of time the excitations have caused the pressure within the box to be slightly above atmospheric. Air will then rush out of the f-holes to equalise the pressure, but the momentum of the moving air will cause the pressure variation to overshoot the equilibrium position and a suction will then be formed in the box. Air will then rush in from the outside and eventually the complete cycle will be repeated. Clearly the moving air will be slowed down by a reduction in the size of the f-holes, so the resonant frequency (f) should increase as the area of the f-holes increases. Similarly, the cycle will take longer if the volume (V) of enclosed air is larger, so that f should increase as V decreases. The theory for this has been worked out by Helmholtz (the theory of the Helmholtz resonator) and extended by Lord Rayleigh (Rayleigh 1894) for the case of elliptic apertures. Although the f-holes in a violin are not elliptic, Rayleigh's formula can be applied by finding the ellipse which most closely resembles their shape (Jansson

1977; Itokawa and Kumagai 1952). The resonant frequency in Hz is then

$$f = 0.27 \, c \, A^{1/4}/V^{1/2}$$

where c is the speed of sound in air measured in metres per second, A is the area of each f-hole in square metres, and V is the enclosed volume in cubic metres. Typical values of A and V are $0.0005m^2$ and $0.00184m^3$, which makes the resonant frequency close to D_4. It has been found that the best position for the MAR is just below the open D string. The value actually predicted by the formula is slightly higher than this for two reasons. Firstly, the f-holes are not actually elliptic in shape, and secondly, the derivation of the formula assumes that the boundary walls are rigid. This cannot be completely true, for if it were there would be no mechanism by which the string vibrations could be transferred to the air. The flexibility of the walls means that the effective volume of air is greater than the actual one and hence f is lowered.

Strictly speaking, the resonance should be considered as a coupling between the air and the different vibrational modes of the body. From the formula it can be seen that the air resonance is not very sensitive to the size of the f-holes; to raise the MAR by just one semitone, for example, would require the area of the holes to be increased by 26%, assuming their shape to be maintained. It is clear from this that it is not practical to make large changes in the position of the air resonance by changing the size of the f-holes. The resonance is a little more sensitive to volume change; e.g. the same semitone shift could alternatively be achieved by reducing the volume by 11%. It can easily be shown that if one of the f-holes is blocked off the resonant frequency is lowered in the ratio $1:\sqrt{2}$, which is almost exactly a tritone, i.e. the MAR is lowered approximately to $A^{\flat}_3$. Caution should be applied when using the Rayleigh formula for quantitative calculations because it has been derived from a greatly simplified model.

The wooden body has very complex resonances which depend on the modes of vibration of the front and back plates and the way in which they are joined as well as the form and positions of the sound post and bass bar. Because of all these factors it is not possible to give one simple formula for calculating the resonances, although certain general trends can be noted. For example, the dominant resonant frequencies of the body will increase with the thickness of the plates and the rigidity of the wood (more precisely Young's modulus) but will decrease as the density of the wood increases. The dominant resonance of the violin sound box is known as the *main wood resonance* (MWR) and it has been found that for a good violin this should be located just below the open A string, i.e. $A_4 = 440$ Hz. This corresponds to the lowest mode of vibration of the body.

In violin construction each individual piece of wood being made into a plate must be worked down to the required thinness. In order to determine how far to go in the thinning process so that the resulting instrument will have the correct wood resonances, the violin maker makes use of *tap tones* (Hutchins et al. 1960). He holds the plate near one end between thumb and forefinger and taps it at various points, listening to the resulting sounds. More scientific methods have also been developed for precise measurements, particularly the technique of holographic interferometry (Hutchins and Stetson 1971). This will be described in connection with the guitar.

If the size of the violin is changed, as in the case of the half or quarter size violins used by children, then the main resonances are moved and the tonal quality deteriorates. For example, in a half size violin the MAR rises almost to F_4, which is far away from the open A string. The effect is seen in Fig. 6.5, which shows frequency spectra of the sound from (a) a full size violin and (b) a half size children's violin, both by the same maker and bowed on the open D string. Notice that with the full size instrument there is a very strong fundamental whereas with the half size violin both the fundamental and the second harmonic are weaker than the third harmonic. Even though the third harmonic is the strongest, the pitch heard is of course still that of the fundamental tone, i.e. D_4.

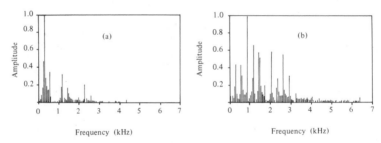

Fig. 6.5. Frequency spectra of the sound produced by (a) a full size violin and (b) a half size violin, both bowed on the open D string.

Glue and varnish

Many people have pondered on the question as to why violins seem to improve in quality with age and why modern makers have found it so difficult to match the superb quality of the instruments produced by the old Italian school. One theory is that the glue plays an important part in this process. Around the edge of each of the plates on a violin there is a shallow groove cut in which *purfling* is inlaid. This is usually in the form of two strips of black dyed pearwood and a strip of white poplar. After many years the glue that holds the purfling in the grooves tends to crack away. Since the wood of the plates is very thin beneath the grooves this effectively creates vibrating plates with very flexible boundaries and it is thought that this could lead to an improvement in tone since the boundary conditions are very important in determining the vibrational modes.

210

Another factor considered to be of importance is the varnish, and some people have gone as far as to state that the superiority of an instrument is primarily determined by the varnish. However, this is not the generally accepted view. In any case, it must be remembered that violins are only varnished on the outside. Varnish has the effect of increasing the mass of the plates and of inhibiting moisture penetration (Itokaura and Kumagai 1952). It also increases the rate at which resonances are damped, which in turn reduces the sharpness of the resonance peaks (see p.189).

Loudness curves

In Chapter 3 we saw how long-time-average-spectra (LTAS) could be used to obtain information about the response characteristics of different instruments. When applied to violins this technique is rather insensitive to the small variations which occur from one instrument to another, and in making comparisons of tonal characteristics, anomalous results can often be obtained. One problem is that an LTAS is constructed from the sound record of a normal musical performance, so the player automatically makes compensations to smooth the tonal response over the range of the instrument. For this reason natural resonances in a particular violin will not always show up as strong peaks on the LTAS. In fact avoiding sudden jumps in tone quality in moving from one note to the next is one of the arts that a violinist must learn.

A much simpler method of comparing different instruments is by reference to their loudness curves. To make a loudness curve the violin is bowed normally, but without vibrato, at semitone intervals over its entire range to produce the loudest tone possible on each note (Hutchins 1962). A sound level meter is then used to measure the loudness of each tone, which is plotted as a function of pitch. Strong resonances in an instrument then show up as peaks on this graph.

In addition to the peaks corresponding to the two main resonances already discussed there is a third, the *wood prime* peak, which occurs an octave below the main wood resonance. This arises because the main wood resonance amplifies the second harmonics of notes in this region and thus increases their volume. The wood prime peak occurs close to the open G string and therefore reinforces notes in the low register. There is no corresponding peak an octave below the main air resonance as this falls outside the range of the instrument.

The measurements are preferably made in a reverberation chamber, which minimises the effects both of standing waves set up in the room and also the directional characteristics of the radiated sound. The latter effect will be dealt with later in this chapter. Fig. 6.6 shows loudness curves for three different instruments: (a) a Stradivarius; (b) a second quality 250 year old instrument; and (c) a poor quality violin. Only the first one shows wholly desirable characteristics with the three main peaks close to the open strings.

There are also other methods of obtaining the resonance characteristics of a particular instrument. One of these is to use a mechanical bow and gradually to increase the bowing pressure on each note until the instrument just speaks. The resulting plot of pressure against frequency has a similar form to the loudness curve and is known as a *Raman curve* after its originator. Another technique is to mechanically vibrate the bridge or top plate and then measure the intensity of the sound emitted at different excitation frequencies.

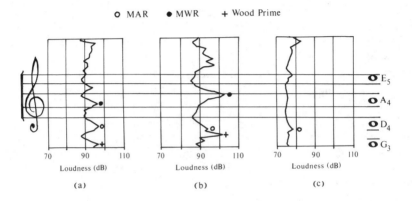

Fig. 6.6. Loudness curves for three different violins: (a) a Stradivarius; (b) a second quality 250 year old instrument; and (c) a poor quality violin (adapted from Hutchins, 1962).

Wolf notes

Some instruments have *wolf notes*, almost always at the frequency of the main wood resonance. When a note of this frequency is played on any string the tone warbles unsteadily, often breaking by a whole octave. This is because of the strong coupling between the string and the body. Instead of the frequency being governed entirely by the string resonance, the vibrations of the body intermittently dominate and give rise to an unstable beating. Wolf notes are liable to appear on any instrument which exhibits large peaks in its loudness curve, although violas and cellos are more prone to wolf notes than violins (Fifth 1978). The pitch of a wolf note can be moved by fixing a small object such as a coin to the body of the instrument with Blu-Tack or tape. This lowers the main wood resonance and correspondingly shifts the wolf note down. The same effects can be obtained with a mute attached to the bridge.

Bowing

When a resined bow is placed on a string and drawn steadily over it, the string alternates between sticking to the bow and sliding against it. As the displacement increases, so does the restoring force and eventually this overcomes the friction of the bow and the string slips back. Then once again the bow grips and the cycle is repeated. The motion of the point on the string which is directly under the bow is shown in Fig. 6.7 as a function of time.

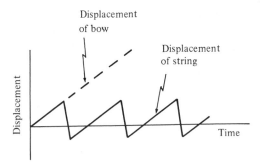

Fig. 6.7. Motion of the bow and the point on the string directly under the bow in upbowing.

The actual shape of the string at different phase positions in the cycle (which repeats itself 440 times a second for A_4) is shown in Fig. 6.8, the full line being the shape of the string. At any instant this resembles the shape it would have if it were pulled aside by the finger. There is a point of discontinuity (this is only an approximation) which moves round a parabolic path (dotted line) and passes under the bow twice each cycle. Each time the discontinuity passes under the bow the status quo is disturbed. If the string is sticking to the bow it will be knocked loose by the discontinuity (position 1). If on the other hand the string is slipping, the passing discontinuity enables the bow once again to grip the string (position 3). Although this motion appears complicated it can in fact be broken down into component sine waves and it is these components which are transmitted through the bridge to the sound box. Since the string is moving rapidly always within the upper and lower limits of the dotted lines, it appears to the eye to fill this area completely, as if it were vibrating only in the lowest mode. This is also shown in Fig. 6.8.

Tone quality is affected by bowing speed, pressure and the distance of the bowing point from the bridge, although as we have already indicated the modern bow is designed to minimise pressure variations. Bowing very close to the bridge (sul ponticello) has the effect of producing a strident tone rich in upper harmonics, whereas bowing closer to the fingerboard (sul tasto) gives a rounder tone with stronger fundamental, since the point of excitation is close to the antinode of the lowest vibrational mode. In this playing position, however, the volume of the sound is least, since the bow is close to the position where the string has its maximum displacement amplitude and of necessity the excursions of the string under the bow are small.

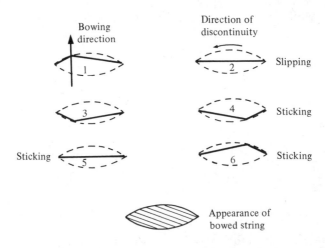

Fig. 6.8. Shape of bowed string at different phase positions in the cycle. In positions 4, 5 and 6 it is sticking, in position 2 it is slipping, and 1 and 3 are positions of discontinuity.

If the string is not bowed perpendicular to its length it will vibrate longitudinally as well as transversely (Lee and Rafferty 1983). Since the speed of longitudinal waves is very much higher than for the transverse waves, this results in a high pitched squeal superimposed on top of the true note. This is a fault often heard in beginners. Further details of violin bowing characteristics are given by McIntyre and Woodhouse (1984), Lawergren (1983), Schelleng (1974) and Saunders (1937).

Playing harmonics

By touching a string lightly in the centre one can damp out modes which have antinodes at this point, i.e. select from the general vibration those modes which have nodes at the centre. These have frequencies $2f_0$, $4f_0$, $6f_0$ etc., where f_0 is the frequency of the open string. As we saw in Chapter 1, these tones form a harmonic series with a new fundamental $2f_0$ (Fig. 1.17), so the ear registers this as a new note one octave above the pitch of the open string. Higher harmonics can be produced by touching the string in other positions; e.g., lightly placing the finger one third of the way along the string will generate the third harmonic.

Natural harmonics in string playing are those which are sounded by playing an open string and touching with a finger at the appropriate position. If the overtones are sounded from a stopped string, i.e. one finger is used to stop the string and another to touch it at a nodal position, then they are referred to as *artificial harmonics*.

Vibrato

Vibrato on the violin is produced by moving the finger back and forth on the string, thus periodically changing its length. This results primarily in a frequency fluctuation (modulation) but accompanied by small fluctuations in amplitude. Because of the mechanics of the way in which vibrato is produced on the violin, it is generally only used on stopped notes. The fuller tone associated with the open string notes tends to compensate for the accompanying lack of vibrato.

In Chapter 3 we examined the measurements that Seashore made for vibrato on the human voice. At about the same time similar measurements were also presented by Arnold Small for the violin (Small 1937) which show a considerable similarity. From an analysis of his own playing he found that pitch modulations were very close to being sinusoidal with a mean frequency of about 6Hz, almost exactly what Seashore had measured for the voice. The pitches varied over a range of about half a semitone, i.e. the sinusoids had amplitudes of about 25 cents. This is about half the value obtained for the voice. He observed that the finger motion responsible for the vibrato was generally initiated by a movement towards the bridge, whereas the final vibrato movement was towards the scroll.

The vibrato frequencies and amplitudes measured by Small are for a single performance and can only be regarded as typical values. The exact modulation used in a particular musical situation is clearly a matter of personal judgement and the accomplished player will have the facility to change his vibrato as the occasion demands. Certain players have a liking for more or less vibrato, jazz violinists often going for a wide modulation.

Directional sensitivity

It is fairly obvious that an instrument such as a trumpet will radiate the sound more strongly in a direction in line with the bell. The violin also has a marked directional sensitivity of sound radiation, due partly to the construction of the instrument and partly to the screening effect of the player. We saw in Chapter 5 that when waves are emitted from the end of a tube the low frequency waves are bent or diffracted more than the high frequency ones. The same principle applies in the case of the violin, so the instrument is more directionally sensitive in the high register than in the low register. This is illustrated in Fig. 6.9, in which the shaded areas indicate the positions measured in the horizontal plane where the sound level never drops more than 3dB below the maximum. These measurements were recorded by Meyer and more details are given in his book (Meyer 1978).

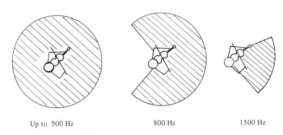

Up to 500 Hz   800 Hz   1500 Hz

Fig. 6.9. Directional sensitivity of the violin in the horizontal plane for notes in three different ranges. Within the shaded areas the sound level never drops more than 3dB below its maximum value.

OTHER MEMBERS OF THE VIOLIN FAMILY

The *viola* and *cello* are essentially scaled up versions of the violin, the strings being tuned a fifth apart, respectively one fifth and one twelfth below the violin. Thus the open strings are

$$\text{Viola } C_3 \text{ } G_3 \text{ } D_4 \text{ } A_4$$

$$\text{Cello } C_2 \text{ } G_2 \text{ } D_3 \text{ } A_3$$

Scaling in simple proportions would lead to a viola which was ½ times the size of the violin and a cello of 3 times the size. These sizes are impractically large and in fact the most usual scaling factors for the viola and cello are approximately 1.1 and 2.1. This tends to lead to weakening of the tone in the low registers since the positions of the wood and air resonances are moved. The violin makers of the old Italian school concentrated their attentions primarily on perfecting the acoustic properties of the violin, somewhat at the expense of the viola and cello. Because of this a good deal of modern research has been directed towards these two instruments to improve their tone quality in line with that of the violin (Firth 1976 a). This has centred around the problem of determining optimum scaling factors in terms of overall dimensions, plate thickness, rib heights, elastic constants etc., so that the main wood and air resonances come close to the two middle open strings.

The *double bass* is not strictly the bass member of the violin family since it has some features in common with the viols and others in common with the violins. Its strings are tuned a fourth apart like the viols', i.e.

Double bass E_1 A_1 D_2 G_2

rather than in fifths as the violins' are. This keeps down the finger spacing and the distances the hand has to travel. It also has sloping shoulders and generally a flat back like the viols, although some double basses have swell backs. On the other hand its wood construction and strings are heavy as on the violin and also it has no frets. Because of these factors its sound is akin to a violin's rather than a viol's and blends with the other members of the violin family in the orchestra. The bow is now generally held overhand as on the violin, although originally it was held underhand as on a viol, and some players still prefer this technique. Fig. 6.10 shows a violin, viola, cello and double bass alongside each other so that their sizes can be compared. The total lengths of these instruments are 60 cm, 65 cm, 124 cm and 183 cm respectively. If the three larger instruments had been directly scaled versions of the violin, then their lengths would have been 90 cm, 180 cm and 283 cm. The outlines of instruments of these sizes have been drawn over the photographs so that the extent of the deviations from direct scaling can be seen.

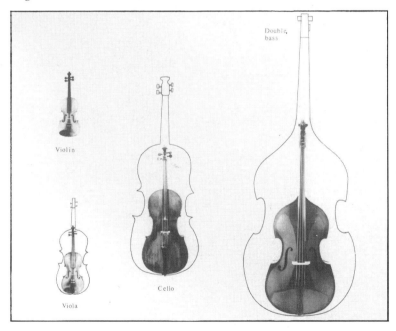

Fig. 6.10. The violin, viola, cello and double bass together with the outline of instruments directly scaled in size from the violin.

An unusual member of the violin family which is now rarely seen is the *kit* or *pochette*. This is illustrated in Fig. 6.4 (a). It is even tinier than the *violino piccolo* (little violin) and is generally tuned about an octave above the violin. It has a small clear tone and was carried by dancing masters in their pockets.

The *huqin* (or *hu-ch'in*) is a bowed string instrument of great import- ance in China, the country of its origin. This employs a skin membrane stretched over a cup-shaped resonating chamber for amplifying the sound, rather like the banjo. The two instruments are shown together in Fig. 6.11 for comparison. The bow cannot be separated from the main body of the instrument since the horse hair passes between the two strings, which are sounded together. The neck is long and passes through the resonating chamber, but there is no finger board, the strings being simply pressed

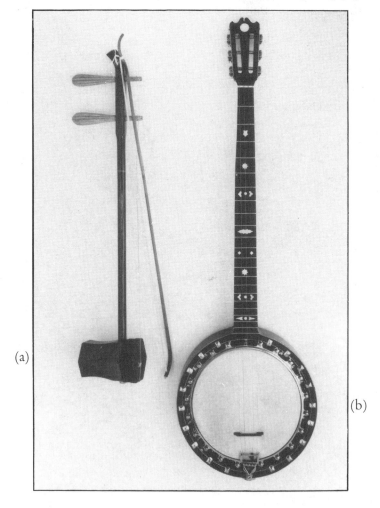

(a)

(b)

Fig. 6.11. Two instruments using a membrane stretched over a cavity: (a) the huqin and (b) the banjo (EUCHMI 2164).

hard to produce the different sounding lengths. Vibrations are transferred from the strings to the membrane by a small bridge which rests on its surface.

THE VIOLS

As was mentioned earlier, the viols were developed before the violins, primarily in the 15th century, and for about two centuries both families of instruments were in popular use. Strictly speaking, the viols should be referred to as 'viole da gamba' (or simply gambas), meaning leg viols, in contrast to the 'viole da braccio' or arm viols, which are the violin family. It is common practice, however, to use the term viola da gamba to mean the bass viol. The bow is held in the underhand position and, as the name implies, all the gambas are held upright either on or between the legs.

Viols generally have six strings tuned in fourths with a major third in the middle, although in the 17th century the number of strings was sometimes increased to seven. There are four members of the family most frequently tuned as follows (Donington):

Treble viol D_3 G_3 C_4 E_4 A_4 D_5

Alto viol C_3 F_3 A_4 D_4 G_4 C_5

Tenor viol G_2 C_3 F_3 A_3 D_4 G_4

Bass viol (A_1) D_2 G_2 C_3 E_3 A_3 D_4

although the tenor viol may be tuned a tone higher. In the Renaissance period musical instruments were generally made in sets or consorts, hence the term 'consort of viols'. The set of instruments would be kept together in one case, referred to as the chest. Often the alto viol was not included in the consort, which typically consisted of 2 basses, 2 tenors and 2 trebles.

In comparison with the violins, the viols have flat backs and sloping shoulders and are generally lighter in construction, making use of thinner wood but with reinforcing crossbars inside. The holes in the belly are C-shaped rather than f-shaped as in the violin, and are known as C-holes. The strings are thinner and slacker. Pieces of fine gut are wound round the fingerboard at semitone intervals to act as frets. These help to sharpen the tone quality on the stopped notes. The tone on the viols is generally quieter but more edgy than on the violins. This lends itself very well to contrapuntal music and in fact much music for viols is of this character.

THE LUTE

As can be seen in Fig. 6.12, the body of the lute resembles a sliced pear in shape and the head containing the pegbox is bent back at an angle to the neck. The strings are plucked with the fingers, although before the 15th century a plectrum was used. The curved back is made from thin strips of wood known as ribs and the soundboard or table is flat, usually made of pine and also very thin, giving the instrument an unusual degree of resonance. The bridge is an integral part of the soundboard and serves as a fixing for the lower ends of the strings. A circular hole known as a rose or knot is cut in the soundboard and this is normally surrounded by elaborate ornamental patterns. The strings are originally of fine gauge gut and are mostly tuned in pairs to the unison or the octave, but there are many different arrangements and tunings. The fingerboard is generally slightly arched and has fine gut frets tied around it, most frequently seven in number.

The lute does not have a powerful sound, mainly because of its light construction and fine strings. However, the sound is rich in upper harmonics and very expressive. Instruments with thin strings tend to lose their tuning very easily and this can be a major problem with the lute.

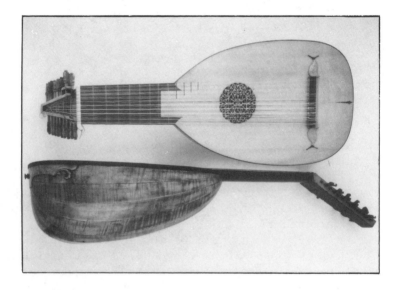

Fig. 6.12. Two lutes from the Edinburgh University Collection. The upper (EUCHMI 305) is by Passauro, the lower (EUCHMI 1721) by an unknown maker.

The lute was an instrument of great importance in Europe from the 15th to the end of the 18th century, being used primarily for solo playing and in the accompaniment of songs. Although it fell into disuse in the 19th century, there has been a revival of interest in recent times. The repertory for the lute is very large, almost rivalling that of the piano.

THE GUITAR

The classical guitar

The origin of the guitar is closely related to that of the lute. During the 17th century the guitar rose in popularity and gradually took precedence over the lute, primarily because of its simpler fingering and more mellow tone. Spain was paramount in the development of the modern classical guitar, which is often referred to as the Spanish guitar. This has changed little in design since the 16th century.

The main elements of the classical guitar are shown in Fig. 6.13 (a). It has six strings made of gut (or frequently nylon nowadays) and they are tuned as follows:

$$E_2 \; A_2 \; D_3 \; G_3 \; B_3 \; E_4$$

The lowest three strings are usually overwound with metal.

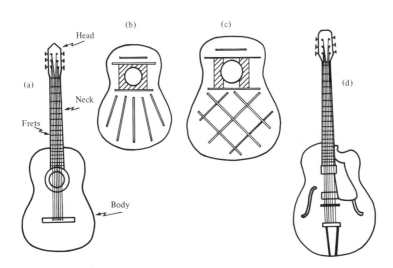

Fig. 6.13. The guitar: (a) elements of the classical or Spanish design; (b) fan bracing used on the classical guitar; (c) cross bracing used on the country and western guitar; and (d) the electro-acoustic f-hole guitar.

221

The bridge is an integral part of the construction of the top plate (sometimes referred to as the table or face), rather than being movable as with the violin, and it serves the dual purpose of transmitting string vibrations to the top plate and being a fastening point for the lower end of the strings. There is no sound post but the inner side of the top plate is reinforced with bracing, which is important in determining the modes of vibration. The traditional design is for the struts to radiate from the sound hole; this is referred to as *fan bracing*. A typical arrangements is shown in Figs. 6.2 (b) and 6.13 (b), but there are many variations which are used by different makers. The back plate and sides are generally of Brazilian rosewood, the neck of cedar and the fingerboard of ebony, one of the hardest of woods. The top plate is of spruce carefully selected for its closeness of grain and in this is cut a single circular sound hole or rose, usually decorated round the edge with mosaic inlay. There are normally 19 nickel silver frets on the fingerboard, giving a total range of three and a half octaves. Guitar music is notated one actave higher than it sounds.

Modern types of guitar

There are a number of popular types of instrument derived from the classical guitar (Collins 1976), all of these being tuned to the same notes, except of course for the *bass guitar*, which has only four strings and is tuned the same as a double bass. The strings on these instruments are steel, requiring a much higher tension, and a plectrum is used for playing. The *country and western* guitar has the same hourglass shape as the classical guitar but is larger in overall dimensions and is flatter at the top. In construction the body is much heavier, to withstand the higher stresses of the steel strings, and for the same reason the traditional fan bracing is replaced by cross bracing as shown in Fig. 6.13 (c). These instruments are frequently fitted with an electric pick-up for feeding to an amplifier system. A variant on the country and western guitar is the twelve string guitar, where the strings are tuned in pairs at the unison, octave or double octave. Electro-acoustic guitars rely primarily on electronic amplification for their sound output, so we shall not discuss them in detail here. They have much thinner bodies, often with a cut-away section near to the end of the fingerboard and f-holes rather than a single rose. This can be seen in Fig. 6.13 (d). Without amplification their sound output is extremely small. In the case of the solid body guitar the sound production is entirely through amplification, so they can essentially be made to any shape and in fact many bizarre shapes have been produced. The most important acoustical feature of their construction is the rigidity of the body. This is essential if adequate sustaining power is to be achieved, for reasons which will be explained in the section on impedance matching in Chapter 7.

Resonances of the guitar

The acoustics of the guitar are complicated by the fact that there is such a range of different designs (Richardson 1983). We shall simplify the situation by considering only the classical guitar, although what is said applies with minor modifications to the country and western designs. It is generally accepted that the resonant response of a guitar to the vibrations induced by the strings is largely governed by the vibrational modes of the top plate together with the Helmholtz resonance of the enclosed air space, the former being the more significant. The back plate and sides have a minor effect and their vibrations are coupled in a complicated way to those of the top plate and enclosed air (Richardson 1984). The back plate vibrations in any case tend to be dampened by the player because of the way the instrument is held.

The formula derived by Lord Rayleigh which we used for calculating the Helmholtz resonance in the violin can be applied in a modified form to the guitar. In this case there is a single sound hole, and since this is circular the factor 0.27 must be changed to 0.17. The resonant frequency is then

$$f = c\,(D/V)^{1/2}/(2\pi) = 0.17\,c\,A^{1/4}/V^{1/2}$$

where D is the diameter of the sound hole measured in metres. Typically the Helmholtz resonance is just above 100 Hz but, as with the violin, the Rayleigh formula overpredicts this frequency. It is generally the lowest vibrational mode of the instrument, but again, as with the violin, it must be emphasised that this vibrational mode is in reality a complex coupling between the vibrations of the body and the enclosed air. The Helmholtz resonance has the effect of enhancing the tone quality in the lowest octave.

In recent times quite sophisticated techniques have been developed by instrument makers and scientists for studying the resonant modes of the body. The measurements are conducted in an anechoic chamber, i.e. a padded room where reflections at the walls are minimised (see Chapter 13). Usually an electrically driven vibrator is attached to the instrument and is controlled by a sine wave oscillator which is scanned through the frequency range of interest, the induced sound being picked up by a microphone placed a short distance from the front plate. When the microphone signal amplitude is plotted against frequency, it shows peaks corresponding to the main resonances. The Helmholtz resonance is generally the lowest and this can easily be verified by blocking off the sound hole and seeing if the lowest peak disappears. The other strong peaks are due to the body, particularly the top plate.

With the oscillator set at a plate resonance, details of the vibrational pattern can be found in a number of different ways. These patterns are of importance to the instrument maker in showing up imperfections of manufacture and also in giving him a detailed comparison between different designs. One method involves simply sprinkling dust over the plate and is used for preliminary investigations rather than for detailed measurements. The dust particles migrate to nodal lines and end up in a pattern known as a *Chladni pattern* (see also p.413). Very much more detailed information can be obtained by the more modern technique of *holographic interferometry* (Reinicke and Cremer 1970). This involves photographing vibrating plates which have been illuminated with the light from an expanded laser beam. Fig. 6.14 shows the patterns of fringes (i.e. dark and light regions) formed on a guitar front plate in its first six main vibrational modes (Richardson and Taylor 1983). These correspond to frequencies of (i) 216 Hz, (ii) 268 Hz, (iii) 431 Hz, (iv) 553 Hz, (v) 628 Hz and (vi) 672 Hz. The dark lines are contours of equal vibrational amplitude, the spacing between contours in these pictures corresponding to a change in vibration amplitude of approximately $1\mu m$ ($10^{-6}m$). For higher modes the plate divides into segments, adjacent segments vibrating $180°$ out of phrase. The lowest mode of the top plate resonance is approximately one octave above the Helmholtz resonance (Firth 1977 (a)).

The Helmholtz resonance can alternatively be found by a slightly simpler means. This requires the use of a *probe microphone*, i.e. a microphone with a long tube attachment which can be used to probe the sound field without causing excessive obstruction. The probe microphone is inserted inside the body of the guitar and a loudspeaker is then placed nearby to excite the air oscillations. The loudspeaker is driven by a sine wave oscillator to produce a pure tone of variable frequency and the resonance is found by adjusting the frequency of the oscillator until the microphone gives a peak response.

Timbre of the plucked string

The fact that the strings of a guitar are plucked gives a sound dramatically different from a bowed violin because of the transient effect. On plucking, the amplitude rises very sharply and then falls back quickly as the sound begins to decay. However, the rate of decay gradually gets less, so the note rings on for a considerable time. This is shown in Fig. 6.15, which is a record of the sound picked up by a microphone close to a guitar plucked with a plectrum on the open A string. The time scale is very compressed in order to show the transient effect, so it is not possible to pick out the individual cycles. It can be seen that even after a period of 3 seconds the amplitude is still approximately one tenth of its peak value.

The harmonic composition of a note can be altered by changing the position of plucking. Plucking near to an antinode for a particular mode will excite it, but not other modes which have a node at that point; e.g. plucking near the centre will accentuate all the odd harmonics including the fundamental. Plucking with a sharp object such as a plectrum accentuates the higher harmonics in contrast to plucking with the finger or a soft

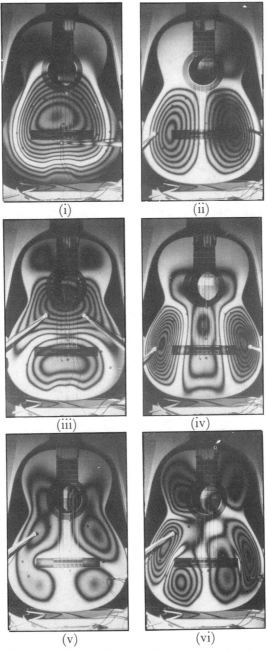

Fig. 6.14. Holographic records of the first six main vibrational modes of a guitar top plate photographed by Bernard Richardson. The resonant frequencies are (i) 216 Hz, (ii) 268 Hz, (iii) 431 Hz, (iv) 553 Hz, (v) 628 Hz and (vi) 672 Hz.

Fig. 6.15. The sound from a guitar plucked with a plectrum on its open A string showing the transient effect.

object. This is because the initial displacement is highly angular in form, as shown in Fig. 6.16. In order to achieve such a displacement curve by the method of superposition (Chapter 5), many higher order modes must be introduced, which would not have been the case if the curve had been more rounded. The sound quality can also be altered by initiating the string motions in different directions. If the direction of release is perpendicular to the plane of the strings, then the harmonics are all more intense (the sound is louder) and they decay more rapidly than when the release is in the plane of the strings. This is because the coupling between the string and the body is greater in this direction, i.e. the bridge impedance is less, so the strings lose their energy more quickly. A player can induce motion in this direction by shaping his nail in the form of a ramp which converts the motion of the fingertip in the plane of the strings to one perpendicular to the strings.

Fig. 6.16. Angular form for the initial displacement of a string plucked with a sharp object.

As with the violin, coupling between string and body can be so great for certain notes that they form a coupled resonant system. In this situation the decay rate is very rapid and there is an unpleasant beating equivalent to the wolf note on the violin.

OTHER MEMBERS OF THE GUITAR FAMILY

The *mandolin* and *ukulele* are very similar in form to the guitar and have similar acoustical characteristics. Both have fretted fingerboards. The ukulele has four strings, typically tuned to G_4, C_4, E_4 and A_4; it has the appearance of a small classical guitar, with the bridge an integral part of the front plate, which has a single circular rose. The mandolin also utilises a resonant sound box which either has a swell shaped back with no sides or is similar to a small f-hole guitar. Its eight strings are metal and are tuned in unison pairs to G_3, D_4, A_4 and E_5. In this case the strings are stretched over a bridge and connected to a tailpiece.

The *banjo* has some similarities to the guitar. The strings are plucked and it has a fretted fingerboard. However, its acoustical characteristics are quite different. Instead of a hollow wooden body it has a shallow metal hoop with a membrane stretched over the top, similar to a drum. This creates a large resonating surface to amplify the sound. Vibrations are transferred to the membrane by means of a bridge, as with the mandolin and the huqin. A banjo is shown in Fig. 6.11 (b).

THE HARP

The harp differs from all the other instruments discussed in this chapter in that it has no fingerboard and the strings are not ordinarily stopped to produce different notes. In its simplest form it comprises a series of strings which are tuned diatonically to the notes of a selected key (Rensch 1969). The upper ends of the strings are attached to tuning pegs on a curved neck. Instruments of this type have a long history of development in Ireland, Wales and the Scottish Highlands. They are often quite small and can be held on the lap when the player is seated. The traditional Irish harp or *clarsach* has wire strings and a brilliant tone, whereas the Celtic harp uses gut strings and has a softer, more mellow tone. These instruments frequently employ a series of hooks fixed below the tuning pegs. If the player turns one of these to press against the string, its pitch will be raised by a semitone. This allows the player to change key without retuning the instrument. Each hook should touch the string at approximately $1/17$th of the string length from the end in order to raise the pitch by a factor 1.06.

The concert harp

Over the generations many chromatic harps have been produced, i.e. instruments where there is a string for each semitone. However, the complexity of the stringing and the playing technique are such that they have not found any lasting favour amongst players. The modern concert harp, which is the normal orchestral instrument of today, was developed by Sébastien Erard (1752–1831) and overcomes the difficulties associated with chromatic notes by an ingenious system of pedals. There are seven pedals operated by the feet, one for each letter name of the scale, i.e. A, B, C, D, E, F and G. These can be seen on the instrument pictured in Fig. 6.17, but in this case there is an additional pedal in the centre which is used to open and close a flap in the back of the soundbox. The remaining pedals operate a series of rods which run through the vertical pillar on the instrument and are linked to rotating discs fixed to the curved neck. There are three positions for each pedal, located by notches.

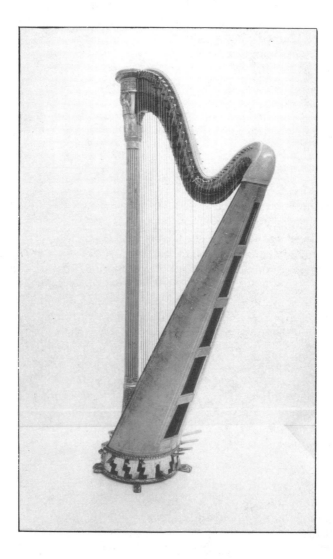

Fig. 6.17. A concert harp by Erard (EUCHMI 176), showing the seven pedals used for raising or lowering the pitch of the strings by a semitone, together with an additional pedal used for opening and closing a flap in the soundbox. In the picture the flap is open.

Depressing by one notch raises the pitch of all the octave strings with that letter name by one semitone, whilst depressing to the second notch raises the pitch by a full tone. The harp is ordinarily tuned to the key of C♭ major, so with all the pedals in the central position it plays in C major. Shortening of the string length is accomplished by having pins on the two rotating discs below each tuning peg, as shown in Fig. 6.18. This illustrates the discs for one string. In 6.18 (a) the pedal is not depressed, so the full string length is utilised. In 6.18 (b) the pedal is depressed by one notch, which rotates the upper disc and raises the pitch by a semitone. Full depression of the pedal (6.18 (c)) rotates both discs and raises the pitch by a tone. The pedal system gives the harp enormous flexibility, in some respects greater than that of the keyboard, since there are actually 21 semitones for each octave.

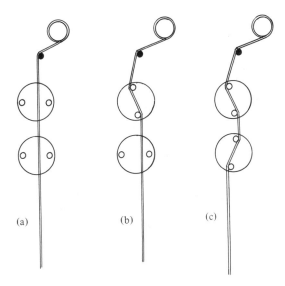

(a)   (b)   (c)

Fig. 6.18. Disc mechanism for a single string on the double action concert harp: (a) with the pedal not depressed, the full string length is utilised; (b) with the pedal depressed by one notch, the pitch is raised by one semitone; (c) with the pedal depressed by two notches, the pitch is raised by one tone.

An earlier version of the modern pedal harp used a single pedal action, i.e. each set of strings for a particular letter name (e.g. all the C strings or all the D strings) could be raised by a semitone by depression of the appropriate pedal. This limited the number of keys in which it could be played. For this reason it was normally tuned to E♭ major, making the major keys of

E♭, B♭, F, C, G, D and A possible without retuning.

Harp strings

The strings on the concert harp are normally of gut or nylon, over-wound in the lower register with wire. To ease identification, C and F strings are of different colours from the rest. The range is nominally C_1 to G_7, i.e. six and a half octaves. We saw in Chapter 5 that if two strings have lengths L_1 and L_2, mass per unit length m_1 and m_2, and tension T_1 and T_2, then the ratio between their frequencies is

$$\text{frequency ratio} = (L_1/L_2)(m_1/m_2)^{1/2}(T_2/T_1)^{1/2} = (L_1/L_2)(d_1/d_2)(T_2/T_1)^{1/2}$$

where d_1 and d_2 are the diameters of the two strings. The last part of this expression assumes that the strings are of the same material, whence the mass per unit length is proportional to the square of the diameter. From the formula it can be seen that if the diameters and tensions of all the strings on the harp were the same, then each octave rise would require a doubling of the string length, meaning that the longest string would be 90 (i.e. $2^{6.5}$) times the length of the shortest string. Because this would make the size unmanageable and also because of other factors which arise, e.g. the *feel* of the string, the diameters and also the string tensions progressively increase towards the bass in approximately the ratios 1.41 (diameter) and 1.47 (tension) per octave. Writing the frequency ratio as 2 in the formula gives the length ratio per octave as

$$L_1/L_2 = 2(d_2/d_1)(T_1/T_2)^{1/2} = 2(1.47)^{1/2}/1.41 = 1.72$$

This is known as the *stringing ratio* or stringing scale. This is adhered to in the central range of the instrument, but in the bass the strings are made shorter than the scaling would predict, the pitch of the bass notes being maintained by overwinding the strings with wire. This leads to the characteristic shape of the harp neck. Stringing in the treble can also deviate slightly from the scaling law.

The feel of a string

The action of playing the harp involves drawing the centre of the string away from its equilibrium position by a small amount and then releasing it. It is in this initial stretching that the question of feel arises, for it is important that the force (F) which must be applied by the player to produce a given displacement (δ) is reasonable. Also, since the displacement is in the plane of the strings, it should not be so large that the strings collide once plucked. Fig. 6.19 shows a string of length L in its displaced position. The *feel* is defined (Firth 1984) as the displacement per unit force, i.e. δ/F. This should not vary too dramatically over the range of the instrument, otherwise the player would feel the restoring action of the strings as being like springs of greatly varying stiffness. The stiffness of a spring in fact is defined as the force per unit displacement. The feel can be written in terms of L and T by the application of some simple principles of mechanics. Balancing the forces gives

$$F \simeq 2T\delta/(L/2) = 4T\delta/L$$

$$\text{i.e. feel} = \delta/F = L/(4T)$$

Since L and T vary by factors of 1.72 and 1.47 per octave respectively, it is seen that the feel will increase by a factor $1.72/1.47 = 1.17$ per octave towards the bass. This is in contrast to the piano, where a typical value is 1.88. The modest variation in feel for the harp makes it comfortable for the player over the entire range, whereas the rise of 88% per octave for the piano would make it virtually unplayable with the fingers.

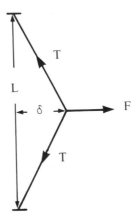

Fig. 6.19. A harp string at its position of maximum displacement. F is the applied force, T the tension of the string, L the overall string length, and δ the maximum transverse displacement from its equilibrium position.

Resonances of the harp

The soundboard on the harp is attached to a soundbox, and on the concert harp the air inside the cavity normally communicates with the atmosphere through five holes in the back of the box. The Helmholtz air resonance generally appears at about 180 Hz and the first main resonance of the soundboard lies above this. The tone quality in the low register is primarily determined by these two resonances (Firth 1977 (b)). The sound output of a particular string depends to some extent on whether it enters the soundboard at a node or an antinode (Bell and Firth 1984). Strings tuned to a particular resonant frequency entering the soundboard at a nodal position in the soundbroad's vibrational pattern (i.e. a position of

231

high impedance) have difficulty in speaking; ideally a soundboard should be designed so that this does not occur.

The lowest resonance on the harp, the Helmholtz resonance, is nearly two and a half octaves above the frequency of the lowest string, making the sound output in the lower frequency range very small. Between the Helmholtz resonance and about 1 KHz it is almost constant; it then dies gradually up to the frequency of the highest note, making the instrument rather weak in the high register. The bass strings are heard primarily through their partials, which lie above the air resonance. Directly after a string has been plucked, the sound output comprises vibrations from all of the body modes. These die within a few tens of milliseconds, each mode at its own decay rate, leaving the more pure sustaining tone of the string. Since strings are normally plucked at their central position, this tends to accentuate the fundamental in the string vibration. For special effects the plucking position can be moved near to one end, which introduces more higher harmonics.

7

Stringed keyboard
instruments

There are three distinct types of stringed keyboard instruments in common usage, the *clavichord*, the *harpsichord* and the *piano*. These have their origins in the *dulcimer* and the *psaltery* which originated about a thousand years ago and are closely related to the harp. Both of these early instruments consist of strings of varying length stretched on a frame over a soundboard. They have no mechanical action, the strings being plucked on the psaltery and struck with light hammers or beaters, held one in each hand, in the case of the dulcimer. Various forms of dulcimer are used today in school percussion and folk groups. *Cimbalom* is the term used for the large concert dulcimer standing on its own legs and fitted with a damper pedal. Fig. 7.1 shows a cimbalom from the Edinburgh University

Fig. 7.1. A concert cimbalom by Schunda (EUCHMI 1797).

collection, together with its wool-covered beaters. The zither is the modern representation of the psaltery. The piano can be thought of as a form of mechanical dulcimer and likewise the harpsichord as a mechanised psaltery.

CLAVICHORD

In general appearance the clavichord is like a small rectangular piano in the form of a box that can be placed on a table for playing, or supported on legs. The clavichord came into prominence in the 16th century, although it is thought to date from the 14th century. Fig. 7.2 shows a typical 18th century instrument made in Germany. The strings run parallel to the longer side, which faces the player.

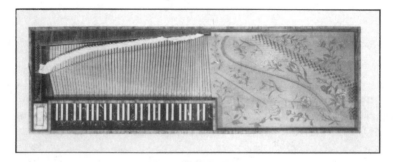

Fig. 7.2. Clavichord by J.A. Hass, Hamburg, 1763, Russell Coll. No. 22.

The principle of the clavichord action is illustrated in Fig. 7.3. The string (or more often a pair of strings tuned in unison) is set into vibration by means of a metal *tangent* (or flag) which is fixed at one end of a wooden lever, the other end being the key. When the key is depressed the tangent is raised smartly against the string and sets it vibrating, the tangent remain-

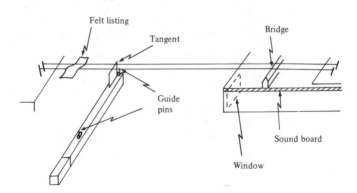

Fig. 7.3. Principle of the clavichord action.

234

ing in contact with the string for the period over which the note sounds. Fig. 7.4 is a close-up picture showing the tangent in the striking position when one of the keys is depressed. The tangent has the dual purpose of setting the speaking length of the string and also initiating the vibrations. The section of the string which does not pass over the bridge is damped by felt (listing). In early clavichords there is usually an economy of strings achieved by having the tangents belonging to two or more adjacent keys striking the same string, or pair of strings. In this case the two notes cannot be played together. Clavichords of this type are referred to as *fretted*. Fretted clavichords are sometimes called *monochords* because of their similarity with the monochord or sonometer (this is a scientific instrument which consists of a sound box and string whose speaking length can be altered by means of a movable bridge). The range of the instrument in the bass was frequently extended by using a short octave, which could be arranged in a number of ways, for instance so that the keys normally used for the notes E_2, $F_2^\#$ and $G_2^\#$ actually sound C_2, D_2 and E_2.

Fig. 7.4. Close-up view of a clavichord showing one of the tangents in the striking position with the key depressed.

The vibrations from the string are transferred to the soundboard by means of a bridge in much the same way as in the violin. The soundboard is generally the top plate of a sound box in which there is an opening known as the window. The frequency of the Helmholz resonance can be adjusted by altering the size of this opening.

The sound from a clavichord is very soft compared with that of the harpsichord or piano, primarily because the strings are very light and low tensioned compared with those of the harpsichord or piano and are struck at nodal positions. Furthermore, the soundboard is small, so its amplifying effect is not very great. However, the disadvantage of small volume is offset by the degree of control which the player can achieve. By altering the key pressure in a vibratory manner, the string tension and hence the pitch can be varied in a form of oscillation similar to the vibrato on a violin. This is referred to by the German term *Bebung* (shaking). The player can also produce fine tonal shades and nuances.

Because of the direct finger control that the player has, the clavichord is particularly well suited to music of a contrapuntal nature. It was a favourite instrument of J.S. Bach and is particularly well suited to the 48 Preludes and Fugues, which can mostly be played on a fretted instrument. The clarity of the sound and the variations of tone colour that can be achieved allow the player to define the different voices with a distinctness that is not possible on the piano.

HARPSICHORD FAMILY

The harpsichord family of instruments (Fig. 7.5) came into prominence at about the same time as the clavichord and they were the favourite stringed keyboard instruments from the beginning of the 16th to the middle of the 18th century.

(a)

Fig. 7.5. Instruments of the harpsichord family from the Edinburgh University Russell Collection: (a) Andreas Ruckers the Elder double manual harpsichord made in Antwerp, 1608, Russell Coll. No.3; (b) Stephen Keene virginal made in London, 1668, Russell Coll. No.8; (c) two views of a spinet made by John Harrison in London, 1757, Russell Coll. No.13.

(b)

(c)

The *virginal* (or virginals) is the earliest and simplest form of harpsichord, with only one string to a note. It is oblong in shape, with the strings running parallel to the keyboard, and it is generally placed on a table, although some virginals rest on a four-legged frame.

The *spinet* resembles the virginals in having only one string to a note but differs in that it is wing-shaped rather than rectangular. The shape roughly follows the varying length of the strings which run at an angle of approximately 45° to the keyboard. This shape permits the use of longer bass strings. The instrument generally stands on legs and resembles the cottage grand piano. The spinet was in use from the late 17th century to the end of the 18th century, when many were made in America.

The harpsichord proper is a more elaborate version of the virginal and spinet. It has two, three or four complete sets of strings operated by separate sets of jacks which are brought into action by means of pedals or hand or knee stops. Where there are two sets of strings these are generally tuned in unison and are described as the eight foot register. Where there are four sets of strings, one is usually tuned an octave higher (four foot register). When brought into action, this adds brilliance to the sound, although the separate pitch is not consciously detected. The reason for this is that the frequencies of the partials for the upper string are simple multiples of twice the fundamental frequency for the lower string, i.e. they just serve to reinforce the even harmonics. Some rare instruments have a separate set of strings tuned two octaves above (two foot register) or an octave below (sixteen foot register). In this case the ear can detect the lower octaves, although the volume of the added strings is small so that they blend in with the eight foot register. Most harpsichords have two manuals, permitting one to play different registers with the left and right hands. Harpsichords frequently have various optional devices for tone colouring, e.g. the strings might be plucked close to one end (*lute stop*). This gives the tone brilliance by introducing more high harmonics. The *harp* or *buff stops* introduce felt or leather pads to dampen the strings.

Fig. 7.5 shows for comparison a harpsichord, a virginal and a spinet from the Edinburgh University collection. Two views are shown of the spinet so that the winged shape can be seen.

Principles of operation

The main components of the harpsichord action are shown in Fig. 7.6. The strings of a harpsichord (or virginal or spinet) are plucked by a *quill* or alternatively a plectrum made of leather. This is carried sideways on an upright *jack* which is raised by a pivoted lever operated at the other end by the key. When the key is released the jack falls back, bringing a small piece of felt into contact with the string to dampen it. The quill mounting has an escapement mechanism so that it bypasses the string when the jack falls and does not therefore repluck it. Fig. 7.7 shows close-up views of the

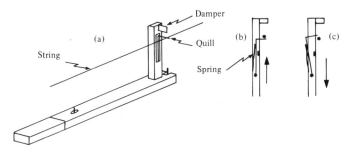

Fig. 7.6. Principle of the harpsichord action: (a) shows the lever mechanism which moves the key upwards when the key is depressed, (b) shows the jack at the moment just before plucking, (c) shows the escapement mechanism which allows the key to be released without the string being replucked.

actions on a harpsichord and a virginal for comparison. The actions are essentially the same, the main difference being that on the virginal there is only one string per note.

The volume of individual notes cannot be substantially altered by a change in touch, although small variations are possible by employing a more or less aggressive finger attack. Groups of notes, however, can be made louder or softer by adding or withdrawing stops or changing manual. The two manuals of the larger harpsichords, which were originally intended to facilitate transposition or performance at different pitch standards (the manuals were out of alignment by a fourth), provide the dynamic contrast required in later baroque music for echo and concertino passages and the accompaniment of solos. In most models the jacks are mounted on horizontal slides which move the quills either a little closer or a little further from the strings. In the closer position the quill plucks more sharply and produces a louder sound.

The strings on a harpsichord are generally made of steel but are much thinner than on a piano, typically ⅓ mm in diameter for the A_4 string as compared to 1 mm for the piano. String tensions are also correspondingly less, typically 40N as compared to 650N on a piano. Their vibrations are transmitted to the soundboard by a bridge, as on the piano, but the soundboard is flat and thinner than the piano one, to match the thinner strings. More will be said about this in the section on impedance matching in connection with the piano. The soundboard is enclosed in the case of the instrument and has a thickness of about 3 mm, although on later instruments it tapers from 4 mm in the bass to 2 mm in the treble.

One of the most important characteristics of the sound from the keyboard stringed instruments is the decay rate. When a string has been plucked its vibrations decay because of energy transfer to the soundboard, sound radiation from the string, internal friction, and air damping due to viscosity (Fletcher 1977 (a)). In the case of very thin strings as on the

(a)

(b)

Fig. 7.7. The action of (a) a harpsichord and (b) a virginal showing one of the keys depressed just after the strings have been plucked.

harpsichord, it is known that air damping is the dominant factor. With air damping the higher modes die away more quickly than the lower ones, which leads to a change in tone colour as the note rings on. Harpsichord strings tend to have a rapid decay, and the instrument has often been criticised for its rather poor sustaining power.

Perhaps the major drawback with the harpsichord and the ultimate reason for its defeat by the piano was that the player had little control over dynamics. Various devices were thought up by ingenious harpsichord makers in attempts to overcome this problem but none was really successful. One such invention was the Venetian swell, which allowed the player to open or close a series of flaps operated by a pedal mechanism and so alter the overall volume. The principle was similar to that of the Venetian blind and is used in the swell box of pipe organs. Another reason for the instrument's decline was that retuning was frequently required, as often as once a week for a domestic instrument, and quills needed frequent replacement.

THE PIANO

The problems of dynamics and quill replacement, and to a certain extent that of tuning, were overcome in the piano. The pianoforte was invented by Bartolommeo Cristofori, a Florentine harpsichord maker, about 1709. Early pianos are often referred to by the Italian name *fortepiano*, this name still being used in Russia for the modern instrument. These early pianos had wooden frames and thin light strings made of brass or soft iron. Cristofori's mechanism contained the main features of the modern piano action, having both *dampers* and an *escapement*, which allows a hammer to rebound immediately after striking the string, thus leaving it free to vibrate.

The piano developed along different lines in Vienna and England, the Viennese pianos having a lighter touch and less sonorous tone. In France, Sébastien Erard developed the English design (after working in London for some time) and over the period 1809–1823 introduced the *double escapement* mechanism. This allows for rapid repetition of notes and is the basis for the piano action as we know it today. Iron frames were introduced in America about 1825, allowing much greater string tensions. Overstringing was introduced about 1835.

Action

In a piano action the hammer is thrown against the string by a lever mechanism and immediately rebounds. In the Viennese design the hammer is mounted on the key itself. This system fell into disuse about 1860. Fig. 7.8 (a) is a schematic diagram of how the mechanism works and Fig. 7.8 (b) is a photograph of one key which has been removed from a

Viennese piano made in 1820. The action of the English design is shown in Fig. 7.9. In this case the hammer is mounted on a pivot which is attached to the frame rather than the key. Once the hammer has rebounded, the back check prevents further rebounds. The modern piano action is in essence the same as this but includes the double escapement. A diagram has not been included because of the complicated nature of the mechanism, but the interested reader may refer to *The New Oxford Companion to Music* (1983). The action of the upright piano is shown in much simplified form in Fig. 7.10. There are two springs, the damper and hammer springs, which need careful setting. These are needed because the hammer and damper do not have the restoring force of gravity as in the grand. For this reason the action of the upright piano is generally considered to be inferior to that of the grand.

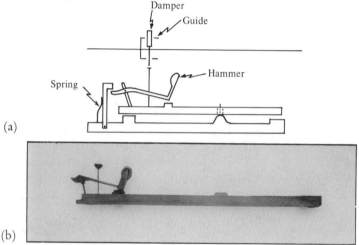

(a)

(b)

Fig. 7.8. Action of the Viennese piano: (a) schematic diagram of the mechanism; (b) a single key removed from an instrument made in 1820.

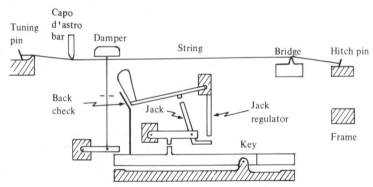

Fig. 7.9. Simplified grand piano action.

Note that in the case of the piano, the hammer is not in contact with the key when the string is struck. For a single note the tone can only be altered by changing the speed at which the hammer strikes the string (depressing the key harder or softer) and by the way in which the damper is lowered, i.e. by the speed of key release (this affects the finishing transient).

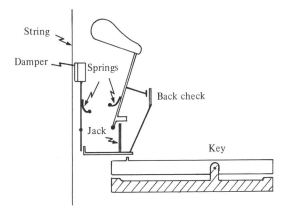

Fig. 7.10. Simplified upright piano action.

Soundboard

The seven and a quarter octave range of the full size piano places severe demands on the acoustical characteristics of a soundboard (Bilhuber and Johnson 1940). The ideal soundboard would have a reasonably flat response over this range, although in practice almost any type of board will discriminate against the higher frequencies. Piano makers over the ages have experimented with almost every conceivable material and device in search for the ideal characteristics. Materials which have been tried include a variety of woods, metals, parchments and plywoods. Separate soundboards for treble and bass have been used, as have double sound-boards and various types of resonator boxes. None of these, however, gives better characteristics than the rather simple soundboard design which is used on the modern piano. This is generally made of laminated spruce, is slightly convex in shape, and is ribbed underneath. Since it is curved upwards, it acts as a spring to withstand the great downward forces of the strings, in contrast to the harpsichord, in which it is a flat plate. The ribs run across the grain on the underside, which has the effect of making the stiffness approximately constant in the grainwise and crosswise direc-tion. The soundboard itself is about 10 mm in thickness, much thicker than on the harpsichord, and is generally tapered to be thinner at the bass end. Notice that the taper is made in the opposite sense to the harpsichord in order to achieve a correct impedance match with the strings. This point will be discussed later in the chapter. Both sides of the soundboard are active in communicating vibrations to the air and because of this the sound quality and volume change significantly when the lid is raised or lowered.

Like the soundboard on a harp or the top plate on a guitar or violin, the resonance characteristics of a piano soundboard are determined by the complex patterns associated with each mode of vibration. The frequency response curve associated with each mode is fairly broad, i.e. each mode can be excited by a broad range of frequencies. These overlap to give an overall response characteristic which is fairly flat over the range of playing frequencies. Any sharp peaks are undesirable since they would lead to preferential amplification of the sound on certain notes.

Vibrations from the strings are transferred to the soundboard by means of a bridge. On overstrung pianos the strings run at two different levels, the longer bass strings being above the shorter treble strings. The two sets have their own bridges, the bass bridge and the treble bridge. This system has a dual advantage. Firstly it allows the maker to use longer string lengths for a given size of case, and secondly it places the bridges more centrally on the soundboard and so enhances its resonance characteristics. The positions of the bridges can be seen in Fig. 7.11, which pictures a Bösendorfer concert grand from above.

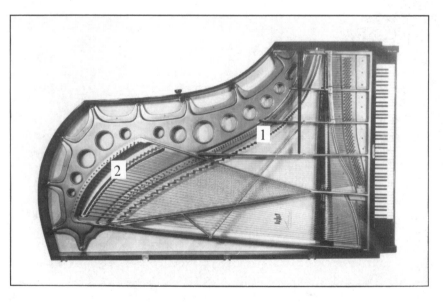

Fig. 7.11. A Bösendorfer concert grand pictured from above showing (1) the treble bridge and (2) the bass bridge.

The tension in a piano string is extremely high; e.g., for C_4 it is approximately 650 Newtons (this tension would be produced by hanging a mass of 65 kg on the end of a string). Because of the manner in which the strings are stretched over the bridge, as shown in Fig. 7.9, the tensions all contribute to produce a *downbearing* force on the soundboard. The magnitude of this downbearing depends primarily on the acuteness of angle of the short length of string between the bridge and the hitch pin. The greater the angle between the string and the soundboard, the greater the force. The downbearing force has the effect of reducing the curvature of the arched soundboard and this in turn alters its elasticity and resonance characteristics. The amount of downbearing on different parts of the bridge can be adjusted by raising or lowering the iron frame to which the ends of the strings are anchored. This is an important factor in the final regulation of the instrument.

Pianos do not generally improve in tone quality with age as do violins, for example. Apart from the problems of wear on the intricate mechanism, this is due to the fact that the great downbearing force of the strings tends to flatten the soundboard over a long period of time, thus causing its resonance characteristics to deteriorate.

Hammers

The wooden hammers on a piano are covered with felt, which is a mixture of wool, silk and hair. The hammers in the treble are harder and thinner than those used in the bass and smaller in overall size. The piano can be *voiced* by needling and ironing the hammers, sometimes after reshaping them with sandpaper. The position at which a hammer strikes the string affects the tone quality significantly, but other important factors are the width and hardness of the hammer and its contact time.

The optimum striking position for a hammer has been found to lie between one seventh and one eighth of the way along the string. We saw with the guitar that optimum excitation of any particular mode occurs when the string is plucked at an antinode. If a nodal point for any particular mode coincides with the plucking point, then it will not be excited. This is often put forward as an explanation for choosing the piano striking position to be what it is. Since the frequency of the seventh normal mode is very much out of tune with the minor seventh on the equally tempered scale it would seem advantageous to suppress this. The first node in this vibrational mode occurs at one seventh of the string length from the end and therefore corresponds approximately with the striking position. In the case of a piano string, however, the problem is complicated by the finite contact time of the hammer with the string. This is long enough to allow standing waves to be set up in the short length of string between the hammer and the capo d'astro bar and to propagate along the whole string length when the hammer has left contact. Assuming the striking distance is exactly one seventh from the end, the frequencies of these standing waves form their own harmonic series and are seven times those which are eventually set up on the complete string length. Since the missing modes caused by striking at a nodal point are the 7th, 14th etc., it is seen that these will all be replaced. In other words, the hammer strikes in such a way that all the normal modes will be present. The magnitude of these vibrations can, however, be varied. Increasing the hammer contact time has the effect of damping the higher modes. The contact time is normally about equal to half a wave period of the fundamental frequency for the note C_4. Increasing the hammer mass has the effect of increasing its contact time, since it is not so quickly thrown off by the spring-like action of the string.

The shape and hardness of the hammer affect the tone quality. If the length of the hammer in contact with the string at the end of the blow exceeds the wavelength of any particular mode, then this mode will not be excited to any significant extent. Thus smaller, sharper hammers produce a tone which is richer in upper partials. In a similar way soft hammers do not excite upper partials to the same degree as hard hammers. Hammers tend to harden with use because of the compression of the felt and eventually will have to be needled in order to restore the tone. In fortissimo playing there is a momentary hardening of the hammer through compression and a corresponding strengthening of upper partials. In pianissimo playing the upper partials tend to be weaker.

Strings

The strings on a modern piano are made from high tensile steel, which allows for increased tension and greater volume than in the old fortepiano. In the middle and upper registers (B_2 to C_8) there are generally three strings per note. In the range $B^\flat$ to $B^\flat$ two springs per note are used and these are overwound with copper in order to increase their mass per unit length. Single overwound strings are used in the lowest register A_0 to A_1.

As with the harp, the string lengths are not increased by a factor 2 for each octave, although in the piano the stringing factor is very much closer to 2, usually about 1.9. The optimum length for the C_4 string is generally considered to be between 60 and 65 cm, giving the highest C_8 string a length close to 5 cm. The string diameters increase by a factor 1.05 per octave towards the bass, matched by a corresponding increase in tension. These stringing rules are modified in the bass register by the overwinding in order to keep the string lengths within practical limits. On a concert grand the lowest string has a length of about 2 metres, less than half that which would be predicted by the scaling rule.

In the idealised model of a vibrating string described in Chapter 5 it was seen that the frequencies of the normal modes were simple multiples of the fundamental. The model used for these calculations assumed that the string was completely flexible, whereas in reality any string possesses some stiffness. The effect of stiffness is particularly important in the piano, where highly tensioned thick strings are used. Such a string vibrates in modes which closely resemble those of the perfectly flexible string but also have some characteristics of the modes for a vibrating bar (Fletcher 1964; Schuck and Young 1943). The result is a progressive sharpening of the partials as the mode number increases, the extent of the sharpening being dependent on the ratio of the string diameter to its length (Shankland and Coltman 1939). The greater this ratio, the greater will be the sharpening. Typically the frequency of the tenth normal mode for the F_1 string on a grand piano would be one third of a semitone sharp and the twentieth mode a whole tone sharp. A small amount of inharmonicity may be considered desirable since it is one of the factors which gives the piano its characteristic sound. It also has the effect of covering imperfections in the tuning of certain intervals caused by the temperament. On the other hand, if the degree of inharmonicity is too great, the pitch of the note becomes less well defined and the sound quality is spoilt. This is particularly noticeable in the bass and is one of the primary factors which makes the sound of the concert grand so much better than the shorter domestic size instrument. On the bass strings the effect of inharmonicity is partly overcome by overwinding. This increases the mass per unit length without dramatically increasing the stiffness. In the mid-range and treble the technique is not really effective because the thin cores of overwound strings could not sustain the required tensions. For the very shortest treble strings the upper partials are extremely sharp, but the hammer and felt used are such that only a few of these are excited. In any case the upper partials lie beyond the audible range.

Multiple stringing (three strings per note over most of the range) is used to increase the volume on the piano (Weinreich 1977 and 1979). The same effect could not be produced by a single string since this would need to be of much larger diameter, which would lead to an unacceptable sharpening of the partials. Each of the three strings has to be tuned separately and it is generally agreed that the most acceptable sound occurs when there is a small degree of mistuning between the strings (Kirk 1959). One to two cents maximum deviation within the strings of any one note is the preferred amount. If the strings are tuned too close, then the sound is dead and also dies away too rapidly. This is because three precisely tuned strings will vibrate in phase, and transfer their energy more rapidly to the soundboard. When the strings are slightly detuned they will initially vibrate in phase and the decay rate will be rapid. After a short time, however, the coherence will be lost and they will vibrate independently, with the decreased decay rate that a single string would have. Piano notes thus exhibit dual decay rates, particularly in the middle register (Hundley et al. 1978; Martin 1947). Fig. 7.12 shows a typical decay curve for C_4

played on a grand piano. There are two easily identifiable slopes indicated by the dotted lines, but in the final part of the decay the curve fluctuates above and below the dotted line, i.e. there is a type of slow vibrato effect (see also Fig. 1.7(b)). This is caused partly by beating between the three strings but also partly by the fact that the plane of vibration of each string rotates as the sound dies away. In this case the two decay rates were measured to be 3.1 dB/s and 18 dB/s. These values are typical of most instruments. For notes above F_5 the two decay rates become indistinguishable and there is only a single slope to the decay curve. From bass to treble there is a general increase in overall decay rate, this being approximately proportional to the frequency of the note in the upper register.

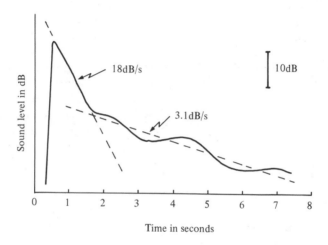

Fig. 7.12. Decay curve for the note C_4 on a grand piano. The initial decay rate is 18 dB/s and the final decay rate 3.1 dB/s.

Impedance matching

The rate at which energy is transferred from the strings to the soundboard is determined by the relative magnitudes of their impedances. In talking about the soundboard we are thinking of the board, the bracing and the bridges as a single unit. This is justified because their impedances are similar, so they essentially vibrate as a single unit. The impedance of the strings is very much smaller than that of the soundboard, so their vibrations are not significantly affected by it. The closer the matching of the string and soundboard impedances, the more rapid will be the transfer of energy from one to the other. If the soundboard impedance were very high, then the energy would be transferred very slowly, so one would hear a sound of small volume but this would be sustained for a long time. This would be the case if the soundboard were made from a very heavy material. A similar situation occurs in electric pianos, where there is no soundboard. These have decay rates significantly less than those of acoustic pianos. In this situation energy loss from the strings is primarily through air damping and internal friction losses. If the soundboard impedance is very low, then the matching with the strings is improved and the sound output level is higher. However, this is accompanied by an increased decay rate, so in an extreme case the note sounds rather like a loud thud. The piano maker has to adjust the impedances so that the most acceptable compromise between these two situations is achieved, taking into account the manner in which the ear responds to sounds of different duration.

In the treble range of the piano the sustaining power is very poor, so much so that the dampers are not employed for the notes above $F_6^\#$. In order to compensate for this the soundboard impedance is increased at the upper end by making it thicker and also by reducing the length of string between bridge and hitch pin to strengthen the downbearing force. At the changeover point from plain to overwound strings the designer has to ensure that there is no sudden change in tone quality, particularly as regards decay times. The wire-wound strings have an impedance which is considerably greater than the plain ones, so this is offset by mounting them on their own separate bass bridge, which is heavier than the treble bridge.

Spectrum structure

In the lower ranges of the piano a large number of partials play a significant role in the sound production, twenty or thirty peaks showing appreciable heights in a spectral analysis (Blackham 1965). For the very lowest notes, however, the fundamental tends to be rather weak and this is accentuated by the poor response of the ear at these frequencies. The number of partials gradually decreases as one proceeds higher in the instrument's compass, and in the C_5 range only about five partials show visible peaks. For the highest note, C_8, only the fundamental and second normal mode frequencies are significant. Once the initial tone has been produced the partials do not decay at the same rate, the mid-range partials generally persisting for longer than the highest and lowest ones. The very highest partials are damped rapidly because of the increased effect of air damping at these frequencies. The lowest partials have an accentuated decay rate because with multiple stringing the vibrations of the different strings remain in phase for longer periods at low frequencies. This effect is accentuated by the fact that the ear is less sensitive at low frequencies, so the tones die more quickly to levels below the threshold of hearing. The result of all this is that there is an audible change in tone quality with the decay of the note, particularly in the middle and low register where the dual decay rate is more pronounced. Another interesting effect is that the listener is often aware of a rise in pitch as the tone rings on. This arises because the partials which persist for the longest time have frequencies which are progressively higher relative to the true harmonics of the fundamental and the listener uses these to judge the instantaneous pitch of the note.

In addition to the discrete frequency components so far discussed, there are other more diffuse sounds which form an important contribution to the overall effect produced by the pianist and characterise both the instrument itself and the touch employed. When the hammer initially strikes the string, an impulse is transmitted through the bridge to the soundboard and also to the frame via the capo d'astro bar. This is in the form of a percussive thud rather than being a series of discrete pitches. Another important contribution is the sound produced by the fingers striking the surface of the key, known as *upper key noise*, in contrast to lower key noise which is the less important contribution introduced by the key striking the bed when it is at the end of its travel. Upper key noise can be used to advantage by the pianist in accentuating the articulation of staccato passages. In cantabile playing upper key noise is not present since the finger, usually the fleshy surface, is gradually brought down on to the key surface, rather than striking it.

It is important for the pianist to realize that, as a result of the way the mechanism catapults the hammer towards the strings, he has no control over its motion at the crucial instant when it strikes the strings. This is in contrast to the clavichord, where the tangent and key are both an integral part of the same lever mechanism. This point has led to confusion over many years about the way in which the pianist can produce a more or less beautiful sound. Teachers frequently use terminology such as hard tone or singing tone and these phrases seem to imply that the tone as well as the volume can be altered by the manner in which the key is depressed. This is not in fact the case, except that upper key noise and the manner in which the key is released are important. The key release determines the manner in which the damper is lowered on to the string and hence the finishing transient. The accomplished pianist produces a beautiful sound by skilfully judging the relative timing and volume of the different notes, i.e. sequences of notes and notes within a chord. On the playing of a single note a listener could not differentiate the sound produced by a beginner from that of a virtuoso pianist. This is one important way in which technique on the piano differs in principle from, say, the flute or violin. On the flute, for example, a great deal of effort can go into improving the tone quality on a single note.

Pedals

Pianos have either two or three pedals. The left pedal is called the *una corda.* On a grand piano this moves the keyboard and action to the right, so that two instead of three strings are struck. In the bass, where there is only one string per note, the sound is still softened because the hammers strike with a softer, less worn part of the felt. On upright pianos one of two actions may occur: either a piece of thick felt called a *céleste* is raised against the strings, slightly damping them, or the hammers are moved nearer to the strings, decreasing the striking distance; the latter is called the *half blow*.

When depressed, the right hand *sustaining pedal* raises the dampers from the strings, allowing them to vibrate freely. As well as sustaining the notes, the pedal alters the tone quality since it allows the strings which are not struck to vibrate in sympathy. The sympathetic vibration occurs because there is a weak coupling between strings both through the bridge and the air. The fact that vibrations are transmitted to the strings through the air can be demonstrated by depressing the sustaining pedal with the piano lid open. If you sing a note loudly in close proximity to the piano, then the vibrations will be picked up by the strings and these will be heard quite clearly when the voice has stopped. Since there are no dampers on the uppermost notes, these strings will always give sympathetic vibrations when a note is played, although their contribution to the overall sound level is very small. When these upper notes are played, application of the sustaining pedal has a marked effect, even though they have no dampers, because the sympathetic vibrations of the lower strings are very strong. Using this pedal the pianist can effect subtle shades of tone colouring as well as sustaining notes, so much so that the sustaining pedal is sometimes called the soul of the piano.

Perhaps the most common mode of application of the pedal is that which is referred to as *legato pedalling*, where the primary object is to maintain a legato line through a series of notes or chords. Here the pedal must be changed on each new note or on each new harmonic progression, depending on the situation. This involves lowering the dampers for a short instant of time when the new note is played in order to damp out the previous sounds. Precise timing is required here to avoid overlaps or gaps between successive notes. In this situation the time required for damping a note is important. In the low register the energy of the heavier and longer string is great, so the time required to damp its vibrations is relatively long compared with that needed for strings in the upper register. This is despite the fact that the dampers are made larger and more massive in the bass. This variation of damping time from bass to treble can be used to advantage in the technique of *half pedalling*. This is used by the pianist when he wants to sustain a bass accompaniment against a more rapidly varying melody line in the treble. A well-known piece where this is often employed is the D♭ Consolation of Liszt. The legato pedalling technique is used for the melody line, but each lowering of the dampers is for only a very short instant of time. This is sufficient to dampen the treble notes but allows the bass notes to ring on.

The central pedal is termed the *sostenuto* pedal. When depressed after a note or chord has been struck, it will catch the dampers that have already been raised, thus sustaining these notes and leaving the player free to use the sustaining pedal on other notes. This obviates the need for half pedalling.

Fig. 7.13. The first four bars of Bartók's 'Harmonics' from his 'Mikrokosmos', vol. IV.

Some composers have used the phenomenon of sympathetic vibrations as a compositional tool. An example is the piece 'Harmonics' in Bartók's 'Mikrokosmos', vol. IV. The first four bars are shown in Fig. 7.13. The notes shown as diamonds are first depressed silently with the left hand and then the right hand vigorously strikes the second chord before playing the melody. Striking the chord initiates vibrations in the B_3, $D_4^{\#}$ and $F_4^{\#}$ strings since their dampers are raised. These sounds form the bakground accompaniment to the legato melody line. The harmonic structure of this background can be studied at the piano by considering the different notes in turn as follows:

(1) Hold B_3 silent. Strike B_2 (staccatissimo). B_3 will sound because its fundamental is the second harmonic of B_2.

(2) Hold $D_4^{\#}$, silent. Strike B_2. $D_4^{\#}$ does not sound, but its second harmonic does because it is the 5th harmonic of B_2.

(3) Hold $F_4^{\#}$ silent. Strike B_2. $F_4^{\#}$ sounds as it is the 3rd harmonic of B_2.

Repeat 1, 2 and 3 striking $D_3^{\#}$ and $F_3^{\#}$ with the right hand.

TUNING KEYBOARD INSTRUMENTS

Because the pitches of the notes are fixed, conventional keyboard instruments must be tuned to a tempered scale. The reasons for this were discussed in detail in Chapter 4. Tuners generally begin by setting the pitch of one note against a tuning fork, adjusting the tension until beats disappear. The pitches of the other notes are then tuned relative to this by listening for beat rates between the partials. Normally one complete octave is tuned using the intervals of a 4th, a 5th and the octave, and then this is used as the basis for obtaining the pitches in the other registers. Tuning this first octave is known as *laying the bearings*. During the complete process there is a continuous sequence of checks using the major thirds and sometimes the major sixths.

Difference tones can also be used to measure the relative pitches of two notes, but these are difficult to detect on stringed keyboard instruments because of the large number of partials present and the short duration of the notes. However, they do affect the overall sound quality produced when a pair of notes is struck simultaneously and this is a useful guide in tuning. Difference tones are most noticeable when the notes are in the high register.

Practical considerations in tuning

Where there is more than one string for a particular note, each string is generally tuned separately. The strings that are not being tuned are damped by the insertion of a felt wedge between them. When one string has been correctly tuned, the others are brought into pitch, but not necessarily to precisely the same frequency since, as we mentioned earlier in the chapter, this tends to lead to a rather dead sound. Beat rates can be measured using a metronome, although the experienced tuner will have learned to recognise beat rates for the most important intervals without any mechanical aids. The appropriate metronome marking is found by multiplying the beat rate in Hz by 60. Slow rates are sometimes difficult to detect accurately. For this purpose the metronome can be set at twice the beat rate and every other pulse made to coincide with a beat. For beat rates exceeding the highest metronome setting of 208, every second beat or possibly every third or fourth can be made to coincide with a metronome pulse. However, very high pulse rates are difficult to gauge against a metronome.

In tuning an interval, one note is assumed correct and the pitch of the other note is adjusted until the beat rate between selected partials is correct for the particular separation of frequencies required. The beat rate, however, does not tell you if the partial of the note under adjustment is high or low compared with that of the note whose frequency is fixed. For example, frequencies of either 99 Hz or 101 Hz will beat at a rate of 1 Hz with a frequency of 100 Hz. To overcome this ambiguity the two frequencies are normally first adjusted for zero beat rate and then the pitch of the string being tuned is brought either up or down as required until the correct beat rate is reached. The order in which the notes are tuned is important here and this can sometimes be arranged so that all of the adjustments are in the same direction, to save confusion.

The clavichord poses its own special problems in tuning since the pressure applied to the key affects the pitch. The higher the pressure, the higher the pitch. When tuning a note the key must be held depressed with approximately the normal playing pressure. This makes precise tuning of the clavichord more difficult than that of the piano or harpsichord. In performance, however, any slight discrepancies tend to be hidden by the pitch variations which occur in the playing process.

There are many electronic tuners on the market and it is possible in theory to tune an instrument entirely by checking the pitch of each string using one of these devices. In practice this process is more difficult than it might appear, for a number of reasons. Firstly, the electronic tuner responds to absolute frequency rather than the frequency differences associated with intervals and even the tiniest percentage deviation in this frequency will spoil the sound of intervals using the note. Secondly, the exact frequency at which each string should be set depends on many factors which are dependent on the mechanics of the particular instrument being tuned. We have already seen, for example, that where there are three strings these should not be set to precisely the same pitch. Another important factor that will be discussed shortly is that of octave stretching.

Tuning intervals

The basic intervals which are used in the tuning process, apart from the octave, are the perfect fifth, perfect fourth, major third and major sixth. We shall now see how the beat rates can be calculated for these intervals in the equal temperament scale. The procedure for calculating beat rates is precisely the same for other temperaments except that the required frequency ratios between the fundamentals for the four intervals will be different. We shall assume for the moment that all the frequencies of the normal modes of vibration of the strings are exact harmonics. The effect of small deviations from this due to string stiffness will be considered later.

For simplicity of explanation we shall assume that the lower note is always C_4 and that this has been set correctly to the frequency 261.63 Hz, which corresponds to $A_4 = 440$ in equal temperament. The C_4 strings are set by adjusting for zero beats with a tuning fork. The problem then is to tune a note which is either a third, fourth, fifth or sixth above the C_4. The notes in question together with their first few harmonics are shown in Fig. 7.14. For the perfect fifth (Fig. 7.14 (a)) the note to be tuned is G_4 and the frequency ratio for a perfect fifth in equal temperament is $2^{7/12} = 1.4983$, i.e. G_4 should be set to the frequency $261.63 \times 1.4983 = 392.00$ Hz. The fundamental of the note being tuned is far from any harmonic of C_4 so there will be no beating at this frequency. However, the second harmonic of G_4 is G_5, coinciding approximately with the third harmonic of C_4, so there will be a beating at this level. There will also be beating between higher harmonics, but this will be less distinct since the amplitudes will be smaller. The frequency of the third harmonic of C_4 (261.63 Hz) is $3 \times$

261.63 = 784.89 Hz and the frequency of the second harmonic of G_4 (392.00 Hz) is 2 × 392.00 = 784.00 Hz. This gives a beat frequency of 784.89 − 784.00 = 0.89 Hz, which corresponds approximately to a metronome setting of 54. The second harmonic of the note being tuned is the lower of the two frequencies, so the procedure will be that the string is first adjusted for zero beating and is then slackened until the 0.89 Hz beat rate is heard.

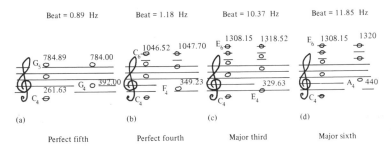

Fig. 7.14 The four most important intervals used in tuning: (a) the perfect fifth; (b) the perfect fourth; (c) the major third; and (d) the major sixth. The lower note of each interval is C_4 and the upper note of the interval is tuned relative to this in equal temperament. The notes above are the harmonics and the frequencies are given at the pitch where beating occurs.

For the perfect fourth the procedure is similar. A perfect fourth above C_4 is F_4 (Fig. 7.14 (b)) and the first coincidence between harmonics occurs at C_6. The correct frequency for F_4 is 261.63 × $2^{5/12}$ = 349.23 Hz and its third harmonic is 3 × 349.23 = 1047.70 Hz. This is slightly higher than the fourth harmonic of C_4, which is 261.63 × 4 = 1046.52 Hz, the beat frequency being 1047.70 − 1046.52 = 1.18 Hz, corresponding to a metronome setting of 69. In this case the note should first be adjusted for zero beats and then raised in pitch until the 1.18 Hz beat rate is achieved.

In the case of the major third the first coincidence of harmonics is at E_6 (Fig. 7.14 (c)) where the fifth harmonic of C_4 has a frequency of 1308.15 Hz and the fourth harmonic of E_4 has the higher frequency of 329.63 × 4 = 1318.52 Hz, giving a beat rate of 10.37 Hz. For the major sixth coincidence also occurs at E_6 (Fig. 7.14 (d)), the frequency of the third harmonic of A_4 being 440 × 3 = 1320 Hz. This gives a beat rate of 11.85 Hz. For both the major third and the major sixth the beat rates exceed the fastest metronome setting of 208. The keen ear can gauge this against a subdivision of the calculated metronome markings of 60 × 10.37 = 622 for the major third and 60 × 11.85 = 711 for the major sixth. However, these high beat rates can be gauged quite accurately by the experienced tuner without a metronome. The overall sound of a correctly tuned major third or major sixth has a shimmering quality which is quite distinctive.

The beat frequencies given here only apply when C_4 is the lower note. If the interval is in a different part of the keyboard then the beat frequency will be correspondingly altered in proportion to the frequency of the lower note; e.g., the beat frequency for the major third G_3 to B_3 would be $10.37 \times 0.75 = 7.78$ Hz, since the interval is a perfect fourth lower than C_4 to E_4.

Laying the bearings

In laying the bearings one complete octave is tuned somewhere near the centre of the keyboard. We shall assume that the octave chosen is G_3 to G_4 and that C_4 has been correctly tuned to a tuning fork. The other notes within the octave are then tuned relative to C_4 using intervals of fourths, fifths and the octave. The notes are tuned in the order of the circle of fifths, i.e. starting from C, G is tuned first, then D, A, E etc. The notes being tuned are kept within the compass of the octave by using fourths as well as fifths, the fifths being upwards and the fourths downwards. The adjustment relative to the zero beat frequency pitch is always downwards since equal temperament fifths are narrow and fourths wide. In addition to tuning the fourths and fifths, checks are made on some major thirds and possibly on major sixths.

A typical scheme for the order of tuning and suitable checks is given in Fig. 7.15. Starting from C_4 the two Gs are tuned and then the fifth above the lower one and so on. When the E has been tuned it is possible to check this against the original C. If this is not correct, then the first steps must be repeated before proceeding further. The beat rates and the pitches at which beating occurs for the different intervals are shown opposite:

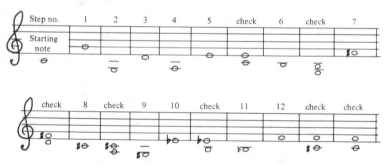

Fig. 7.15. A typical tuning sequence for laying the bearings with a number of checks.

In equal temperament the enharmonically equivalent sharps are flats have the same pitch, so in step 10 for example the interval $F_4^{\#}$ to $E_4^{\flat}$ can be considered as a perfect fifth for the purpose of calculating the beat rate. All of the checks listed, apart from the last, are using major thirds, which have very high beat rates in equal temperament. In practice the notes of these intervals can be tuned down an octave before checking, so that the beat rates are halved.

TABLE 7.1

Step no.	Interval	Pitch at which beating occurs	Beat rate in Hz
1	C_4–G_4	G_5	0.89
2	G_4–G_3	No beat	
3	G_3–D_4	D_5	0.67
4	D_4–A_3	A_5	1.00
5	A_3–E_4	E_5	0.75
Check	C_4–E_4	E_6	10.37
6	E_4–B_3	B_5	1.12
Check	G_3–B_3	B_4	7.78
7	B_3–$F^\#_4$	$F^\#_5$	0.84
Check	D_4–$F^\#_4$	$F^\#_6$	11.64
8	$F^\#_4$–$C^\#_4$	$C^\#_5$	1.26
Check	A_3–$C^\#_4$	$C^\#_6$	8.72
9	$C^\#_4$–$G^\#_3$	$G^\#_5$	0.94
10	$G^\#_3$–$E^\flat_4$	$E^\flat_5$	0.71
Check	B_3–$E^\flat_4$	$E^\flat_6$	9.79
11	$E^\flat_4$–$B^\flat_3$	$B^\flat_5$	1.06
12	$B^\flat_3$–F_4	F_5	0.79
Check	$C^\#_4$–F_4	F_6	10.99
Check	C_4–F_4	F_6	1.18

It must be emphasised that the scheme just described for laying the bearings is only an outline scheme and there are many variations. Normally a professional tuner will use additional checks to the ones given, particularly using major sixths. Once the bearings have been laid, the remainder of the keyboard is tuned in octaves.

The procedure for tuning in other temperaments is similar. Detailed tables of beat rates for both equal temperament and a number of other temperaments are given in the books by Kellner (1980) and Fisher (1975).

Octave stretching

The tuning of a stringed keyboard instrument is based on matching the pitches of partials for notes at various intervals. We have already seen that these partials tend to be sharp compared with the true harmonics because of the stiffness in the strings. This is particularly so in the case of the piano, where thick highly tensioned strings are used. It follows from this that in a properly tuned instrument the notes will be progressively sharper in the treble compared with the frequencies calculated for a particular tempered scale (Schuck and Young 1943). Likewise in the bass the notes will become progressively flatter. This effect is known as octave stretching. The highest notes on a piano can be as much as 30 cents sharp and the lowest notes 30 cents flat. Fig. 7.16 shows a typical deviation across the keyboard range on a 158 cm grant piano. In this case the high notes are about 15 cents sharp and the low ones 15 cents flat. The stretching effect is usually most pronounced on smaller pianos since the short strings make the upper partials extremely sharp. On concert grands the effect is less marked because of the long strings.

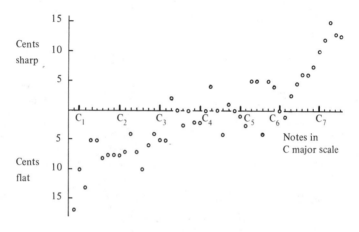

Fig. 7.16. Octave stretching on a 158 cm grand piano. The lowest notes are about 15 cents flat and the highest notes about 15 cents sharp compared to the calculated equal temperament pitches.

8

Woodwind instruments

The woodwinds are part of the aerophone class of instruments. There are two distinct types of woodwind, those where the resonance is excited by a mechanical reed and those where the excitation is by an air reed mechanism. Mechanical reeds can be either of the single type, as in the clarinet and saxophone, or the double, as in the oboe and bassoon. The air reed instruments are essentially the flutes, recorders and ocarinas.

The term woodwind is in fact something of a misnomer since it implies that the instrument is made of wood. Nowadays most flutes are made of metal and many clarinets are plastic. In fact plastic or metal can be used for many of the woodwinds with only second order effects on tone quality. Materials other than wood were also used for many of the early baroque flutes.

REED WOODWINDS

In the reed woodwinds the oscillations are excited by a reed which is clamped at one end and free to vibrate at the other. Reeds are generally made from a particular variety of cane which is mainly grown in France, although they can be of plastic. In the case of the single reed instruments the reed is clamped to a mouthpiece having a curved face such that there is a gap between the tip of the reed and the face which allows air to pass through into the bore of the instrument to which the mouthpiece is attached. In the double reed instruments the two pieces of cane are attached to each other so that there is a gap between the two free ends. In either case the reed or reeds act as a form of valve which allows the high pressure air from the player's mouth to enter the instrument in a series of pulses which inject energy to initiate and maintain the oscillations within

259

the tube. The oscillations of the reed are strongly influenced by the oscillations within the air column, i.e. there is a strong coupling between them. This is in contrast to the reeds used in an accordion or reed organ where each reed vibrates essentially at its own natural frequency, separate reeds being used for each note. The woodwind reed always follows the pressure variations between the player's mouth and the mouthpiece cavity, provided that the oscillation frequencies are lower than its own natural resonant frequency. If the reed is blown without damping, however, then it can vibrate at its own resonant frequency and a high pitched squeak results.

The pressure in the player's mouth is relatively high compared with the pressure inside the mouthpiece and is approximately constant. Inside the mouthpiece, however, the pressure is oscillatory. Fig. 8.1 shows the cycle of events as the reed or pair of reeds oscillates throughout one cycle.

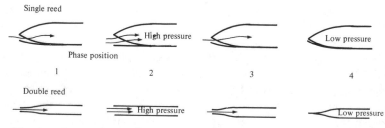

Fig. 8.1. One cycle in the oscillation of a reed. The top four sketches show the motion for a single reed attached to a mouthpiece and the lower four show the same cycle for a double reed.

At phase position 1 the reed is partially closed and there is a flow of air from the high pressure region of the player's mouth to the lower pressure in the tube. This lower pressure is approximately atmospheric. One quarter of a cycle later the pressure has risen to its maximum inside the mouthpiece, forcing the reed to its most open position and causing an increase in flow rate which feeds the pressure build-up. At phase position 3 the mouthpiece pressure has again dropped to atmospheric, causing a partial closure of the reed. In the last quarter of a cycle the pressure has fallen below atmospheric, causing the reed to close and the flow to be cut off. Notice that the puffs of air produced by the valve-like action of the reed come at phase positions which reinforce the pressure oscillations. At phase position 2 the high speed of flow over the reed causes a suction which assists in drawing the tip of the reed upwards. This is known as the *Bernoulli* effect and is particularly important in the double reed instruments.

Because a mechanical reed is pressure operated it will only function when the pressure fluctuations in the tube to which it is attached are a maximum at the reed end, i.e. the reed must be situated at a pressure antinode. From the point of view of determining standing wave patterns in a tube, fixing a reed to one end can be thought of as the same as terminating the tube by a closed end (Benade 1960 (a)).

In Fig. 8.1 the single reed is shown as closing the mouthpiece aperture completely in the last part of the cycle. This in fact only happens in fortissimo playing or when the embouchure is very tight. In the playing position the lower lip presses on the reed and forces it closer to the curved *facing* on the mouthpiece. If the embouchure is tight the reed is forced closer to the facing than it is with a loose embouchure. When the instrument is blown the reed vibrates about this mean position. In pianissimo playing the tip of the reed generally does not touch the face, so the airstream is never completely cut off. In fortissimo playing the amplitude of the reed oscillation is much greater and the tip of the reed remains in contact with the face for a significant part of the cycle. The reed motion is then less smooth, which encourages the formation of upper harmonics. With a double reed the upper harmonics also tend to be very strong and in addition there is a very characteristic starting transient.

The significance of resonances in the player's vocal tract in producing the sound has been a point of debate for many years. Clinch et al. (1982) conclude that in saxophone and clarinet playing the sound produced is highly dependent on the shape of the vocal tract and that the tract resonance should match the frequency of the note played. However, there are many varied opinions on this point (see pp. 287 and 325).

SHAWMS AND CRUMHORNS

The *shawm* and the *crumhorn* are both examples of double reed woodwinds which have not found a place in the modern orchestra but are used a good deal by early music enthusiasts.

The shawm is a double reed instrument with a conical bore and is the predecessor of the modern oboe. Fig. 8.2 shows two examples, one a European instrument and the other from China. In Europe the shawm was used extensively during the 14th to 17th centuries, mainly for playing outdoors at ceremonial occasions. In China the instrument is still used at theatrical performances, weddings and funerals. The reed is not held between the lips as with the oboe but is set in a type of holder known as a pirouette. The lips are pressed against the flat face of the pirouette, allowing the reed to vibrate freely in the mouth. This gives a sound which is more powerful than that of the oboe, but the player lacks the degree of control provided by lip pressure on the reed.

The crumhorn is a hook-shaped wooden instrument, as seen in Fig. 8.2 (b and c). It has a narrow cylindrical bore about 5–8 mm in diameter which widens out towards the end. The instrument maker bends the wood to form the hook by a steaming process. The finger holes are essentially the same as on the recorder, seven small holes on the front and one thumb hole on the back. It is not overblown, so the range is just an octave plus one note. Six of the holes form the basic scale, as discussed in Chapter 5, together with the lowest hole, which completes the octave. The eighth hole give the one additional note above the octave compass. In the instrument illustrated, a further note can be obtained by operating a key covering a ninth hole. The reed is placed inside a wooden cap which has a slot in it for blowing through, so it is not actually placed in the mouth.

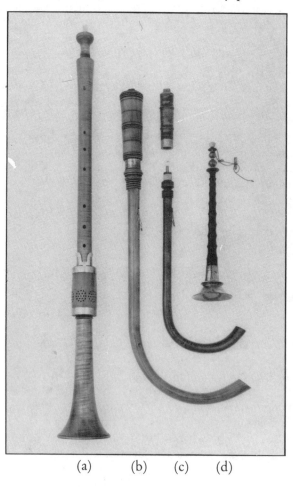

(a) (b) (c) (d)

Fig. 8.2. Double reed woodwind
 (a) Renaissance shawm by Hanchet
 (b) Tenor Crumhorn by Körber
 (c) Alto crumhorn by Wood, with wind cap removed
 (d) Chinese shawm

However, the notes can be articulated by tonguing against the slot as with the recorder.

The curved end of the crumhorn is pierced by side holes which cannot be reached by the fingers, and are therefore permanently open. The acoustical effect of this perforated extension is to darken the sound of the lowest notes (cf. p.270). A typical harmonic spectrum for a mid-range crumhorn note is illustrated in Fig. 3.61.

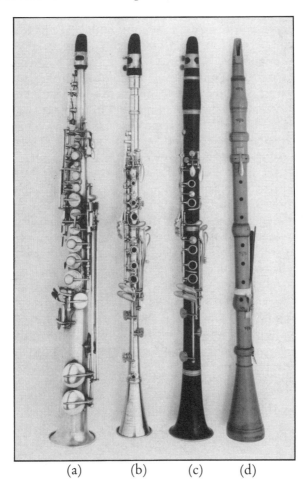

(a) (b) (c) (d)

Fig. 8.3. Single reed woodwind instruments
 (a) Soprano saxophone (EUCHMI 2316)
 (b) Metal clarinet by Hawkes (EUCHMI 2312)
 (c) Wooden Boehm clarinet by Marigaux (EUCHMI 127)
 (d) Early five-keyed clarinet by Collier (EUCHMI 100/1154)

THE CLARINET

The history of the clarinet is somewhat obscure, but the first recognisable instruments were probably made in Germany during the late 17th century by J.C. Denner. Mozart was one of the first great composers to exploit the clarinet but it was not until Beethoven's time that it became a fully established member of the orchestra. The clarinet has become the leading instrument in the military band, taking the role that the violin has in the symphony orchestra. Fig. 8.3 (d) shows an early boxwood clarinet made by Collier. This has just five keys and most of the chromatic notes need to be formed using cross-fingerings. These early instruments were played with the reed uppermost, the reed itself being smaller than the one used today. From about 1840 onwards the technique of having the reed below the mouthpiece and controlling it with the lower lip became more or less universally accepted. The standard modern instrument is of the Boehm design shown in Fig. 8.3 (c), although another keywork scheme known as the Simple or Albert system was preferred by many players until quite recently and is still used to some extent in Germany.

The most commonly used clarinet is pitched in B♭, sounding a tone lower than written. The Boehm model shown in Fig. 8.3 (c) is in B♭. For orchestral work it is normal to have two instruments, one pitched in B♭ and the other in A. The sound from these is virtually identical and the same mouthpiece is generally used for both. When a composition is in a sharp key it is most often scored for the A clarinet and likewise for the B♭ instrument when in a flat key. In this way the number of sharps or flats in the written score is kept to a minimum, which leads to greater fluency in the performance. There is also a clarinet in E♭, sometimes referred to as the clarinetto piccolo because of its small size. This sounds a minor third higher than written. It is used mostly in military bands but is also called on in a number of well-known orchestral compositions, e.g. Berlioz's 'Symphonie Fantastique'. The bass clarinet is in B♭, pitched an octave lower than the standard B♭ model, and resembles a tenor saxophone in appearance. The main body is of wood and the crook and horn of metal. Fig. 8.4 shows a bass clarinet and a tenor saxophone for comparison. Note that with the saxophone the bore flares out along its length like a cone, whereas with the clarinet it is essentially constant apart from the bell section. The lowest member of the family is the contra-bass clarinet, pitched either in E♭, a fifth below the bass clarinet, or in B♭, an octave below. These are generally constructed from metal throughout. The *basset horn* is really a clarinet pitched in F, a fourth below the standard B♭ instrument. In appearance it is like the bass clarinet, but it is smaller in size and the crook has just a single bend, rather as on an alto saxophone.

In discussing the construction and acoustics we shall confine ourselves to the modern B♭ instrument, although the main features apply equally to the other members of the clarinet family.

(a)   (b)

Fig. 8.4. (a) Bass clarinet
          (b) Tenor saxophone

Construction

The bore of the clarinet is approximately cylindrical, of diameter 15 mm or slightly less, and there is a small flared bell at the lower end. The tube is effectively closed at the mouthpiece end, so it only resonates at the odd harmonics. The bell only has a significant effect on the lowest notes, where it assists with the impedance matching between the resonator tube and the surrounding air and also lowers the resonant frequency. The complete instrument is made up of five components, as shown in Fig. 8.5. The main barrel carrying the keywork is in two sections, the bottom joint and the top joint, and these are connected to the mouthpiece by means of a short barrel. Tuning can be accomplished by pulling out the mouthpiece or barrel a short distance. The bell is separate and fits on the lower end, making the total length of the B♭ clarinet 67 cm to the tip of the mouthpiece. The sounding length is a little less than this, giving a bottom note sounding D_3 (written E_3). From E_3 (written) upwards the tube length is progressively shortened by opening holes in succession to give all the semitones up to A_4. A further semitone up to $A_4^\#$ is obtained by opening the uppermost hole with the left hand thumb key. This low range is known as the *chalumeau* register. To proceed higher the uppermost hole is kept open to act as a speaker key and the instrument is overblown. Since the clarinet only sounds the odd harmonics, it overblows the twelfth, so the next note B_4 in the scale is sounded with all holes closed except for the speaker key. The speaker hole is located a distance 15 cm down the tube and when it is opened the fundamental resonance is shifted upwards to such an extent that the pitch will jump to the next resonance. This point will be discussed in more detail later. Since the speaker hole is very small and close to the mouthpiece it is liable to clogging from moisture running down the tube caused by condensation of the player's breath. To avoid this the hole is drilled into a short length of metal tube which projects into the bore. The middle range, known as the *clarinet* register, is obtained again by successively opening finger holes in order up to C_6. Above this the fingerings are obtained from the fifth and seventh harmonics of the fundamental notes, but additional holes are opened to produce a venting which discourages formation of the lower modes. In all there are fourteen holes on the upper joint including speaker and thumb holes and nine on the lower joint. The full range is nearly four octaves, although the uppermost notes are rarely used in orchestral playing because here the instrument loses its fine tone quality.

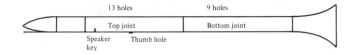

Fig. 8.5 The compondents of a B♭ Boehm clarinet.

Traditionally clarinets are made of wood, African blackwood being used for good quality modern instruments. It is often said that the clarinet has a woody sound, but this is due to the shape of the bore and finger holes together with the end condition imposed by the reed, rather than anything to do with the material. This is not to say that the material has no effect on tone, but certainly its effect is of secondary importance. This is also the case with the flute, which we shall examine later in this chapter. Cheaper modern clarinets are frequently made of plastic, and metal is also used sometimes. Fig. 8.3 (b) shows a metal clarinet. It resembles somewhat the soprano saxophone (Fig. 8.3 (a)), but notice that the bore does not flare out, so it is much narrower at the low end.

Mouthpiece

The mouthpiece is generally made of either ebonite (vulcanised rubber) or hard plastic, the reed being clamped on the facing by means of a metal ligature as shown in Fig. 8.6. This gap between the reed and facing, through which air is blown, is determined by the curved shape of the facing at the tip, known as the *lay*. The lay is one of the most important characteristics of a mouthpiece and even minute changes in shape can have fairly dramatic consequences. Wide lays generally allow for wider reed vibrations and a bigger sound but are difficult to control in pianissimo passages, especially if the reed is hard. Jazz and dance band instrumentalists often prefer a wide lay. Another important feature is the shape of the cavity inside the mouthpiece, known as the *tone chamber*. Sometimes the shape is such as to give a smooth transition to the bore of the barrel, but in other designs there is a constriction, often opening up with a sharp step. This leads to a separation of the air stream from the wall and high speed oscillations which enhance the upper harmonics. Mouthpieces of this design are said to have a greater *edge* than those of the straight through type.

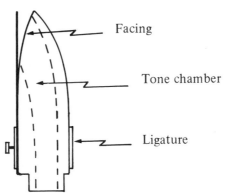

Facing

Tone chamber

Ligature

Fig. 8.6. Clarinet mouthpiece with reed attached.

Fixing a mouthpiece and reed to a resonator tube has the effect of lowering the resonant frequency. This is similar to what we saw in the violin, where vibrations of the body lead to an effective enlargement of the resonant cavity. The effective volume that is added to the tube is found to be approximately constant over the playing range but is considerbly greater than the actual volume of the tone chamber.

Some players place great importance on the type of ligature and there are many different designs on the market. An interesting ligature patented fairly recently uses a flexible strap made from polyester fabric impregnated with neoprene to hold the reed to the mouthpiece. This can be tightened up using a metal thumb screw. The manufacturers claim that this method of fixing allows the reed to swell and shrink without distorting the reed body and thus reduces the likelihood of leakage at the lay due to reed distortion. In many ways this method of fixing is similar to the old technique of binding the reed to the mouthpiece with twine.

Tone quality

In a clarinet the reed vibrations are dominated by the resonance characteristics of the tube and these in turn determine the pitch and spectral composition of the sound (Smith and Mercer 1974). The response of the tube to different frequencies of excitation can be quantified by measuring the impedance of the instrument at the mouthpiece end. We saw in Chapter 5 that acoustic impedance is equal to the pressure fluctuation divided by the volume velocity. For a progressive wave moving down a long tube this quantity is independent of the position along the tube and the frequency. However, in the case of the clarinet, standing wave patterns are formed at certain resonant frequencies. At resonance the mouthpiece end will be characterised by large pressure fluctuations and very small particle velocities. The impedance will then be very large, so if a graph is plotted of impedance versus frequency, the resonances will show up as a series of sharp peaks. An impedance curve can be measured by injecting a small oscillatory flow of constant amplitude into the mouthpiece using a capillary tube attached to a pressure transducer (Backus 1974). The resulting pressure fluctuations inside the mouthpiece are then measured using a probe microphone whose output is recorded as the frequency of the oscillation is varied.

Fig. 8.7 shows a typical impedance curve for the note C_4 (sounding B$\flat_3$) on a clarinet. Note that only the peaks corresponding to odd numbered modes are present, but that these become progressively flatter at the higher frequencies. In addition to this, only the first five peaks are of significant height. These two features can be explained by the presence of the length of tube below the first open hole. This is perforated with a number of open holes and acts as a high pass filter to the sound waves, i.e. high frequency waves can travel down this section of the tube but low frequency ones cannot, since their energy leaks out through the holes to the surrounding atmosphere. The result of this is that only the low frequency waves are strongly reflected at the first open hole and produce standing waves of significant amplitude. These low frequency waves, however, extend further and further into the open hole section as the frequency increases, so the wavelength of the higher partials becomes progressively longer and the frequency correspondingly lower. The frequency at which attenuation of the higher mode standing waves begins is known as the *cutoff frequency*. If the same impedance curve is repeated with the speaker key open, i.e. for the note G_5 one twelfth higher, then the result is similar except that the funamental is raised by something over a tone and a half. This is indicated by the dotted line in Fig. 8.7. Since the lowest components do not now form a harmonic series, the pitch jumps to the twelfth above. It is actually possible to obtain the fundamental with the speaker key open if one blows very softly to suppress the upper tones. The note sounded is then approximately $C_4^\#$ instead of the $B_3^\flat$ sounded with the speaker key closed.

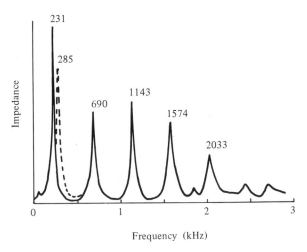

Fig. 8.7. Impedance curve for the note C_4 on a clarinet. The dotted line indicates how the curve changes when the speaker key is depressed, i.e. G_5 is fingered. The numbers above the peaks indicate the peak frequencies in Hz.

An impedance curve can tell us a great deal about the playing characteristics of an instrument. When a sustained note of constant pitch is played, the tube is being excited by the reed at a large number of frequencies simultaneously, but all of these of necessity form a harmonic series since the complex waveform is periodic. The amount of amplification given to any harmonic by the tube resonance is determined by the height of the impedance curve at that frequency. Thus if the frequency of a particular impedance peak coincides with a discrete multiple of the fundamental, then this harmonic will be strongly amplified within the tube. Note that the sound of a steady note on a clarinet contains only pure harmonics because of its periodicity. This is in contrast with the piano, for example, where the amplitude of the signal continually changes and the partials do not in general form part of a harmonic series.

Although the spectrum of the sound measured within the instrument, with a probe microphone, shows strong attenuation above cutoff, the externally radiated sound does not to any great extent because these higher frequencies are radiated more efficiently. Nevertheless, it has been shown that instruments with high cutoff frequencies are considered by musicians to have a 'bright' timbre, while those with low cutoff frequencies are felt to be 'dark' in timbre (Benade 1976). Since the cutoff frequency can be raised by increasing the diameter of the finger holes, instruments with large side holes have a brighter sound than those with small side holes. The radiated sound is actually only a few percent of the total sound power within the instrument. Most of the sound is radiated through the first open hole, with the major part of the remainder coming through the second hole.

The relative strengths of the harmonics depend not only on the impedance curve but also on the dynamic level at which the instrument is played. Worman (1971) has shown that when a clarinet is blown fairly softly, the pressure amplitude P_n of the nth harmonic measured in the mouthpiece is proportional to the nth power of the fundamental amplitude P_1. For very quiet notes, P_1 is very small, and the higher harmonics are amost insignificant; as the volume is increased, the upper harmonics grow more rapidly than the fundamental, and the timbre becomes richer.

From the impedance curve characteristics it will be seen that in the lower register of the clarinet many harmonics are present, but these are predominantly the odd ones because of the closed end condition at the mouthpiece. In the upper registers there are only a few harmonics present, but the even ones become more significant, since the resonances of the tube deviate progressively away from the discrete multiples of the fundamental. In fortissimo playing the waveform shape of the reed vibrations becomes more complex, which accentuates the higher harmonics.

Because of its rich tone quality the clarinet is usually played without vibrato in orchestral works. Jazz and dance band clarinettists invariably use a vibrato, which is produced by a periodic variation in lip pressure, sometimes strengthened by pulsations from the diaphragm.

Bore variations

The inside bore of a clarinet is not in reality the smooth cylinder which is assumed in the simple idealised theory (Benade 1959). The pads do not close flush with the inside, so a small cavity is left under each closed pad. Also there is often a cavity left when the barrel or mouthpiece is pulled out for tuning purposes. These small perturbations all affect the tuning of the various harmonic components in the sound. Instrument makers can also make fine adjustments to the tuning of a clarinet by changing the bore diameter at appropriate places.

The effect of a bore contraction or enlargement depends on whether it is at a pressure node or antinode for any particular mode of oscillation. If a contraction coincides with a pressure antinode, then a given motion of air particles at some position further along the tube will give rise to an increased pressure fluctuation at the antinode. In effect the springiness of the system will be increased, giving rise to an increase in frequency. This is analogous to the case of a mass vibrating on a spring. If the stiffness of the spring is increased, then the frequency of oscillation also rises. A contraction in the vicinity of a pressure node will however cause a lowering of the frequency for the mode in question. The opposite effect occurs with an expansion. Enlarging the bore near a pressure antinode reduces the springiness and hence the frequency, rather like increasing the volume of a container in which there is a Helmholtz resonance. Enlargements near to pressure nodes, on the other hand, cause the frequency to rise. It is possible to draw out curves for each separate mode showing the effect on frequency of making changes in bore size at any particular point along the resonator tube. These are helpful in the design stage and in the final regulation of an instrument.

THE SAXOPHONE

The saxophone was invented by the Belgian instrument maker Adolphe Sax and patented by him in Paris in 1846, a year before Boehm brought out his revolutionary flute design. There are seven models of saxophone, the smallest being the sopranino in E^b. Then comes the B^b soprano, E^b alto, B^b tenor, E^b baritone, B^b bass and the largest, the E^b contrabass. All of these are transposing instruments with a basic range of two and a half octaves, written $B^{\natural}_3$ to F_6. In addition, there is the non-transposing C melody saxophone, which lies between the alto and tenor in size. This is not made nowadays, although a few models exist and are played by enthusiasts. By far the most commonly used members of the family are the alto and tenor.

Saxophones are traditionally made of brass which is either lacquered or plated, although some years back one company produced a plastic saxophone. This was not generally considered to have a good tone quality. The tone holes are large, e.g. the lowest hole on the alto has a diameter of 4 cm, more than half the tube diameter at this position. Pads are generally made of leather, often with metal discs in the centre to minimise sound absorption.

The bore of the saxophone is conical, except for a very short flare at the end of the bell. The bore diameter is larger and the expansion angle greater than with other conical bored instruments. On the alto saxophone, for example, the diameter at the mouthpiece end is 13 mm as compared to just 4 mm on a bassoon, and the expansion angle is about four times as great. These factors, together with the large tone holes, give the instrument an extremely full and powerful sound. Since the resonator tube is a truncated cone, the saxophone overblows the octave so that the same fingering is used for the notes written D_4 to $C_5^\#$ as for the notes written D_5 to $C_6^\#$, except that in the higher register the speaker key is depressed with the left thumb. Although there is only a single speaker key on the modern instrument, there are two separate speaker tone holes, an upper one for the notes written A_3 and above, a lower one for the notes below. These are brought into action automatically as the appropriate notes in the scale are played. However, two separate speaker keys are found on some old instruments. In the normal fingering only the second harmonics are employed in the upper register, separate keys being used for the notes written D_6, $D_6^\#$, E_6 and F_6. These are operated with the bottom joints of the first three fingers on the left hand and the first finger on the right hand. The notes are played with the speaker key depressed and are in fact second harmonics of notes which are not used in the fundamental. However, they can be used in the lower octave for alternative fingerings, e.g. trilling from $C_5^\#$ to D_5. Separate keys are also used to extend the range down to $B_3^\flat$ and baritone saxophones frequently have a low A key sounding C_2. Although only the fundamental and second harmonics are used in the standard fingering, virtuoso players make use of higher harmonics to extend the range up a further octave.

The different members of the saxophone family lie alternately a fifth and a fourth apart, so their sounding lengths increase in the ratios of $3/2$ and $4/3$. The sounding length is measured from the vertex of the cone, so account must be taken of the missing section if measurements of an actual instrument are used to calculate its pitch. The position of the vertex can be found by measuring the bore diameter at both ends and extrapolating back to the point where the diameter would have been zero. As an example, matching alto and tenor saxophones by the same maker had the following dimensions:

	Bore diameter mouthpiece end	Bore diameter open end	Measured tube length	Total extrapolated length
Alto	1.3 cm	8 cm	102 cm	124 cm
Tenor	1.8 cm	10.5 cm	141 cm	170 cm

From these it is seen that the frequency of the lowest note on the alto comes to approximately $346/(2 \times 1.24) = 139\,\text{Hz}$ corresponding to $D_3^\flat$ and on the tenor $346/(2 \times 1.70) = 102\,\text{Hz}$ corresponding to $A_2^\flat$.

In comparison with the alto's the mouthpiece for the tenor is shorter than direct scaling would predict because a mouthpiece is made to match the size of the reed. The reed for a tenor is about $\sqrt{4/3}$ (i.e. 1.15) times as long as an alto reed, since the frequency of vibration of a bar, which is essentially the same, varies as the inverse square of the length. A matching pair of alto and tenor mouthpieces owned by one of the authors was found to measure 8.9 cm and 10.1 cm in overall lengths, giving a scaling ratio of 1.13.

THE OBOE

The oboe is a development from the shawn and first appeared in the mid-17th century when instrument makers in France abandoned the pirouette and redesigned the bore. Oboes of the baroque and classical period had just two keys, but gradually more were added. The simple system, which has thirteen keys and two rings, was developed in the early part of the 19th century but was soon superseded by the conservatoire and thumb-plate systems which are used today. Fig. 8.8 shows an early English two-keyed

(a)   (b)   (c)   (d)

Fig. 8.8. Four instruments from the oboe family: (a) an early English two-keyed oboe (EUCHMI 63); (b) a conservatoire oboe by Strasser, Marigaux and Lemaire (EUCHMI 1555); (c) an oboe d'amore by Mahillon (EUCHMI 957); and (d) a conservatoire cor anglais by Triébert (EUCHMI 74).

oboe (8.8 (a)) and a conservatoire model (8.8 (b)) for comparison. With some musicians, particularly those in military bands, the simple system remained in favour for about a century. The thumb-plate mechanism is generally used by musicians in Britain, but in many other countries the conservatoire is preferred. The basic range of the oboe is B♭₃ to G₆ and its music is written at sounding pitch.

The resonator on an oboe is a tube with an approximately conical bore (Nederveen 1967) and since this is effectively closed at the narrow end by the reed, a complete harmonic spectrum is produced and overblowing is to the octave as with the saxophone. The bore on the oboe is very much narrower than on a saxophone and the hole diameters much smaller. The maximum loudness is therefore much less. The oboe has two speaker holes and there is a choice of mechanisms available for opening and closing these. In the simplest arrangement there are two separately operated speaker keys. Most players, however, prefer either the fully automatic system, similar to that on the saxophone, or the semi-automatic arrangement where there is a linkage between two separate octave levers which closes the lower hole as the upper one is opened.

The oboe's double reed is bound to a thin tube known as a *staple* which is conical in bore and is generally made of brass, although silver, copper and various alloys are also used. When inserted into the body it makes the total length similar to that of the clarinet, although the oboe sounds higher because of its conical bore. The body itself is in three sections consisting of upper joint, lower joint and bell. Careful measurments of bore diameter have been made on selected instruments by inserting calipers into the wide end of the tube (Nederveen 1967). These have shown that there are always deviations from the true conical shape but that these are rather small on the modern instrument. The most consistent deviations occur at the top of the upper joint, where there is a constriction of the bore. Just above this, however, there is a sudden expansion at the transition from upper joint to staple. Both the staple and the bell have angles of expansion which are considerably greater than the expansion angle for the upper and lower joints.

The double reed excitation is complex in form, so the oboe's tone is rich in upper harmonics. In the low register the fundamental is rather weak, but this increases in strength as the scale is ascended. At B♭₅ the fundamental has approximately the same strength as the second harmonic and above this pitch it is the strongest peak in the spectrum. A feature of the oboe sound is that the harmonic spectra for different notes are characterised by formants which accentuate certain frequencies. The dominant formant is centred around 1100 Hz, corresponding approximately to the second formant for the vowel sound 'a' but a little higher pitched (see p.482). There are also secondary formant peaks at 2700 Hz and 4500 Hz (Meyer 1978). Together these give the oboe a rich tone, but with a somewhat nasal edge.

The sound from the oboe is radiated with pronounced directional characteristics like the sound from the clarinet. As with the clarinet, there is a cutoff frequency above which sound waves in the tube are not reflected at the first open hole. For the baroque oboe, the cutoff frequency can be as low as 1000 Hz (Benade 1976); for a modern instrument it lies in the region of 1500. At frequencies below this, e.g. at 1000 Hz, sound is radiated mainly from the open holes as shown in Fig. 8.9 (a) (Meyer 1978). At higher frequencies the sound is directed more along the axis of the bell towards the ground, and for frequencies of 8000 Hz and above the radiation is almost entirely within a narrow cone propagating from the bell, as seen in Fig. 8.9 (b). It is very important to take account of the directional characteristics of instruments when positioning microphones for sound recording.

The two other commonly used members of the family are the *oboe d'amore* and the *cor anglais* or English horn. An easily recognisable feature of both of these is their pear-shaped bell (see Fig. 8.8 (c) and (d)). The oboe d'amore is built a minor third lower than the oboe and the cor anglais a fifth lower. Both instruments have a somewhat veiled sound quality. Much more rare is the *heckelphone*, which is a form of baritone oboe, having a wider bore and more powerful sound.

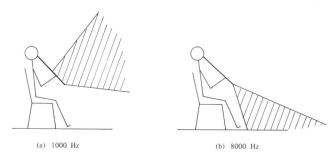

(a) 1000 Hz   (b) 8000 Hz

Fig. 8.9. Directional characteristics of the oboe at two different frequencies: (a) 1000 Hz and (b) 8000 Hz. Within the shaded areas the sound level does not drop more than 3dB below its maximum value. Adapted from Mayer (1978).

THE BASSOON

The bassoon dates from the mid-17th century. It has a conical bore and uses a double reed like the oboe. Its overall tube length is just over two and a half metres, providing for a bottom note of B_1^b, but it stands only just over half this height since the tube is bent back on itself like a hairpin. The complete resonating tube, as shown in Fig. 8.10, is in five sections:
(1) the crook, or bocal, made of metal and having a diameter of approximately 4 mm at the small end; (2) the wing joint, named because of its

flattened shape; (3) the butt joint or boot, which contains two parallel tubes joined at the bottom by a metal U-section; (4) the long joint; and (5) the bell, which has a diameter of approximately 4 cm at the open end. The bulge on the bell is to strengthen the wooden wall and is of no acoustical significance.

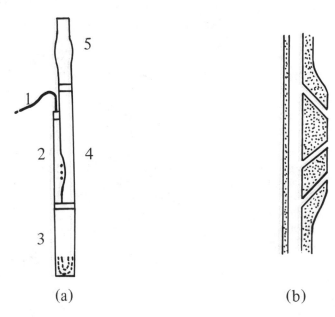

Fig. 8.10. The bassoon. (a) shows the five sections: (1) crook, (2) wing joint, (3) butt joint, (4) long joint, and (5) bell; (b) shows the way in which the holes are drilled in the wing joint.

A lengthened bell joint is sometimes used to extend the range down to A_1. The wing joint contains three holes to be covered by fingers of the left hand. These would be too far apart to be covered by the fingers if drilled at right angles to the surface of the wood. To overcome this problem the wood is thickened in the form of a wing and the holes are drilled at a slanting angle, as shown in Fig. 8.10. To increase further the effective distance between the holes, the lowest one sometimes has a smaller diameter so that the effective length of the tube when it is opened is well below the point where it meets the internal bore.

The narrow holes tend to restrict the sound which is radiated through them, and since most of the low frequency harmonics are radiated through the side holes, this leads to an accentuation of upper harmonics. Like the oboe, the sound spectrum is characterised by strong formants. The dominant formant peak is around 500 Hz and this corresponds in shape to the lowest formant for the vowel 'o'. This is one of the main reasons why the bassoon's sound has strong voice-like features. On the lowest notes this frequency range is only reached by the sixth or seventh harmonics and the lower components are all weak. There are also many high frequency formant peaks, the most important ones being centred around 1150, 2000 and 3500 Hz, which add brightness to the timbre.

A predecessor of the modern bassoon is the *curtal* or *dulcian*. This has all the essential features of the bassoon but has a short bell and is constructed in one piece. Fig. 8.11 shows a curtal and also a reproduction of an early three-keyed bassoon for comparison.

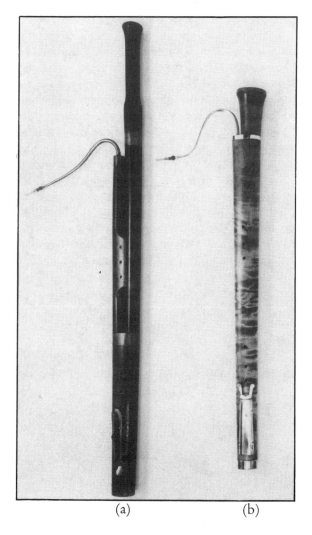

(a)   (b)

Fig. 8.11. (a) a three-keyed bassoon; (b) a curtal by Simon Carlyle.

The only other member of the family to be used extensively is the *contrabassoon*, which has a tube length approximately twice that of the standard instrument. This is in five parallel sections connected by U-joints. Its music is written an octave higher than sounding pitch, in contrast to bassoon music which is written at sounding pitch.

BAGPIPES

Bagpipes have a long tradition in all the European countries, although the Scottish Highland pipes are the best-known and most widely used (Firth and Sillitto 1978; Lenihan and McNeil 1954; Carruthers 1977 and 1978). These have three drones and a chanter, all attached to a sheep or goatskin bag which is inflated from the mouth through a blowpipe. The drones are tuned to sound fixed notes, the two tenors A_3 and the bass A_2. These have cylindrical bores and are fitted with a sliding joint for tuning. Wooden stocks tied to the bag hold the single reeds and also act as joints for attaching the drones. The chanter itself is supplied with a double reed and its conical bore gives it a complete harmonic spectrum in contrast to the drones, which are rich in odd harmonics like the clarinet. The chanter has an idiosyncratic nine-note scale from G_4 to A_5: it is not overblown. Practice chanters have a narrow cylindrical bore so that they sound softer and lower.

Bagpipes from other regions frequently use a cylindrical chanter instead of the conical chanter of the Highland pipes. The Northumbrian pipes, for example, have a cylindrical chanter with a double reed. These pipes are smaller than the Highland instruments and are blown with bellows. The

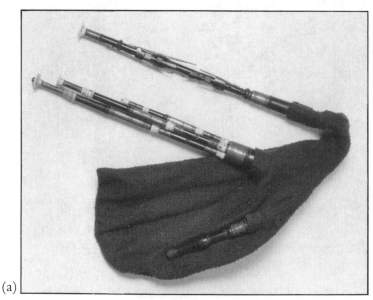

(a)

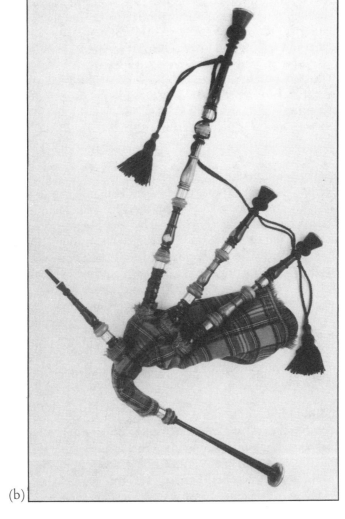

(b)

Fig. 8.12. Bagpipes from (a) Northumbria (EUCHMI 1716) and (b) the
Scottish Highlands (EUCHMI 1512). The chanter is conical
on the Highland pipes and cylindrical on the Northumbrian,
which are shown here without the bellows.

chanter has the novel feature of being blocked at the end, so that when all
the holes are closed it is silent. This allows notes to be separated by silence,
a very useful facility since this cannot be achieved by tonguing. Fig. 8.12
(a) shows a set of Northumbrian pipes for comparison with the Highland
pipes (8.12 (b)). In pipes of Eastern European origin the chanter is
generally cylindrical and uses a single reed like the drones. The sound

from these cylindrical bore chanters is weak in even harmonics, so the quality differs a good deal from the complete spectrum produced by the conical chanter. One interesting version of the bagpipes is the French *musette*, used in the 17th and 18th centuries in wealthy society. This is driven by bellows and employs a set of drones referred to as a *shuttle drone*, in which the bore runs up and down a series of cylindrical holes drilled into a block of wood or ivory. Double reeds are used for both chanter and drones. The chanter has a cylindrical bore, like the drones, and is fitted with keys for playing semitones.

THE FLUTE

Renaissance flutes were cylindrical tubes with six holes to give the basic scale. Such instruments were frequently used for military purposes, the military version being known as the fife. They were generally made in one piece from wood and often had a rather narrow bore giving them a shrill sound. Their tuning was generally poor and chromatic notes could only be produced by using cross-fingering. Fifes are still used in 'fife and drum' bands, but the modern instrument has a conical bore.

The first fundamental changes in flute design came about at the end of the 17th century and were primarily due to the French flautist and instrument maker Jacques Hotteterre (Fairley 1982). In order to eliminate the shrillness of the early instruments and to improve the tuning, he replaced the cylindrical tube with a conical bore, narrowing towards the lower end. The blowhole on the baroque instrument was set in a separate section known as the headjoint, which was slid into the main body and could be pulled in and out for tuning purposes. The headjoint still retained its cylindrical bore, as shown in the schematic illustration of Fig. 8.13 (a). As well as producing tonal advantages, the conical taper of the body allowed the finger holes to be placed closer together, thus reducing uncomfortable finger stretches. The flutes of this period were generally made of wood, but other materials, particularly ivory, were frequently used. Fig. 8.14 shows three early flutes, one in stained wood, one in ivory and one in glass, for comparison with the modern flute. Hotteterre also added the first key, a D key operated with the little finger of the right hand. His instrument was pitched in D, the fundamental note being D_4. The compass was effectively D_4 to D_6, although a few higher notes could be obtained with difficulty. The tuning of these early instruments was based on the mean tone scale.

From the time of Hotteterre's innovation up until Boehm, the inventor of the modern flute, numerous minor modifications were made, mainly in the addition of more keys. By the beginning of the 19th century the instrument had become completely chromatic, using equal temperament tuning, although many of the old cross-fingerings persisted with some keys being used primarily for ornaments.

It was Theobald Boehm (1794–1881) who redesigned the flute to the form in which it is used today. The story is that Boehm went to hear the great virtuoso Charles Nicholson and was so impressed with his enormous sound that he investigated his instrument. Boehm decided that it was the large tone holes which were responsible for the power. However, the tuning of the flute was poor, so it could only be handled effectively by a master such as Nicholson. This inspired Boehm to redesign the instrument completely, using large tone holes covered by pads. After some preliminary trial models which were eventually discarded, Boehm introduced his radical new design in 1847. This remains essentially unchanged to this day. The Boehm flute has a cylindrical body and a tapered headjoint, as indicated schematically in Fig. 8.13 (b). Boehm's original design was for a 20 mm bore, but he later changed this to 19 mm. This made for easier blowing in the upper register, since the strength of resonance depends on the amount of reflection at the ends, which is determined by the ratio of the wavelength to the tube diameter.

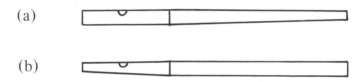

Fig. 8.13. Body and headjoint tapers in (a) the baroque flute developed by Hotteterre and (b) the Boehm 1847 flute.

The orchestral flute of today is of the transverse type, i.e. it is side-blown. End-blown flutes have been produced, the most famous inventor being Carlo Giorgi. In 1888 he brought out a keyless flute with a cylindrical bore where the embouchure hole and lip plate were fitted on the end so that the instrument was held in much the same way as a recorder.

Components of the Boehm flute

The Boehm concert flute is pitched in C and has a range of three octaves from C_4 to C_7, although most players can extend the range into the fourth octave (Bate 1969). The body is in one piece and contains holes for the notes of the basic scale plus additional holes for all the chromatic notes, ten large holes (about 13 mm in diameter) in all plus a small hole for $C^{\#}_5$ and two small holes for trill keys. On the end of the body is fitted the foot joint, which has three large holes, one for $D^{\#}_4$ and the other two to extend the range down from D_4 to C_4. Longer B foot joints with an additional hole are also quite common. The headjoint is generally made of

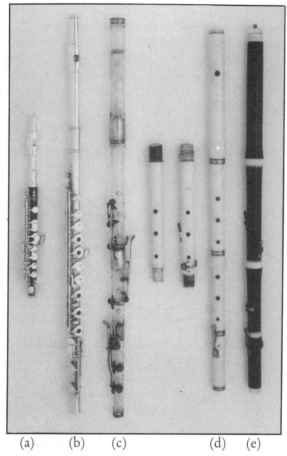

(a)   (b)   (c)   (d)   (e)

Fig. 8.14. Instruments from the flute family. From left to right: (a) a Boehm piccolo by Yamaha; (b) an open-holed Boehm flute by Sankyo; (c) an eight-keyed glass flute (EUCHMI 55); (d) a single-keyed ivory flute by Cahusag with interchangeable joints (EUCHMI 1014); (e) a single-keyed flute in stained wood by Clement (EUCHMI 1536).

metal and slides into the body, as shown in Fig 8.15, its end being plugged by a cork whose position is adjustable. The player's lower lip rests on a lip plate which is raised above the headjoint tubing and is connected to it by a chimney. The internal shape is thus similar to that which would be produced by boring through the thick wall of a wooden tube, although the sides of the chimney are sloping to give a slight expansion towards the inside of the tube.

The lowest note C_4 has a wavelength of $346/262 = 1.32$ m. The length of the instrument from embouchure hole to open end should therefore be 66 cm, since to a first approximation the flute responds like a cylindrical tube open at both ends. The actual length is closer to 62 cm because of the combined corrections of the tone hole chimneys, the cavity between the embouchure hole and the cork, and the open end of the tube. Boehm constructed a graph which he called his *schema* for calculating the positions of the holes on a flute tuned to any required pitch (Boehm 1964, p.41). The standard pitch at his time was $A_4 = 435$ Hz. The hole positions have been recalculated by various flute makers since the time of Boehm, in particular the English flute maker Albert Cooper (Cooper 1980). His tuning is sometimes referred to as the Cooper scale.

Since the flute overblows the octave, the fingering in the middle register is the same as in the lower one, except that for the note D_5 the first finger key is opened on the left hand, acting as a speaker key. In the top register the notes are obtained from the third, fourth and fifth harmonics, as indicated in Fig. 8.16. The fingering for each high note is essentially the same as for the fundamental, but one or two additional holes are opened for venting to aid the formation of the upper harmonic and to make fine adjustments in the tuning. For example, D_6 has the same fingering as G_4 except for one extra hole being opened.

Actually there are no simple and universally accepted rules for determining the pitch used for naming an instrument and experts often disagree over this question, especially when it comes to flutes. In the case of the baroque flute there are, in essence, just six holes, which play the scale of D major when opened in turn, chromatic notes being formed by cross-fingering. This clearly puts the pitch at D since the instrument lends itself most readily to playing music in this key. In later baroque models it is true that keys were added for producing accidentals and for extending the range down to C_4, but these do not alter the basic layout of the instrument. Although the modern Boehm flute is usually described as being pitched in C, it is argued by some that it would be more correct to say it is in D, since it is a development of the baroque flute. However, on the Boehm instruments the mechanism is so arranged that on lifting each key in turn one ascends the scale of C major, the $F^{\#}$ requiring a cross-fingering. The instrument thus lends itself naturally to playing music in C major.

Modern flutes can be obtained with either open or closed holes. On the open hole version five of the keys are perforated, and need to be covered by the fingers. On the closed hole type all the holes are fully covered by pads.

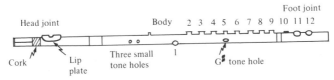

Fig. 8.15. Components of the Boehm flute.

Fig. 8.16. The harmonics on which the fingering in the upper registers of the flute are based. D_6, for example, has a fingering similar to the fundamental G_4.

Air reed mechanism

The mechanism by which vibrations in the resonating tube of the flute are excited is extremely complicated and as yet not fully understood. High speed photographs recorded in the laboratory have shown that the overall air movements are somewhat similar to those which occur with a mechanical reed, hence the term air reed. Fig. 8.17 illustrates the cycle of events for comparison with Fig. 8.1. At phase position 1 the pressure inside the flute is its mean value, i.e. approximately atmospheric. The airsteam is then split evenly, with about half of the jet entering into the flute and producing a mean flow through the instrument. This corresponds to phase 1 in Fig. 8.1. Because of the standing wave in the tube (see Fig 5.7) there is an additional *acoustic velocity* into the flute, drawing the jet inwards so that it is at its innermost position when the high pressure phase of the cycle is reached (phase 2). At phase 3 the acoustic velocity is outwards and the jet has returned to the position where it is split by the edge. At phase 4 the acoustic velocity is zero and the jet flows outside the embouchure hole. Note that the velocity of the jet in or out of the flute lags behind the acoustic velocity by one quarter of a cycle in these sketches. This phase lag, which can be thought of as being due to the inertia of the jet, may in practice be smaller, the exact value being dependent on the geometry of the jet and the embouchure hole and the mode being excited (Coltman 1968 (a) and (b)).

Although the cycle of events for the air reed appears very similar to that of the mechanical reed, there is one essential difference. The mechanical reed is pressure controlled and will only operate under conditions where the pressure variation is large. The impedance therefore reaches a maximum at resonance. The air reed, on the other hand, is flow controlled, the impedance being a minimum at resonance. The pressure node at the embouchure end of a flute occurs a short distance outside the embouchure hole, the pressure variation across the jet being small.

The flow patterns depicted in Fig. 8.17 are a greatly simplified representation of the pattern of lines which are everywhere tangential to the velocity, known as streamlines. The motions can be examined in the

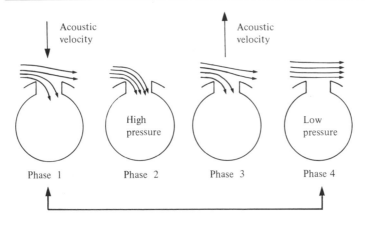

Fig. 8.17. One complete cycle of the air reed on a flute.

laboratory by sounding a flute with a mechanical blower and injecting a smoke stream into the jet. High speed photographs then show the positions of the smoke particles at any given phase position, known as streak lines. Since the streamline patterns are fluctuating periodically, the streak lines appear as wavelike patterns. Photographs at two extreme phase positions are shown in Fig. 8.18 (Campbell et al. 1984).

The speed V at which the air jet issues from the player's mouth and the distance d between the lip aperture and the far edge of the embouchure hole are related to the frequency of sound generation. For maximum excitation of the tube the wavelength of the disturbance which moves along the air jet should be approximately 2d; if it is less, movements at different locations across the hole will not reinforce each other. The situation is complicated, however, by the fact that the wavelike disturbances move at a speed of only about 0.4 V (Fletcher and Thwaites 1979). Thus the maximum excitation will occur at frequencies around 0.4V/2d = V/5d. If this coincides approximately with the fundamental frequency of the tube, the fundamental will be sounded. If V/d is gradually increased, then the note will at first continue to sound, but eventually there will be a sudden jump to the next higher harmonic. This can be seen in Fig. 8.19, which graphs the frequencies sounded by a mechanically blown flute where the distance d was maintained constant and V was varied. Varying velocities were obtained by altering the pressure P of the air behind an artificial embouchure. Since it is known that V is proportional to $\sqrt{P}$, the frequencies have been plotted against this parameter. Pads were closed corresponding to the fingering for the note A_4. Two separate graphs are shown, the first with a relatively large value of d and the second with a smaller d value. Following the first graph from left to right, there are three short curved sections on the left. These are known

285

as *whistle tones,* being extremely quiet sounds which are produced when the instrument is blown very lightly. After the first whistle tone at the fundmental frequency there is a brief region of silence followed by another a fourth below and then a third an octave higher. Whistle tones are sometimes used for special effects in recordings. They are very difficult to control, but some flautists can play whistle tone melodies. Moving to the right, the full fundamental tone is produced, represented by the long line. Eventually this becomes unstable and then breaks up to the octave above. Notice that there is a small rise in frequency as the air speed is increased.

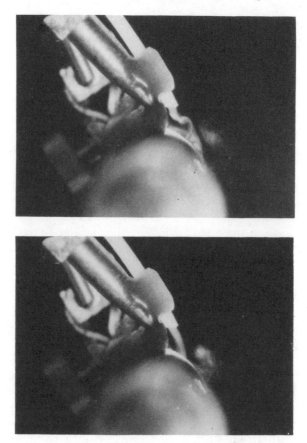

Fig. 8.18 Streak line photographs of the flow over a flute embouchure hole. The upper corresponds to phase 4 and the lower to phase 2 in Fig. 8.17.

In Fig. 8.19 (b) the mouth of the jet is closer to the embouchure hole. In this case no whistle tones are produced and the fundamental and the octave above sound at lower blowing pressures. At $\sqrt{P} = 22$ the pitch breaks up to the third resonance (indicated by the arrow pointing upwards) and this pitch is maintained and slightly sharpened as the pressure increases further. When the pressure is lowered, however, the note does not fall back to the octave at $\sqrt{P} = 22$ but at the lower pressure indicated by the downward pointing arrow. This phenomenon is known as hysteresis and is well known to the flautist. When blowing a high note extra energy must be expended to start it sounding, but the blowing pressure can then be reduced.

Many players feel that the mouth resonance is important in tone production and they associate a certain shaping of the mouth cavity with a particular sound quality. Experiments have been conducted using both flutes and recorders (Coltman 1973; Bak 1969) to test the validity of these assertions. From the results of these the general conclusion is that the cavity shape has little effect, although marked resonances do occur in flute playing in the region of 1 KHz. It may well be that the main effect of changing the shape of the mouth cavity lies in the focusing of the air jet.

We have already said that the air reed gives rise to a mean flow through the flute. This moves down the tube in a swirling motion, as can be seen in Fig. 8.20, which shows dust particles swirling through a transparent flute without tone holes. This photograph was for the third harmonic of C_4. Notice that the dust collects at three positions corresponding to the displacement nodes associated with the third mode of oscillation.

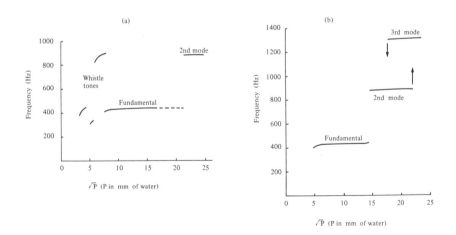

Fig 8.19. Variation of pitch with blowing pressure for the note A_4. The distance d between the lip aperture and the far edge of the embouchure hole was greater for graph (a) than for (b). Full lines indicate stable regions and dotted lines unstable.

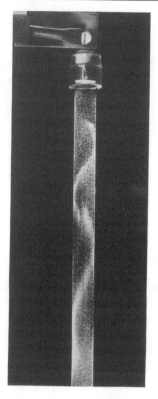

Fig. 8.20 Swirling flow in a flute for the third mode of oscillation.

Tone quality

Although it is often said that the flute sounds a very pure note, this in fact is only true in the upper register, as can be seen in Fig. 8.21, which shows spectra of the sound issuing for notes played in the three different registers. Similar measurements have been published by Fletcher (1975). For D_6 the spectrum has only one strong peak at the fundamental, indicating that the wave pattern is almost purely sinusoidal. The second, third, fourth and fifth harmonics are seen to be present, but these have extremely low amplitudes. For the note D_5, on the other hand, the first three harmonics are all strong and for the lowest note C_4 the second harmonic is stronger than the fundamental. This gives the instrument a rich, almost reedy, sound in the low register. The skilled player can vary the shape of these spectra quite considerably by changing the shape of the air jet, but these essential characteristics remain.

Another interesting facet of the flute's sound is the starting transient. Fig. 8.22 (a) shows that waveform for the start of a tongued note, in this case D_4. Notice that on the first few cycles the wave resembles a sinusoid

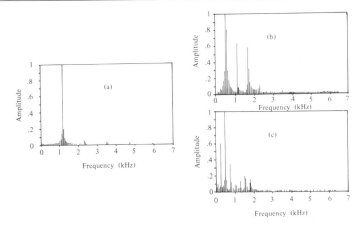

Fig. 8.21. Spectra for the sound of a flute played on notes (a) D_6, (b) D_5 and (c) C_4.

and it is only after a number of wave periods have elapsed that the more complex pattern, showing the formation of higher harmonics, begins to emerge. This seems to be characteristic of the low impedance source, the starting transient for a reed instrument being different. Fig. 8.22 (b) shows the starting transient for the written note G_4 on an alto saxophone. Note that the wave form starts by being extremely complex, reminiscent of noise, but after some time it settles down to a periodic pattern.

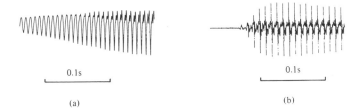

Fig. 8.22. Starting transients for the sound from (a) a concert flute playing D_4 and (b) an alto saxophone playing the written note G_4. Both notes were tongued.

Standing wave patterns

To a first approximation the flute behaves as a cylindrical tube open at both ends (Coltman 1968 (a)) with the resulting standing wave patterns that were described in Chapter 5 (Fig. 5.8). In a real instrument, however, the end conditions differ from this idealised case (Brindley 1971; Coltman 1979). Except when playing the lowest note C_4, the open end is terminated by a section of tube containing open holes and, as with the clarinet, the higher mode standing waves will penetrate into this. At the blowing end, the embouchure hole is set in the side of the tube, whose end is terminated by a cork. At the cork itself there must be a pressure antinode, accompanied by zero motion of the air particles. On the other hand, at the embouchure hole the pressure must drop, but not to zero, since the pressure node will occur at some distance outside the hole. These combined effects produce pressure patterns, as indicated in Fig. 8.23 (Benade 1976). The effective length of the tube is a little more than the distance from the cork to the first open tone hole. Thus in the fundamental mode there is a pressure antinode half way between the cork and the first open hole and the pressure distribution in the central region is the same as the distribution for a plane tube open at both ends, indicated by the dotted lines. The nodal points for this lie a little beyond the cork and the first open hole. For modes 2 and 3 the pressure node at the open end extends further into the section with the open holes because of the high pass filter effect in this section (see p.268).

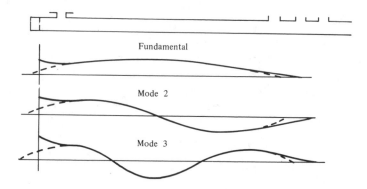

Fig. 8.23. Pressure standing waves in a flute (schematic representation).

At the blowing end the low pressure region at the embouchure hole comes progressively closer to the first pressure antinode as the mode number increases, which has the effect of lowering the amplitude of the resonance. When the antinode coincides with the centre of the embouchure hole the resonance almost completely disappears, resulting in a frequency band where the resonances are strongly attenuated. This effectively limits the playing range of the instrument. For the baroque flute the cork to embouchure hole distance is usually about 25 mm and the attenuated frequency band is centred just above 2000 Hz (corresponding to C_7), which is a little above the instrument's playing range. With the Boehm tapered headjoint the cork is set at a distance of 17 mm (or one tube diameter) from the hole, which makes the attenuated band higher and allows the range to be extended up as high as F$^\sharp$. Pulling the cork out further lowers the pitch of the highest note which can be reached.

The cork position also affects the tuning over the range of the instrument. If the cork is pulled out, then the speaking length is increased and all notes are flattened. However, the flattening effect on the upper modes is greater than on the lower ones since for the higher modes the effective position of the pressure node at the blowing end is beyond the cork. Fig. 8.24 shows the amount of sharpening or flattening of the first six resonance modes with a Boehm tapered headjoint and the cork in three different positions 6.4 mm, 16.4 mm and 26.4 mm from the centre of the embouchure hole. The contracted tube diameter at the cork was 16.4 mm, so this was the normal cork setting. The measurements were recorded for the note A$_4$, resonating the tube with a miniature loudspeaker fitted to a probing tube which was inserted into the flute barrel. The instrument was retuned to A = 440 Hz each time the cork position was moved. Notice from the graph that pulling out the cork beyond its normal position flattens all the upper harmonics, whilst pushing it in sharpens them.

Moving the cork also changes the relative pitch of different notes. Pulling out the cork, for example, will flatten the left hand notes, e.g. A and B, more than the right hand ones because their tube length is shorter and so they are more sensitive to small changes in end correction.

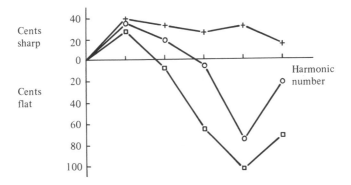

Fig. 8.24. Pitch of the first six modes in relation to the true harmonics for a flute with a Boehm tapered headjoint tuned to A$_4$, with the cork + 6.4 mm, ○ 16.4 mm and □ 26.4 mm from the centre of the embouchure hole.

Lip movements

Of paramount importance in playing the flute is the embouchure, especially since the flautist has a very large degree of control over the note, both in its pitch and in its tone colour (Krell 1973; Fletcher 1974 (a)). Although there are many schools favouring different techniques, nearly all flautists today favour the relaxed embouchure where the lower lip is in effect spread along the length of the lip plate. The sides of the mouth are then dropped by eliminating muscular tension, in contrast to the flautists smile, often depicted in early pictures. The lower lip covers approximately one third of the embouchure hole, the exact amount of lip cover being important in determining the pitch. Covering more of the hole reduces the capacity of the opening to lessen the pressure, and the boundary condition at the blowing end more closely resembles that of a closed tube, resulting in a lowering of the pitch. Similarly, uncovering more of the hole raises the pitch. In determining the effective amount of cover the upper lip position is important as well as the lower lip. In order to overblow the fundamental tone to reach a note in the upper register, the flautist must contract the size of the lip aperture and increase the blowing pressure to give a higher air speed. The rise in pressure forces the lips forward and increases the lip cover. This can be seen in Fig. 8.25, where the shape of the lips has been drawn for three notes F_4, F_5 and F_6. The outlines were obtained by photographing a professional flautist and tracing over the pictures. It is seen that the lip cover is progressively greater for the higher notes.

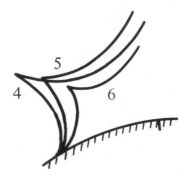

Fig. 8.25. Lip positions for three notes, F_4, F_5 and F_6 (indicated by 4, 5 and 6 respectively), traced from photographs of a professional flautist.

Headjoints

Just as the mouthpiece design is of extreme importance to a clarinet or saxophone player, so the headjoint is to the flautist. Although headjoints are normally purchased with a flute, they can also be bought separately and there are many instrument makers who specialise in handmade headjoints. Some flautists feel that the headjoint is of equal importance to the main body of the instrument in determining the overall playing characteristics. We shall discuss here some of the features of the headjoint used on the Boehm flute.

As we have already said, the normal headjoint used for a Boehm flute is tapered down towards the blowing end (Benade and French 1965). In his original design Boehm gave values for the tapering diameter at different positions along the tube and these are published in his book *The Flute and Flute Playing* (Boehm 1964). The headjoint taper is generally referred to as parabolic since it is curved to give a smooth transition from the cylindrical section, which slides into the body of the instrument, down to the cork. In reality the shape only vaguely resembles the curve of a parabola. The reason for the taper can be seen from Figs 8.24 and 8.25. For the high register notes the lip covers more of the embouchure hole and so flattens the pitch. The notes in the second register have the same fingering as those in the low register, but the frequencies of the second normal modes are sharp compared to the true harmonics, compensating for the effect of lip cover. With a cylindrical headjoint it is extremely difficult to bring the upper register into tune. Fig. 8.26 shows the pitch of the resonance modes with a cylindrical headjoint alongside those of the Boehm taper for comparison.It is seen that all of the partials are flat in relation to the true harmonics.

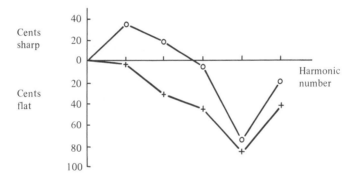

Fig. 8.26. Pitch of the first six modes in relation to the true harmonics for a flute fingered for A_4 with the cork at a distance 16.4 mm from the centre of the embouchure hole; ○ Boehm tapered headjoint + cylindrical headjoint.

In the top register the tuning is complicated by the fact that the fingerings are not precisely the same as those of the fundamental. However, the overall tuning pattern of the flute is characterised by a gradual sharpening towards the top notes. This can be seen in Fig. 8.27, which shows the natural resonant frequencies of all the notes in the scale for a typical student model instrument. Notice that the notes played with the fingers of the left hand, e.g. A and B, are particularly sharp and those played with fingers of the right hand are relatively flatter.

Although the experienced flautist compensates for the sharpening in the high register, beginners often have difficulty in making the correct adjustments and tend to play the high notes sharp and the low notes flat (Coltman 1966, 1976 (b)). In Fig. 8.27 the circles represent the average pitch of notes sounded by three beginner flautists who were asked to play up the scale. These follow the general shape of the natural resonance curve, although the deviations from the correct tuning are less, as might be expected.

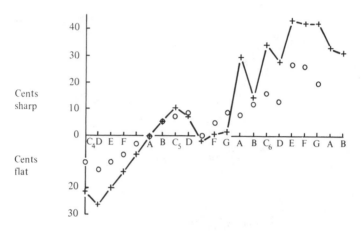

Fig.8.27. Natural resonant frequencies for a typical Boehm flute measured by exciting an instrument with a loudspeaker. The circles represent the pitches played by beginner flautists, found by taking the average of three players.

The other crucial elements in headjoint production are the embouchure hole, the lip plate, and the chimney which joins the two. On Boehm flutes the embouchure hole is either elliptic in shape or rectangular with rounded corners. The length along the axis of the flute is approximately 12 mm and the width 10 mm. The depth of the chimney is approximately 5 mm and the side walls generally slope at a small angle (about 7°) so that the hole is larger on the inside. The shape and size of these two elements vary considerably from one maker to another as does the shape of lip plates. Like the lay on a clarinet or saxophone mouthpiece, the embouchure hole and chimney are very sensitive to small modifications and filing away even the minutest amount of metal can completely spoil a headjoint.

Over the years many different ideas have been thought up for modifying the design of headjoints. One which has recently been patented and given a good deal of publicity is the capped headjoint. This dispenses with the cork, the tube being effectively cut off at the normal cork position and stopped with an adjustable cap. Only the appearance of the instrument is likely to be affected by this alteration. Another interesting idea has been to make the headjoint from a double walled metal tube, rather like a kind of double glazed headjoint. The inventors of these ideas have usually claimed an increase in output sound intensity. However, it is extremely difficult to test this scientifically because of the dependence of output intensity on the precise manner of blowing. Performers given these instruments to test frequently give differing verdicts as to whether they offer an improvements or not.

Construction materials

Nearly all Boehm flutes today are made of metal, the most common metal for student flutes being nickel silver (an alloy of copper, nickel and zinc, sometimes referred to as German silver), often plated with either nickel or silver. More expensive professional instruments are most frequently made from one of the noble metals, silver, gold or platinum, solid silver being by far the most common. In Boehm's time and before, wood was favoured by many players and some flautists today still prefer a wooden instrument. The most popular woods were cocus (cocoa) wood, South American grenadilla, boxwood and ebony. All manner of other materials have been used to a greater or lesser extent at different periods, including ivory, crystal-glass, porcelain, various plastics and unusual metals. Papier-maché, rubber and even wax have been tried. Glass and ivory flutes are shown in Fig. 8.14. Quite often the headjoint is made of a different material from the body. A solid silver headjoint is frequently put on to a nickel silver instrument.

It is generally accepted that the construction material has only a secondary influence on tone quality, the dimensions of the resonating tube being the dominant factor which determines this (Coltman 1971). However, even small differences in playing characteristics can be important to the performer, who is often prepared to pay large sums of money for a noble metal flute. These are generally considered to play better than nickel silver instruments, although there is still much debate over whether this is really so. Generally these more expensive instruments are made to a far higher standard of craftsmanship, which may be of more significance than the metal itself. Wooden instruments definitely respond differently from metal ones, but again this may be because the wall thickness and construction method lead to a resonating tube of slightly different dimensions from the metal version. The resonating tube does vibrate when the flute is blown, but the amplitude of these oscillations is extremely small and the sound level they induce very low (Løkberg and Ledang 1984). Whether or not they influence the standing waves set up in the air column is not really known.

There are other characteristics of the material which are of importance to the player and may affect tone in an indirect way. Silver, for example, has a very high thermal conductivity and warms up quickly. It also has a pleasant feel and is not slippery, an important consideration because the flute is balanced rather than being held. Any tendency for sliding, particularly the embouchure plate on the lip, will upset the embouchure formation.

Avant-garde techniques

The flute lends itself very well to avant-garde techniques of performance because of its great flexibility in tone production. The most common is the *flutter tongue* effect produced by trilling an 'r' whilst playing a note or sequence of notes. This is often used as an alternative to double tonguing in rapid scale passages such as in the Berkeley Sonatina. Also frequently used are *microtones*: intervals of less than a semitone formed using a non-standard fingering. Microtones are easiest on open holed flutes since the perforated keys can be depressed without covering the central hole, thereby reducing their flattening effect.

An interesting technique which has gained popularity in recent years is that of *multiphonics*, where two or even three notes are sounded simultaneously. It has already been seen that a complete set of modes can be blown with a single fingering. By suitably spreading the air jet it is possible to excite more than one of these at a time. An extensive set of multiphonic fingerings has been published by Robert Dick (1978). These do not always correspond to the regular fingering for any of the notes in the multitone since holes must usually be opened or closed to make minor corrections in tuning or to give venting to assist in the formation of the higher tones.

The very quiet whistle tones have already been referred to. There are also some more bizarre effects which are occasionally employed in modern music. These include blowing the flute like a trumpet with the lips completely covering the embouchure hole, covering the end of the lowest note to form the octave below C_4, and singing at the same time as playing.

The piccolo

The piccolo resembles the concert flute but is pitched an octave higher and has no separate foot joint, the lowest note being D_5. Two separate designs are available for the resonating tube. In the most commonly used of these the body is tapered like the pre-Boehm flute and is matched with a cylindrical headjoint. The alternative is a cylindrical body and tapered headjoint, as with the Boehm flute. With this latter design the sound tends to be somewhat on the shrill side. Fig. 8.14 (a) shows a Boehm piccolo with a plastic tapered body and metal cylindrical headjoint.

FIPPLE FLUTES

The simplest form of fipple flute is the *flageolet*, the *recorder* being a more sophisticated version of this. The word fipple (or beak) refers to the whistle-type cutaway which acts as the sound generator.

Flageolet

The flageolet dates back to the 16th century. In the 17th and 18th centuries it became very popular, particularly in France. These early instruments were generally of conical bore with six finger holes. An interesting adaptation was the English double flageolet, which comprised two separate resonating tubes on a common headpiece. These were arranged for playing melodies in harmony, with the difference tones sounding in the bass.

In its modern version the flageolet is what was formally referred to as the penny whistle. This has six tone holes cut in a cylindrical bore tube, normally made from fine gauge metal with the fipple head piece in plastic. The six holes are so arranged that the major scale can be played by uncovering each one in turn. The idea of producing a basic scale from six holes was discussed in Chapter 5. In the case of the flageolet the major third is played when the lower two holes are opened and the hole sizes are varied to give a comfortable spacing for the fingers. The third hole from the bottom is thus smaller than the others to give the semitone between the mediant and the subdominant. When this is opened the tube is effectively cut off at a position below the actual hole.

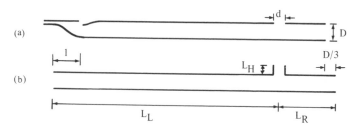

Fig. 8.28. Schematic representation of a flageolet with one hole open showing (a) the actual tube and (b) the equivalent tube.

It is interesting to examine in more detail how holes of finite size will affect the pitch of a note (Benade 1960 (b); Leppington 1982). For a tube it is known that the pressure node at an open end lies at a distance of approximately one third of a diameter (D) outside the tube. The effective end of the tube is then one third of a diameter beyond the actual end. In the same way an open hole can be thought of as being equivalent to a short length of tubing extended by one third of its diameter. Fig. 8.28 (a) shows a flageolet with one open hole of diameter d and Fig. 8.28 (b) indicates the equivalent tube. This is longer than the actual tube because of the end correction (1) which has to be applied at the mouthpiece and also because of the correction at the open end. In the case of the modern flageolet the wall is thin, so the length of the side tube equivalent to the open hole is $L_H \approx d/3$. Now it will be seen that the effective length of the tube with the hole open is going to be greater than L_L since the two branches at the right hand end offer a resistance to the flow. On the other hand it will be less than $L_L + L_R$ because opening the hole lessens the resistance and hence raises the pitch. If the effective length is $L_S = L_L + L_x$ then it can be shown by analogy with electrical circuitry (Nederveen 1969) that

$$S_1/L_x = S_1/L_R + S_H/L_H$$

where S_1 is the area of the main tube, i.e. $\pi D^2/4$ and S_H is the area of the side hole, i.e. $\pi d^2/4$. L_S is referred to as the length of the substitution tube. Once the length of the substitution tube has been calculated with the lowest hole open, the procedure can be repeated in precisely the same manner with the hole above opened and so on for all the remaining holes.

In the case of the modern flageolet the holes are relatively large, so the effect of the term S_1/L_R in the equation for evaluating L_x is small and can be ignored for rough calculations. In terms of diameters rather than areas the expression for L_x with $L_H = d/3$ is then

$$L_x = (D/3)(D/d)$$

In the extreme case when $d = D$ this gives $L_x = D/3$, which is simply the end correction for an open tube, as one might expect. When $d = D/2$, corresponding approximately to the larger holes on most flageolets, then $L_x = 2D/3$. One point to note is that if a hole is almost as large as the tube diameter, it effectively cuts off the tube at that point, so the pitch cannot be lowered by closing holes further down the instrument; this makes cross-fingering ineffective. In fact the flageolet is not designed to be played with cross-fingering. The instruments are made in a range of pitches and the appropriate one must be chosen for the key in which the music is written.

It should be pointed out that only the outline method of calculating the effect of tone holes has been given. If accurate results are required, then various corrections must be applied. The most important of these takes account of the viscous nature of the air, which gives rise to a very thin boundary layer along the wall of the tube, within which the velocity is changing rapidly from the tube velocity to zero velocity at the wall itself. The effect of this is to reduce slightly the resonant frequency of the tube, in effect increasing the value of L_x. Without accounting for this, all of the calculated frequencies are slightly too high.

The recorder

The recorder as we know it today is in essence the same as the baroque instrument. In the 19th century the recorder passed almost into disuse but it was revived by Arnold Dolmetsch in the 1920s. The instrument is generally in three sections, although cheaper school models combine the foot joint with the body so that the instrument is in two sections. The resonating tube tapers down slightly from top to bottom, but for most practical purposes can be considered as a cylindrical tube open at both ends. The earlier renaissance instrument has a wider bore and generally the degree of the taper is less. Fig. 8.29 (b) shows a Van Heerde treble baroque recorder in stained boxwood and Fig. 8.29 (a) a renaissance recorder for comparison.

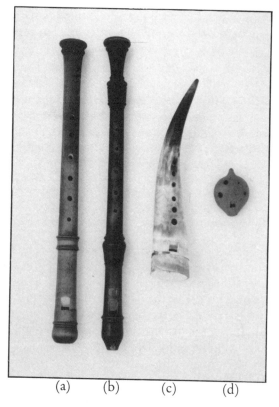

(a)   (b)   (c)   (d)

Fig. 8.29. Instruments with fipple sound generators: (a) a reproduction renaissance recorder by Hopf; (b) a baroque treble recorder by Van Heerde in stained boxwood (EUCHMI 257); (c) a gemshorn by Fitzpatrick; and (d) an ocarina.

Recorders in common use, with their ranges, are the sopranino (F_5–G_7), the descant or soprano (C_5–D_7), the treble or alto (F_4–G_6), the tenor (C_4–D_6) and the bass (F_3–D_5). The garklein (a fifth higher than the sopranino) is also available, together with various "great bass" instruments descending to C_3, F_2 or even C_2 (Munrow 1976).

Fig. 8.30 shows the construction of the descant recorder. It has eight holes, the lower two being divided, i.e. drilled as two separate small holes. By covering only one of the small holes, chromatic semitones can be produced above the lowest two notes. For the higher chromatic notes, cross-fingerings are used. These are quite effective on the recorder, in contrast to the flageolet. The recorder overblows the octave, so the fingering is essentially the same in the upper octave as it is in the lower. For the high notes the thumb hole at the back acts as a speaker hole and is half closed by pressing the thumb nail into the hole. The six upper holes at the front give the basic scale, but with the minor third rather than the major third used on the baroque flute and the flageolet. The lowest hole is not used for the upper octave.

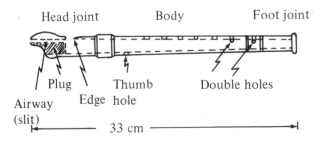

Fig. 8.30. The descant recorder.

Since the resonating tube is essentially cylindrical and open at both ends, the distance between the window (the opening in the front of the headjoint) and the bottom end corresponds approximately to a half wavelength for the lowest note. For the descant recorder the lowest note is C_5 with frequency 523 Hz, the corresponding half wavelength being $346/(2 \times 523) = 0.33$ m. In fact the distance between window and lower end is 28 cm, the shortfall being due primarily to end effects.

Ocarina and gemshorn

Two rather uncommon but interesting instruments which have fipple type sound generators are the ocarina and the gemshorn. Both of these are classed as *vessel flutes*, since the resonator is a hollow cavity of some fairly arbitrary shape, rather than a cylindrical or tapered tube. These instruments operate on the Helmholtz resonance principle, their resonant frequency being determined by the volume of the vessel and the area of the open holes.

The ocarina was invented in Italy in the mid-19th century and was a development of the earthenware bird whistle. An example is shown in Fig. 8.29 (d). This instrument has four holes of different size; by opening various combinations of these holes a diatonic scale of an octave can be obtained. Some models have a plunger at one end which can be pushed in or out to adjust the reasonance volume and hence the pitch. The instrument had something of a revival in the 1940s when it was sold under the name 'hot potato' and used in dance bands. The gemshorn is similar to the ocarina but is made from an animal horn. The open end is cut off square and made into a fipple using a wooden bung. Fig. 8.29 (c) shows a typical modern reproduction instrument. These usually have six or more holes.

The ocarina and gemshorn have an unusually pure tone because of their lack of harmonics. A curious feature of both which arises because of the Helmholtz principle is that opening different holes gives the same rise in pitch, provided they are of the same size.

9

Brass instruments

One of the most striking visual features of a symphony orchestra is the array of polished golden bells and glittering tubing which characterises the brass section: it is clear why the section is so named. In a jazz big band, trumpets and trombones are joined by a phalanx of saxophones of equal metallic splendour; yet the saxophone is technically not a 'brass' instrument, but a 'woodwind'. In fact, what distinguishes the brass and woodwind families is not the material of contruction, but the method of sound generation.

We saw in Chapter 5 that wind instruments ('aerophones') could be subdivided into three classes: mechanical reed, air reed and lip reed. Brass instruments (in the usual musical sense) fall into the category of lip reed aerophones – instruments in which a column of air is excited by the vibration of the lips of the player.

Brass and woodwind instruments have many acoustical features in common, although there are also many differences which have significant musical consequences. The term 'lip reed' suggests an analogy between the vibration of the lips in a brass instrument and that of a double mechanical reed in an instrument such as the oboe. We start by discussing the way in which the lips interact with the tube which is being excited; many of the features most characteristic of brass instruments arise from the particular nature of this interaction. We then survey the wide variety of shapes found in the tubing of brass instruments, examining the effect of variations in mouthpiece design and bell flare on intonation and tone quality. The use of crooks, slides or valves to extend the sounding length of a brass instrument introduces problems which have frequently been misunderstood; we discuss these problems in general terms, before proceeding to review the acoustical properties of specific families of brass instruments.

THE LIP REED

Pressure-controlled valves

Let us consider first a wind instrument with a single longitudinal standing wave in its air column. Air is oscillating up and down the tube; left to itself, the standing wave would quickly die out as its energy was dissipated by friction at the walls of the tube, or radiated as sound from its openings. In order to keep the oscillation going, energy must be supplied from outside. In practice, the source of this external energy is the air injected into the instrument by the player.

A steady flow of air down the instrument would not help to maintain the oscillation; it would add energy during one half of the oscillation cycle, but would take it away again during the other half. To make a positive net energy contribution, the air must be injected predominantly during the appropriate half cycle of the standing wave oscillation.

Lip reed instruments, like mechanical reed woodwinds, have a pressure antinode at the mouthpiece: that is, the embouchure behaves acoustically like a closed end. During one cycle of oscillation, the pressure exerted on the reed by the air in the mouthpiece fluctuates above and below its mean value. The reed is designed to respond to this pressure fluctuation by opening and closing in such a way that air flows strongly into the instrument when the mouthpiece pressure is high; when the mouthpiece pressure falls below average, the air flow is reduced, or even cut off entirely by the closure of the reed. The reed is behaving as a *pressure-controlled valve*.

We can see that the behaviour just described will reinforce the strength of the standing wave by considering Fig.9.1. This illustrates the lowest frequency standing wave in a cylindrical tube open at the lower end, with a small aperture in the otherwise closed upper end. The variation with time of the pressure just below the aperture is shown in the upper curve. At five particular instants during one oscillation cycle the distribution of pressure in the tube is represented by the depth of shading in the diagrams in the lower part of the figure.

At the instant represented by (a) in Fig. 9.1, the pressure is uniform throughout the tube. Air is flowing in through the lower end, however, and since it cannot escape through the effectively closed upper end, the pressure at the top of the tube begins to rise. At the instant represented by (b), the pressure at the top of the tube has reached its maximum value. (Note that the pressure at the open end remains constant, since it is a pressure node.) If, at this stage in the cycle, air is also flowing into the tube through the aperture, as illustrated by the black arrow in Fig. 9.1 (b), there will be an even greater quantity of air squeezed into the space at the top of the tube, and the pressure difference between the two ends of the tube will be increased.

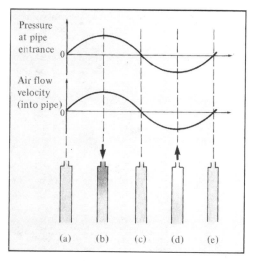

Fig. 9.1. When the air flow velocity is in phase with the pressure at the entrance to the tube, energy is supplied to the standing wave.

Similarly, at stage (d) the pressure at the top of the tube has fallen to its minimum value; the minimum will be further lowered if air is sucked out of the aperture during this phase of the cycle. We can thus draw the conclusion that if the flow of air into the mouthpiece of an instrument through a reed (mechanical or lip) is *in phase* with the pressure in the mouthpiece, the standing wave will be reinforced. The optimum phase of the air flow is shown by the lower curve in Fig. 9.1 Here we have assumed that the air speed has a simple sine curve variation; the situation in real musical instruments is usually more complicated, as we shall see shortly.

Fig. 9.2 illustrates what happens if the air flow through the reed is completely *out of phase* with the pressure at the entrance to the tube. At stage (b), the standing wave is trying to create a high pressure region at the top of the tube; since air is now allowed to flow out through the aperture, the height of the pressure maximum will be reduced. At stage (d) when the pressure at the antinode has its minimum value, air flowing in through the aperture partially replaces the air which has retreated towards the open end, so that the minimum is not as deep as it would otherwise be. Thus the out-of-phase air flow weakens the standing wave instead of strengthening it.

The argument is essentially unchanged if a steady flow of air is added to the oscillating flow; as long as more air is flowing into the instrument during the high pressure half cycle than during the low pressure half cycle, the net effect will be to reinforce the standing wave. An equilibrium can then be achieved in which the extra energy supplied to the standing wave just balances that lost through friction and sound radiation. This equilibrium corresponds to the production of a stable note of constant loudness.

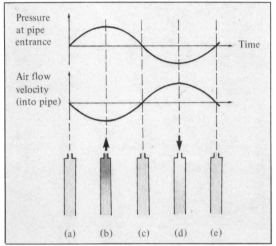

Fig. 9.2. When the air flow velocity is 180° out of phase with the pressure at the entrance to the tube, energy is drained from the standing wave.

The manner in which a woodwind reed or brass embouchure controls the air flow into the instrument so as to reinforce the standing waves in the air column was first explained clearly by Helmholtz (1863). The details of the process were further investigated, theoretically and experimentally, by Bouasse (1929 (a)), Benade and Gans (1968), Backus and Hundley (1971), and Worman (1971): the results of these investigations have been elegantly summarised by Benade (1973, 1976). The discussion of the operation of the lip reed which follows draws largely on this work, and on the recent studies by Fletcher (1979) and Elliott and Bowsher (1982).

Inward striking and outward striking reeds

To help clarify an important distinction between brass and woodwind instruments, we begin by recalling the discussion of a woodwind double reed in Chater 8 (p.260). Fig. 9.3 illustrates the opening and closing of a double reed under the combined influence of the fluctuating pressure in the tube and the pressure in the player's mouth. We assume that the mouth pressure is constant and always much larger than the tube pressure (see also Fig. 8.1). At time (a) the reed is slightly open, allowing a moderate flow into the instrument; as the pressure from the tube builds up towards its maximum at (b), the reed is forced wider and wider open, and the flow of air from the high pressure reservoir in the mouth increases. At time (d), on the other hand, the tube pressure has dropped to its minimum and the excess pressure from the mouth side is sufficient to close the reed. Comparing Fig. 9.3 with Fig. 9.1 shows this mechanism is just what is required to keep pressure and air flow in phase, supplying energy to the standing wave.

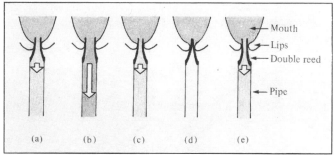

Fig. 9.3. Air flow (represented by the length of the arrow) and pressure (represented by the depth of shading) in a double reed, vibrating well below its natural resonant frequency.

If the mouth pressure is slowly increased while the tube pressure remains constant, the reed will gradually close. Such a reed is known as an *inward striking reed*. Single and double mechanical reeds of the type found on woodwind instruments are of the inward striking type.

When we come to examine the behaviour of the brass instrument lip reed, we find a fundamental difference of considerable musical significance. Normally the lips are stretched across some kind of mouthpiece, as shown in Fig. 9.4. If the mouth pressure is slowly increased, the lips bulge further into the mouthpiece, and the gap between them gradually opens. This is the characteristic behaviour of an *outward striking reed*.

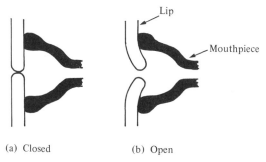

(a) Closed   (b) Open

9.4. The motion of the lips on a brass instrument mouthpiece

The importance of the distinction between inward and outward striking reeds is apparent when we apply the discussion accompanying Fig. 9.3 to the case of the lip reed, illustrated in Fig. 9.5. At a time when the mouthpiece pressure is high (Fig. 9.5 (b)), we would expect this high back pressure to close the lips, cutting off the flow of air. Only when the pressure in front of them was at its lowest (Fig. 9.5 (d)) would the lips open widely, allowing a large air flow into the mouthpiece.

We are then faced with a problem. Comparing Fig. 9.5 with Fig. 9.2 shows that mouthpiece pressure and air flow are out of phase when the lip is operating as we have described; the air flow is thus draining energy from the standing wave instead of reinforcing it. We appear to have demonstrated that stable notes on brass instruments are acoustically impossible.

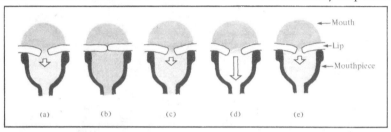

Fig. 9.5. Air flow and pressure when a lip reed vibrates below its natural resonant frequency.

Lip reed resonance

Experience tells us that a strong standing wave can certainly be excited and maintained in a tube by buzzing the lips against one end. The flaw in the preceding argument lies in the assumption that the bending of the lips is in phase with the pressure difference across them. We took it for granted that in Fig. 9.5 (b) the lips would bend upwards in response to a high pressure from below, while in Fig. 9.5 (d) they would bend downwards in response to a low pressure below. This is indeed the way that the lips will respond if the standing wave frequency is sufficiently low. However, the lips have their own natural resonant frequency, which depends on their mass and on the tension with which they are stretched across the mouthpiece. In a way which is characteristic of all such resonant systems (French 1971, p.85), a phase difference gradually develops between the pressure variations and the resulting lip movements as the standing wave frequency is raised towards the natural resonance frequency of the lips. When the standing wave frequency coincides with the lip resonance frequency, the lip movements lag behind the pressure variations by 90°; when the standing wave frequency is much higher than the lip resonance, the lips are moving almost completely out of phase with the pressure variations.

The latter situation is illustrated in Fig. 9.6. When the upward pressure on the lips is greatest (Fig. 9.6 (b)) they are bent downwards; when the net downward pressure is greatest (Fig. 9.6 (d)) they have their maximum upward displacement. Comparing Fig. 9.6 with Fig. 9.1 shows that we now have the necessary phase conditions for supplying energy to the air column. A stable standing wave can thus be maintained by a lip reed, provided that the standing wave frequency is *above* the natural resonance frequency of the lips.

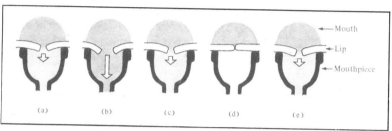

Fig. 9.6. Air flow and pressure when a lip reed vibrates above its natural resonance frequency.

By following a similar argument, it can be seen that an inward striking reed, such as that on the oboe or clarinet, can generate a stable standing wave only at a frequency *below* the natural reed resonance frequency. In practice, the reed resonance frequency in woodwind instruments is usually chosen to be well above the playing range of the instrument, so that this condition is always satisfied. The lips in a brass instrument mouthpiece constitute a much more massive vibrator, which only responds strongly to the pressure variations in the mouthpiece at frequencies close to the natural lip frequency. To feed energy into a particular standing wave on a brass instrument it is therefore necessary for the player to adjust his lip muscles so that the lip resonance frequency is just below the frequency of the standing wave.

The frequency of a standing wave maintained by a lip reed operating above its natural resonance frequency is a little higher than the standing wave frequency which would be measured if the mouthpiece end were completely closed. We can understand this effect by considering a compression pulse travelling up the tube from the open end. As the pulse reaches the mouthpiece, it finds the lips moving towards it: it is thus reflected slightly earlier than it would have been if the lips were stationary. The period T of the standing wave oscillation, which is the time taken for the pulse to travel up the tube and back down again, is therefore reduced by the lip vibration, and the frequency f (= 1/T) is increased. The opposite effect occurs with a woodwind reed operating below its natural resonance frequency: the playing frequency is below that measured with the reed end closed (see p.267).

At this point, experienced brass players may become a little uneasy.

Our theory so far implies that a stable note can be produced only at a pitch slightly above one of the natural resonances of the tube. How is it, then, that a player can 'lip' a note so as to pull it a semitone or more below its normal pitch? We shall defer a discussion of this important question until later in the chapter.

Harmonic generation by the lip reed

In Chapter 3 we examined the waveform of a trumpet, playing the note A_4 at various dynamic levels (Fig. 3.6). We saw that the waveform is simplest (closest to a sine curve) when the note is played very quietly; during a crescendo the waveform becomes more and more complex. Even at the pianissimo level, however, the waveform is not a pure sine curve. This means that the sound radiated by the trumpet normally contains several harmonic components. The same is true of other members of the brass instrument family. Yet our discussion of the operation of the lip reed implied that by choosing the resonance frequency of the lips properly the player could feed energy into only one of the possible vibration modes (standing waves) of the air column in the instrument. A single mode would radiate only a pure sine wave; where do the other harmonics come from?

Fig. 9.7. Cross-section of an idealised conical brass instrument.

To simplify our discussion, let us consider the case of an idealised brass instrument consisting of a long cone, open at the wide end and fitted with a mouthpiece at the narrow end (Fig. 9.7). There is, in fact, a real lip reed instrument which is very close to this idealised case: the Swiss alphorn (Fig. 9.8). We saw in Chapter 5 that for a cone complete to the vertex the standing wave frequencies form a complete harmonic series. The input impedance curve for the cone has thus a set of sharp peaks at whole number multiples of the lowest (fundamental) standing wave frequency. Fig. 9.9 shows the input impedance curve for an alphorn in $A^\flat$.

To sound the lowest note of the alphorn, the player adjusts his embouchure so that the lip resonance frequency is just below that of the first impedance peak; for the $A^\flat$ alphorn, this peak is at about 50 Hz. He then sets his lips vibrating by blowing a stream of air through them. The interaction between the lips and the pressure fluctuations in the cone encourages the development of the first air column mode, with its frequency raised slightly above 50 Hz by the lip reed effect previously mentioned.

In the 1940s, Martin carried out a classic experiment in which he filmed

Fig. 9.8 Swiss alphorn in A♭ (left) by Emmenegger; straight sectional horn in F (right) by Köhler (EUCHMI 490/656).

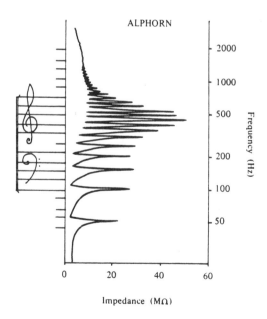

Fig. 9.9. Impedance curve for an A♭ alphorn.

the lip movements of a cornet player through a transparent mouthpiece. Analysis of the film showed that the lips vibrated in such a way that they only just closed once during each cycle (Fig. 9.10). The opening between the lips varied smoothly between zero and a maximum value which increased with loudness. The area of the lip opening is plotted as a function of time in Fig. 9.10; it can be seen that the open area varies almost sinusoidally about its average value.

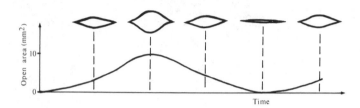

Fig. 9.10. Variations of the open area between the lips of a cornet player sounding the note $B^\flat$. Adapted from Martin (1942).

It should be emphasised that this nearly sinusoidal variation of the lip reed aperature is found for loud notes as well as for quiet notes. This is in sharp contrast to the behaviour of woodwind reeds, which for loud playing close completely during a considerable fraction of the cycle. It is easy to understand how woodwind reeds generate upper harmonics when blown strongly: the air is injected into the instrument as a series of detached puffs. Such an air flow will have a rich harmonic spectrum. Thus if the fundamental frequency is 50 Hz, there will also be a second harmonic component of the air flow at 100 Hz; if a standing wave mode exists with a frequency just above 100 Hz, the second harmonic component will feed energy into it, and it will build up. The same argument applies to the higher frequency components.

At first sight it appears that this explanation cannot apply to lip reed instruments. If the pressure inside the mouth is always much larger than that in the mouthpiece, we might expect the air flow through the lips to be simply proportional to the area of the gap between them. This would give a sinusoidal variation in the air flow, at the frequency of the lip vibration; there would be no upper harmonics in the excitation of the tube.

Using a technique known as hot wire anemometry, Elliott and Bowsher (1982) have recently measured the air flow in a trombone mouthpiece. A tiny probe containing a thin wire through which a current could be passed was inserted into the throat of the mouthpiece. The resistance of a wire depends on its temperature; when a current passes through it, it heats up and its resistance increases. The hot wire probe is connected to a device which monitors its resistance. When air flows past the wire, it conducts heat away from it, and the resistance falls; the speed of the air flow can be deduced from the resistance change. The result of such a measurement for the note B$\flat_2$ on the trombone is shown by the lower curve in Fig. 9.11; the upper curve shows the mouthpiece pressure, which was measured simultaneously by a probe microphone. Clearly the air flow is far from sinusoidal. In fact, the speed of the air in the mouthpiece throat hovers around 20 ms^{-1} for most of the cycle, dropping only briefly to zero (when the lips close). Such a waveform has a rich harmonic spectrum.

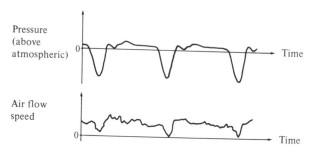

Fig. 9.11. Pressure and air flow velocity measured simultaneously in the throat of a trombone mouthpiece while the note B$\flat_2$ was played (Elliott and Bowsher 1982, p.209, Fig. 19).

How is it then that a smooth sinusoidal opening and closing of the lips results in a complex, spiky air flow? In our previous discussions, we assumed that the pressure in the player's mouth was always much higher than that in the instrument. Measurements made during the playing of a trombone, with probe microphones in the mouthpiece and in the mouth of the player, have demonstrated that this assumption is invalid (Elliott 1979). Indeed, the curves in Fig. 9.12 show that for a considerable fraction of the cycle of vibration the pressures inside and outside the lips are approximately equal; at a certain point the mouthpiece pressure even rises above that in the mouth. We might then expect to find that the direction of

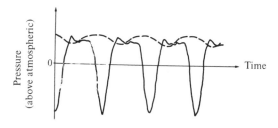

Fig. 9.12. Pressure measured (a) in the throat of a trombone mouthpiece (solid curve) and (b) in the mouth of the player (dashed curve). The note played was F$_3$. (Elliott 1979, p.C8-343, Fig. 4.)

313

the air flow reverses; measurements with the hot wire anemometer have confirmed that, for a small part of the cycle, air can actually flow out of the mouthpiece and into the player's mouth.

We can now see how the lip reed, by its very nature, tends to generate upper harmonics in the mouthpiece of a brass instrument. We return to the example of the alphorn in $A^\flat$. The first impedance peak occurs at 50 Hz; the lip reed will be able to sustain a standing wave at a slightly higher frequency (say 52 Hz) if the lip resonance frequency is chosen to be just below 50 Hz. Let us assume that the player's lips are temporarily frozen, and the alphorn is excited by an external loudspeaker radiating a sine wave of frequency 52 Hz. The pressure variation in front of the lips will then be sinusoidal. When the lips are unfrozen, they will respond to the pressure variation by opening and closing sinusoidally with a frequency of 52 Hz. If the excess pressure in the player's mouth is comparable with the amplitude of the mouthpiece pressure variation, the initial airflow through the lips will have a complex waveform, something like the shape of the lower curve in Fig. 9.11.

The complex air flow can be considered as a harmonic series of sine wave components, with fundamental frequency 52 Hz. Fig. 9.13 illustrates the relationship between the frequencies of these components and the frequencies of the impedance peaks of the alphorn (see p.311). The fundamental components has the frequency required to excite a strong standing wave based on the first impedance peak, as we have already seen. This standing wave will therefore build up strongly; we can switch off the external loudspeaker, since the air column vibration will now be sustained by energy fed in by the air flow.

When we turn our attention to the upper harmonic components of the air flow, we find that each of those also lies just above an impedance peak. Remembering that the relationship between pressure (p), volume air flow velocity (U) and impedance (Z) is

$$p = ZU, \text{ (see p.195)}$$

we can see that a component of air flow at a particular frequency will generate a large pressure variation if the impedance is large at that frequency. Thus each upper harmonic of the air flow will generate a strong standing wave at its own frequency.

Mode locking and co-operative regimes of oscillation

The foregoing discussion has shown how a self-sustaining oscillation at the first mode frequency results in the feeding of energy into higher modes of the air column. It is not necessary that these upper mode oscillations should be self-sustaining, provided that the fundamental mode is extracting enough energy from the air flow both to sustain itself and to supply energy to the upper modes. The situation is analogous to that of a mother bird with a nest of chicks: the mother must foray outside the nest to find food not only for herself but for her offspring, who themselves supply nothing.

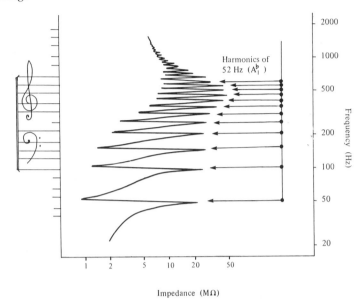

Fig. 9.13. The alphorn in A♭ has impedance peaks at multiples of 50 Hz. The harmonic components of the note A♭ are multiples of 52 Hz: each component lies just above an impedance peak. Note that the impedance is plotted on a logarithmic scale; this makes it easier to see the details of the minima in the curve.

It may be, however, that some of the higher modes are also capable of extracting energy from the lip reed in such a way as to become self-sustaining. If we consider the case in which first and second modes are both self-sustaining, we find that these two modes can supply energy not only to the remaining (energy-draining) modes, but also to each other. Father and mother are both feeding the chicks, and are exchanging particularly tasty morsels.

Remembering that the self-sustaining condition depends on the achievement of the correct phase relationship between lip vibration and pressure, we can see that two or more modes can be sustained simultaneously only if all the mode vibrations are 'locked' into a fixed phase relationship with the lips (Fletcher 1978). In the case of the alphorn note illustrated in Fig. 9.13, we might well have six or eight self-sustaining modes in action, each having a fixed phase relative to the lip vibration, and each interacting with all of the others through their common control of the air flow through the lips. Benade has suggested that this mutual aid society

315

of standing waves should be called a *regime of oscillation* (Benade 1973).

It is important to note that if the components of such a co-operative regime are to maintain fixed phase relationships, they must have frequencies which are exact members of a harmonic series. In a real brass instrument, the impedance peaks will not be exactly spaced at equal frequency intervals; indeed, in most brass instruments the first impedance peak is usually separated by much more than an octave from the second. Fig. 9.14 gives an example of a $B^\flat$ tenor trombone with the slide in first position; it will be seen that although the second and higher impedance peaks are close to the harmonics of $B^\flat_1$, the first peak occurs at a frequency of 39 Hz, a fifth below the fundamental of $B^\flat_1$ at 58 Hz.

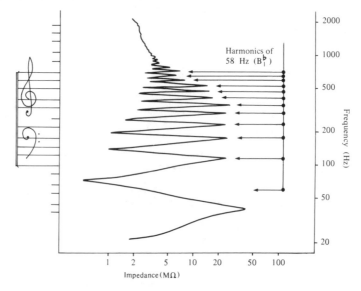

Fig. 9.14. Impedance curve for a $B^\flat$ tenor trombone in first position, illustrating the regime of oscillation which corresponds to pedal $B^\flat_1$.

Despite this deviation, the reason for which will become clear later in the chapter, it is possible to set up a co-operative regime which will sound the pedal note $B^\flat_1$. The player chooses a lip resonance frequency just below 58 Hz and sets his lips vibrating. The fundamental component of the air flow finds an impedance minimum at its own frequency, and so cannot sustain a standing wave. However, the upper harmonics set up a strong co-operative regime, since several are close to impedance peaks. The exact frequency of the vibration of the lips will normally be that which gives the strongest co-operative regime (although the player can 'lip' the pitch up or down to some extent); this frequency will be close to 58 Hz.

If the lip resonance frequency is lowered to just below 39 Hz, a weaker self-sustaining oscillation based on the first impedance peak can be set up (Fig. 9.15). Once again the lip reed will modulate the air flow, in a way which introduces components at multiples of about 40 Hz (just above the first impedance peak); in this case, however, these upper harmonics lie in the dips between the impedance maxima, and none of them can excite a self-sustaining oscillation. Only the 40 Hz mode will have a large amplitude. The absence of a co-operative regime of phase locked modes means that the lip vibration is much less strongly controlled by the tube; the player can lip the note up or down by several semitones. Such a note is often described as 'lacking centre': centring, in this sense, is dependent on the creation of a co-operative regime based on several strong impedance peaks.

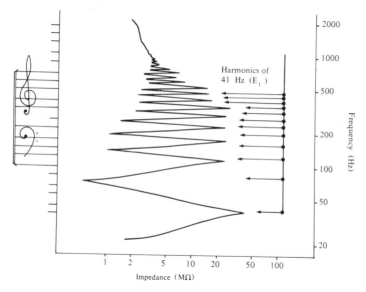

Fig. 9.15 With a relaxed lip, a trombonist can play the note E_1 on a tenor trombone in first position. Only the fundamental component is supported by an impedance peak.

Natural notes and privileged notes

By adjusting the lip resonance frequency, the player can choose from a wide variety of possible co-operative regimes; a range of different pitches can thus be obtained from a tube of fixed length. For example, Fig. 9.16 shows the regime set up on the A^b alphorn when the lip frequency around 156 Hz is chosen. The first three harmonic components of the airflow are close to the third, sixth and ninth impedance peaks of the instrument; a co-operative regime is thus set up which gives a strong, stable note at pitch E_3^b. This is one of the *natural notes* of the instrument: a note whose fundamental repetition frequency is close to the frequency of an impedance peak of the air column. The natural notes of the alphorn form an almost exact harmonic series. It should now be clear that any instrument which relies on co-operative regimes to stabilise its tones must give a set of natural notes which are reasonably close to a harmonic series; if this were not so the impedance peaks would not have the correct spacing to allow mode-locking to occur.

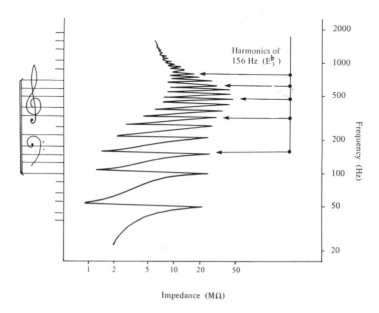

Fig. 9.16. The co-operative regime of oscillation which gives the note E_3^b on the alphorn.

Every brass player is familiar with the natural notes of his instrument – they provide the basic structure around which the playing technique is developed. Many players are unaware, however, that there is another set of notes which can be elicited from a brass instrument. These notes are sometimes called *privileged notes* (Bouasse 1929 (a), Benade 1960 (c)); they are much weaker than the natural notes, since they involve co-operative regimes of oscillation in which the fundamental component of the air flow is not supported by an impedance peak.

We have already met one rather special example of a privileged note in the pedal B_1^b of the tenor trombone. Another example is illustrated in Fig. 9.17: the note C_3, played on the A^b alphorn. The fundamental frequency of C_3 is 131 Hz; it is difficult to persuade the lips to vibrate at this frequency, which is intermediate between the second and third impedance

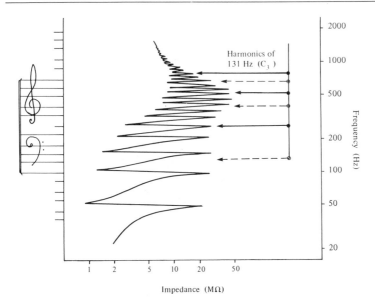

Fig. 9.17. Co-operative regime of oscillation supporting the privileged note C₃ on the alphorn. Dotted lines and open notes indicate components not sustained by impedance peaks.

peaks (at 104 Hz and 156 Hz respectively). The air column exerts a strong influence on the lips, trying to entice them into a co-operative regime in which the lip vibration frequency coincides with one or other of the peaks. The player who can avoid these attractions is rewarded by discovering that it is possible to play a relatively stable (although not very strongly centred) C_3. From Fig. 9.17 we can see that the second harmonic of the air flow coincides with the fifth impedance peak, while the fourth harmonic coincides with the tenth peak. We can therefore find a co-operative regime in which the even numbered components are self-sustaining. Of course, if only the even components were present, the note would sound as C_4, an octave higher: the mixing effect of the lip reed valve supplies energy to the odd components as well, so that we hear a note of pitch C_3, with prominent even harmonics (Fig. 9.18).

In principle, a privileged note can be found at any frequency which is equal to a natural note frequency divided by a whole number. There are thus many privileged notes on all brass instruments. Because of the difficulty in starting and maintaining these notes, they are not used in normal playing. They do occasionally feature as special effects, and can be used in an emergency to supply a note not otherwise available on the instrument (see p.385).

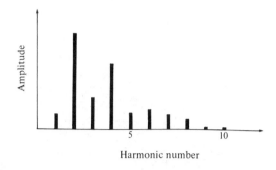

Fig. 9.18. Harmonic spectrum of the privileged tone C_3 played on the $A^\flat$ alphorn.

Mouthpiece pressure waveforms and harmonic spectra

Having gained some understanding of the way in which harmonics are generated in a brass instrument mouthpiece, we can now look in a little more detail at the waveforms and spectra of the mouthpiece pressure under different playing conditions. We must bear in mind that the mouthpiece spectrum tells us only what is going on inside the instrument – the radiated sound may have a very different spectrum, transformed by the properties of the radiating aperture (or apertures). We shall discuss the nature of this spectrum transformation later in the chapter. It is perhaps worth noting that, while the radiated spectrum relates directly to how the sound is heard by a listener, the mouthpiece spectrum relates directly to how the instrument feels to the lips of the player.

Fig. 9.19 shows the waveforms, and the corresponding spectra, measured with a probe microphone in the mouthpiece of a $B^\flat$ tenor trombone playing the notes $B^\flat_1$, $B^\flat_2$, $B^\flat_3$ and $B^\flat_4$. The pressure variation for the lowest two pitches shows the sharply peaked waveform that we have already seen in Figs. 9.11 and 9.12, associated with a spectrum rich in upper harmonics. On the other hand, the highest pitch has a waveform which is almost a pure sine curve, corresponding to a spectrum in which only the first harmonic is significant. It is clear that the lip reed valve is behaving very differently in these two extreme cases.

John Bowsher and his colleagues at Surrey University have made an extensive study of brass instrument mouthpiece acoustics, and have shown that the average resistance to air flow of the lip opening is an important factor in determining the nature of the mouthpiece pressure waveform (Elliott and Bowsher 1982). If the amplitude of the lip vibration is large, average resistance is low: air can pass relatively freely through the lips, and the pressure drop across the lips is small except during the small fraction of the cycle when they are nearly closed. If the amplitude of lip

320

vibration is small, a large pressure drop is needed to force air through the much higher resistance offered by the lips even at their widest opening.

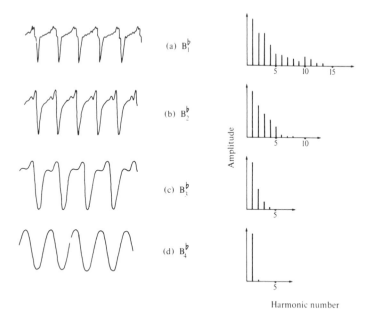

Fig. 9.19. Waveforms (left) and harmonic spectra (right) of the pressure variations in a trombone mouthpiece during the playing of four notes.

The average lip opening in brass instrument playing is largest for notes of low pitch, and decreases steadily as the pitch of the note being played rises (Martin 1942). The average resistance R_o therefore increases with pitch; this is shown by the dashed curve in Fig. 9.20, based on measurements of trombone playing made by Elliott and Bowsher. Also shown in Fig. 9.20 is a typical impedance curve for a B^b tenor trombone. A comparison of these curves shows that for the note B^b_2 the average lip resistance is very much less than the impedance of the instrument at the fundamental frequency of 119 Hz (the second lowest peak shown). This corresponds to the case illustrated by Fig. 9.12; the assumption that mouth pressure is always much greater than mouthpiece pressure is invalid, and the waveform of mouthpiece pressure has the characteristic sharp downward spike (Fig. 9.19 b).

For the note B^b_4, on the other hand, the magnitude of Z at the fundamental frequency of 466 Hz is about the same as that of R_o. In this case, there will always be a large pressure drop between the mouth and the mouthpiece. We can therefore expect the variation of the air flow through

321

the lips to follow more closely the (nearly sinusoidal) variation of the lip opening; harmonics are generated less strongly in the mouthpiece, and the resulting waveform is almost a pure sine curve (Fig. 9.19 (d)).

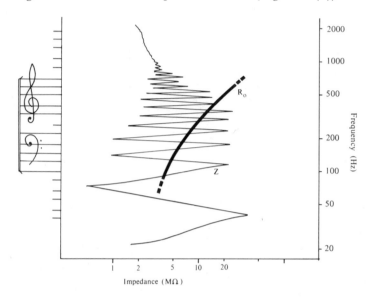

Fig. 9.20. Comparison between the impedance Z of a tenor trombone and the average resistance R_0 of the lip opening. Values of R_0 were obtained from Elliott and Bowsher (1982), p.209, Fig. 20.

The low pitch case

Although an exact theory of the operation of the lip reed is not yet available, the nature of the mouthpiece spectrum has been calculated for some simplified cases. One remarkable result relates to the low pitch case described above, for which R_0 is much less than Z. Elliott and Bowsher have shown that, in this case, there is a simple relationship between amplitudes of the different harmonic components of mouthpiece pressure. If we call the amplitude of the nth component P_n, then

$$P_n = (P_1/4P_s)^{n-1} P_1$$

(where P_s is the difference between atmospheric and mouth pressure, assumed constant).

To illustrate the significance of this result, let us consider a note for which $P_1 = P_s$: the pressure amplitude of the fundamental component is equal to the magnitude of the mouth pressure. Then $P_1/4P_s = \frac{1}{4}$. The

322

amplitude of the second harmonic is given from the formula by putting $n = 2$:

$$P_2 = (P_1/4P_s)\, P_1 = \tfrac{1}{4}P_1$$

Similarly,
$$P_3 = (P_1/4P_s)^2\, P_1 = \tfrac{1}{16}P_1$$

$$P_4 = (P_1/4P_s)^3\, P_1 = \tfrac{1}{64}P_1$$

The harmonic spectrum for this note, shown in Fig. 9.21 (black circles), is characteristic of a trombone $B^\flat_2$ played pp.

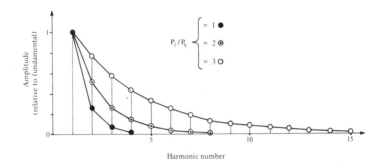

Fig. 9.21. Harmonic spectra for a low pitch trombone mouthpiece waveform, calculated from the theory of Elliott and Bowsher (1982) for three different values of the parameter P_1/P_s.

To increase the dynamic level of the note, the player increases the blowing pressure P_s. The average amplitude of the lip vibration also increases; measured mouthpiece waveforms imply that P_1 grows more rapidly than P_s (Elliott and Bowsher 1982, p.202). The effect on the mouthpiece spectrum of increasing the ratio P_1/P_s is shown in Fig. 9.21: the note becomes increasingly rich in upper harmonics.

A striking feature of this result is that the mouthpiece spectrum does not depend on the details of the impedance curve of the instrument to which the mouthpiece is coupled. The harmonic spectra of Fig. 9.21, and the corresponding waveforms, will be the same for any brass instrument which has impedance peaks sufficiently high to justify the approximation that Z is much greater than R_o.

The high pitch case

For notes of higher pitch, the assumption that P_s is always much greater than P_1 is justified. We then have a situation similar to that of the reed woodwinds. In Chapter 8 we saw that, for low to medium amplitudes of vibration of the reed, the height of a particular harmonic in the mouthpiece spectrum of a reed woodwind is proportional to the height of the relevant impedance peak; we can expect the same to be true for brass instruments. Thus, in contrast to the low pitch case, the mouthpiece spectrum for higher notes will reflect the structure of the impedance curve for the particular instrument being played.

As with the woodwinds, the harmonic spectrum is relatively pure for quiet playing, becoming steadily richer as the dynamic level is increased. There is, however, one important difference to note between the woodwinds and the brass. Above a certain critical blowing pressure, the reed of a woodwind instrument closes completely for a significant part of its cycle. At this critical blowing pressure the player notices a 'change of feel'; the tone quality of the note develops a hard edge which reflects the spikiness of the mouthpiece waveform (Benade 1976, p.442). With the outward beating lip reed a similar 'change of feel' is experienced for notes in the middle register. This is not due to an increased closure of the lips, however: we have seen that the lip vibration adjusts automatically, so that for quiet or loud playing it only just closes once in each cycle. Instead, the change occurs when the average lip opening has increased to such an extent that a large pressure drop across the opening can no longer be maintained. We are then back in the low pitch case, with its spiky waveform.

For notes in the highest register of the instrument, such a large lip amplitude cannot be attained, and the waveform remains close to sinusoidal even for fortissimo playing. The relative purity of the waveform is accentuated by the fact that the standing wave is supported only by the impedance peak at the fundamental frequency, the peaks at the frequencies of the upper harmonic components being much too small to contribute to a regime of oscillation (see Fig. 9.14).

Mouth and throat resonances

Much theoretical and experimental work is at present being carried out on the behaviour of the lip reed, and some aspects of the simplified theory outlined above will almost certainly require revision as our understanding develops. We close our discussion by mentioning briefly two other aspects of lip reed acoustics which are recognised as having considerable musical significance.

In the first instance, acousticians are only now catching up with practical brass instrumentalists, who have long insisted that the shape of the player's mouth and throat has a considerable influence on the stability and tone quality of the note produced (Hall 1955; Elliott and Bowsher 1982). As long as the lungs, throat and mouth are treated purely as a means of supplying air at constant pressure behind the lips, it is difficult to see why their shape should be relevant. However, we can look on the player's windway as effectively a second 'brass instrument', with the air flowing in the 'wrong' direction (that is, towards the lips rather than away from them) (Fig. 9.22). The tubes and cavities of the windway will also have an acoustic impedance, and therefore the fluctuations in the air flow introduced by the lip vibrations will cause a fluctuating pressure difference between the lungs and the mouth.

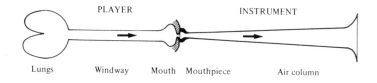

Fig. 9.22. Schematic diagram showing the relation of the player's windway to the instrument. The arrows show the direction of the average air flow.

The fluctuation of the pressure in the mouth has already been seen in Fig. 9.12. By adjusting the mouth and throat, it is possible for the player to modify the resonances of the windway so as to amplify one or other of the components of the mouth pressure. Benade and Hoekje (1982) and Clinch et al. (1982) have claimed that windway resonances can significantly influence woodwind timbre (see p.261), although this view has recently been challenged by Backus (1985).

Dramatic changes in the spectrum of the mouth pressure produce only subtle changes in the mouthpiece spectrum of a woodwind instrument, because of the high average resistance of the reed opening. The effect is likely to be more significant in the low pitch regime of brass instruments, where mouth and mouthpiece are at almost the same pressure for most the cycle. Also of great importance is the role that a strong windway resonance can play in helping to create or stabilise a regime of oscillation. The player has at his command an additional high impedance peak which can be adjusted in pitch to fit in harmonically with whatever the instrument has provided; since the lip vibration is controlled by the pressure *difference* between mouth and mouthpiece, a strong resonance on the mouth side contributes to the stability of the co-operative regime in essentially the same way as do the instrument resonances. To maximise the pressure difference across the lips, it is of course necessary that the mouth pressure fluctuations should be 180° out of phase with the mouthpiece pressure fluctuations; the measurements of the two quantities presented in Fig. 9.23 show that the expected phase difference is indeed found (Elliott and Bowsher 1982).

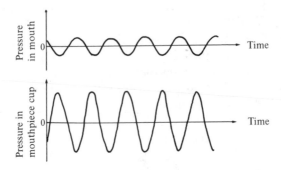

Fig. 9.23 Measurements by Elliott and Bowsher (1982), p.205, Fig. 16
(b), showing that, when the note $B^{\flat}_4$ is played on a tenor
trombone, the variation of pressure in the player's mouth is
180° out of phase with the variation in the mouthpiece cup.

We can thus understand how adjustments of the mouth and throat can
affect the tone quality of a note on a brass instrument, and can make it
easier to produce a note at a pitch for which the instrument on its own
cannot generate a self-sustaining regime. The process is clearly very
similar to that used by singers to create different vowel sounds. It is worth
noting, however, that when singing vowels, the lips are normally fairly
open, while the larynx is almost closed (see Chapter 12); when playing a
brass instrument, the larynx is open to allow a free flow of air, and the lip
opening is very small. The mouth position which gives formant resonance for a particular vowel sound (p.482) will therefore give different
mouth resonance frequencies in brass instrument playing.

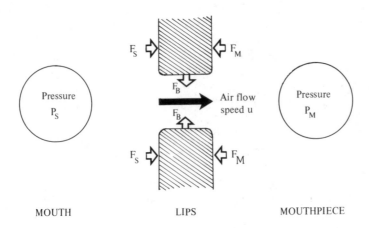

Fig. 9.24. The Bernoulli force F_B, created by the flow of air between the
lips, tends to pull the lips together.

The Bernoulli force

Our discussion of the behaviour of the lip reed up to this point has assumed that the air exerts only two forces on each lip: a force F_S, due to the mouth pressure P_S, pushing the lip into the mouthpiece, and a force F_M, due to the mouthpiece pressure P_M, pushing in the opposite direction (see Fig. 9.24). There is, however, a third force acting on the lip when air is flowing through the opening: this is the Bernoulli force F_B which tends to pull the lips together. We saw in Chapter 8 that the Bernoulli force has a small but significant effect on the operation of woodwind reeds. What is its role in lip reed behaviour?

The magnitude of the Bernoulli force is given by

$$F_B = \tfrac{1}{2} \varrho \, u^2 \, A$$

where u is the air flow speed, ϱ the density of the air and A the effective area of each lip parallel to the direction of flow. The air flow speed is determined by the pressure difference across the lip opening; it can be shown that the relationship is approximately given by (Backus 1963; Fletcher 1979)

$$u^2 = (2/\varrho) \, (P_S - P_M)$$

We can thus combine these two equations to eliminate u^2, giving

$$F_B = (P_S - P_M) \, A.$$

(Elliott and Bowsher 1982).

From this equation we can see that, if the mouthpiece pressure P_M rises towards P_S, the force F_B will be reduced. The lip opening will therefore widen. If the mouthpiece pressure falls, increasing the pressure difference $P_S - P_M$, the increase in F_B will tend to close the lips. Thus the Bernoulli force makes a contribution to the control of the air flow for which the phase relationship between pressure difference and lip opening is that of an inward striking rather than an outward striking reed (see Figs 9.1 and 9.2).

Benade has suggested that the brass player's ability to lip a note above or below the pitch of the relevant impedance peak of the instrument could be explained by the use of the Bernoulli force (Worman 1971, p.111; Elliott and Bowsher 1982). We saw previously that, when the Bernoulli force F_B is negligible in comparison with the direct pressure forces F_S and F_M, the lip resonance frequency must be chosen to be below that of the impedance peak; the sounding pitch is then above the peak. If the player can adjust his lips (for example, by increasing the area A) in such a way that the Bernoulli force becomes dominant, the lip reed valve will adopt the characteristics of an inward striking reed; a self-sustaining oscillation will require a lip resonance frequency above the impedance peak, and the sounding pitch will be below the peak.

We do not yet know enough about the detailed motion of the lips in a brass instrument mouthpiece to be sure that this is the correct explanation of lipping technique. It is certainly clear that adjustments of the lips can produce drastic changes in the behaviour of a brass instrument. Indeed, this is one of the most striking differences between the woodwind instruments and the brass: in the woodwind class, the reed has more or less fixed properties, and is dominated by the air column of the instrument; in the brass the effective mass, area and springiness of the lips can be widely varied by the player, and the lips play a much more powerful role in the interaction with the air column.

A good player who has all these variable factors well under control can compensate to a considerable extent for the imperfections of a particular instrument, and can extend its range well beyond what appear to be the technical limits. The playing of a pedal note, as we saw, relies on the player's ability to sustain a lip vibration at a frequency which is between the first and second impedance peaks; many other low pitch 'fakes' can be obtained by forcing the lips to vibrate at frequencies which are not close to an impedance peak of the instrument.

Fig. 9.25. Extract from the first trumpet part of Richard Strauss's 'Alpensinfonie' (sounding a tone lower than written).

At the upper extreme of the range, the player can make use of the Bernoulli force to create notes which are too high to be sustained by a co-operative regime of oscillation (Benade 1976, p.447). The orchestral repertoire occasionally calls for the note D_6 (sounding pitch) on the $B^\flat$ trumpet (e.g. the extract from Strauss's 'Alpensinfonie', Fig. 9.25). The impedance curve of a typical $B^\flat$ trumpet is shown in Fig. 9.26: although the tenth peak provides some support for the fundamental component of the note D_6, the peaks diminish rapidly above this pitch, and there are no helpful air column resonances coinciding with the second or higher harmonics. In the absence of the powerful mode locked regime which stabilises notes of lower pitch, the Bernoulli force is the dominant lip control mechanism. The stratospheric exploits of some jazz virtuosi, who venture up to an octave higher, show that it is possible to create notes in this way without even a small peak for the fundamental to lean on.

THE SHAPES OF BRASS INSTRUMENTS

The resonating air columns in woodwind instruments come in two basic shapes: cylindrical or conical. In Chapter 5 we saw that only these two

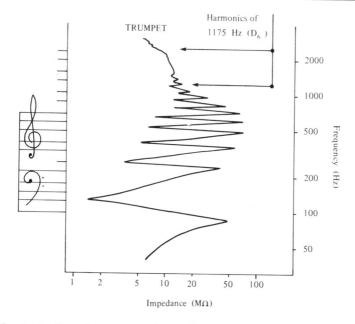

Fig. 9.26. Impedance curve for a B♭ trumpet, showing the lack of support for the highest note in Fig. 9.25.

types of column allow a fixed set of finger holes to be used to play scales in more than one register.

The air columns of lip reed instruments are more difficult to classify. Instruments like the cornett and the serpent, on which finger holes are used in the same way as on woodwind instruments, have essentially conical air columns, as do some natural (i.e. fixed length) instruments such as the alphorn and the bugle. In general, however, the air column of a brass instrument consists of several sections of varying profile. A column typical of the trumpet or trombone is shown schematically in Fig. 9.27. First comes a *mouthpiece* in the form of a cup with a narrow throat; an

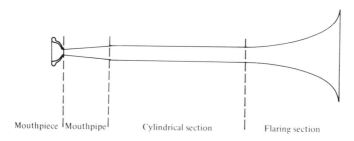

Fig. 9.27. Schematic diagram of the air column of a brass instrument (not to scale).

approximately conical *mouthpipe* acts as a transition between the mouthpiece throat and a *cylindrical section*. If the instrument has valves, they are places in the cylindrical section. Finally comes the *flaring section*; the diameter of the column increases more and more rapidly, ending in a wide bell.

We have seen that a successful brass instrument must have an air column whose normal mode resonance frequencies are reasonably close to a harmonic series. A conical tube satisfies this criterion; on the other hand, it is by no means obvious that the tube sketched in Fig. 9.27 will do so. In fact, the resonance frequencies of such a tube can deviate substantially from a harmonic series, particularly at low frequencies (see Fig. 9.14). Over the centuries, brass instrument manufacturers have discovered by trial and error that certain combinations of mouthpiece, mouthpipe, cylinder and flare give an acceptable approximation to a true set of harmonics. In the last thirty years, the physical principles underlying these empirical choices have been clarified, and this scientific understanding has led to some significant improvements in the design of brass instruments (Kent 1961; Cardwell 1970; Benade 1973, 1976; Smith and Daniell 1976).

The mouthpiece: impedance multiplication

The most characteristic feature of brass instruments, common to both conical instruments and to those of more general profile, is the mouthpiece. The detailed form varies greatly from one instrument to another: Fig. 9.28 contrasts the cup shape of a typical trumpet mouthpiece with the funnel shape more characteristic of the horn. The important feature in all cases is that a substantial volume of air exists between the player's lips and a relatively narrow throat which communicates with the main tube of the instrument.

(a) Trumpet   (b) Horn

Fig. 9.28. Cross-section of typical brass instrument mouthpieces.

The most obvious function of the mouthpiece is to provide a supporting frame against which the player's lips can be pressed. More significantly, it acts as an *impedance multiplier*, boosting the height of the impedance peaks in the middle register of the instrument. It performs this function because the volume of air bewteen the player's lips and the mouthpiece throat acts as a Helmholtz resonator (see p.208) (Cardwell 1970).

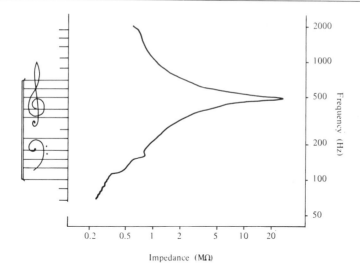

Fig. 9.29. Impedance curve for a trombone mouthpiece.

When a trombone mouthpiece alone is mounted on the impedance measuring equipment described in Chapter 8 (p.268), an impedance curve such as that shown in Fig. 9.29 is obtained. At the Helmholtz resonance frequency, in this case around 500 Hz, a strong impedance peak is found. The mass of air in the throat of the mouthpiece is bouncing on the spring provided by the air trapped in the cup (see Fig. 9.30); at the natural resonance frequency, there is a large amplitude of vibration (and therefore, a large volume velocity) in the throat. On the other hand, the air

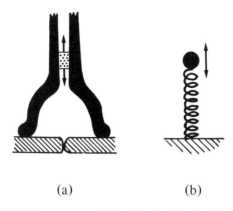

(a)   (b)

Fig. 9.30. (a) A segment of air vibrating in the throat of a trombone mouthpiece; (b) the forces on the air are similar to those on a ball supported by a spring.

331

there is relatively free to move in and out, so that the pressure fluctuations are small. This corresponds to a very low impedance in the throat ($Z = p/U$). At the position of the lips, the opposite condition prevails: the volume velocity is practically zero, and large pressure variations occur. Thus the lips feel a very large impedance Z at the resonance frequency.

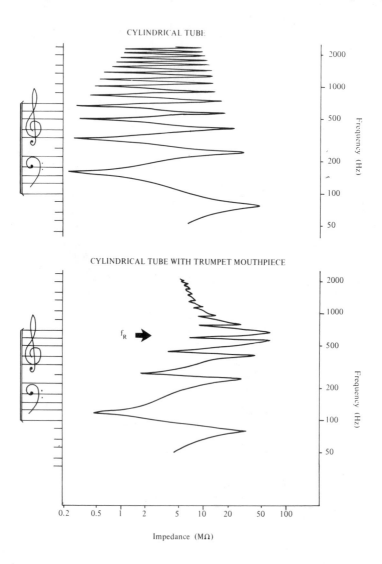

Fig. 9.31. Impedance curves for a cylindrical tube one metre long (upper curve) and for the same tube fitted with a trumpet mouthpiece (lower curve). The mouthpiece resonance frequency f_R is marked by an arrow.

When the mouthpiece is coupled to an instrument, the situation is more complicated, since the throat opens into a tube with its own set of resonances. At frequencies far from the mouthpiece resonance, the heights of the impedance peaks are little affected by the properties of the mouthpiece. Around the mouthpiece resonance, however, the impedance peaks are strongly modified by the mouthpiece: Fig. 9.31 shows how the peaks of a cylindrical tube are raised by the addition of a trumpet mouthpiece.

Bearing in mind that a stable note on a brass instrument requires a co-operative regime of oscillation based on a set of strong impedance peaks, we can see that a well-designed mouthpiece is a vital part of the instrument. It is clearly important to choose the right mouthpiece resonance frequency, so as to obtain impedance multiplication where it is most useful. The mouthpiece resonance frequency is sometimes called the 'popping frequency' since it can be estimated by listening to the pitch of the popping sound heard when the mouthpiece is slapped against the palm of the hand (Benade 1973). (It is easy to misjudge this highly damped sound as being an octave below its true pitch.)

Mouthpiece effects on intonation

Careful examination of Fig. 9.31 shows that the addition of a mouthpiece to a cylindrical tube alters not only the heights but also the frequencies of the impedance peaks. The intonation of an instrument is thus critically dependent on the design of the mouthpiece. To clarify the nature of this dependence, let us return to our simple example of the conical alphorn.

We assumed earlier that the resonances of a conical instrument were exact harmonics; this assumption cannot be strictly valid for a real instrument, since the apex of the cone must be cut off in order to provide an aperture for the lips. For most conical wind instruments, the cutoff part is about 10% of the total length of the cone; when the narrow end is closed by the lips, the resonating tube has the shape shown by the solid line in Fig. 9.32 (a).

At very low frequencies, the resonances of such a truncated cone (length L) are very close to those of the equivalent complete cone (length L_o) – it is as if the sound waves being reflected up and down the tube did not notice that the apex section was missing (Benade 1959; Nederveen 1969). The higher frequency resonances are increasingly affected by the absence of the apex section, and at very high frequencies the resonances are close to those of a cone of length L rather than L_o. The gradual sharpening of the resonances is illustrated in Fig. 9.33, for the case of the A^b alphorn. The pitches of the resonances which would be obtained if the cone were complete to the apex are shown by black circles; the corresponding pitches, calculated on the assumption that 10% of the cone is missing, are shown by the open circles lying on the curve marked (a). The horizontal displacement of each open circle from the vertical line shows how much the resonance has been sharpened by the removal of the apex section.

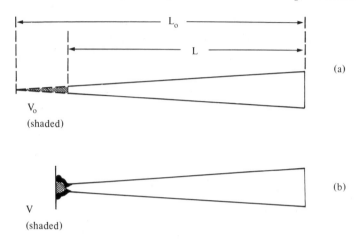

Fig. 9.32. (a) An ideal complete cone of length L_o is reduced to a length L by removal of the apex. The volume lost is V_o. (b) The addition of a mouthpiece restores a volume V.

An $A^\flat$ alphorn whose eighth harmonic had a pitch of $A^\natural$ would be of little musical use. Fortunately, the addition of a suitable mouthpiece brings the resonances back into a reasonably harmonic relationship. For frequencies well below the mouthpiece resonance, the only significant feature of the mouthpiece is the total volume of air which it contains; let us call this volume V. If we make V equal to the volume V_o of the missing apex section, we find that the resonances are shifted to the pitches shown in Fig. 9.33 by the open circles on curve (b). The first four are now practically true harmonics of $A^\flat$, although the tenth resonance is still 55 cents sharp.

If we make the mouthpiece volume bigger, the high resonances are improved, but the lower ones become too flat; this is illustrated by the circles on curve (c) in Fig. 9.33, corresponding to the case $V = 1.5V_o$. Adjusting only the volume of the mouthpiece cannot bring all the resonances into a harmonic relationship.

In the foregoing discussion, we have assumed that the mouthpiece resonance is much higher in pitch than the resonances we are studying. The Helmholtz resonance frequency of the mouthpiece depends not only on the volume of the cup, but also on the diameter of the throat; by keeping the volume constant while reducing the throat diameter it is possible to lower the pitch of the mouthpiece resonance, bringing it into

the playing range of the instrument. Indeed, as we saw earlier, the impedance multiplying function of the mouthpiece demands that the resonance
frequency should be in the region of the eighth impedance peak of the
instrument tube.

When the resonant property of the mouthpiece is taken into account, it
is found that the impedance peaks of the tube are flattened by an amount
which increases with frequency up to, and beyond, the mouthpiece resonance frequency (see p.342). By careful choice of the size of the
mouthpiece throat, and the profile of the tapering backbore which joins
the throat to the instrument, it is possible to bring the higher resonances of
curve (b) in Fig. 9.33 sufficiently close to the true harmonics of A♭ for the
instrument to function as though it were indeed an ideal, complete cone.

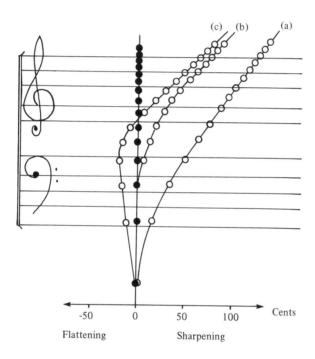

Fig. 9.33. When the cone is complete, the resonances are harmonic
(black circles). Removing 10% of the length distorts the
pitches of the resonances (curve (a)). Adding a mouthpiece
with $V = V_o$ gives the correction shown by curve (b). Increasing the mouthpiece volume to $3V_o/2$ flattens the lower resonances (curve (c)). The calculation of the effect of mouthpiece
volume is based on Nederveen (1969), p.39, Eqn. 27.2, and
does not take into account the Helmholtz resonance of the
mouthpiece.

Equivalent cone length

A satisfactory brass instrument must have a set of resonances whose frequencies are close to a complete harmonic series. A conical tube fitted with a suitable mouthpiece has such a set of resonances. The conical tube therefore provides a useful reference against which the properties of tubes with more complicated profiles can be judged.

Let us consider a specific example: the B^b tenor trombone whose impedance curve is shown in Fig. 9.14. Apart from the two lowest impedance peaks, the resonances are close to a harmonic series with fundamental frequency 58 Hz (B^b_1). This harmonic series would be obtained from an ideal cone (complete to the apex) with a length of 2974 mm. We can thus say that, for the third and higher resonances, the trombone has an *equivalent cone length* (L_e) close to 2974 mm.

The second impedance peak of the trombone occurs at 112 Hz; a cone of length 3080 mm would have its second harmonic at this frequency. The equivalent cone length of the trombone has therefore increased to 3080 mm at 112 Hz. At 39 Hz, the frequency of the first impedance peak, the

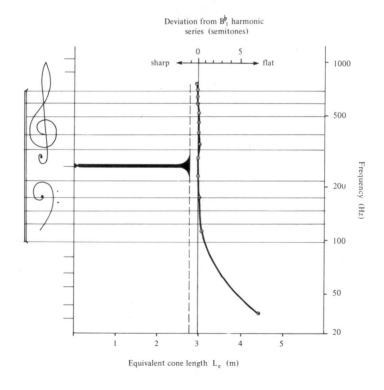

Fig. 9.34. The variation with pitch of the equivalent cone length L_e of a B^b tenor trombone.

equivalent cone length of the trombone has increased to 4423 mm, since a cone of this length would have a fundamental resonance frequency of 39 Hz.

In general, if the nth resonance of an instrument occurs at a frequency f_n, the equivalent cone length at that frequency is given by the formula

$$L_e = nc/2f_n$$

where c is the speed of sound (Pyle 1975).

The variation of equivalent cone length with frequency for a tenor trombone is shown in Fig. 9.34. The principal advantage of such a diagram is that it enables one to see at a glance the extent to which the resonances of a given instrument deviate from an exact harmonic series. An increase in L_e is equivalent to a flattening of the corresponding resonances; the magnitude of this flattening (in semitones) is indicated by the upper horizontal scale on the diagram.

The physical length of the trombone tube, marked in Fig. 9.34 by the dashed vertical line, is 2770 mm (from mouthpiece rim to bell). Thus for frequencies above the second resonance, the trombone behaves like an ideal cone whose length is about 7% greater than the physical length of the instrument. It is remarkable that the complicated trombone profile (Fig. 9.35 (a)) yields the same resonances as a simple cone (Fig. 9.35 (b)) over so much of its playing range. To aid our understanding of how this correspondence is achieved, and why it breaks down at the lowest resonance, it is useful to consider the contributions to the total equivalent length of the trombone due to the various sections of the tube: mouthpiece, mouthpipe, cylinder and flare.

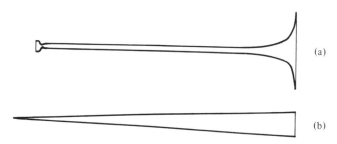

Fig. 9.35. (a) The profile of a trombone (horizontal and vertical scales are different). (b) The equivalent cone, giving almost the same resonances at high pitches.

Handel on the hosepipe

There can be few brass instrumentalists who have not occasionally amused themselves (and others) by 'getting a few notes' from a piece of hosepipe or metal tubing. The hosepipe is equivalent to the purely cylindrical section of the trombone, with the mouthpiece, mouthpipe, and flaring sections removed; how close does it come to being a useful musical instrument?

Since the playing end of the pipe is effectively closed by the lips, the resonance frequencies constitute the odd members of a harmonic series with fundamental frequency

$$f_1 = c/4L$$

L being the length of the pipe. The second resonance thus had frequency $f_2 = 3 \, (c/4L)$, the third resonance a frequency $f_3 = 5 \, (c/4L)$; in general, the nth resonance had a frequency $f_n = (2n-1)(c/4L)$. As n becomes larger, $(2n-1)$ becomes closer and closer to 2n: when n = 10, for example, $2n-1 = 19$ while $2n = 20$, a difference of only 5%. The nth resonance frequency then approaches $(2n) \, (c/4L) = n \, (c/2L)$, which is just the nth resonance frequency of an ideal cone of length L. In other words, the equivalent cone length of our hosepipe trumpet is close to its actual length for resonance corresponding to large values of n.

The general formula for the equivalent cone length at the nth resonance of the hosepipe, valid for all values of n, is

$$L_e = \{2n/(2n-1)\} \, L.$$

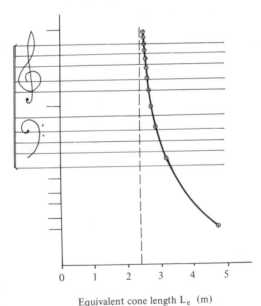

Equivalent cone length L_e (m)

Fig. 9.36. Equivalent cone length of a cylindrical 'hosepipe trumpet'.

The variation of L_e with frequency is shown in Fig. 9.36, for a hosepipe of length 2350 mm. The practical musician, perhaps a little suspicious of the mathematical manipulations of the preceding paragraph, can check experimentally that Fig. 9.36 really does describe the behaviour of a hosepipe trumpet. On a piece of fairly sturdy tubing about 13 mm in diameter, the resonances from the second to the tenth can be readily obtained by an experienced brass player. We should remember that the playing frequencies are not necessarily exactly those of the impedance peaks of the tube, because of the lip reed effects previously discussed; nevertheless, the pitches of the notes which can be obtained from a 2350 mm tube are very close to those shown in Fig. 9.36.

The best way to appreciate the musical significance of the variation of the equivalent cone length of the hosepipe is to attempt to play on it a piece of music intended for the natural trumpet or bugle. The bugle call illustrated in Fig. 9.37, for example, makes use of notes which are the 3rd, 4th, 5th and 6th harmonics of C_2. How will this sound on the hosepipe?

Fig. 9.37. Bugle call: part of the British Army 'Retreat' (normally written an octave higher).

The pitch of the 5th resonance for the particular length of pipe we have chosen is very close to E_4. The interval between this and the 4th resonance, which we have to use as C_4, is 434 cents, 49 cents bigger than a just intonation major third. Similarly, the interval between E_4 and the 6th resonance, which must serve as our G_4, is 32 cents larger than a just intonation minor third. Thus the tuning is 'stretched' by the variation in effective length. Our 'perfect fifth' (C_4–G_4) will be over 80 cents too wide; the octave span of the melody (G_3–G_4) is extended by 165 cents – nearly two semitones.

The hosepipe bugle is clearly an abysmal failure. On the other hand, a part written for the baroque natural trumpet, such as the obbligato in 'The trumpet shall sound' from Handel's oratorio 'Messiah', can be tackled with somewhat greater success on the hosepipe. The first two bars of Fig. 9.38 are still problematical, since they require the use of the 4th, 5th and 6th resonances, where the equivalent length is varying substantially. However, from the third complete bar onwards, the example uses only resonances above the 7th; although the average tonality has drifted up from C to C#, the relative mistuning is much less severe. The interval from the 8th to the 12th resonance, which must serve as a perfect fifth, is only 38 cents too wide; a skilled player could lip this interval into tune.

Fig. 9.38. The obbligato part for trumpet in D from 'The trumpet shall sound' in Handel's 'Messiah'.

Adding a mouthpiece to the hosepipe

The tuning is not the only problem of the hosepipe trumpet: the notes are difficult to excite, and the tone quality is muffled. This is because the impedance peaks are too low and too widely spaced to allow a strong regime of oscillation to develop. We saw earlier that the lips require a mouthpiece in order to interact properly with the tube; we also saw that the mouthpiece had a flattening effect on the upper resonances of a conical instrument like the alphorn. The addition of a trumpet mouthpiece to the hosepipe gives a dramatic increase in the strength of the notes which can be played, and also improves the tuning of the high register. These changes correspond to the raising and shifting of the impedance peaks, as shown in Fig. 9.31.

Mouthpiece design is perhaps the most controversial aspect of brass instrument manufacture. Every player has his own favourite mouthpiece, and makers produce a bewildering array of different types. It is therefore worth looking in a little more detail at the way in which a mouthpiece alters the resonance frequencies of a cylindrical tube; the principles are the same in a complete instrument such as the trumpet or trombone.

Adding a mouthpiece increases the effective length L_e of the cylindrical tube. For the lowest pitched resonances, the additional length due to the mouthpiece is equal to that length L_o of the cylindrical tube which would have the same volume V as the mouthpiece (Fig. 9.39) (Bouasse 1929 b; Benade 1959). In other words, at very low frequencies the shape of the mouthpiece has no effect on the tuning of the instrument: only its volume is significant.

As the playing frequency rises towards the resonance frequency of the mouthpiece, the increase in L_e due to the mouthpiece becomes greater than L_o. At the mouthpiece resonance frequency f_R, there is a pressure

_____Checkout Rece

Tech Community College
27/07 02:57PM
****
RON: 23312000428963

musicians' guide to acoustics /

lection: abg
1 No: ML 3805 .C24 1988
code: 33312000362467
 Time:
 Date: 12/11/07

_____

AL: 1Checkout Receipt
Tech Community College
27/07 02:57PM
****
RON: 23312000428963

musicians' guide to acoustics /

ection: abg
 No: ML 3805 .C24 1988
ode: 33312000362467
 Time:
 Date: 12/11/07

_____

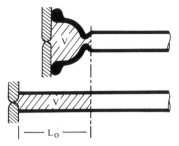

Fig. 9.39. At low frequencies, adding a mouthpiece of volume V to a cylindrical tube is equivalent to extending the tube by a length L_o giving the same increase in volume.

antinode at the lips, and a pressure node at the mouthpiece throat; the mouthpiece is thus behaving as though it were an extension of the cylindrical tube of length $L_R = \lambda/4$ (Fig. 9.40). Since at the frequency f_R, $\lambda = c/f_R$, the mouthpiece increases the effective length of the tube by an amount $c/4f_R$ at this frequency (Cardwell 1970; Pyle 1975).

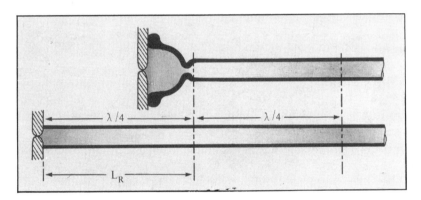

Fig. 9.40. At its resonance frequency, the mouthpiece effectively extends the tube by a quarter of a wavelength.

Let us take a particular example: a trumpet mouthpiece with volume $V = 1500$ mm^3 and resonance frequency $f_R = 800$ Hz, fitted to a cylindrical tube 12 mm in diameter. A section of the tube 13 mm long has a volume of about 1500 mm^3, so $L_o = 13$ mm. A quarter wavelength at the frequency $f_R = 800$ Hz gives $L_R = 108$ mm. Thus the effective length has increased by 95 mm between the low frequency limit and 800 Hz.

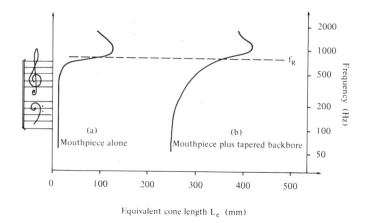

Fig. 9.41. Variation of effective length L_e with pitch for (a) a trumpet mouthpiece without backbore; (b) the same mouthpiece with a tapering backbore and mouthpipe 300 mm long. Based on Pyle (1975), pp.1314, 1315.

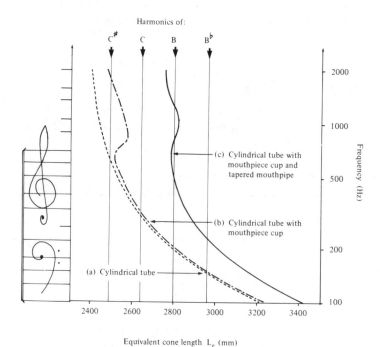

Fig. 9.42. Variation of effective length L_e with pitch for (a) a cylindrical tube closed at one end; (b) the same tube terminated by the mouthpiece cup of Fig. 9.41 (a); (c) the same tube with the mouthpiece cup, backbore and mouthpipe of Fig. 9.41 (b).

The variation of the effective length added by this mouthpiece is shown in Fig. 9.41 (a). Above C_5 the length increases rapidly, up to and beyond the mouthpiece resonance at G_5; near C_6 it peaks, then decreases slowly. Such a variation is too abrupt to be useful in compensating for the relatively slow decrease in the effective length of the cylindrical tube with increasing pitch (see Fig. 9.42, curves (a) and (b)).

So far, however, we have ignored one crucial aspect of mouthpiece design. In Fig. 9.39 we showed the mouthpiece throat opening directly into the full bore of the cylindrical tube. In practice, a carefully designed tapering *backbore* forms a continuous transition between the two elements. Frequently the initial segment of the instrument tube is also a tapered *mouthpipe* (see Fig. 9.27).

The effect of this tapered section is twofold: it increases the total variation in effective length of the mouthpiece-mouthpipe combination, and it spreads the variation over a larger pitch range on either side of the mouthpiece resonance (Fig. 9.41 (b)). As a result, the overall effective length of the mouthpiece plus mouthpipe plus cylindrical tube can be made almost constant in its usable upper register (Fig. 9.42 (c)).

Benade has made the interesting observation that, since the shape of the mouthpiece effective length curve is almost completely determined by V and f_R, the musical properties of a mouthpiece are little affected by fairly major changes in profile which leave these two quantities unaltered (Benade 1976, p.418). Widening the throat of a mouthpiece without changing the cup volume raises the resonance frequency f_R, and decreases L_R ($=c/4f_R$); since L_0 remains constant, the overall change in effective length is reduced in magnitude and spread over a wider pitch range. This reduces the flattening effect of the mouthpiece on the higher resonances. Decreasing the cup volume while leaving the throat unaltered has a similar effect, although in this case both L_0 and L_R are reduced.

Changing a mouthpiece affects not only the intonation of an instrument's upper register, but also the tone quality and stability of the notes produced. These different aspects of the instrument's performance are, of course, related by the requirement that a co-operative regime of oscillation must feed on a set of harmonically related resonances. We should also remember that a change which increases f_R (reducing the cup volume or increasing the throat area) moves the region of impedance multiplication to a higher pitch. Such a change also increases the multiplying factor (Lurton 1981, p.146, Fig. 6); the presence of a set of strong impedance peaks at high pitches results in a sound with a harder, more brilliant quality.

The flaring section

While the addition of the mouthpiece and mouthpipe to the cylindrical tube has given us an instrument whose equivalent length is reasonably constant in the high register, the lower resonances are still much too flat to serve as harmonics. It is the role of the flaring section, leading to the bell of the instrument, to compensate for this variation of effective length at low pitch.

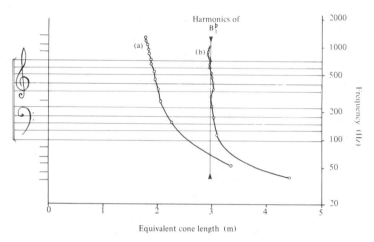

Fig. 9.43. Effective length L_e of a trombone (a) without and (b) with its flaring section.

The extent to which this compensation is achieved can be judged by comparing the two curves in Fig. 9.43. Curve (a) shows the variation of L_e with pitch for a trombone with the flaring section removed (but including its normal mouthpiece). This curve has the same shape as that of the hosepipe trumpet. Curve (b) shows L_e measured for the complete instrument. The addition of the 1150 mm flaring section has increased L_e by 1060 mm at 585 Hz (the 10th resonance of the complete trombone), but by only 590 mm at 110 Hz (the 2nd resonance). As a consequence, the effective cone length of the instrument is close to 3000 mm at all resonances from the 2nd upwards; only the fundamental remains obstinately flat.

The open circles in Fig. 9.43 represent the frequencies of impedance peaks measured in the mouthpiece of the trombone. A trombone player can verify the conclusion simply by removing the bell section of the instrument and sounding quietly the first position notes obtainable from the slide section only.

Why is it that at low frequencies the increase in effective length due to the flaring section is so much less than its physical length? The properties of sound waves in flaring tubes are considerably more complicated than those in tubes of cylindrical or conical bore. One of the most striking differences is that whereas in a cylinder or a cone the sound wave travels at the same speed as in the open air, in a tube with a flaring profile the speed of the wave increases by an amount which depends on the curvature of the wall. The lower the frequency, the greater the increase in speed produced by a given flare (Morse 1948, pp.265–288).

A sound wave entering the flaring section of the trombone from the cylindrical section finds itself in a tube whose rate of widening at first gentle, becomes more and more pronounced as the bell is approached. For a high frequency wave, the resultant change in speed is small; the wave reaches the bell, and most of its energy is radiated into the surrounding air.

For a low frequency wave, on the other hand, a point in the tube is reached where the speed of the wave becomes infinitely large. The wave is reflected at that point, rather as though the tube were cut off there; only a small fraction of the sound energy penetrates through the 'forbidden zone' beyond, to reach the bell. The point of reflection moves further from the bell as the frequency of the wave is decreased (Benade 1973; Benade and Jansson 1974).

The effect of this shift in the reflection point on the first four resonances of the trombone is illustrated in Fig. 9.44. The increase in the additional effective length due to the flaring section as the pitch rises is clearly evident. The art of the instrument maker lies in achieving a rate of flare for which this increase just compensates for the decrease in effective length with increasing pitch in the remainder of the instrument. We can see why this compensation cannot extend to the lowest resonance by noting that, even with the flaring section completely removed, the lowest resonance of the trombone in Fig. 9.43 has a frequency around 50 Hz, which is about a tone below $B^\flat_1$; however little the flaring section adds, the fundamental resonance of the complete instrument will always be lower than this. In practice, the flare is chosen to bring the resonances from the 2nd upwards close to a harmonic relationship, leaving the 1st up to a fifth flatter than the fundamental of the harmonic series.

Radiation of sound from a brass instrument bell

Up to this point, our discussion has concentrated on the standing waves set up inside a brass instrument tube by the interaction between a wave travelling towards the bell and a reflected wave travelling back towards the mouthpiece. We have seen that the lip reed valve functions best when these standing waves are strong and their frequencies approximately harmonic.

The purpose of the instrument is not, however, to generate a set of internal standing waves which feel good to the lips of the player — it is to radiate into the surrounding atmosphere a wave which sounds good to the ears of the listener. We must now examine the relationship between what goes on inside the instrument and what emerges from the bell.

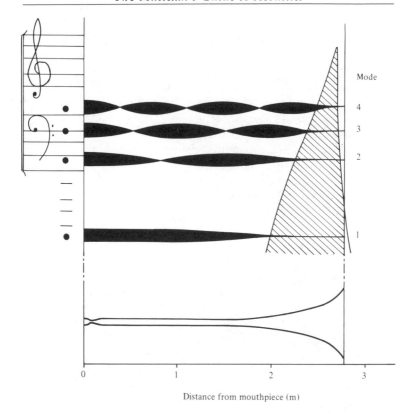

Distance from mouthpiece (m)

Fig. 9.44. Standing wave patterns for the lowest four resonant modes of a B♭ tenor trombone. The shaded area represents the 'forbidden zone', which reflects most of the low frequency sound energy arriving at the bell.

The height of the 'forbidden zone' in Fig. 9.44 determines a *cutoff frequency* (f_c) for the instrument. Internal waves with frequencies much below f_c are almost completely reflected in the flaring section; this gives very strong standing waves, but relatively little radiation out of the bell. On the other hand, a wave with frequency well above f_c is almost completely transmitted by the bell; the absence of significant reflection makes for a very weak internal standing wave.

A comparison of Fig. 9.14, which shows the impedance curve for a trombone, with Fig. 9.31, which shows the impedance curve for a cylindrical tube, reveals that the cylindrical tube has a much larger retinue of high pitch peaks than does the trombone. The 'forbidden zone' at the open end of the cylindrical tube is very narrow, but very high in pitch; even at the 20th resonance, there is still enough reflection to produce a sizeable impedance peak. The cutoff frequency for the trombone is around 700

Hz, so that above the 10th resonance the impedance peaks die away rapidly.

A small reflection means a large transmission; we can thus see that the bell radiates high frequency sounds much more efficiently than those of low frequency. Below the cutoff frequency the sound wave has to 'tunnel' through the barrier of the 'forbidden zone'. The lower the pitch, the thicker and higher the barrier, and the smaller the fraction of the internal sound which tunnels through to the outside world.

The pressure transfer function

The relationship between the sound trapped inside the instrument and that radiated from the bell can be studied using the experimental set-up shown in Fig. 9.45. Here a trombone mouthpiece has a probe microphone fitted to it, so that the sound in the mouthpiece cup can be examined; at the other end of the instrument, a second microphone just outside the bell measures the radiated sound. Of course, the sound radiated along the axis of the instrument will not in general be the same as that radiated at an angle to the axis. However, it has been shown that the sound picked up by an axial microphone one bell radius away from the end plane of the bell (see Fig. 9.45) has more or less the same spectrum as that which would be obtained by averaging over all directions of emission (Benade et al. 1977).

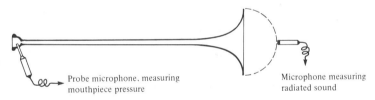

Probe microphone, measuring mouthpiece pressure

Microphone measuring radiated sound

Fig. 9.45. Experimental arrangement for measuring the pressure transfer function of a trombone.

If we record the output from the two microphones while the instrument is being played, we can subsequently compare the two signals. The *pressure transfer function* T is defined as the ratio of p_o, the 'output' pressure measured beyond the bell, to p_i, the 'input' pressure in the mouthpiece (Elliott et al. 1982). Usually the pressure ratio is expressed in decibels:

$$T = 20 \log (p_o/p_i)$$

In Fig. 9.46(a) we show a measurement of T for a tenor trombone. In this case, the sound was generated, not by playing the instrument, but by injecting into the mouthpiece a pure tone of continuously varying pitch. It will be seen that, above the cutoff frequency (around 800 Hz), T has a nearly constant value of about −35 dB. This means that the sound pressure level 93 mm (one bell radius) from the end of the bell is some 35 dB less than that in the mouthpiece. This reduction is simply a consequence of the fact that the sound is radiating out in all directions from

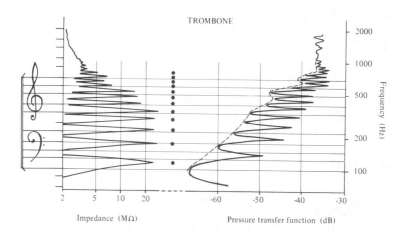

Fig. 9.46 (a). Measured impedance (Z)and pressure transfer function (T) for a B♭ tenor trombone. The natural notes of the instrument are shown by black circles. The dashed line indicates the trend of the minima in T. The lowest impedance peak is not shown.

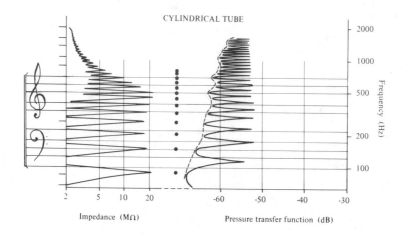

Fig. 9.46 (b). Measured impedance and pressure transfer function for cylindrical tube of length 2770 mm with a trombone mouthpiece.

the bell, and the sound energy is spread over a much larger area than the cross-section of the mouthpiece throat.

As the frequency of the injected sound falls below the cutoff frequency, an increasing proportion of the sound energy travelling down the instrument from the mouthpiece is reflected by the 'forbidden region' in the bell (Jansson and Benade 1974, p.194, Fig. 4). Since this reflection is necessary for the establishment of strong standing waves, it is not surprising to find that the impedance curve of the instrument (the left hand curve in Fig. 9.46 (a)) shows sharp peaks only below the cutoff.

The pressure transfer function (the right hand curve in Fig. 9.46 (a)) also has pronounced peaks and dips below the cutoff. A careful comparison of the two curves reveals that at the pitch of each impedance peak, corresponding closely to one of the natural notes of the instrument, the pressure transfer function is near to a minimum (that is, a large negative value). This is understandable, for at an impedance peak the reflection at the bell is particularly strong.

Superimposed on the variations due to the standing waves is a general downward trend in the transfer function with decreasing frequency. The 'forbidden zone' becomes thicker and effectively higher as the pitch drops, until almost no sound can leak through it.

Thus when a note is blown on the instrument, the high frequency components in the mouthpiece spectrum are radiated much more efficiently than the low frequency components. This 'treble boost' contributes greatly to the cutting brilliance of a loud trumpet or trombone note. For example, the trombone describe by Fig. 9.46 (a) has a transfer function of -58 dB at the pitch F_3 and -38 dB at the pitch F_5. If the mouthpiece spectrum of a played note contained components with equal pressure amplitude at each of these pitches, the amplitude of F_5 in the radiated sound spectrum would be 20 dB greater than that of F_3.

The crucial importance of the flaring section and bell is illustrated by a comparison of Figs. 9.46 (a) and 9.46 (b). The latter displays the impedance and pressure transfer function for a piece of cylindrical tubing of the same length as the trombone (2770 mm) attached to the mouthpiece used in the measurements on the trombone. The microphone measuring the radiated sound was the same distance from the end of the tube (93 mm) as in the trombone measurement. It will be seen that, although the pressure transfer function is about the same magnitude for trombone and cylindrical tube at very low pitches, the 'treble boost' is very much weaker in the case of the cylindrical tube. Even at very high pitches, most of the sound energy remains trapped inside the tube. The role of the flaring section of a brass instrument is thus twofold: it brings the instrument's internal resonances into harmonic order, and it improves the radiation of the higher frequencies which are essential components of the instrument's characteristic tone quality.

CROOKS, SLIDES AND VALVES

An instrument like the alphorn makes use only of the natural notes of its fixed length of tubing. To play a diatonic scale, the player is forced to ascend above the 8th harmonic; even then, the 11th harmonic must serve as a very sharp subdominant. To find a chromatic scale, it would be necessary to go beyond the 16th natural note. Even the Swiss are reluctant to venture so high.

Remembering that the frequency of the nth mode of a cone is $f_n = nc/2L$, we can see that there are two ways of changing the frequency, without altering n. We can decrease the length L of the cone, by cutting a piece off; this will raise f_n. Or we can extend the cone, by adding an extra length; this will lower f_n.

The first expedient – amputation – is too irreversible to be practically useful. It does, however, form the basis of the finger hole system which is used in nearly all woodwind instruments, as we saw in Chapter 8. To a first approximation, opening a large hole in the side of the tube is equivalent to cutting it off below that point. This system is also used in certain lip reed instruments. Much more characteristic of the brass family, however, is the second expedient − extending the tube.

Crooks

The simplest method of extending the effective length of a brass instrument is to add an additional length between the mouthpiece and the narrow end; this addition is called a *crook*. If, for example, we wish to lower the entire set of resonances of the $A^\flat$ alphorn by one semitone (frequency ratio 1.059), we must increase the effective length by 5.9%. The fundamental of the instrument's harmonic series is $A^\flat_1$, with frequency 51.9 Hz; its effective length is therefore $L_e = c/2f_1 = 3324$ mm. The increase in effective length required to give a new harmonic series based on G_1 is $0.059 \times 3324 = 196$ mm.

This calculation was of practical use to one of the authors a few years ago, when he encountered a fellow alphorn player possessing an alphorn in G. Since the author's instrument is in $A^\flat$, the prospect of exploring the splendid repertoire of alphorn duets seemed remote. However, an impromptu crook was manufactured from a piece of cylindrical paxolin tubing which accepted the mouthpiece at one end and fitted into the alphorn at the other. When the length was cut so that the mouthpiece was displaced by 196 mm from its usual position (Fig. 9.47), the two instruments were found to play acceptably in tune with each other.

Some time later, a similar opportunity arose – but this time the other instrument was in $G^\flat$ (there seems to be an unfortunate lack of standardisation in the pitching of alphorns). Since a pitch interval of two semitones is equivalent to a frequency ratio of 1.122, a second crook was manufactured, this time extending the length by 3324 × 0.122 = 406 mm. Although this crook did bring the A♭ instrument roughly into G♭, it had the unfortunate side-effect of disturbing the relative pitches of the resonances; some were too sharp to be true harmonics of G♭, while others were too flat. Only by constant 'lipping' could the crooked instrument be played in tune.

Fig. 9.47. The playing end of the alphorn, with (a) the mouthpiece in its normal position; (b) a cylindrical crook between the mouthpiece and the instrument.

Here we have come across a fundamental problem inherent in the idea of a crook. If the same mouthpiece is to be usable with or without a crook, the tube of which the crook is made must clearly be cylindrical (see Fig. 9.47). However, as the proportion of cylindrical to conical tubing is increased, the resonance frequencies will deviate more and more from those of a pure cone (that is, from a true harmonic series).

When a crook is used with an instrument (such as the trumpet) which already includes a section of cylindrical tubing, the net effect is to increase the proportion of the total tube length which is cylindrical, and to decrease the proportion which is flaring. If the flaring section has been chosen to compensate for the variation in effective length of the instrument without crooks, the compensation will become increasingly inadequate as the crook length is increased (Benade 1976, p.412). We can see the nature of this problem by imagining a ridiculously long crook which made the instrument almost completely cylindrical, with the flaring section comprising only one tenth of the total length. Such a relatively short flare could have only a slight influence on the resonant frequencies, which would be close to those of a purely cylindrical tube closed at the mouthpiece end. That is, the intervals between successive resonances would be wider than those of a complete harmonic series, the deviation being most severe for the lowest resonances.

An instrument designed to be used with a large range of crooks (for example, the natural horn in Fig. 9.94) will have its flare chosen for optimum performance with a crook of medium length. Intonation problems can then be expected only with the shortest or longest crooks. By including a mouthpipe section of varying bore in each crook, the discrepancies of tuning can be brought within usable limits for a range of crooks which allows the basic pitch of the instrument to be raised or lowered from the median pitch by about a fifth (Baines 1976, p.163).

Slides

The principal disadvantage of a crook is that it cannot be changed very quickly. The slide section of the trombone (or the slide trumpet) provides a means of increasing the cylindrical part of the tube continuously and almost instantaneously. The principle of the trombone slide is illustrated by Fig. 9.48. The two straight sections of the moveable bow provide a close but smoothly sliding fit over the two sections of cylindrical tube within. When the bow is pushed away from the mouthpiece by a length L, the total cylindrical section of the instrument is increased by 2L.

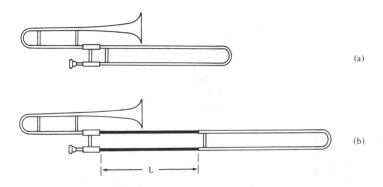

(a)

(b)

Fig. 9.48. Trombone with slide in (a) first position; (b) seventh position.

Although the slide can provide a continuous variation in the pitch of the resonances, there are seven *positions* of the slide which are conventionally defined. In the first position, the slide is fully in, and the instrument has its shortest effective length; for a $B^\flat$ tenor trombone, as we saw earlier, this is $L_e = 2960$ mm. The second position moves the pitches of the resonances down by one semitone, giving approximately a harmonic series based on A_1. To achieve this, L_e must be increased by 176 mm, to 3136 mm; the slide must therefore be moved by half this amount, or 88 mm.

Table 9.1 shows the slide extensions required to move the 'fundamental' down in semitone steps from $B_1^\flat$ to E_1 (the quotation marks enclosing 'fundamental' are a reminder that there is in fact no resonance at that pitch). It will be seen that successive positions of the slide are separated by increasing distances. This is due to the fact that moving the slide out from one position to the next lowers the pitch by one semitone, and thus increases the effective length by a constant factor of 5.9%. From the sixth to the seventh position, the required increase in L_e is 5.9% of the *sixth position* length; this increase is clearly much greater than that required in the move from first to second position, where L_c must increase by only 5.9% of the *first position* length.

TABLE 9.1

Theoretical slide positions of a B^b tenor trombone

Position no.	'Funda-mental'	L_e (mm)	ΔL_e	Slide displacement (mm) from 1st pos.	from prev. pos.
1	B^b_1	2960	0	0	0
2	A_1	3136	176	88	88
3	A^b_1	3323	363	182	94
4	G_1	3520	560	280	98
5	$F^\#_1$	3730	770	385	105
6	F_1	3952	992	496	111
7	E_1	4187	1227	614	118

In the foregoing discussion, we have ignored the intonation problem which we met when discussing crooks. We have assumed that an increase in the cylindrical section of the trombone simply increases L_c by that amount at all frequencies. However, the alteration in the relative proportions of cylindrical and flaring sections has the same effect as when it is accomplished by the insertion of a cylindrical crook. The lower resonances become increasingly flattened relative to the upper resonances (Backus 1976). This effect is illustrated by Fig. 9.49, which shows the deviations from expected pitch of the resonances of a B^b trombone with the slide in first and in seventh position. It can be observed that the interval from the second to the eighth resonance (which should be two octaves) is 39 cents too wide in first position, but 112 cents too wide in seventh position.

Of course, on the trombone the pitch of a note can be adjusted by a small movement of the slide. In playing the interval $E_4 - E_2$ in seventh position, the slide can be drawn in a little between the sounding of the upper and lower notes to compensate for the flatness of the second rsonance peak in this position. The tone quality and stability of the note E_2 will, however, be adversely affected by the fact that the resonance peaks are so widely separated, since this inhibits the setting up of a strong co-operative regime of oscillation. In general, low notes played in extended positions on the trombone are less well centred and more difficult to start than notes of similar pitch which can be obtained in first position.

Valves

The majority of modern brass instruments make use of valves to extend

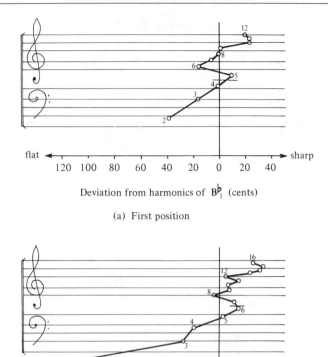

Deviation from harmonics of $B^\flat_1$ (cents)

(a) First position

Deviation from harmonics of E_1 (cents)

(b) Seventh position

Fig. 9.49. Deviations in pitch of the impedance peaks of a King tenor trombone from true harmonics of (a) $B^\flat_1$, (b)E_1.

their cylindrical sections by the insertion of fixed lengths of tubing (see, e.g., Bate 1966, Ch. 8). Two types of valve are in common use: the piston valve and the rotary valve. In both types, the movement of a cylinder within the tightly fitting valve casing diverts the sound wave through an additional section of tube; in the piston valve, the cylinder is displaced along its axis, while in the rotary valve it is rotated about its axis. The operation of both types is illustrated in Fig. 9.50. Normally the valve is spring-loaded so as to return to the 'out' position when not activated by finger pressure; it is then known as a *descending* valve, since its activation lowers the pitch of the instrument. Some valve systems make use of *ascending* valves; with these valves, the additional tubing is removed by depression of the valve and reinserted when the pressure is released.

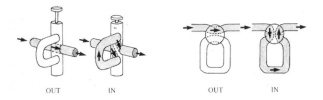

Fig. 9.50. Two types of descending valve: left, piston valve; right, rotary
valve. Shading indicates the passage of the sound wave through
the valve.

The most common valve system makes use of three descending valves;
examples of instruments using this system are illustrated in Figs. 9.64, 9.73
and 9.83. The first valve (normally operated by the index finger), when
used alone, extends the tubing of the instrument by a length sufficient to
lower the pitch by two semitones; the second (operated by the middle
finger), when used alone, lowers the pitch by one semitone; the third
(operated by the third finger), when used alone, lowers the pitch by three
semitones.

The effect of these valves on the resonances of a trumpet in C is
illustrated by Fig. 9.51 (only the second to the sixth resonances are
shown). By using the second, first and third valves in succession, the major
third between the fifth resonance (E_5) and the fourth resonance (C_5) of the
natural tube can be subdivided chromatically. The perfect fourth between
the fourth and third resonances of the natural tube cannot, however, be
bridged chromatically using only one valve at a time; there is no way of
obtaining the note $G_4^\#$.

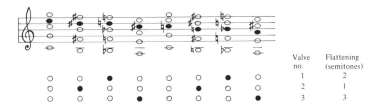

	Valve no.	Flattening (semitones)
	1	2
	2	1
	3	3

Fig. 9.51. Notes obtainable using only one valve at a time on a C
trumpet. The black notes give a chromatic scale descending
to A_4. The symbols beneath each note indicate the valve
depressed.

To extend the chromatic compass of the instrument down to and below
the second resonance, the valves are used in combination. The second and
third valves are depressed together to lower the pitch by four semitones;
the first and third are used to give a five semitone drop; while all three

valves depressed together provide the six semitones necessary to bring the pitch of the third resonance to within a semitone of the second.

Unfortunately, there is an inherent flaw in the apparently simple arithmetic of valve combinations. The second valve introduces a piece of tubing which is 5.9% of the effective length of the *unextended* instrument (that is, the length with no valves depressed). This gives the required increase in length (a factor of 1.059) to lower the pitch by a semitone. But if we start with the third valve already depressed, and wish to lower the pitch by a further semitone, the required additional length is 5.9% of the *extended* instrument (basic length plus tubing inserted by third valve). The tubing inserted by the second valve is too short to serve this purpose.

The information in Table 9.1 (p.353) can be used to give an idea of the scale of this problem. The fourth column in the table shows the additional length ΔL_e introduced by various positions of the slide of a B^b tenor trombone. On the valve trombone, the slide is replaced by a fixed set of valve-controlled extensions. Using the three-valve system, the second valve should add 176 mm, the first 363 mm and the third 560 mm; depressing the valves separately in the order 2–1–3 would then be equivalent to extending the slide through the first four positions. Depressing the second and third together would add 560 + 176 = 736 mm; however, the fifth position of the slide adds 770 mm. The tubing added by the combination of second and third valves is 34 mm short of the ideal length: this is equivalent on the slide trombone to misplacing the slide by 17 mm.

The calculated pitch discrepancy due to the combined use of second and third valves is 16 cents. When the first and third are used together, the calculated discrepancy rises to 30 cents, while the theory predicts that using all three valves together should give pitches which are 54 cents (more than half a semitone) too sharp. Since these values depend only on the relative lengths of the different sections of tubing, the pitch discrepancies – according to this simple theory – should be the same for all brass instruments with three valves, from the piccolo trumpet to the contrabass tuba.

How do these predictions agree with the performance of real musical instruments? For the low pitched brass instruments, such as the tuba or sousaphone, the theory appears to work quite well (Young 1967): the sharpness of notes obtained by valves in combination is a familiar practical problem to players of brass basses without some form of compensating system (see p.370). On the other hand, a well-made trumpet does not display this effect. Indeed, for notes in the low register, the opposite effect is frequently found: the notes A^b_3, G_3 and $F^{\#}_3$ on the C trumpet, for example, are often distinctly flat when no attempt is made to correct their intonation by slide adjustments or by lipping (Benade 1976, p.413).

The basic reason for the failure of the simple theory in the case of the trumpet is that it does not take into account the alteration in the relative proportions of cylindrical and flaring sections which occurs when valves are depressed. Increasing the proportion of cylindrical tubing, as we saw when discussing crooks and slides, reduces the sharpening influence of the flaring section; the resonances then come out flatter than the simple theory predicts. By careful design, this flattening effect can be made to compensate for the sharpening effect due to the valve combinations in the middle register. Since the flattening effect increases as the number of the resonance decreases, the lowest register will then be too flat: this agrees with experience. Conversely, in the high register, notes obtained with valve combinations will tend to be sharp; this is a less serious problem, however, since valve combinations are not so frequently used in this register.

Why, then, do the brass basses appear to obey the simple theory? These instruments are normally constructed largely from conical tubing, with only a small proportion of cylindrical tubing; the flattening effect of an additional length of cylindrical tubing depends less on the harmonic number for such a bore profile. There are, however, other factors which make the intonation problem with valve combinations more serious in large instruments. One is the increased mass of air in the resonating column: if the note has to be lipped into tune, the lips have to work harder to pull a large air column away from its natural resonances. Another factor which has a significant effect on the tuning of the instrument is the warming effect of the player's breath. Different parts of the instrument warm up to different extents: in particular, the valve sections, through which warm air passes only intermittently, are normally cooler than the rest of the instrument. It has been suggested (Young 1967) that this effect, which is more noticeable on small instruments, improves the intonation of valve combinations, although any such improvement, depending as it must on the predominant key signatures of the music and the ambient temperature of the room, will be at best somewhat variable.

Two important conclusions emerge from the foregoing discussion: notes produced by valve combinations may be sharp or flat, and the effect will probably be different for different notes played using the same combination of valves. The exact nature of the effect depends on the interaction of different factors, not all of which are well understood theoretically.

Because of the problem associated with valve combinations, some instruments use *independent* systems of valves (Bate 1966, pp.166, 172). In these instruments, only one valve is used at a time; six valves are required to replicate the seven positions of the trombone slide. The principal disadvantage of independent systems is that they require much more tubing; the total length of tubing in a six-valve independent system valve trombone is nearly 16 metres.

Even with the independent system, problems associated with the use of a single flaring section with different lengths of cylindrical bore remain.

357

The final logical step is to have each valve switch in not only an extended cylindrical section, but also a proportionally extended flaring section and bell. The marvellous 'Distin multiple horn', illustrated in Fig. 9.52, was built on this principle; rather than embrace such a hydra, however, practical instrumentalists have accepted the necessity of lipping the odd note into tune on more conventional instruments.

Fig. 9.52 The Distin multiple horn.

INSTRUMENTS WITH PREDOMINANTLY CONICAL BORE

The lip reed family encompasses many diverse types of instrument. Having surveyed some of the principles common to most of these types, we now examine briefly the way in which these principles are put into effect in the more important instruments of the family. It is convenient to divide the instruments into three categories, depending on the bore profile:

(i)   instruments with predominantly conical bore;
(ii) instruments with predominantly cylindrical bore;
(iii) instruments with hybrid bore.

The first class, with which we begin our review, contains those instruments whose tubing tapers almost uniformly from one end to the other, with perhaps a short cylindrical section when valves are incorporated. The second class contains the trumpet and trombone families, with a large fraction of the tubing of cylindrical bore and a relatively short flaring section. The third class contains instruments of the horn family; in this class, conical, cylindrical and flaring sections are likely to be of comparable length.

Natural cones: the alphorn

We have already discussed the acoustics of the *alphorn* (Fig. 9.8) as a typical example of a natural conical instrument (that is, one which relies only on its natural notes). As we would expect from a cone, the fundamental resonance is in tune. This resonance is not normally used, however; a relatively small mouthpiece is chosen, whose high 'popping' frequency means that the multiplying effect of the mouthpiece on the heights of the impedance peaks is centred above the sixth resonance (see Figs 9.9 and 9.13). The instrument thus plays most easily in the region between fourth and twelfth harmonics. The almost total absence of a bell gives a high cut-off frequency, which strengthens the upper resonances within the instrument, but reduces the efficiency with which high harmonics are radiated; as a result, the tone quality is remarkably pure.

Fig. 9.53 (a) illustrates a traditional Swiss alphorn melody. Although it is notated in C, it would of course be played in the natural key of the instrument, which could be from a tone to a sixth lower. That is, the alphorn plays as a transposing instrument. Fig. 9.53 (b) illustrates what is probably the best-known alphorn melody, although many people who recognise it as a theme from the last movement of Brahms's 1st Symphony are unaware that the composer heard it on the alphorn while on a holiday in Switzerland. The use of the natural eleventh harmonic, which is not a degree of the diatonic scale, is an interesting feature of the original; in the symphonic version, this note is sharpened to become an augmented fourth above the tonic.

(a) Traditional alphorn tune from Wäggithal (notated by E. Heim 1876).

(b) Traditional alphorn tune from Rigi (notated by J. Brahms 1868).

Fig. 9.53. Two alphorn tunes.

Posthorn and bugle

Various shorter instruments of essentially conical bore have flourished at different times, often serving practical as well as purely musical functions. As examples of this class, we choose the posthorn and the bugle. The *posthorn* developed in the 16th century, when it was used to signal the arrival and departure of the horsemen who transported mail between cities. In its early form, its tube length was only about 400 mm, giving a fundamental pitch around A_4. The conical bore gave a second resonance an octave above, and this octave interval became the recognised posthorn call. In the 18th century longer tubes were used, bringing the fundamental down to A_2 or lower; the instrument could then be played up to the eighth harmonic, and made occasional forays into the concert hall (Fig. 9.54). By this stage, however, the posthorn incorporated significant sections of cylindrical and flaring tubing and should therefore be considered acoustically as a hybrid bore instrument (p.391).

Fig. 9.54. Part for posthorn in A from Mozart's Serenade No. 9 K.320.

The *bungle* evolved in Germany in the 18th century as a military signalling instrument. In its present day version, it is a conical tube of length around 1300 mm, giving a fundamental $B_2^\flat$. Its compass normally extends from the second to the sixth harmonic (Fig. 9.37 (a)); however, the fundamental is available, and is occasionally called for in bugle calls (Fig. 9.55).

Fig. 9.55. Two excerpts from Prussian Light Infantry bugle calls; from Kastner (1846), quoted in Baines (1976), p.27.

Cones with side holes: the cornett

The prototype of most of the short conical instruments is the animal horn, opened out at the narrow end to form a rudimentary mouthpiece. In many primitive instruments of this type, several holes have been bored in the side of the horn; normally closed by the fingers, these can be opened to raise the sounding pitch.

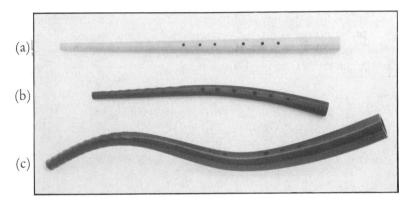

Fig. 9.56. Reproduction cornetts by Christopher Monk: (a) mute cornett; (b) treble cornett; (c) tenor cornett. The treble and tenor cornetts are shown without mouthpieces.

From this simple beginning developed the supreme virtuoso wind instrument of the Renaissance: the *cornett*. The standard form of the instrument (Fig. 9.56 (b)) echoes the curve of the animal horn, although it is constructed by hollowing the bore out of two separate lengthwise sections of wood, which are subsequently glued together and bound with leather. There are six finger holes on the front of the instrument, and one hole for the left hand thumb on the rear.

The bore is not strictly conical; usually, the section from the mouthpiece to the thumb hole tapers outwards rather more rapidly than does the remainder of the instrument. In this the cornett resembles the oboe, although the cornett tube has a considerably larger average diameter. The length of the treble cornett is typically 600 mm (excluding mouthpiece); because of the 'missing apex' effect described on p.333, the equivalent length at its lowest resonance (A_3) is extended to 784 mm. Since the small air volume added by the tiny cup shaped mouthpiece is insufficient to compensate for the volume of the missing apex, the upper reasonances are somewhat sharp (the fourth resonance with all holes closed is $B_5^\flat$, a semitone above the fourth harmonic of A_5). However, with a fairly elaborate system of cross-fingering, a complete chromatic scale can be obtained from A_3 to D_6.

The power of the lips to dominate and modify the resonances of the tube is particularly significant in the case of the cornett, with its short air column. This gives the instrument a unique flexibility of intonation – many of the notes can be lipped easily over a range of at least a fouth. Indeed, the compass of the instrument in fingering charts of the renaissance period includes the notes G_3 and $G_3^\#$, obtained by lipping down the fundamental A_3. The starting transient can also be made very short, since the time taken by the initial pulse of air to travel down the instrument and be reflected back to the lips is less than in instruments with greater tube length. Very rapid divisions and ornaments are therefore possible on the cornett (Leguy 1979). Fig. 9.57 illustrates the type of music which was written for the cornett in the 17th century.

Fig. 9.57. Cornett parts from Monteverdi's Vespers of 1610.

The small volume of the traditional cornett mouthpiece (Fig. 9.58 compares the sizes of typical cornett and trumpet mouthpieces) has an important influence on the tone quality of the instrument. The high 'popping frequency' emphasises the impedance peaks above 1000 Hz, yielding a clear bright sound which has often been compared to the voice of a child. On the mute cornett (Fig. 9.56 (a)), a deeper, more conical mouthpiece is bored directly into the body of the instrument; the lowering of the mouthpiece resonance frequency strengthens the lower peaks at the expense of the higher, resulting in a more 'muted' sound (Fig. 9.59). In both cases, the complete absence of any terminal flare inhibits the radiation of the high frequencies which give the 'brassy' quality to lip reed instruments with bells.

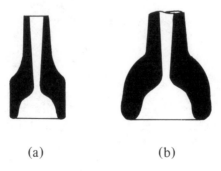

(a)   (b)

Fig. 9.58. Cross-sections of (a) a typical cornett mouthpiece, (b) a typical trumpet mouthpiece.

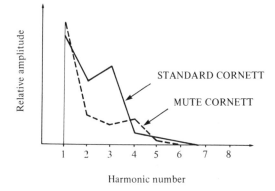

Fig. 9.59. Average spectrum envelopes typical of the standard cornett and the mute cornett, for the note E₅ played mf.

The cornett family contains a variety of sizes of instrument. Apart from the treble, the most important are the *cornettino* (a fourth higher than the treble), and the *tenor cornett* or *lysarden* (a perfect fifth below the treble). On this latter instrument, the tube has to take a sinuous form to bring the finger holes into a position where they can be reached by a player of normal proportions (see Fig. 9.56 (c)). Although a few cornetts of lower pitch have survived from the Renaissance period, the inherent weakness of the instrument in its lowest register makes the sackbut (the early trombone) a more satisfactory bass for a group of cornetts. Much of the repertoire of early music performed by modern brass groups was originally written for ensembles of cornetts and sackbuts.

The serpent

The application of the finger hole principle to a long conical tube is embodied in the *serpent*, surely the strangest of the many strange shapes in the lip reed family. The average bore is proportionally wider than that of the cornett, and a relatively deep cupped mouthpiece gives a secure and well-centred fundamental (usually C₂). In order to bring the lower end of the instrument within reach of the hands, the tube has three 180° bends, followed by a wide, almost circular arc (Fig. 9.60 (a)).

There are two serious problems in the design of the serpent: both are associated with the finger holes. The ideal spacing of the holes would be about 150 mm apart; a spacing of roughly 50 mm is as much as the average hand can manage. In addition, the finger holes should ideally have a diameter which is a considerable fraction of the bore diameter; this is clearly not feasible on the lower reaches of the serpent, if the holes are to be covered by human fingers.

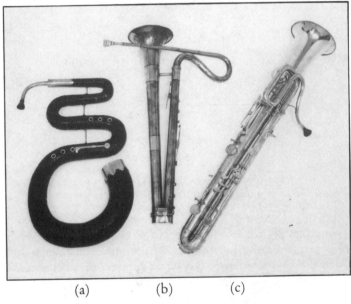

(a)   (b)   (c)

Fig. 9.60. (a) serpent by Haye (EUCHMI 1156/1157); (b) bass horn (EUCHMI 193/627); (c) ophicleide, 9 key, in B♭ (EUCHMI 2157/2158).

On the basic serpent, these problems are simply ignored. The holes are placed in two clumps of three, with a wide gap between the two clumps; the spacing and diameter of the holes are chosen to lie conveniently under the player's fingers. Unfortunately, the relatively accurate harmonic relationship of the resonances with the finger holes closed is drastically disrupted once one or two holes are opened (see Fig. 9.61). The possibility of setting up a co-operative regime of oscillation disappears, and the centring and tone quality of the notes are much inferior to those obtained from the complete tube. In fact, with several holes open, the air column exerts such a weak influence on the lips that it is easy to lip a continuous glissando over more than an octave. Clearly, musical results on such an instrument can only be achieved by a player with good lip control and a keen musical ear.

Despite its acoustical flaws, the serpent played a useful role in the 18th and early 19th centuries, supporting the singing in churches and providing a bass in military bands and orchestras. Although the bass trombone can also descend to D_2, its harmonic spectrum contains a much higher propor-

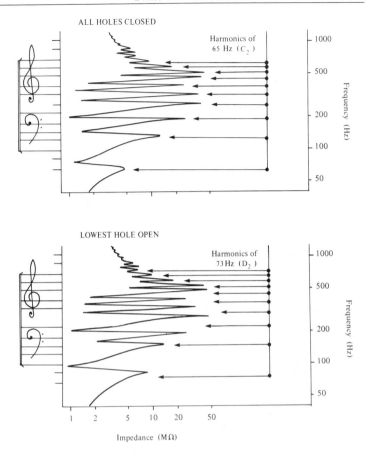

ALL HOLES CLOSED

Harmonics of
65 Hz (C₂)

LOWEST HOLE OPEN

Harmonics of
73 Hz (D₂)

Impedance (MΩ)

Fig. 9.61. Impedance curves for a serpent. In the upper curve, obtained with all holes closed, the peaks are close to harmonics of 65 Hz (including the fundamental), giving a strong co-operative regime for the note C₂. Opening one hole, to play the note D₂, gives the lower curve; the harmonic relationship of the peaks has been disrupted. The second harmonic of D₂ is the only component supported by an impedance peak.

tion of upper harmonics than does that of the serpent (Fig. 9.62). The serpent therefore added a fullness of tone which was otherwise lacking in the bass region of the 18th century brass section; as late as 1842, Wagner pressed the instrument into service in the scoring of 'Rienzi' (Fig. 9.63). It is probable that the instrument intended by Wagner was in fact the V-shaped version of the serpent which was developed in the late 18th century (Fig. 9.60 (b)). Equipped with several extra holes closed by key controlled pads, this was commonly made of brass, and was known as the

365

bass horn. A thicker walled wooden version had the somewhat confusing title of *Russian bassoon*.

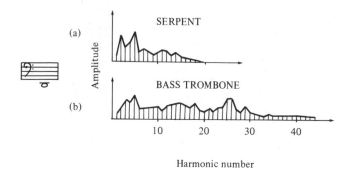

Fig. 9.62. Average spectrum envelopes for the note D_2 played on (a) a serpent in C; (b) a bass trombone in G (slide in 6th position).

Fig. 9.63. Excerpt from the serpent part in the overture to Wagner's 'Rienzi'.

The keyed bugle and the ophicleide

The keys on the later versions of the serpent family supplemented the open holes, improving chromatic notes otherwise obtainable only by lipping. In 1810 Joseph Halliday, an Irish bandmaster, patented a design for a *keyed bugle*, in which all the holes were closed by key operated pads. Since the position and size of the holes were no longer controlled by the limitations of the hand, the instrument could be designed in an acoustically satisfactory way; six holes opening at regular intervals along the tube allowed the interval between second and third harmonics to be bridged chromatically. Later versions, equipped with additional keys, had a compass extending down to the fundamental (usually C_3 or $B_2^\flat$); a seven-keyed instrument is illustrated in Fig. 9.64 (b).

Since the holes are large enough to preserve the harmonic relationship of the resonances in the shortened tube, practically all the notes available on the instrument are stable and well focused, with a clear, mellow tone typical of a conical instrument played with a relatively deep mouthpiece. The keyed bugle was widely used in military and amateur bands in Europe and America up to the middle of the 19th century; Fig. 9.65 shows an example of a mid-19th century piece of American keyed bugle music.

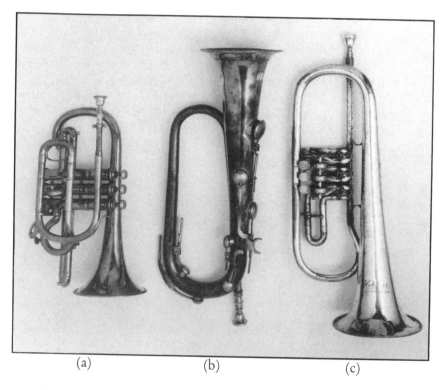

(a) (b) (c)

Fig. 9.64. (a) flügelhorn in B♭ by Kohlert; (b) keyed bugle in C, crooked in B♭ (EUCHMI 1134/1135); (c) cornet in B♭ by Gisbone (EUCHMI 1610/1611).

Fig. 9.65. Excerpt from 'Yankee Doodle Variations' for solo keyed bugle, by R. Willis (arr. H. Gainer).

The battle of Waterloo not only brought an end to the Napoleonic war; it also contributed indirectly to an important step in the design of bass brass instruments, by bringing British bands playing the new keyed bugle to France. The Parisian maker Halary was quick to copy them; in 1817 he invented a bass version, with a fundamental pitch of either C_2, or $B^\flat_1$, which he called the *ophicleide*. Although the keyed bugle was rarely called upon to descend below its second harmonic, the ophicleide quickly found a role as a replacement for the serpent in the bass register. To provide a satisfactory chromatic scale in the fundamental octave, the number of keys was increased from seven to eleven, with nine being a standard compromise (Fig. 9.60 (c)). In this form it is a highly satisfactory instrument, both acoustically and musically, and was much used by orchestras and bands throughout the 19th century (see Fig. 9.66).

Fig. 9.66. Ophicleide solo part from the 'Cavatine de pasquarello' in Berlioz's opera 'Benvenuto Cellini'.

Valved cones

In 1815, Heinrich Stölzel demonstrated in Breslau a horn equipped with two mechanical valves. From this beginning developed a revolution in the contruction of brass instruments. In the course of the next twenty or thirty years, as the new invention was improved, every existing type of brass instrument appeared in valved versions, and a myriad of essentially new instruments with valves came on the market.

The classification of brass instruments in terms of their tube shape becomes exceedingly difficult at this point. As we have already seen, valve systems almost inevitably introduce a considerable cylindrical section into the instrument; thus there is no such thing as a purely conical valved instrument. Furthermore, since in a valved instrument all the sound emerges from the single aperture at the open end, it is possible to increase the radiating efficiency by flaring the tube into a wide bell; this possibility was fully exploited in the 19th century quest for greater volume from orchestral instruments.

Nevertheless, there is a large group of valved brass instruments whose overall bore profile remains sufficiently close to conical to justify their inclusion in this section. These instruments retain many of the characteristics of the natural cones; in particular, the equivalent length remains reasonably constant down to the lowest resonance frequency, so that the fundamental is a strong note supported by a solid co-operative regime. The tubes used normally taper fairly rapidly outwards, so that the bell end is proportionately wide even in the absence of a pronounced flaring section. The mouthpieces used are typically deep cupped, with a low resonance frequency which results in amplification of the first few impedance peaks. All of these factors contribute to a rounded, mellow tone quality, and to an absence of high harmonics from the spectra.

The characteristic soprano instrument of this class is the *flügelhorn*. The example illustrated in Fig. 9.64 (a) has a bore profile very similar to that of the keyed bugle shown on the same figure; frequently the bore tapers more slowly and ends in a more pronounced flare. The flügelhorn equipped with only three valves cannot descend chromatically to its fundamental pitch of B♭₂; the compass in the lower register in thus the same as that of the B♭ trumpet or cornet. However, its characteristic tone quality has ensured it an independent existence in jazz and popular music, and in the brass band. Twentieth century composers have also occasionally made use of its individual sound (see Fig. 9.67).

Fig. 9.67. Excerpt from the part for flügelhorn (alternatively described as 'bugle C-alto') in Stravinsky's 'Threni'.

Instruments of the *tuba* family also come into the 'approximately conical' category, although the designation 'tuba' covers a wider variety of instruments than any other to be found in an orchestral score. Many of the early tubas were basically valved ophicleides, preserving the relatively narrow conical shape of the keyed instrument. By the end of the 19th century, the bore was usually much wider; Fig. 9.68 illustrates a four valve E♭ bass tuba by Boosey and Co. Fig. 9.69 illustrates typical harmonic spectra for several notes on this instrument; the absence of upper harmonics gives the higher register a bare, somewhat plaintive sound which is sometimes used as a special effect (Fig. 9.70).

The tuba comes into its own, however, as a firm, solid foundation for the orchestra or band. For this purpose, it is often given a fourth valve, which introduces sufficient additional tubing to lower the fundamental pitch of the instrument by a fourth, from E♭₁ to B♭₀. By using this valve in combination with the other three, it is possible to play chromatically down to $E^\flat_1$, and even a few semitones below (Fig. 9.71).

Fig. 9.68. 4-valve $E^\flat$ bass tuba by Boosey and Co., with mute.

Since the fourth valve increases the effective length of the instrument by one third, the intonation problem associated with valve combinations is much more serious than in a three valve instrument. Like many brass basses, the tuba shown in Fig. 9.68 has a *compensating system* (Bate 1966, pp.165–169) which introduces additional lengths of tubing only when the fourth valve is used in combination with others. The ingenious plumbing which achieves this need not concern us, although some of it can be seen in Fig. 9.68; the important point is that the amount of lipping required to play in tune in the lowest register is very much reduced.

Several alternatives to the bass tuba in $E^\flat$ or F are in common use in different parts of the worlds. Some instruments are built as three-valve basses with a fundamental pitch of $B^\flat_0$ or C_1; in France, the standard orchestral tuba was until recently a relatively short instrument with a fundamental pitch of C_2, but equipped with six valves. In Britain, the tenor tuba with fundamental pitch $B^\flat_1$ is known as the euphonium, and has an honoured history as a solo instrument (Fig. 9.72).

370

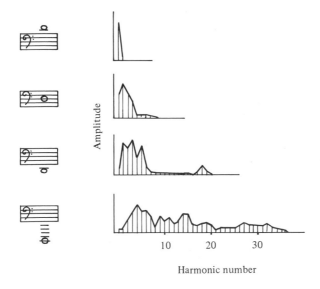

Fig. 9.69. Average spectrum envelopes measured for the notes D_4, D_3, D_2 and D_1, played on an E^b bass tuba.

Fig. 9.70. Tuba solo in 'Peasant with bear' from Stravinsky's ballet 'Petroushka'.

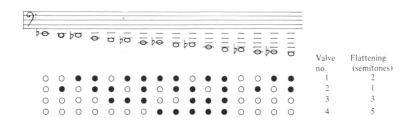

Fig. 9.71. Lowest register of the four-valve E^b bass tuba.

371

Fig. 9.72. Excerpt from the euphonium (tenor tuba) part in Holst's suite 'The Planets'.

Although many of the 'conical' instruments have a final section which flares very rapidly to a wide bell, the basic tonal character of the instrument is affected only if the flaring section extends over a significant fraction of the instrument's length. The *sousaphone* is a version of the bass tuba (in E♭ or B♭) in which the tube is coiled around the player, ending in a gigantic bell which projects forward over the player's left shoulder (Fig. 9.73). Although the visual effect is magnificent, it must be admitted

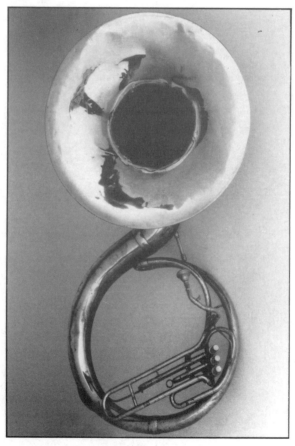

Fig. 9.73. Sousaphone in E♭ by Lafleur.

that the only acoustical purpose likely to be served by this large area of brass is to make the instrument more directional in its radiation of frequencies around 400 Hz, where the wavelength is comparable to the bell diameter.

Of the many other approximately conical valved instruments developed by Adolphe Sax and other fertile instrumental designers of the 19th century, we have space to mention only the *Wagner tubas*. These instruments were originally conceived by Wagner to fulfil his requirement for a particular type of brass sonority in the scoring of 'The Ring'; they have subsequently been used by numerous other composers. They are essentially tenor and bass tubas with fundamental pitches of $B_2^\flat$ and F_1 respectively, usually equipped with four rotary valves. Two features distinguish them from the tubas described above. Firstly, the average bore is considerably smaller than that of the euphonium or F tuba. Secondly, and more importantly, the mouthpipe tapers down to a much smaller diameter at the playing end, and takes a horn mouthpiece. In 'The Ring', the scoring calls for eight horn players; four of these double on the Wagner tubas. The narrower bore and smaller mouthpiece volume transfer more of the tonal content into the upper harmonics, without losing the rounded firmness characteristic of the conical family.

INSTRUMENTS WITH PREDOMINANTLY CYLINDRICAL BORE

The natural trumpet

Although instruments with long cylindrical sections and relatively short flaring bells existed in Greek and Roman times, there is no evidence that the flare was chosen to bring the resonances into a harmonic relationship, or indeed that more than one note was sounded on these instruments. In the 13th century, the cylindrical trumpet reappeared in Europe, probably imported from the Moslem world by knights returning from the Crusades. Over the course of the next two centuries, the trumpet developed an important military role as a signalling instrument, and from the nature of the calls (musical motifs) it can be deduced that the resonances down to the second were acceptable harmonics.

In fact, no instrument survives from this early period, and the first clear notation of trumpet calls dates from the 16th century (Baines 1976, p.120). In the 15th century however, numerous vocal compositions explicitly imitate the sound of trumpets; in Dufay's Gloria 'Ad modum tubae', for example, the two lower parts consist entirely of fanfares using the third, fourth, fifth and sixth harmonics of C_2 (Fig. 9.74). It is clear that, by this time, the sound of the trumpet was associated with a well-tuned harmonic series.

Fig. 9.74. Closing bars of Dufay's 'Gloria ad modum tubae'.

In the 17th century, every European court with any pretensions had a corps of trumpeters for ceremonial purposes. All the players in a corps used instruments of the same length; this was frequently about 2250 mm, giving a harmonic series based on C_2 at the high pitch of the time. Different players specialised in different registers of the instrument, some providing essentially a drone accompaniment on second and third harmonics, while others played fanfare motifs using harmonics from the third to the eighth. At the top of the ensemble came one or two parts described as 'clarino', using the diatonic compass up to the twelfth harmonic or beyond. The most magnificent recorded example of music for such a corps is that used by Monteverdi to open his opera 'Orfeo' in 1607 (Fig. 9.75).

Fig. 9.75. Toccata for trumpets from Monteverdi's opera 'Orfeo'.

From the acoustical point of view, the most important feature of the trumpet corps is the uniformity of the instruments playing parts at all pitches. This implies a wide range of tonal quality; the instruments playing at the bottom of their range have a harmonic spectrum rich in upper components, but deficient in fundamental, whereas the instruments playing the clarino parts have a relatively pure tone with only a few harmonics in the spectrum. This gradation of tonal quality is illustrated in Fig. 9.76, which shows the spectra of notes played on a Haas trumpet of 1687 (Fig. 9.77 (b)). On the other hand, the fact that all the instruments share the same formant regions introduces a unifying quality quite different from that obtained with a homogeneous group of scaled instruments (such as the soprano, alto and tenor saxhorns), for which the pitch of the formant varies with the size of the instrument.

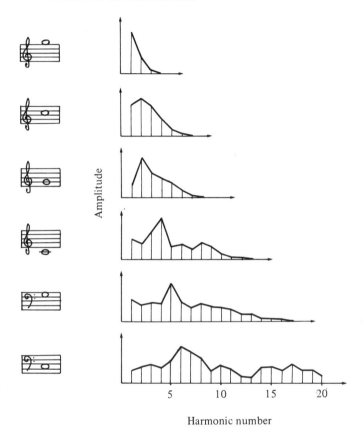

Fig. 9.76. Average spectrum envelopes for six notes on a 17th century natural trumpet, played mf. The written pitch of each note is shown to the left of the corresponding spectrum. Since the trumpet was in E♭, the sounding pitches are a minor third higher.

In the 18th century, the clarino register of the trumpet was further developed by players and composers, culminating in the virtuoso parts written for the instrument by Bach and Handel. The mouthpieces used at this time seem to have been rather smaller than those typical in the 17th century, although still large in comparison with modern trumpet mouthpieces (Smithers et al. 1986). The reduction in mouthpiece volume is consistent with cultivation of the highest register of the instrument (Fig. 9.78), since it raises the heights of the higher impedance peaks (see p. 343).

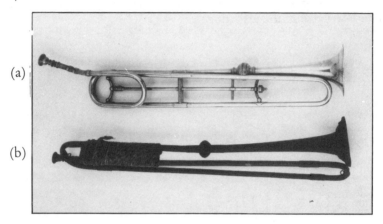

Fig. 9.77. (a) 19th century slide trumpet in F, crooked in E♭ by Cubitt (EUCHMI 2159/2160); (b) 17th century natural trumpet in E♭ by Haas (EUCHMI 996/997).

The bore of the baroque trumpet is characterised by a gentle, almost conical expansion in the bell branch, culminating in a rapid flare in the last few centimetres of the bell (Fig. 9.77 (b)). This abrupt transition reflects sound back into the instrument with greater efficiency than the more gradually flaring bell of later instruments (Figs. 9.77 (a) and 9.83). As a consequence, the baroque trumpet has useful impedance peaks at considerably higher pitches than does the modern trumpet (Benade 1976, p.404), providing additional security in the clarino register.

The modern interest in authentic performance of baroque and classical music has stimulated considerable research into the acoustical properties and playing techniques of the natural trumpet (Bate 1966, Ch. 6; Baines 1976, Ch. 5; Smithers 1973; Benade 1985; Smithers et al. 1986). It is important to remember that the baroque natural trumpet was normally a much longer instrument than the trumpet in common use today. The part illustrated in Fig. 9.78 was written for a trumpet about 2500 mm long, with a fundamental pitch of C_2; the first note of the example, D_5, is therefore the 9th natural note of the instrument. On a modern B♭ trumpet, of length 1340 mm, this is the 5th natural note. Frequently a piccolo B♭ trumpet about 700 mm long is used for playing very high parts; on this instrument D_5 is obtained with the first and second valves depressed, and is the 3rd natural note of the resulting air column.

Fig. 9.78. Excerpt from the part for trumpet (clarino) in C in K.G. von Reutter's 'Servizio di Tavola' (1757).

Bearing in mind that the impedance peaks of a trumpet grow up to about the sixth and then die away, we can see that the fundamental component of D_5 will tend to be more dominant in the spectrum of the baroque trumpet than in either of the modern instruments. This effect is emphasised by the large mouthpiece with its relatively low resonance frequency. On the other hand, measurements by Smithers et al. (1986) have shown that very high frequencies (above 8000 Hz), which are almost totally absent from the sound of the piccolo trumpet, add significantly to the brilliance and clarity of the natural trumpet played in an authentic manner. Thus the baroque instrument has a timbre at once warmer and clearer than a modern short trumpet. This is particularly important when the trumpet is required to play the role of a chamber music partner to instruments such as the violin and recorder (Fig. 9.79); in this company, it is expected to sound 'as sweet as an hautboy' (Baines 1976, p.136).

Fig. 9.79. Excerpt from the first movement of Bach's Brandenburg Concerto No.2.

Careful examination of Figs 9.78 and 9.79 reveals that by no means all of the pitches required from the trumpet are natural notes of the instrument. Controversy has raged for more than a century over the question of how these 'missing notes' were obtained (if indeed they were). It has been suggested that players might have hand-stopped the instruments, or opened secret pinholes to move the mode frequencies around (see Benada 1976, pp.123-124).

Smithers et al. (1986) have pointed out that irregularities of bore inevitable in the hand-made baroque instruments result in impedance peaks which are much lower and less sharply tuned than those of modern instruments (including machine-made reproductions). The lips thus receive less assistance from the air column in setting up a strong co-operative regime of oscillation. On the other hand, notes can be lipped into tune much more easily, and with less effect on their timbre. Don Smithers has demonstrated that, with an appropriate technique, all the notes required by baroque composers can be obtained satisfactorily on original natural trumpets. It is ironic that the principal fault with modern reproductions appears to be that they are too carefully manufactured.

Slide trumpets

Several compositions of the 15th century include relatively low pitched parts marked 'trumpet', apparently requiring the instrument to play diatonically from the third natural note upwards (e.g. Fig. 9.80). Although scholars disagree on whether these parts are truly instrumental (rather than vocal imitations of trumpet music), it has been widely accepted that they were probably played on a natural trumpet equipped with a cylindrical mouthpiece sliding inside the main tube of the instrument. By pushing the main body of the instrument away from the player, the tube length could be extended and the fundamental pitch lowered (Fig. 9.81).

Fig. 9.80. The part marked 'contratenor trompette' in the Rondeau 'J'ayme bien celuie qui s'en va' ascribed to Pierre Fontaine (c. 1440).

No trumpets with sliding mouthpieces have survived from the Renaissance, but numerous illustrations of the period show trumpeters apparently using such instruments (Sachs 1950). Estimates of the dimensions of the instruments depicted, taken together with the known limitations of the human arm, permit deductions to be made about the length of tubing added in the most extended position. It is dangerous, however, to draw conclusions about the pitch changes resulting from this extension by using the simple theory based on the fractional change in tube length (see p. 356). The increase in the ratio of cylinder to flare will lower the pitch of the extended position, by an amount which depends on the details of the instrument's bore profile. Thus an increase in tube length of 20%, which according to the simple theory would lower the pitch by three semitones, could in fact be sufficient (perhaps with a little downward lipping) to provide the four semitone interval necessary to bridge chromatically the gap between third and fourth harmonics (Baines 1976, pp.94–98).

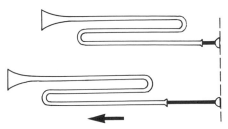

Fig. 9.81. The principle of the medieval slide trumpet.

The existence of slide trumpets in the Renaissance has been hotly disputed (Downey 1984). In the baroque period however, trumpets with sliding mouthpieces were certainly used by German town musicians, under the title of *Zugtrompeten*. One surviving instrument, dated 1651, allows an extension sufficient to lower the basic pitch by four semitones. Several of Bach's church cantatas contain trumpet parts requiring a non-natural diatonic compass in the lower register; some of these parts are marked *tromba da tirarsi*. It seems probable that the instrument intended was a *Zugtrompete*.

The principal practical problem with a sliding mouthpipe is the necessity of moving almost the whole of the instrument backwards and forwards. In 17th century England the trombone slide principle was applied to the trumpet. On the *flat trumpet*, used by Purcell in his music for the funeral of Queen Mary in 1695, the trumpet bow which lay over the player's left shoulder could be extended backwards (Fig. 9.82). This not only reduced the mass of the moving part of the instrument, but halved the displacement necessary to achieve a given pitch change.

At this point it becomes necessary to clarify the distinction between the trumpet and trombone families. The flat trumpet had about the same length of tubing as the tenor trombone, and possessed a double slide: what made it a trumpet rather than a trombone?

Trumpets and trombones do indeed share many common characteristics, being basically cylindrical tubes with short flaring sections. The method of tube extension cannot be used to separate the two classes; we have valve trombones as well as slide trumpets. A distinction can, however, be drawn on the basis of design features which give greater emphasis to high harmonics in the tonal spectrum of the trumpet family than in that of the trombones. The flaring section usually occupies about a quarter of the total tube length of a trumpet; in a trombone this fraction is typically around one third. The bore of the cylindrical section is narrower in a trumpet than in a trombone of the same length. Most importantly, the relative proportions of typical trumpet and trombone mouthpieces are different. Although the resonance frequency of a B♭ tenor trombone mouthpiece is usually less than an octave below that of a B♭ trumpet mouthpiece, the cup volume is relatively much larger in the case of the trombone. This has the effect of reducing the impedance multiplying factor of the trombone mouthpiece. In addition, the raising of the impedance peaks takes place over a wider pitch range, below rather than around the mouthpiece resonance (Backus 1976; Elliott et al. 1982). The resulting difference between characteristic trumpet and trombone impedance curves can be seen by comparing Figs 9.26 and 9.14.

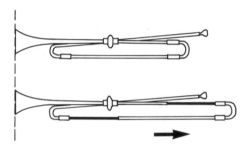

Fig. 9.82. Principle of the English 17th century 'Flat trumpet'.

Since these are all questions of degree rather than of kind, the demarcation line between trumpets and trombones is inevitably blurred. Many modern trumpets have a flaring section which takes up almost half the tube length, and a bore which is similar to that of a 19th century tenor trombone; some players also use a deep cupped mouthpiece on the trumpet. The resulting 'trumpet' sound is fuller and more rounded than that of the classic instrument whose properties are described above. Likewise, some jazz trombonists use a relatively narrow bored instrument with a small volume mouthpiece to achieve a harder, more biting sound.

The design of the flat trumpet of Purcell imposes at least one characteristic trumpet feature: the short flaring section. Since the double slide is on the second (backward) bow of the instrument, the tubing must remain cylindrical until about half way along the final straight section. On the trombone, the slide is on the first (forward) bow, and the flare can start much earlier.

In the late 18th century a further development of the slide trumpet took place. The slide was fitted with a mechanism (originally a spring, later a rubber cord) which returned it automatically to the closed position. In this form (Fig. 9.77 (a)) it became the standard English orchestral trumpet, and remained so throughout most of the 19th century. When fully extended, the slide lowered the pitch by about two semitones; it was used principally for correcting the intonation of the natural notes of the instrument. The fundamental pitch was normally F_2; crooks were used to lower the pitch as far as G_1.

The keyed trumpet

The use of key operated side holes to reduce the effective playing length of the tube was not confined to conical instruments such as the keyed bugle. In fact, the invention of the keyed trumpet preceded that of the keyed bugle by several years. The trumpet concerto of Haydn was written for such an instrument in 1796, and keyed trumpets were demonstrated by several solo performers in the early part of the 19th century.

From the acoustical point of view, the keyed trumpet suffers from two problems not shared by the keyed bugle. In comparison with the bugle, the trumpet has a narrow bore and a wide bell; there is thus a gross disparity between the sound radiated from the bell with all keys closed, and that radiated from a small hole opened some distance along the tube. Furthermore, since the opening of a hole greatly reduces the influence of the section of tubing beyond the hole, the effect of the flaring section in correcting the intonation of the natural notes changes as the keys are depressed. Although the tuning could in principle be controlled by cross-fingering, the 'open key' notes are weakened by the absence of the harmonically related resonance peaks necessary for a co-operative regime.

These problems are least serious when only holes near the bell are opened; the instrument can therefore play well in the upper register, using the keys to provide chromatic notes in the diatonic region of the natural notes. In this context, it offers a viable alternative to the slide trumpet (since it raises rather than lowers the pitches of the natural notes, it could be described as a 'sharp' rather than a 'flat' trumpet).

Valved trumpets

As early as 1824, valved trumpets were in use in German military bands, and three years later they were playing in the orchestra of the Paris Opéra. At first, the orchestral use of the valve trumpet echoed that of the natural trumpet: the basic instrument had a fundamental pitch of F_2 or G_2, and a range of crooks was available to facilitate playing in other keys. As valve systems improved, the instrument came to be treated as fully chromatic, and the use of crooks declined. Oddly enough, composers continued for some time to write for 'trumpet in E♭', 'trumpet in D♭', etc.; all these parts were played on a single instrument without crooks, the player transposing the part at sight. Fig. 9.83 illustrates two orchestral F trumpets of the 19th century, one using rotary valves, the other piston valves.

(a)

(b)

(c)

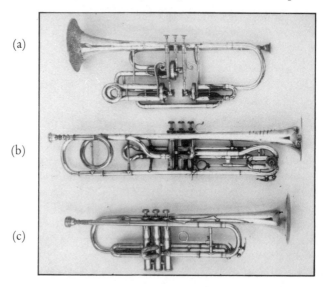

Fig. 9.83. (a) 19th century disc valve trumpet in F by Köhler (EUCHMI 869/886); (b) 19th century piston valve trumpet in F, with E♭ crook, by Mahillon (EUCHMI 2321/2322); (c) 20th century piston valve trumpet in B♭ by Vega.

Towards the end of the century, a shorter trumpet with a fundamental pitch of $B_2^\flat$ gradually supplemented the F trumpet. The B♭ trumpet (Fig. 9.83 (c)) provides greater security and brilliance in the upper register, for reasons which we have already discussed. The modern trumpeter's arsenal is also likely to include even shorter instruments: trumpets with fundamental pitches of C_3, D_3, F_3 and even $B_3^\flat$ (the *piccolo trumpet*) are in regular use.

The fact that modern trumpets have considerably shorter tube lengths than their classical and romantic forbears gives rise to some practical problems for the orchestral trumpeter. For example, the third trumpet part in Schumann's 'Manfred' overture descends to $E_3^\flat$ in the final bars (Fig. 9.84). This is the second natural note of the E♭ trumpet prescribed in the score; it is, however, a semitone lower than the lowest note obtainable on the B♭ trumpet. It is usually possible to cope with such isolated notes by extending the tuning slides of the B♭ instrument, converting it temporarily into a trumpet in A.

Fig. 9.84. Excerpt from the third trumpet part in Schumann's overture 'Manfred' (sounding pitch).

It must be accepted, however, that the short modern trumpet does provide a different tone quality from that expected by composers writing for the longer instruments. Articulation and phrasing are also liable to be affected by the substitution: a melody which can be played using only the natural notes of the long E trumpet, for example, will require frequent valve changes on the B♭ instrument.

An interesting example of the contrasting sounds of long and short, natural and valved trumpets is provided by the Pastoral Symphony of Vaughan Williams. The scoring of the first, third and fourth movements employs three trumpets in C (i.e. with fundamental pitch C_3). In the second movement, however, a long and highly atmospheric solo passage is given to an E♭ trumpet (Fig. 9.85). It is worth quoting in full the composer's instruction in the score:

It is important that this passage should be played on a true E♭ Trumpet (preferably a natural Trumpet) so that only natural notes may be played and that the B♭ (7th partial) and D (9th partial) should have their true intonation. This can, of course, be also achieved by playing the passage on an F trumpet with the 1st piston depressed. If neither of these courses is possible the passage must of course be played on a B♭ or C Trumpet and the pistons used in the ordinary way. But this must only be done in case of necessity.

Fig. 9.85. The solo for E♭ natural trumpet from the second movement of Vaughan Williams's Pastoral Symphony.

The solo passage lingers several times on the 'out-of-tune' 7th natural note. As we have seen, the laws of acoustics do not guarantee that this note will be a true 7th harmonic of E♭; the exact pitch of this, as of the other natural notes of the instrument, depends on the details of the bore profile. The composer clearly intended that the written B♭$_4$ should have the true

383

7th harmonic pitch 231 cents below the written C_5, and therefore about a third of a semitone flatter than the corresponding note played (in equal temperament) on a B^b valve trumpet. Since the cellos are playing a continuous E^b_2 during most of the trumpet solo, the true 7th harmonic will already be present in the accompanying sound. It can therefore be reasonably argued that it is in fact the B^b valve trumpet note (concert A^b_4) which is 'out-of-tune' in this context.

One long trumpet has preserved an occasional place in 20th century orchestration. This is the *bass trumpet*, conceived by Wagner for use in 'The Ring'. The most common instrument has a fundamental pitch of C_2, an octave below the C trumpets mentioned above. Although it has roughly the same tube length as the tenor trombone, its bore profile and mouthpiece proportions are usually characteristic of the trumpet rather than the trombone family (p.379). Thus, although it is customarily double by a trombone player, its sound is distinguished from that of the valve trombone by a greater emphasis on upper harmonics, giving a 'harder, brighter, narrower' tone quality (Wick 1984).

The trombone

Although valve trombones are occasionally to be found in crowded theatre pits or bicycling bands, the slide instrument is almost invariably used in orchestral, jazz and popular music. The standard instrument is the B^b *tenor trombone*, with a fundamental pitch of B^b_1 (Fig. 9.86 (a)); the acoustical properties of this instrument have been extensively discussed earlier in the chapter.

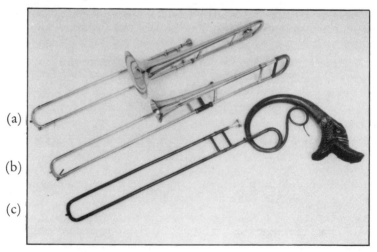

Fig. 9.86. (a) B^b trombone by Conn; (b) trombone with section of bell removed to simulate sackbut; (c) 'Buccin' trombone(EUCHMI 214).

The normal playing range of the tenor trombone extends upwards to D_5 (the 10th natural note). Although an athletic player can ascend further, orchestral trombone parts in this very high register are usually written for the *alto trombone* (fundamental pitch E^b_2). The use of the alto trombone was common in the classical and early romantic periods, but had almost died out by the end of the 19th century. Its present-day revival is largely due to an increasing awareness of the individual tone quality which the shorter instrument brings to such passages as Fig. 9.87.

Fig. 9.87. Excerpt from the alto trombone part in Schumann's 3rd Symphony (fourth movement).

The downward compass of the B^b tenor trombone can be derived from Fig. 9.88 (a), which shows the lowest four natural notes obtainable from each slide position of the instrument. The second natural note in first position is B^b_2 which can be lowered in semitone steps to E_2 in seventh position. The first natural note is the pedal B^b_1, which can also be lowered chromatically to E_1. However, a gap exists between E_2 and B^b_1, It is possible to fill in this gap by using privileged notes. For example, the note E^b_2 can be played with the slide in third position, since the second harmonic of this note (E^b_2) coincides in pitch with the third impedance peak of the tube when the slide is in this position. Since most of the other harmonics fall near impedance minima, these privileged notes are difficult to sound, and are not normally considered part of the instrument's compass.

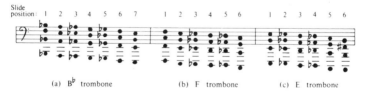

Fig. 9.88. The lowest four notes obtainable with each slide position for trombones in B^b, F and E.

A pedal note has its own characteristic quality, due to the fact that the first harmonic is not supported by an impedance peak (see p. XXX). This quality is sometimes specifically called for, as in the excerpt from Berlioz's 'Symphonie Fantastique' quoted in Fig. 9.89. Here the usual roles of trombone and tuba are reversed: the lowest note of the brass chord at the beginning of the fifth bar quoted is given to the tenor trombone, a sixth below the tuba. The dramatic effect of this fortissimo pedal note, with its profusion of upper harmonics, would have been even more striking when executed on the narrow bore trombone used in France in Berlioz's time.

Fig. 9.89. Excerpt from Berlioz's 'Symphonie Fantastique'.

The modern tenor trombone is frequently provided with a rotary valve, operated by the left hand thumb, which inserts sufficient additional tubing to lower the fundamental pitch (with the slide in first position) to F_1; it is then described as a $B^\flat$/F tenor. With this additional tubing in place, the slide positions are, of course, further apart: the seventh position is 'off the end of the slide', and the sixth may be difficult for the player to reach. The natural notes provided by the available six positions of the F trombone are shown in Fig. 9.88 (b). Disregarding the pedal notes, a chromatic compass is now obtainable down to C_2. Notorious passages such as Fig. 9.90, requiring the player of a $B^\flat$ trombone to alternate rapidly between first and seventh positions, become straightforward on the $B^\flat$/F instrument, since with the F valve depressed B₂ and A♯₂ can be played in second and third positions respectively.

Comodo
con sord.

ppp

Fig. 9.90. Excerpt from the second trombone part in Bartók's Dance
Suite (fifth movement).

A complaint frequently levelled against the B♭/F trombone is that notes obtained using the F valve are of inferior tone quality to those obtained using only the basic B♭ tubing (Wick 1984, p.71). There are certainly good acoustical reasons for expecting a change in tone quality when nearly one metre of additional cylindrical tubing is inserted into the instrument. If the flaring section occupies 30% of the basic B♭ tube length (in first position), it will form only about 16% of the tubing used with the F valve depressed and the slide in sixth position. The flare will thus be less effective in tuning the impedance peaks to produce a strong co-operative regime when the F valve is used.

The insertion of a valve usually introduces sharp bends and con-strictions into the bore of the instrument. This problem is, of course, shared by all valved instruments. Such bore changes affect the resonance frequencies of the instrument in a complicated way: a constriction raises the resonance frequency of standing waves with a pressure antinode near the constriction, but lowers the resonance frequency of standing waves which have a pressure node in this vicinity. Sharp bends also affect the tuning of the resonances, and a significant amount of acoustical energy is lost due to friction between adjacent layers of air when the wave is abruptly diverted (Keefe and Benade 1983). Finally, any sudden change in the bore of an instrument results in the partial reflection of sound waves at that point (Elliott et al. 1982). A clean start to a note depends on the first pressure pulse travelling without disturbance to the bell, with a strong reflection returning to the lips; a premature reflection from the valve confuses this signal to the lips, and makes a short starting transient more difficult to achieve (Benade 1976, p.425).

A carefully designed and well-constructed valve reduces these problems to a level at which the difference in performance between valved and unvalved instruments is a matter of some subtlety. Nevertheless, many players continue to use the simple B♭ tenor, partly because the additional plumbing of the B♭/F trombone considerably increases the weight of the instrument.

Bass and contrabass trombones

The most frequently used bass trombone in the modern brass section is, like the tenor, a $B^\flat$/F instrument. It has a considerably larger bore than the tenor, and a longer and wider flare; it is also played with a mouthpiece of larger volume. These differences give it an increased ability to exploit the lower pitch range: strong pedal notes can be obtained down to E_1, and even a few semitones below this are possible.

Turning again to Fig. 9.88, we can see that a complete chromatic scale down to E_1 is not possible using the $B^\flat$ and F tubings. Because the seventh position is unavailable with the F tubing, the note $B^\natural_1$ is missing To supply this note, an extra long tuning slide is sometimes provided, which when extended lowers the fundamental pitch of the F tubing by a semitone (see Fig. 9.88 (c)). This is clearly not usable unless several seconds are available for adjustment of the slide. More commonly, a second rotary valve is arranged to insert or remove this extra tubing; the instrument is then described as a $B^\flat$/F/E bass.

Until recently, bass trombones were frequently constructed in G or F with a long, swivelling handle which allowed an extension to the seventh position. Alternatively, a double slide was employed: two parallel bows were moved simultaneously by the player, so that the distance between adjacent slide positions was halved. To satisfy the requirements of Wagner's 'Ring' a *contrabass trombone* was specially constructed, with a double slide and a fundamental pitch of $B^\flat_0$. Double slide instruments are rarely found in present-day use; the modern contrabass trombone is usually a single slide instrument with a fundamental pitch of F_1 and a valved extension to C_1. Some instruments have a second valve, taking the fundamental pitch down to $B^\flat_0$, as in Wagner's original contrabass. In fact, the contrabass trombone is not required to aescend below E_1 in 'The Ring', and the part can be (and often is) played on a normal $B^\flat$/F/E bass; however, the use of the shorter tube length inevitably involves some sacrifice of tonal weight.

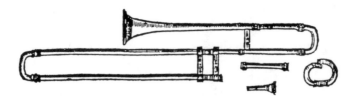

Fig. 9.91. Illustration of a tenor trombone (sackbut) with mouthpiece and crooks from Praetorius's 'Syntagma Musicum', Vol.II (1618).

The sackbut

The trombone developed from the Renaissance slide trumpet during the 15th century; by the end of the 16th century it was extensively used in court and church music, and it was included in the scoring of Monteverdi's operas. At this time it was known in Britain as the *sackbut*, and the title has come to be applied to the particular design of instrument in use during the period. The growing interest in authentic performance of early music has prompted a number of instrument makers to manufacture reproduction sackbuts.

As can be seen in the illustration from Praetorius's 'Syntagma Musicum' (1618), shown in Fig. 9.91, the sackbut was remarkably similar to the modern trombone. The bore of the cylindrical section of the tenor instrument was typically between 10 mm and 12 mm in diameter, the latter figure corresponding roughly to a present-day medium bore trombone. The flaring section lacked the final rapid expansion of the modern instrument, the bell being usually about 100 mm in diameter. The mouthpieces used with these instruments appear to have had cup and throat diameters similar to those found on many modern mouthpieces, but a relatively small cup depth and a sharp discontinuity between cup and throat (Fischer 1984).

Fig. 9.92 shows the results of measurements of input impedance and pressure transfer function carried out on a reproduction sackbut manufactured by Christopher Monk. These curves can be usefully compared with the corresponding curves for a modern trombone of about the same bore (Fig. 9.46 (a)). In both cases, the same mouthpiece was used (a modern Denis Wick 6BS).

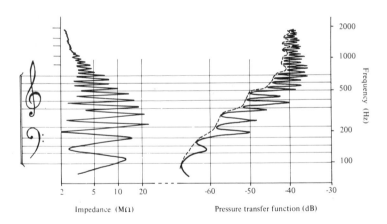

Fig. 9.92. Input impedance and pressure transfer function of a sackbut by Christopher Monk. The bell radius of the sackbut was 51 mm, but the PTF was measured 93 mm from the plane of the bell to facilitate comparison with Fig. 9.46. The lowest impedance peak is not shown.

Considering first the impedance curves, it will be seen that the fourth mode (corresponding to the third peak illustrated) is the same magnitude for both instruments. For the modern trombone, this is the central member of a group of five peaks of almost equal height; for the sackbut, the second peak is only half the magnitude of the first, while the peaks above the fourth fall steadily. The small bell of the sackbut traps sound energy above 800 Hz, while sound waves of such high frequencies leak freely through the wide bell of the modern trombone; as a consequence, the sackbut has several additional usable impedance peaks above the treble clef.

For the same reason, the pressure transfer function is about 5 dB lower for the sackbut than for the trombone at the mode frequencies above 800 Hz. These measurements are in accord with the musical experience of playing the instrument. The extended retinue of impedance peaks gives the security and responsiveness associated with a strong regime of oscillation, especially in the upper register, while reduction in pressure transfer function reduces the brilliance of the sound in comparison with that of a modern trombone.

It should be noted that Fig. 9.92 represents the acoustical behaviour of only one reproduction sackbut. Much more study is required, of both reproductions and originals, in order to clarify the differences between Renaissance and baroque instruments and those of the present day. In particular, the acoustical effects of wall material, thickness and treatment need investigation (Fischer 1984) (see p.404).

Many of the 'sackbuts' used in professional performances of early music at the present time are in fact 19th or 20th century narrow or medium bored trombones which have been modified by the removal of the last few centimetres of the flaring section. Figure 9.86 (b) shows a modern tenor trombone modified in this way.

Clearly modifications so near the open end will have little effect on the low pitch modes, since the sound waves associated with them are reflected earlier in the bell. In fact, the impedance curve below 800 Hz is almost completely unaltered by the amputation illustrated in Fig.9.86 (b). Fig. 9.93 shows that, above this frequency, the properties of the 'sawn-off sackbut' are in fact quite similar to those of the careful Monk reproduction. Both instruments are capable of creating a sound quality consistent with the advice of Mersenne in 1635:

> [The sackbut] should be blown by a skilful musician, so that it may not imitate the sounds of the trumpet but rather assimilate itself to the sweetness of the human voice, lest it should emit a warlike, rather than a peaceful sound (*tr.* Galpin 1906, p.21).

The fact that the final section of the bell has little effect on the intonation of the instrument has allowed makers to experiment widely with the tonal effects of different shapes and sizes of bell. The most grotesque result of such experiments was the 'buccin' trombone, in which the bell took the form of a brightly enamelled serpent's head (Fig. 9.86 (c)). The popularity of this instrument in French and Belgian military bands of the 19th century must have owed more to its spectacular appearance than to its musical performance, which is disappointingly similar to that of a conventional instrument.

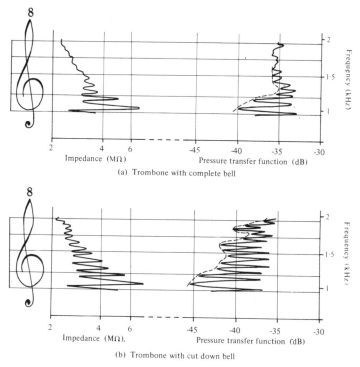

Fig. 9.93. Input impedance and pressure transfer function measured for a King tenor trombone with the bell cut back by 30 mm and re-rimmed (b). The new bell radius was 50 mm, but the PTF was measured 93 mm from the plane of the bell to facilitate comparison with a similar measurement on the unaltered instrument (a). Only the region above 1000 Hz is shown.

INSTRUMENTS WITH HYBRID BORE

The horn

We have no space to follow the development of the modern orchestral horn from its origin in the animal horn used from prehistoric times for hunting signals (Morley-Pegge 1960; Baines 1976, Ch. 6). It is worth noting, however, that the natural horns in common use in France in the 17th century were single looped instruments with fundamental pitches in the range F_2 to D_2. The tubing, about 2 metres in total, consisted of a long conical section followed by a short terminal flare. The repertoire of these instruments was restricted to hunting calls and fanfares: on such a short tube, natural notes above the tenth are difficult to secure. The development which led the horn from the hunting field to the concert hall was the extension of the tube length to around 4 metres, lowering the fundamental pitch to the vicinity of F_1; this extension was achieved by incorporating a substantial cylindrical section into the middle of the instrument, rather like a permanently inserted cylindrical crook. Thus, even before the development of elaborate systems of crooks and the invention of the valve, the horn had acquire what we have described as a hybrid bore: a long, approximately conical initial section, a central cylindrical section (or an alternation of cylinders and cones), and a final flaring section.

The acoustical theory of the horn is correspondingly more complicated than that of most of the instruments which we have discussed so far in this chapter; we shall limit ourselves to noting some of the ways in which the horn differs from its cousins in the brass family. The most significant difference is in the nature and function of the mouthpiece.

The trumpet mouthpiece, together with its short tapering mouthpipe, plays an important role in correcting the intonation of the instrument through the variation of its effective length with frequency (see Fig. 9.41). This function is largely unnecessary in the horn, since the bore profile can be designed to give an almost constant effective length in the upper register. The resonance frequency of the horn mouthpiece is therefore normally chosen to lie at the upper end of the playing range; below this frequency the variation of effective length is relatively small. If the high notes of the instrument run sharp, a mouthpiece with narrower throat or larger volume will give a lower resonance frequency, and will flatten these notes by bringing the variation of effective length into a lower pitch range (Pyle 1975).

The other important function of the mouthpiece is its amplification of the impedance peaks of the instrument. The deep funnel shaped horn mouthpiece (see Fig. 9.28), tapering smoothly into the narrow conical bore of the initial section of the horn, gives rise to a strong impedance multiplication effect, but one which is concentrated on the lowest three or four peaks (Lurton 1981). It is a characteristic of narrow bored cones that the low pitched impedance perks are very weak (Caussé et al. 1984); without the multiplication due to the mouthpiece, the low natural notes of the horn would be very difficult to sound. The role of the mouthpiece here is quite different from that which it plays in the trumpet: in the latter instrument, the impedance multiplication is in the vicinity of the mouthpiece resonance (around G_5 on the B^b trumpet), contributing much to the brilliance of tone which distinguishes it from the horn.

The natural horn

The classical orchestral horn was, of course, a natural instrument, supplied with a wide range of crooks so that the fundamental pitch of the instrument could be adapted to suit the prevailing tonality (Fig. 9.94). With the longer crooks, the compass of the instrument extended beyond the 20th natural note (Fig. 9.95).

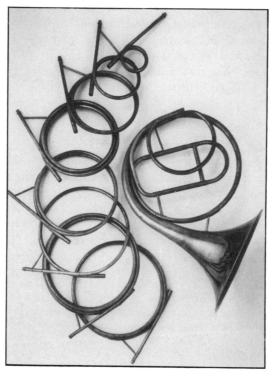

Fig. 9.94. Natural horn by Kretzschmann with crooks (EUCHMI 1804/1805).

Fig. 9.95. Except from the part for horn in E♭ in Haydn's Sextet No.14 in E♭ for wind and string.

Around the middle of the 18th century, the technique of *hand-stopping* revolutionised the art of horn playing, allowing chromatic intervals to be obtained from the 4th natural note upwards. The basis of the technique is encapsulated in an excerpt from *New Instructions for the French Horn*, published in the 1770s:

> Should you want to make the cromatic tones . . . one hand must be within the edge of the Bell ready to put into the Pavilion or Bell of the Horn as the notes require . . . (quoted in Morley-Pegge (1960), p.73).

The introduction of the player's right hand into the bell flattens the pitch of the natural notes to an extent which depends on the degree of insertion; the acoustical reason for this flattening, and the details of the musical technique based upon it, are discussed in the section below on 'Muting and hand-stopping on brass instruments'.

The valved horn

By the beginning of the 19th century, the art of hand-stopping had been developed to a remarkable degree: in the 9th Symphony of Beethoven, the fourth horn is required to modify the natural notes of the E♭ instrument to give a diatonic scale of B major (written A♭) (Fig. 9.96). Nevertheless, even the most skilled players were not always successful in disguising the changes in tone quality resulting from different degrees of hand-stopping. Writing in 1803, Dr Charles Burney commented:

> It must, however, be discovered by every discriminating hearer, that the factitious half notes that are made by the hand in the mouth of the instrument, are sounds of a different quality from the natural tones of the instrument. We have often thought that Ponto [the leading virtuoso of the day], with all his dexterity, produced some of these new notes with similar difficulty to a person ridden by the night mare, who tries to cry out but cannot (Burney 1803).

Fig. 9.96. Except from the part for horn in E♭ in Beethoven's 9th Symphony (third movement).

It is understandable, therefore, that the first recorded application of valves was to the horn (see p.368). The earliest valved horns were constructed with two valves, lowering the fundamental pitch by a semitone, a tone or (in combination) a minor third. Many features of hand horn technique were retained with the new instrument: the right hand continued to be placed within the bell, playing an important role in modifying both tone quality and intonation. The valves were regarded as quick change crooks, permitting the basic horn in F to be transmuted into a horn in E, E^b or D.

Although three-valved horns were fairly rapidly developed, they did not meet with general acceptance until the middle of the 19th century. The early valves, with their constrictions and sharp bends, added considerably to the resistance of the instrument, and to the problems of attack associated with premature reflections; these difficulties increased with the number of valves. As the design of valves improved, composers and performers embraced the chromatic possibilities of the three-valved horn, although not without reluctance; as late as 1865, Wagner, in an introductory note to the score of 'Tristan und Isolde', wrote:

The composer desires to draw special attention to the treatment of the horns. This instrument has undoubtedly gained so greatly by the introduction of valves as to render it difficult to disregard this extention of its scope, although the horn has thereby indisputably lost some of its beauty of tone and power of producing a smooth legato. On account of these grave defects, the composer (who attaches importance to the retention of the horn's true characteristics) would have felt compelled to renounce the use of the valvehorn, if experience had not taught him that capable artists can, by specially careful management, render them almost unnoticeable, so that little difference can be detected either in tone or smoothness (*tr*. Blandford 1922).

The standard instrument of the present day is a *double horn*, usually in B^b/F. On this instrument, a fourth valve operated by the left hand thumb removes sufficient tubing to raise the fundamental pitch from F_1 to B^b_1. It is clearly necessary that, when the fourth valve shortens the basic tubing, the length of tubing introduced by the other three valves should be reduced in proportion. This may be achieved by a compensating system, similar to that used on the tuba. In the full double horn (Fig. 9.97) the finger operated levers control rotary valves each with two sets of passages; one introduces the additional tube length required for the F horn, the other the shorter length required for the B^b horn. Which part of the valve is in the active air column is determined by the position of the fourth valve.

In the hands of a good player, the modern double horn is free from most of the 'grave defects' of which Wagner complained. There remains the acoustical problem associated with the insertion or removal of a long section of cylindrical tubing by the fourth valve (see p.351): if the flare is adjusted to compensate for the variation of equivalent length with pitch when the B^b tubing is used, the compensation will be inadequate for the longer F tubing (Backus 1976). Fine adjustments of tuning based on the old hand horn technique are used to correct for these and other deficiencies of intonation.

Fig. 9.97. Double horn in B♭/F.

Some modern players use a single horn with fundamental pitch $B_1^\flat$, equipped with four or five valves to permit chromatic playing in the lower register. The tone quality obtained on such an instrument is, of course, considerably different from that produced by the longer tubing of the F horn, for which much of the classical and romantic horn repertoire was written; on the other hand, the increased spacing of the harmonics (in a given pitch range) reduces the likelihood of 'cracking' a note on the B♭ instrument. This principle is carried even further on the *descant double horn*, in which the fourth valve switches between an instrument with fundamental pitch $B_1^\flat$ and one in 'F alto' with a fundamental pitch F_2. This type of horn is sometimes used by players specialising in high register playing.

Occasionally, modern composers write music which can only be played on the long F horn, since it uses natural notes which are unobtainable on a shorter tube. Vaughan Williams did so, in the same movement of the Pastoral Symphony from which Fig. 9.85 quotes. The outstanding example is the Serenade Op. 31 by Britten, in which the Prologue and Epilogue, for unaccompanied horn in F, are 'to be played on natural harmonics' (Fig. 9.98).

Fig. 9.98. Prologue to Britten's Serenade Op. 31.

The cornet

Of the many other types of hybrid bore brass instrument, we can mention only the *cornet*. This instrument was developed by the application of valves to the small posthorn (see p.360). The basic tube length of the early cornet was about half that of the orchestral horn, with crooks supplied to give fundamental pitches ranging from $B_2^\flat$ down to D_2; the lengths of tubing introduced by the valves could be adjusted by tuning slides to match the chosen crook.

By the second half of the 19th century, the longer crooks had been largely abandoned, and the cornet was used principally in $B^\flat$, A or $A^\flat$. The instrument, which had been built in a variety of shapes, had settled into the form of a rather stubby trumpet (Fig. 9.64 (c)). The smaller *soprano cornet*, with fundamental pitch $E_3^\flat$, is also used in brass bands, and both $B^\flat$ and $E^\flat$ cornets feature in the orchestral scoring of composers from Berlioz onwards.

The $B^\flat$ cornet has many similarities to the $B^\flat$ trumpet; the principal distinguishing features of the cornet are the long initial conical taper, and the relatively deep cupped mouthpiece normally used. These features give the cornet some of the acoustical properties of the horn: in particular, the tone quality lacks the brilliance which the small mouthpiece volume and short mouthpipe contribute to the trumpet. However, changes in musical taste have in recent years led to a desire for a fuller, more rounded trumpet tone; as a result, trumpets have developed longer conical mouthpipes and deeper mouthpieces, and the distinction between trumpet and cornet is correspondingly less acute than it was in the 19th century.

MUTING AND HAND-STOPPING ON BRASS INSTRUMENTS

Mutes

In the scoring of the toccata which opens his opera 'Orfeo' (Fig. 9.75), Monteverdi calls for 'trombe sordine' – muted trumpets. Thus, as early as 1607, a mute was part of the Italian court trumpeter's equipment. Mersenne's *Harmonie Universelle*, published 29 years later, contains a sketch of a trumpet mute (Fig. 9.99 (a)). Although the internal design of this early mute is not clear from the drawing, it was presumably similar to the surviving baroque mute whose cross-section is illustrated by Baines (Fig.9.99 (b)) – a wooden plug with a narrow cylindrical tube bored through it.

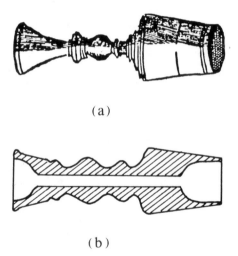

(a)

(b)

Fig. 9.99. (a) Mersenne's drawing of a trumpet mute; (b) cross-section of a baroque wooden trumpet mute (from Baines 1976, p.123).

A mute of this type has two effects on the behaviour of the instrument into which it is inserted: it raises the pitch of the natural notes by a tone (Munrow 1976, p.67) and strongly modifies the volume and tone quality of the sound produced. The latter effect is due mainly to the reduction in the radiating area at the open end of the instrument; the small hole through which the sound must escape can only radiate efficiently at very high frequencies, so that high harmonics are dominant in the muted timbre.

We shall return to the question of the pitch change introduced by the baroque mute in our discussion of horn hand-stopping. Modern trumpet and trombone mutes are designed in such a way that their insertion does not alter the pitches of the notes obtainable from the instruments. Backus (1976) has investigated this question both theoretically and experimentally, and has shown that the dimensions of the internal cavities and apertures of non-transposing trumpet mutes are empirically chosen so that they do not alter the trumpet's impedance curve significantly between 200 Hz and 1000 Hz. The impedance peaks in this region are those which establish the co-operative regimes of oscillation possible in the instrument, and therefore determine the pitches of the natural notes.

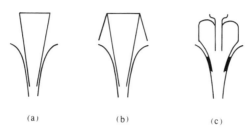

(a)   (b)   (c)

Fig. 9.100. (a) straight mute; (b) cup mute; (c) Harmon mute. Straight and cup mutes are supported in the bell by small cork pads, not shown.

Three common types of trumpet mute are illustrated in Fig. 9.100; similar mutes are used on trombones, and straight mutes are available for most brass instruments (see Fig. 9.68). The timbre modifications introduced by such mutes have been studied by Ancell (1960), Backus (1976) and Caussé and Sluchin (1982). On a trumpet, for example, each type of mute strongly reduces the output of sound energy below about 800 Hz. This effect occurs partly because of the reduction in area of the radiating surface, as discussed in the case of the baroque mute. There is, however, another reason for the decrease in radiating efficiency at low frequencies.

Blowing across the narrow open end of a straight trumpet mute excites the Helmholtz resonance of the air cavity. This is normally at a frequency around 220 Hz (pitch A_3). In this frequency region the mute is particularly efficient at absorbing sound energy from the trumpet air column and radiating it back towards the mouthpiece. Since the frequency width of the Helmholtz resonance is large, this process introduces a wide minimum into the curve of radiating efficiency as a function of frequency. Other minima at much higher frequencies have also been associated with resonances of the mute cavity (Causse and Sluchin 1982).

The effect of the straight mute on timbre can be summarised by describing it as a 'high-pass filter' (Backus 1976). Frequencies above about 1800 Hz are passed without much hindrance, while lower frequencies are trapped. The cup mute behaves similarly below 800 Hz, but allows through a band of frequencies between 800 Hz and 1200 Hz; above 1200

Hz it traps sound much more efficiently than the straight mute. Thus the cup mute has a characteristically gentle sound (except when played ff), with a pronounced formant in the region of C_6.

The Harmon mute has an open pipe at the centre. Resonances of this pipe correspond to maxima in radiating efficiency; three such formants have been identified, at around 1500 Hz, 3000 Hz and 4500 Hz (Ancell 1960). Partially closing the end of the pipe with the fingers lowers these resonances and modifies the timbre considerably. The change in the lowest formant is similar to the change of the second vocal formant when the vowel [a] ('ah') is altered to the vowel [u] ('oo') (see Fig. 12.8). Hence opening and closing the central tube of the Harmon mute gives a characteristic 'wah-wah' effect.

Hand-stopping

Another way in which the radiating efficiency of a brass instrument can be modified is by the insertion of the hand into the bell. This technique is almost exclusively confined to French horn players. Benade (1973) has given an excellent account of the technique, explaining that the hand performs several important acoustical functions. It reduces the efficiency of radiation of the high spectral components by increasing the height of the 'forbidden zone' barrier in the bell (see also Roberts 1976). In consequence, the impedance peaks of the air column extend to higher frequencies, making it easier to achieve co-operative regimes of oscillation in the high register. These regimes can be further stabilised by small adjustments of the hand position, bringing the peaks into a proper harmonic relationship.

One question which has been a perennial source of debate among horn players concerns the effect of inserting the hand on the pitch of the note (see, e.g., Morley-Pegge 1960; Aebi 1976). Since the open end of a brass instrument is a velocity antinode (a pressure node), restricting its area should lower the frequencies of all the modes of the air column. Gradually inserting the hand while playing a note on the horn does indeed force the pitch of the note downwards. When the hand is firmly pressed in as far as it will go, however, it appears that (at least on the F horn) all the natural notes of the instrument have risen by a semitone!

An explanation of this effect much favoured by some horn players is that pressing the hand in has shortened the effective length of the air column, thereby raising the pitch. It is difficult to see how this can be reconciled with the observation that partially inserting the hand makes the pitch fall.

Scientific studies of hand-stopped horns by Aebi (1971) and Backus (1976) have provided a convincing resolution of this apparent paradox. To aid our understanding of how the resonances of an air column behave when the open end is gradually closed, let us consider first the simple case of a cylindrical tube. Fig. 9.101 (a) shows the measured input impedance curve for a tube of length 1040 mm and diameter 25 mm, closed at the input end and completely open at the other end. The peaks occur at frequencies which are odd integer multiples of 81.5 Hz, as we should expect.

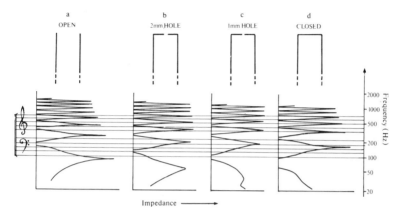

Fig. 9.101. Input curves for a cylindrical tube, closed at the lower end, showing the effect of different degrees of closure of the upper end.

When the output end of the tube is closed by a disc with a 2 mm diameter hole in it, the curve shown in Fig. 9.101 (b) is obtained. All the impedance peaks have moved to lower frequencies; the change (in terms of pitch interval) is greatest for the lowest peak. When the hole in the disc is reduced to 1 mm (Fig. 9.101 (c)), the lowest peak falls even further in pitch, becoming broader and lower in amplitude. When the hole is completely closed, the original first peak has dropped right out of the picture, and the lowest resonance remaining is that which started as the second (Fig. 9.101 (d)). By this stage, of course, we have arrived at a tube closed at both ends, and as expected the peaks in Fig. 9.101 (d) correspond to a complete harmonic series with a fundamental frequency of 164 Hz.

The changing pitches of the first six resonances are shown in Fig. 9.102 as a function of the diameter of the open end. This diagram clearly displays the continuous downward pitch glide of each resonance from the completely open to the completely closed state.

The technique used in obtaining the measurements displayed in Figs. 9.101 and 9.102 was based on the work of Backus, who examined the gradual closing off of a horn bell (Backus 1976, pp.478–480). This is a more complicated case than the cylindrical tube, since for the lowest resonance the sound wave is reflected before reaching the bell, and is

401

therefore less affected by what goes on within it. However, Backus was able to demonstrate that upper resonances of the horn glided steadily downwards as an aperture within the bell was gradually closed.

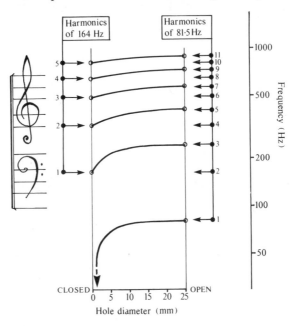

Fig. 9.102. Illustrating the continuous downward pitch glide of the first six resonances of a cylindrical tube as the output end is gradually closed.

As part of an investigation into the effect of baroque mutes, we have carried out a similar measurement on a sackbut. A cylindrical tube extending 100 mm into the bell was fitted with a variable aperture at its inner end (Fig. 9.103). With the bell unobstructed, the usual set of impedance peaks was found (Fig. 9.92): with the exception of the lowest, at 39 Hz, they occur close to harmonic multiples of 58.3 Hz ($B_1^\flat$). Inserting the tube, open at both ends, reduced the upper mode frequencies, by effectively lengthening the air column. The pitch glide of the first six resonances as the inner end of the tube was gradually closed is shown by the solid curves in Fig. 9.103. As complete closure was approached, the lowest impedance peak diminished in both amplitude and frequency, and finally disappeared. The striking feature in the pattern of the remaining resonances is that (with the exception of the lowest) they form a new harmonic series, with an apparent fundamental of 61.7 Hz ($B_1^\natural$); this is just a semitone above the apparent fundamental of the open instrument. The original 3rd harmonic of $B_1^\flat$ has moved down to become the 2nd harmonic of $B_1^\natural$, while the higher modes have undergone a similar transformation both of pitch and of harmonic number.

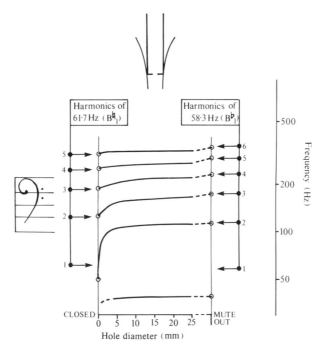

Fig. 9.103. Illustrating the continuous downward pitch glide of the first six resonances of a sackbut as an aperture within the bell is gradually closed.

With a 1 mm diameter hole at the end of the 'mute', the sackbut was playable, though with a very high resistance. The natural notes were indeed harmonics of $B^\natural_1$. Similarly, Backus found that on an F horn the 'stopped' hand position transforms the 3rd, 4th, 5th . . . harmonics of F_1 into the 2nd, 3rd, 4th . . . harmonics of $F^\sharp_1$.

Morley-Pegge (1960, p.136) has emphasised that the rise of pitch on a stopped note will not occur unless the note is attacked 'with a slight tensing of the lip muscles'. Otherwise, he says, 'we get a heavily blanketed, dull note half a tone to a tone lower than the open note'. As the degree of closure increases, the pitch interval between adjacent modes widens (see Fig. 9.103), so that an attempt to use the second mode resonance as a 2nd harmonic becomes less and less satisfactory. The quotation from Morley-Pegge is a graphic description of a note produced without the help of a co-operating set of harmonically related resonances. The slight adjustment of lip tension allows the lip reed to lock into the alternative, well-tuned regime at the higher pitch.

THE EFFECTS OF BELL MATERIAL, TREATMENT, THICKNESS AND FINISH

In 1854 the Royal Marine Artillery carried out on Woolwich Common a series of comparisons of the carrying power of bugles made from different materials. At the time, this was a question of considerable military importance. According to Rose (1894, pp.102–103):

> Buglers were told off, each carrying a bugle of brass and one of copper, the instruments having all been made by the same workman, on the same mandril, etc. The buglers sounded these instruments at various distances. This was the result. The atmosphere being still (i.e. no perceptible breeze blowing), the copper bugles were clearly heard two miles off, whilst the brass instruments were unaudible at less than half the distance.

Despite this apparently unequivocal conclusion, the question of whether or not the material of construction of a 'brass' instrument significantly affects its sound power output or timbre has remained under active discussion up to the present day. It is generally accepted (at least among acousticians) that wall material vibrations play a very minor role in the sound production of woodwind instruments (see Chapter 8); on the other hand, no one has seriously questioned the crucial importance of body or soundboard resonances in stringed instruments. Brass instruments fall into an intermediate category: the large area of thin metal in a trombone bell bears a tempting resemblance to the shape of a loudspeaker cone. It must be borne in mind, however, that the primary source of sound energy in a wind instrument is the air column. If the walls do vibrate significantly, they may generate their own sound, but such vibrations could also reduce the overall sound output by dissipating some of the energy of the air column's standing waves.

This dichotomy is reflected in the diversity of manufacturers' claims about the effects of different bell materials (Bowsher and Watkinson 1982). Some makers boast of 'live' bells, clearly assuming that bell vibration is a good thing; on the other hand, one famous manufacturer states that 'as far as the overall instrument is concerned, the more inert it is to vibration, the better it is'.

When a trumpet or trombone is played fortissimo, it is easy for the player to feel the vibration of the bell, and tempting to identify the characteristic 'brassy' blare with this metal vibration. As we have already observed, it is in fact the rapid growth of high harmonics with increasing loudness which is responsible for this aspect of brass timbre. Grasping the instrument firmly just behind the bell does not stop it blaring when played very loudly, even though it must seriously dampen the wall vibrations; Knaus and Yeager (1941) covered the external wall of a cornet with putty, and reported a negligible change in timbre.

On the other hand, more recent measurements have shown that bell vibrations can under certain circumstances contribute measurably to the sound radiated by some brass instruments. Some of the most interesting and important work in this field has been carried out by Richard Smith (1978; 1981; 1986). Using the technique of interference holography (see Chapter 6), Smith has been able to observe and measure on trombone bells the vibrations which arise as a consequence of the 'pumping' effect of the pressure variations in the air column. Because of the nature of the technique, the instruments were not blown by a live performer, but sounded by an artificial acoustic driver.

Examples of Smith's interferograms are shown in Fig. 9.104. The lower two photographs are side and end views of a brass trombone bell with a wall thickness of 0.3 mm. The air column vibration at 240 Hz coincided here with a strong vibration mode of the bell, with four-fold cylindrical symmetry. The upper pair show similar views of another mode of the bell, which was excited by an air column vibration at 630 Hz. In this case the bell mode has six-fold symmetry. Computer calculations have shown that vibration patterns of the type shown in Fig. 9.104 are to be expected in brass instrument bells (Watkinson and Bowsher 1982).

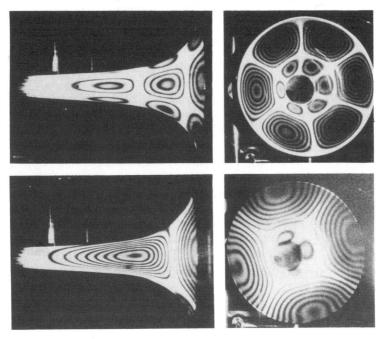

Fig. 9.104. Time-averaged interferograms for the vibrations of a brass trombone bell, wall thickness 0.3 mm. Lower: 240 Hz; upper: 630 Hz (reproduced by kind permission of Richard Smith).

The fringe spacing on interference holograms decreases with increasing vibration amplitude. Making use of this fact, Smith has measured amplitudes of vibration for several bells of different thickness, and has shown that the amplitude (for a given forcing air pressure) increases very rapidly when the wall thickness is reduced below 0.4 mm (Fig. 9.105). This curve agrees with a theoretical prediction that wall vibration amplitude should be inversely proportional to the fourth power of the wall thickness (Smith 1978).

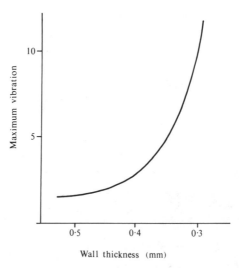

Fig. 9.105. Dependence of wall vibration amplitude on wall thickness for a brass trombone bell (from Smith, (1978)).

Is the sound generated by the vibrations shown in Fig. 9.104 measurable? And is it audible? Smith has shown that the sound radiated along the axis of the bell is not significantly altered in either volume or timbre by changes in bell thickness. However, measurements made with a microphone at the position normally occupied by the player's left ear show that harmonics in the vicinity of 240 Hz (the frequency of the strongest bell vibration mode) were boosted by several dB when a 0.5 mm bell was replaced by an 0.3 mm bell of identical internal bore. The player might therefore be aware of a difference, even if the audience was not.

The curve in Fig. 9.105 is of considerable significance for the discussion of the acoustical difference between modern and 16th century trombones. The majority of modern trombones have bells with wall thickness of 0.4 mm or over, while many surviving sackbuts have bells whose walls taper to well under 0.3 mm. Fischer (1984) has argued strongly that the resulting strength of wall vibration is an important feature of true sackbut timbre; this hypothesis awaits scientific verification.

If the thickness of the bell wall is of primary importance in determining the extent to which it vibrates, other aspects of the wall have also been found to cause measurable changes in the radiated sound. Pyle (1981) carried out careful comparisons of silver plated and lacquered bells on French horns, and showed that lacquering the bell reduced the amplitudes of spectral components above 500 Hz, some by as much as 6 dB. Silver plating did not have a measurable effect. Wogram (1979) found a 3 dB difference in spectral components in the range of 3 kHz to 5 kHz between instruments made of brass and those made of nickel silver. Lawson and Lawson (1985) found that the extent to which the bell of a French horn is annealed can also introduce deviations of the order of 3 dB into the sound spectrum.

The current consensus is therefore that differences in wall material, treatment, thickness and finish can all affect the radiated spectrum of a brass instrument. It is not yet established, however, that these differences are musically significant. In a carefully controlled blindfold test, Smith (1986) used ten highly experienced trombonists to compare the playing properties of six trombones with bell thicknesses ranging from 0.3 mm to 0.5 mm. The bells were made on the same mandrel, and precautions were taken to equalise the weight and balance of the instruments. It was found that, despite the spectral differences previously described, none of the players could reliably distinguish between thick and thin bells.

In an echo of the 19th century buglers' trials, Smith subsequently included an electroformed pure copper bell in the test set. Blindfold, the players could not distinguish this from the brass bells. When the blind-folds were removed, however, magical properties were ascribed to the copper bell! In this area it is particularly difficult to disentangle acoustical facts from players' prejudices.

10

Percussion instruments

Praise the Lord!
Praise him with tambourine and dance!
Praise him upon the loud cymbal!
Praise him upon the high sounding cymbal!
(Psalm 150)

The earliest records of musical activity show performers exploiting the range of sounds obtainable when different objects are struck or rattled together. The ensemble described by the Old Testament psalmist apparently includes two types of cymbal with distinctive musical properties, as well as some kind of drum; composers of the present day occasionally call for a percussion section containing more than fifty different instruments. Despite their musical importance, percussion instruments have received relatively little attention from acousticians; although the general principles which govern their behaviour are well understood, many questions of musical significance remain unresolved. In this chapter, we offer a brief review of the present state of knowledge concerning that section of the orchestra known affectionately as 'the kitchen'. Most of the references to historical developments and playing techniques are drawn from the volume *Percussion Instruments and their History*, by one of the greatest of modern orchestral percussionists, James Blades (1984).

Strictly speaking, any instrument excited by striking is a member of the percussion class. Instruments such as the dulcimer, cimbalom and piano, in which strings are struck by hammers, are technically *percussion chordophones*, and have been discussed in earlier chapters. The instruments normally considered as members of the orchestral percussion section are either *percussion membranophones*, in which the struck object is a stretched membrane, or *percussion idiophones*, in which the natural reso-

409

nance of some rigid object is exploited. We discuss first the percussion membranophones – in other words, the drums.

DRUMS

The essential element in every drum is a membrane which is stretched over a frame. Traditionally, the membrane has been a carefully prepared animal skin, although synthetic materials are used in most modern orchestral drums. In some of the earliest pictorial records of drums, the skin is stretched over a rectangular frame. In practically all drums of musical significance, however, the frame is circular; we shall therefore consider only the acoustical properties of a circular membrane.

Vibrations of a circular membrane

In Chapter 1 we looked briefly at the behaviour of a struck drumhead. The impact of the stick pushes the head downwards; because the head is under tension, the downward displacement generates an upward force which causes the membrane to spring back to its original-position and beyond. The nature of this restoring force is illustrated by Fig. 10.1, showing a cross-section through the centre of a circular drum. Before the stick strikes, a small segment of the membrane at the point O is pulled from right and left by equal and opposite forces due to the tensioning of the head. After the stroke, the point O is lower than the points A and B on the frame. The two tension forces are now on longer in opposite directions: although the rightward pull due to one is balanced by the leftward pull due to the other, each exerts an upward pull on the segment at O.

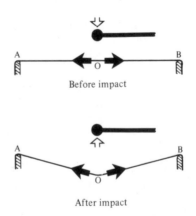

Fig. 10.1. When a drumhead is struck at the centre, the central segment (O in the diagram) is displaced downwards. The tension forces on O (represented by black arrows) then exert a net upward pull.

The behaviour of a struck membrane is thus very similar in principle to that of a struck or plucked string. The crucial difference is that the string is a one-dimensional vibrator (that is, its thickness can be neglected in comparison with its length), whereas a membrane is a two-dimensional vibrator (the length and breadth of a circular head are equal, although its thickness is still negligible in comparison).

The two-dimensional nature of the vibrating drumhead has one very important musical consequence. The normal mode frequencies for an ideal (very thin, completely flexible) string are members of an exact harmonic series; in contrast, the normal modes of an ideal circular membrane have frequencies which are strongly inharmonic (Kinsler et al. 1982, pp.82–85). Hitting the head at an arbitrary point will excite a large number of normal modes simultaneously; we should therefore expect the sound radiated to contain many inharmonically related frequencies, and to lack any definite sense of pitch.

This expectation is not borne out by experience: under the right circumstances, a drum can produce a clearly pitched note. In the first bar of Beethoven's Violin Concerto (Fig. 10.2), for example, the four strokes on the kettledrum establish the tonality of D before the entry of any other instrument. It is often thought that the bowl of the kettledrum is responsible for the fact that its sound has a definite pitch, but we shall see that this is not so. Indeed, in the 19th century Adolphe Sax invented a set of timpani in which the membranes were stretched over thin circular frames without any bowls. These instruments also gave clearly pitched notes; Sax called them 'timbales chromatiques', since the set could be tuned to play chromatic scales (Blades 1984, pp.278, 352).

Fig. 10.2. The opening bars of Beethoven's Violin Concerto.

In order to understand why a circular drumhead can produce a definite pitch, we must look in more detail at the nature of the vibration patterns of such a membrane. In doing so, we shall also gain some useful insights into the playing techniques of the timpanist and other drummers.

411

Normal modes of a circular membrane

The mode frequencies and vibration patterns of an ideal, undamped circular membrane were first calculated in the 19th century (Clebsch 1862; Rayleigh 1894). The vibration patterns of the first twelve modes are shown in Fig. 10.3. Points on the membrane which remain at rest during the vibration of a particular mode lie on *nodal lines*, the two dimensional equivalents of the nodes on a vibrating string.

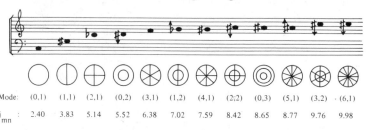

Mode:	(0,1)	(1,1)	(2,1)	(0,2)	(3,1)	(1,2)	(4,1)	(2,2)	(0,3)	(5,1)	(3,2)	(6,1)
j_{mn} :	2.40	3.83	5.14	5.52	6.38	7.02	7.59	8.42	8.65	8.77	9.76	9.98

Fig. 10.3. The first twelve normal mode patterns of an ideal undamped circular membrane. Above each pattern is shown the approximate pitch of the mode, assuming a first mode pitch of C_3. Below each pattern is shown the mode description (m, n) and the value of the number j_{mn} (see text). From Rayleigh (1894), Vol.1, pp.330, 331.

For a circular membrane of uniform thickness and tension, the nodal lines are either circles concentric with the frame, or diametral lines passing through the centre of the head. Since the head is fixed at the outside rim, this rim is a nodal circle for all the modes. The first mode has no other nodal lines; the whole membrane rises and falls as a unit. It is this motion which is illustrated in Fig. 1.18.

The second mode has an additional diametral line, dividing the membrane into two equal segments. The two segments vibrate with opposite phase, one rising while the other falls. The third mode has two such lines, perpendicular to each other; in this mode, two diametrically opposite segments vibrate in phase, while the remaining two segments vibrate with the opposite phase.

The fourth mode displays a different pattern: there are no diametral nodal lines, but the membrane is divided into two segments by an additional nodal circle. As with the second mode, the two segments vibrate with opposite phase, the central disc rising while the outer ring falls. The fifth mode has six segments separated by three diametral nodal lines, while the sixth mode combines one nodal diameter with two nodal circles. Succeeding modes show the membrane being divided into smaller and smaller segments by increasing numbers of nodal diameters and circles.

It is conventional, and convenient, to describe each mode by two numbers: the first gives the number of nodal diameters, the second the number of nodal circles. Thus the first mode, with no nodal diameters and only one nodal circle, is the (0,1) mode; the sixth mode, with one diameter and two circles, is the (1,2) mode.

Patterns of nodal lines are often called *Chladni figures*, after the German acoustician who first showed that the patterns could be made visible by sprinkling sand on a vibrating plate. The sand is thrown up on the vibrating areas, and collects around the nodal lines (see Fig. 10.22). Thomas Rossing, who with his colleagues at Northern Illinois University has contributed greatly to the present day understanding of percussion instruments, has published photographs of six Chladni figures of a kettledrum head, demonstrating that the patterns of nodal lines are indeed those given in Fig. 10.3 (Rossing 1982 (a)).

Resonant frequencies of an ideal undamped drumhead

The frequency of a particular normal mode of a circular drumhead can be calculated, if the properties of the membrane are known. For a membrane of radius a metres, with surface density ϱ kilograms per square metre, under a tension equivalent to a force of T newtons across a line of unit length on the membrane, the resonant frequency of the (m,n) mode is given by

$$f_{mn} = (1/2\pi a) (T/\varrho)^{1/2} j_{mn}$$

where j_{mn} is a number (known to mathematicians as 'the nth root of the mth Bessel function') depending on the number of nodal diameters (m) and circles (n) in the pattern. This calculation assumes that the membrane is completely flexible, and is not acted on by any forces tending to damp out the vibrations.

The formula quoted above tells us several useful things about drumheads. The fact that the frequency is inversely proportional to the radius a shows that doubling the radius of a drum (keeping thickness and tension constant) will halve the frequency of a given mode; in other words the pitch will drop by an octave. The tension T on the head appears to the power $1/2$; in order to raise the pitch by an octave, the tension must be increased fourfold.

If the size, thickness and tension of the drum are kept constant, the frequency of a particular mode depends only on the number j_{mn}. Values of this number are given under the corresponding nodal patterns in Fig. 10.3. These numbers are clearly not harmonically related. To make this more obvious we have shown the pitches of each of the modes on the stave above, assuming that the drum is tuned so that the (0,1) mode has a pitch C_3. None of the other modes illustrated have pitches which are harmonics of C_3; the mode frequencies are much more closely spaced than a harmonic series.

413

The effect of air damping on real drumheads

If a real drum radiated the set of pitches shown in Fig. 10.3 the sound would not only lack a definite pitch, but would be rather nasty; the clash between $D_4^\flat$ and the flattened $D_4^\sharp$ and the cluster of pitches around A_4, would give rise to a high degree of beating and roughness The musical quality of a well-tuned drum is due principally to the influence of a factor which we have so far neglected: the damping effect of the surrounding air.

In discussing the force on a segment of the drumhead (Fig. 10.1), we assumed that only the forces due to the tension on the membrane need be considered; the resonant pitches shown in Fig. 10.3 were calculated on this assumption. However, when the drumhead moves upwards, it compresses the air above it, and reduces the pressure of the air below (Fig. 10.4). As a result, the surrounding air exerts a net downward force on the membrane, tending to oppose its motion. It is this interaction between the membrane and the air which is responsible for the radiation of a sound wave; the energy originally imparted to the membrane by the stroke of the drumstick is gradually converted into sound energy (apart from that lost through friction), and the vibrations die away.

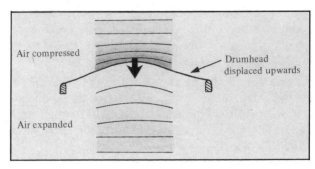

Fig. 10.4. A net downward force (represented by the arrow) results from the pressure difference across the drumhead.

The force exerted on the drumhead by the air does not merely cause the amplitude of the vibrations to diminish; it also reduces the frequencies of the normal modes (Morse 1948). It is intuitively obvious that the head will vibrate more sluggishly when it has to push the air up and down than it would do if it were vibrating in a vacuum. If the tension of the drumhead is very high, the force exerted by the air is small in comparison and the changes in normal mode frequencies are slight. For the tensions used on orchestral timpani, the air damping force has an important effect, lowering the pitch of the low frequency modes much more than the modes of high frequency (Rossing 1982 (a)). Thus the pitch intevals separating the normal modes of a real drum are wider than those shown in Fig. 10.3.

Lord Rayleigh noticed that most of the sound from a struck kettledrum appeared to come from the (1,1) mode, with the (2,1) and (3,1) modes also contributing significantly (Rayleigh 1894, Vol.1, p.348). Christian et al. (1984) have shown that these and other modes with only one nodal circle (at the rim) decay much more slowly than do modes with more than one nodal circle. Thus, after a second or so, the only modes left contributing to the ringing aftersound of the drum are the (n,1) modes (with n = 1, 2, 3 ...).

Examination of Fig. 10.3 shows that, if the membrane were undamped, this aftersound would be fairly discordant. By a remarkable and fortunate coincidence, the effect of air damping on a kettledrum is to widen the spacing of the (n,1) modes so that they become almost exactly members of a harmonic series. This is illustrated in Fig. 10.5, where for convenience the pitch of the (1,1) mode has been chosen as C_3. The quasi-harmonic nature of some kettledrum resonances has been noted by various writers (Rayleigh 1894, Vol.1 p.348; Kirby 1930, p.43; Blades 1984, p.355). The musical validity of Fig. 10.5 was demonstrated to one of the authors some twenty years ago by the timpanist Andrew Shivas, singing into a carefully prepared calfskin head; measurements by Benade (1976, pp.143–144) have revealed the same harmonic relationship in the frequency spectrum of the radiated sound from a struck kettledrum.

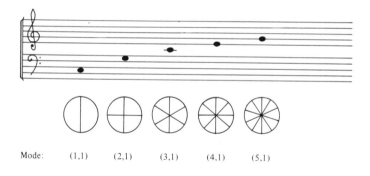

Fig. 10.5. The modes of vibration principally responsible for the sense of pitch of a drum note. Above each mode pattern is shown the approximate pitch of the mode on a real (air damped) kettledrum tuned to C_3.

The pitch assigned to the drum, known as the *nominal*, is in fact that of the (1,1) mode, with one nodal diameter. The influence of the air damping can be seen by comparing the intervals of Fig. 10.5 with those shown for the undamped case in Fig. 10.3: the interval between (1,1) and (2,1) modes has been stretched from 514 cents to around 700 cents, while that between (1,1) and 5,1) has increased from 1435 cents to around 1900 cents.

Effect of the drum body on mode tuning

The effect of air damping on the pitches of the modes of a drumhead is greater when the head is mounted on a kettle or other body than when it is isolated. This is understandable, since the air trapped inside a kettle offers more resistance to the motion of the head than the open atmosphere. Christian et al. (1984) have studied this effect both experimentally and theoretically; Fig. 10.6 is based on some of their experimental measurements on a 26″ diameter Ludwig kettledrum. In this diagram the pitches of the modes (1,1) to (5,1) are plotted vertically in the usual way, assuming a pitch of C_3 for the (1,1) mode. (In the actual measurements of Christian et al., the (1,1) mode pitch varied between C_3 and F_3.) Horizontal displacements indicate the extent to which the pitch of each mode deviates from the 'ideal' value given in Fig. 10.5.

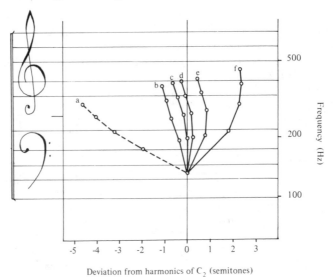

Fig. 10.6. Pitches of the (n,1) modes of a kettledrum head, with n = 1, 2, 3, 4, 5.
(a) Calculated for isolated undamped membrane.
(b) Measured on drumhead without kettle.
(c) Measured on drumhead with kettle volume $V_0 = 0.14 \text{ m}^3$.
(d) Measured on drumhead with kettle volume $0.75 V_0$.
(e) Measured on drumhead with kettle volume $0.5 V_0$.
(f) Measured on drumhead with kettle volume $0.25 V_0$.
Measurements from Christian et al. (1984), scaled to give common pitch of C_3 for (1,1) mode.

The points joined by line (a) are the pitches calculated without taking air damping into account; the (5,1) mode, which according to Fig. 10.5

416

should give G_4, is 4 semitones too flat. Line (b) joins points corresponding to measurements on the head without a kettle attached. Even for this isolated drumhead, air damping has brought the mode pitches quite close to the vertical line representing exact harmonics. The brain's tolerant pitch processor would identify a definite pitch in this sound, probably somewhat flatter than C_3 (see p.87).

When the head was fitted to its kettle, the relative mode pitches were found to be those joined by the line (c). The (2,1) mode is now exactly a fifth above the (1,1), and the (3,1)–(1,1) interval is only 17 cents less than a true octave. The kettle thus brings the mode pitches even closer to true harmonics, resulting in a clearer sound.

By partially filling the kettledrum bowl with water, Christian et al. examined the effect of bowl volume on mode pitches. The results are summarised in curves (d), (e) and (f) of Fig. 10.6. Reducing the volume of air below the head to 75% of its original value made little difference to the relative pitches of the modes. Reducing the volume to 25%, however, meant that the higher modes were much too sharp to be acceptable to the brain as members of the same harmonic series as the (1,1) mode. Clearly the normal, approximately hemispherical bowl is approaching the minimum acceptable volume.

Before leaving our discussion of Fig. 10.6, we should perhaps re-emphasise that although all the sets of measurements in this figure have been scaled to give a common pitch of C_3 to the (1,1) mode, the effects of air damping are in fact greater on low pitch modes than on high pitch modes. Thus, for example, reducing the bowl volume to 25% hardly affected the frequency of the (5,1) mode, but reduced the (1,1) mode frequency from 170 Hz to 148 Hz.

The nominal pitch of a drum

We stated that the nominal pitch of a drum is that of the (1,1) mode. Looking again at Fig. 10.5, however, we can see that although the pitch of the (1,1) mode is C_3 in this example, the (2,1) and (4,1) pitches are not harmonics of C_3. In fact, all five pitches are members of the harmonic series with fundamental pitch C_2. In the light of our discussion of the pitch sensing mechanism of the brain in Chapter 3, we should expect the set of tones in Fig. 10.5 to be perceived as a note of pitch C_2, despite the fact that the fundamental is missing. Why is the perception normally that of a note an octave higher?

This is one of the cases, which occur not infrequently in music, where the brain has to make a decision based on information which is open to more than one interpretation. Since the fundamental is missing, the principal clue suggesting an overall pitch of C_2 rather than C_3 is the existence of the tone with pitch G_3, radiated by the (2,1) mode. Since all the modes of a struck drumhead decay fairly rapidly, the brain has only a short time in which to decide whether this component exists with sufficient strength to justify the perception of the pitch C_2 rather than C_3. Usually the decision is in favour of the higher pitch; however, the inherent ambiguity can lead to disagreements among listeners over the actual pitch at which drums sound. The written pitch is that of the nominal, and Berlioz found it necessary in his *Traité de l'instrumentation* ('Treatise on instrumentation') to emphasise that this was in fact the sounding pitch:

> The sound of the kettledrum is not very low, it is played as it is written in the F clef in unison with the corresponding notes on the violon-cellos, and not an octave below as musicians have supposed (Berlioz 1844, p.247).

The importance of the position of striking

The sense of pitch associated with a drum note is due principally to the modes with one nodal circle and one or more nodal diameters. What of the other modes of vibration? These contribute little to the sound radiated by a drum under normal playing conditions. Modes with no diametral nodal lines, such as the (0,1), (0,2) and (0,3) modes, are relatively highly damped, and contribute principally to the initial 'thump' rather than to the ringing aftersound on which the pitch assessment is based (Rossing 1982 (a)). If a drumhead is struck exactly at its centre, none of the modes with nodal diameters will sound, since the point of excitation is a node for each of these modes. Only the initial short, pitchless thump remains. Needless to say, the normal striking position is not at the centre of the drumhead, although, on the bass drum, this position is chosen if a succession of short notes is called for (Blades 1984, p.368); in this case, the sense of pitch is unimportant, and indeed undesirable.

Modes with nodal diameters are less highly damped. The reduction in strength of the undesirable modes such as (1,2), (2,2) and (3,2), which have two nodal circles and would contribute inharmonic components to the sound, is achieved by a careful choice of the striking position. The inner nodal circle has a radius of 0.55 times the radius of the head for the (1,2) mode; this ratio increases to 0.61 for the (2,2) mode, and to 0.65 for the (3,2) mode (see Fig. 10.7). The normal striking position is about two thirds of the way from the centre to the rim, and thus lies close to these nodal circles. As a consequence the corresponding modes are only weakly excited. In contrast, the modes with only one nodal circle develop with an orientation such that the striking position is halfway between two adjacent nodal lines, giving a highly efficient excitation.

In our discussion so far, we have emphasised that any circular drumhead, tensioned and struck appropriately, will give a pitched sound. We now pass on to review briefly the different types of drum in modern orchestral use; we shall see that while in some cases this sense of pitch is a valued feature, in others steps are taken to suppress it.

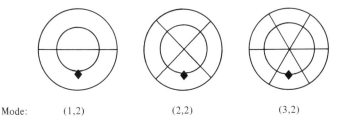

Mode: (1,2)   (2,2)   (3,2)

Fig. 10.7. The normal playing spot on a kettledrum head (marked ◆) is close to the inner nodal circle of the (1,2), (2,2) and (3,2) modes. These inharmonic modes are therefore only weakly excited.

Kettledrums

In the orchestral kitchen, the chef de cuisine is undoubtedly the timpanist. The kettledrums were introduced into the European orchestra during the 17th century, and were the only percussion instruments regularly included in the scores of Bach and Handel. The normal complement of timpani at this time consisted of two drums, their diameters differing by about 10%. The two drums were tuned either a fourth or (more rarely) a fifth apart, giving the tonic and dominant of the prevailing key. In the writing of Bach the pitch of the smaller drum ranges between E^b_3 and B^b_2, and that of the larger between B^b_2 and F_2. The tension of the head was controlled by five or more square topped screws placed symmetrically around the outside of the head. Tuning was a fairly laborious business, involving the separate application of a tuning key to each of the screws; the drums were tuned to the most useful pitches at the beginning of a work, and remained at these pitches throughout the work. Only towards the end of the 18th century did it become customary to expect the timpanist to change the tonality of his drums between movements.

The nature of the sound produced by an 18th century kettledrum was considerably different from that of a modern instrument. The diameter of the head (around 600 mm) was fairly small by present standards, and the tension much less than that normally used on today's synthetic heads. The use of an animal skin, however carefully prepared, inevitably introduces small variations in density over the surface of the head; although the player can to some extent compensate for these by subtle adjustments of the tensioning screws, the modes of vibration lack the high degree of symmetry obtained with a uniform membrane.

As a consequence of these differences, the sound of the 18th and early 19th century drums lacked the sharp clarity of pitch which has become an accepted and valued feature of the 20th century timpani sound. Problems can arise when modern drums are used in performing classical works, since occasionally composers made use of one of the two drums at their disposal despite the fact that it gave technically the 'wrong' note (Del Mar 1984, pp.345–346). For example, in modern editions of Beethoven's 'Coriolan' overture the timpani are silent in bars 220–223 (Fig. 10.8). According to James Blades, the original timpani part contained written Gs in these bars, clashing with the Fs on bassoon and double bass. Beethoven scored for the usual complement of two drums, tuned to G and C; he must have expected the pitch of the drum to be suppressed at this point by the rest of the orchestral sound. With a modern drum, however,

Fig. 10.8. Excerpt from the score of Beethoven's overture 'Coriolan'.

the note rings out as a disturbing dissonance. Blades records that when Britten was conducting this work, he asked Blades to play the offending passage on a third drum tuned to F (Blades 1984, p.274).

The role of the kettle in the kettledrum

The shining copper bowls of the timpani add considerably to the spectacle of the symphony orchestra. Their role in the acoustical performance of the drums has been a matter of intense debate among scientists and musicians for centuries (Rayleigh 1879; Richardson 1929; Kirby 1930; Taylor 1964), and many plausible sounding theories have been advanced without any real scientific justification. The experiments and calculations of Benade (1976) and Christian et al. (1984) have clarified the position considerably.

First of all, we should dispose of the idea that the bowl of the kettledrum acts as a resonator, with the natural frequencies of the enclosed air matched to those of the vibrating head (Wood 1962, p.150). Since the volume of the bowl remains the same while the head is tuned over a range of more than a fourth, resonant amplification could clearly be achieved only over a small part of the compass of the drum. In fact, the various resonances of the enclosed air are usually much higher in frequency than those of the membrane, and therefore have only a small effect on the radiation of the sound (Rossing 1982 (a), p.152).

The role of the kettledrum bowl in tuning the pitches of the modes of the head has already been discussed. Although the volume has been identified as the principal factor involved, work is continuing on the possibility of subtle effects based on the shape of the bowl (Christian et al. 1984).

The most important acoustical function served by the kettle is to make the drum a more efficient radiator of sound (Rayleigh 1879). Paradoxically, it does this by preventing the radiation of a sound wave from the underside of the drum. Fig. 10.9 (a) shows the cross-section of a simple drumhead (without kettle) vibrating in its (0,1) mode. The air in the region of A, just above the centre of the drum, is compressed when the head rises, and expanded when it falls. We can then consider the air at A to act as a secondary source of sound, since the compressions and expansions result in a sound wave travelling outwards from A in all directions; the wave travelling to the right is illustrated schematically by the upper sine curve in Fig. 10.9 (a). The air in the region of B, below the head, acts as a similar secondary source of sound waves, with one crucial difference: when the head rises, the air at B *expands*, and when the head falls it is *compressed*. In other words, the source at B generates a wave which is 180° out of phase with that at A. The lower curve in Fig. 10.9 (a) shows the wave radiated from the underside of the head to the right; since its crests coincide with the troughs of the wave from the upper side, the two waves cancel. As a result, no sound is radiated in this direction, or in any other direction lying in the plane of the drumhead.

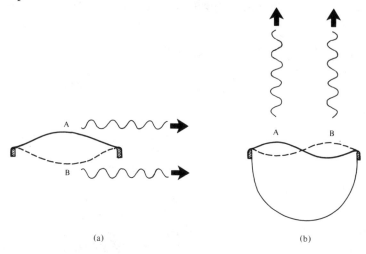

(a)   (b)

Fig. 10.9. (a) An unshielded drumhead vibrating in the (0,1) mode; (b) a drumhead shielded on the lower side by a bowl, vibrating in the (1,1) mode. In each case, sound waves radiated from regions A and B interfere destructively in the directions shown by the arrows.

This argument can be applied not just to the (0,1) mode, but to any other mode: each vibrating segment of the head is equivalent to a pair of sources of sound of opposing phase (known as an *acoustic dipole*) (Kinsler et al. 1982, pp.169–172). By shielding the lower side of the drum with a kettle, one half of each dipole is suppressed, and the cancellation no longer takes place. For the same reason, a loudspeaker is usually mounted in a cabinet which prevents sound radiation from the rear of the loudspeaker cone.

The decay time of a kettledrum note

Interference between waves generated by different segments of the modal pattern are important even when the head is mounted on a kettle. In the (1,1) mode, for example, the two halves of the drumhead on either side of the nodal diameter vibrate with opposite phase; this gives rise to two secondary sound sources of opposing phase above the drumhead (at points A and B in Fig. 10.9 (b)). The waves emitted in the vertical direction will thus cancel each other, as will those emitted in the horizontal plane along the direction of the nodal diameter. For other directions in the horizontal plane, the situation is more complicated, since the waves from the two sources do not travel the same distance to reach the listener. If the distance between A and B in Fig. 10.9 (b) were half a wavelength (in air) of

422

the note emitted by the (1,1) mode, the two waves emitted to the right would arrive in phase, giving constructive rather than destructive interference. In practice, however, the wavelengths of the important low pitched components are much longer than the dimensions of the drum, and the interference is predominantly destructive in all directions.

Simply by considering the symmetry of the normal mode patterns, it can be seen that any mode with one or more nodal diameters will give rise to a lot of destructive interference. It may seem odd that it is just these modes which are important in generating the characteristic sound of the kettledrum. However, we have seen that the method of striking the kettledrum head is such as to impart most of the energy of vibration to modes with nodal diameters; the fact that destructive interference renders these modes relatively inefficient as radiators of sound energy means that the stored energy will take correspondingly longer to diminish. The modes without nodal diameters are more efficient radiators, and the small amount of energy given to them by the stroke of the stick is radiated away in a few hundred milliseconds; the inefficient but harmonically related modes with nodal diameters continue to radiate for several seconds, prolonging the decay of the sound and giving it its sense of pitch.

The tone quality of a kettledrum note

The timpanist uses a variety of techniques for controlling and varying the tone quality of the note obtained from a given kettledrum (Shivas 1957; Blades 1984). Several different types of stick are employed, ranging from the *hard stick* with a small wooden ball at the striking end to the *soft stick* with a larger ball covered by several layers of felt. The instant after a blow with a hard stick, the membrane is left with a sharply defined depression (see Fig. 10.10 (a)). The set of normal modes corresponding to this

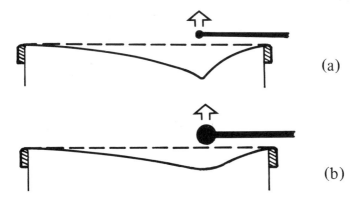

Fig. 10.10. The state of a drumhead immediately after the impact of (a) a stick with a small hard end; (b) a stick with a large soft end. (Displacement of membrane greatly exaggerated.)

excitation contains strong components with high frequencies, and the lowest frequency modes are only weakly represented. The resulting sound is dry and hard. A stroke with a large, soft ball leaves the membrane with a much shallower depression (Fig. 10.10 (b)), corresponding to a predominance of low frequency modes and a fuller, more booming sound. The diminution of the high frequency modes is accentuated by the damping of the skin which occurs during the short time of contact with the soft felt covering: a similar effect occurs during the contact between a piano hammer head and the strings of the instrument (see p.245).

The position of striking has also an important bearing on the tone quality of the note. In Chapter 6 we saw that striking or plucking a string close to one end accentuates the high frequency modes, while exciting the string near the centre concentrates the vibration energy in the low frequency modes. The same is true in the two dimensional case of the drumhead; the corresponding variation of drum timbre has been utilised at least since the 17th century (Blades 1984, p.212). The timpanist is, however, restricted in his choice of playing spot by a further requirement which does not apply to the string player: the need to suppress the inharmonic modes with more than one nodal circle. Moving the playing spot towards the rim emphasises upper frequencies, while moving it towards the centre throws more energy into the low frequency modes; but if the spot strays too far in either direction, the sense of pitch deteriorates.

Frequently the player is instructed to *damp* or *mute* the timpani. This effect is normally achieved by placing a piece of felt or other soft material on the surface of the drumhead. James Blades describes two degrees of damping, corresponding to different positions of the felt (Blades 1984, p. 364). In the first, the felt is placed to the left of the playing spot, as shown in Fig. 10.11; this gives sufficient damping for most circumstances, while the pitch remains distinct. Considering the vibration patterns of the first three modes of the drumhead, we see that this position of the felt lies across a nodal line for the (1,1) and (3,1) modes; those modes are therefore only lightly damped by the felt. The (2,1) mode, on the other hand, is heavily damped, since the felt lies on an antinode. This type of damping

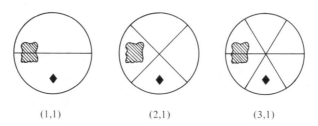

(1,1)   (2,1)   (3,1)

Fig. 10.11. Light damping of a kettledrum; felt positioned at 90° to playing spot (◆).

thus consists mainly in the removal of the fifth above the nominal; the nominal itself, and the octave above, remain relatively strong, which explains the retention of pitch clarity.

In the second type of damping, the felt is placed at the opposite side of the head to the playing spot (Fig. 10.12). Because of the symmetry of the mode patterns, this position is an antinode for all the modes of the head; as a result the muting effect is much more severe, and the sense of pitch is lost.

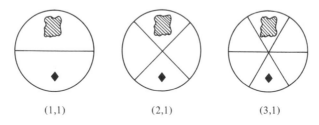

(1,1)   (2,1)   (3,1)

Fig. 10.12. Heavy damping of kettledrum; felt positioned at 180° to playing spot (◆).

Machine and pedal timpani

In the course of the 19th century, the demands of composers for increased flexibility in the tuning of timpani led to experiments with mechanical systems by which the tension of the head could be adjusted by the movement of a single lever or screw. By the beginning of the 20th century, such *machine drums* had become fully accepted in orchestral circles, and were specifically requested by Nielsen and Mahler. The most common type of kettledrum in the modern orchestra is the *pedal drum*, in which the pitch changing mechanism is controlled by a foot operated lever; frequently a tuning scale is provided, enabling the player to set the pitch approximately to the desired value before completing the fine tuning by ear.

In some designs of pedal drum, the mechanical system is entirely outside the drum; in others; the controlling levers pass inside the bowl, connecting with the pedal through a small hole in the base. It has been claimed that the former system is preferable, since the resonance of the bowl is undisturbed (Blades 1984, p.350). In view of the minor role now ascribed to the bowl resonances, it seems unlikely that there is really a significant acoustical difference between the two types of design.

The hole found at the bottom of most kettledrums serves one obvious function in equalising the ambient pressures inside and outside the instrument. It has sometimes been suggested that it also has a significant effect on the acoustical performance of the drum. Players have on the whole been sceptical about such claims, pointing out that plugging the hole with

425

a cork makes no noticeable change in the sound (Blades 1984, p.353). The most likely effect would be on the (0,1) mode of the drum, since the rise and fall of the membrane as a unit exerts the maximum degree of compression and expansion of the air inside the bowl. It is plausible that loss of energy through friction as the air flows in and out of the hole might contribute significantly to the damping of the (0,1) mode (Benade 1976, p.143); if this were so, plugging the hole should increase the time taken for the (0,1) mode to decay. Measurements by Rossing (1982 (a)) have shown that no such change takes place.

Modern scores frequently call for timpani ranging in pitch from D_2 to D_4, and higher and lower pitches are not unknown. Although a pedal drum can usually be tuned over a range of an octave, a satisfactory sound is obtained only over the central fifth, for reasons previously discussed. Four or five drums are therefore necessary to cover the complete spectrum. With such an equipage, the timpanist can engage in some remarkable chromatic acrobatics, such as those prescribed by Britten in his 'Nocturne' (Fig. 10.13).

Fig. 10.13. Excerpt from the obbligato part for timpani in Britten's 'Nocturne' Op. 60.

The bass drum

The timpani are the only drums whose pitches are normally specified in orchestral scores. The other two common types of orchestral drum, the bass drum and the snare drum, are described as instruments of indeterminate pitch. We have seen, however, that any circular drumhead is liable to produce a pitched sound; we must therefore ask why these types of drum do not do so.

The *bass drum* consists of two heads of equal diameter, stretched on either side of a wide, shallow barrel. A typical orchestral bass drum might have a diameter of one metre, and a depth of half this. Striking one head results in a compression of the air inside the drum, which in turn results in an outward displacement of the unstruck head; both heads are thus set into vibration, and subsequently radiate sound. The single headed bass drum (the 'gong drum') was at one time a common alternative; it lost favour, significantly, because it tended to produce a pitched note (Blades 1984, p.367). On the double headed drum, the tension of one head is adjusted to be slightly different from that of the other, so that the mode frequencies of the two heads do not coincide: the ear is content to accept the resulting mixture of radiated frequencies as an unpitched sound.

The playing spot on a bass drum is normally about halfway between the centre and the rim. This is closer to the centre than the usual striking position on a kettledrum, and is less effective in suppressing the inharmonic modes; it also imparts a greater part of the energy of striking to the modes of lowest frequency, including the strongly radiating (and therefore heavily damped) (0,1) mode. The typical bass drum sound is therefore characterised by a predominance of low frequencies, a relatively rapid rate of decay, and a lack of definite pitch (Fletcher and Basset 1978).

We have already noted that the bass drum is occasionally struck in the centre; all of the energy is then given to the rapidly decaying circularly symmetric modes, and a very short pitchless sound is produced. In contrast, Stravinsky asks at one point in 'The Rite of Spring' for the bass drum to be struck near the edge with a hard stick (Blades 1984, p. 429). This is one of the rare occasions on which a pitch is specified for the bass drum note, in this case 'in the region of B^b'. To comply with this instruction, the previously described precautions for reducing the sense of pitch must be reversed. The heads should be tuned to the same nominal pitch of B^b_2; the striking position suggested by the composer is close to the nodal circles of several of the inharmonic modes, and will reduce their effectiveness in clouding the sense of pitch.

The snare drum

The small, double headed barrel drum, used to accompany dancing throughout the Middle Ages and the Renaissance, was known in English as the *tabor*. To increase the volume and duration of the sound produced by this drum, it was customary to stretch a cord of gut (called the *snare*) across the playing head (Fig. 10.14). The vibration of the cord against the head gives a characteristic rattling or buzzing sound. The interaction between the vibrating string and the membrane is acoustically complicated, and has not been studied scientifically; an important practical point is that the resulting sound is almost pitchless.

The principle of the snare finds an application in the modern *snare drum*, also called the *side drum* (from its playing position in the military band). In this case, the snare is a set of parallel strings or wires stretched over the unbeaten head of the drum (Fig. 10.15). A mechanism allows the snares to be lifted from the head; when the drum is played with the snares

427

Fig. 10.14. Tabor with gut snare by Williamson.

Fig. 10.15. Snare drum with transparent plastic head by Ludwig, showing wire snares and internal damper.

off a set of distinct pitches can usually be distinguished. The tensioning of the heads and the method of striking give rise to several slowly decaying modes which are responsible for these pitched tones. The important function of the snares is to disguise the pitches while exploiting the prolonged decay time.

The snared head can be excited into vibration by sound waves emanating from outside the drum as well as by those which arise from the striking of the playing head. If a snare drum is left with its snare in contact with the head, an unwanted rattle occurs every time a note corresponding in pitch to one of the head resonances is played by an adjacent instrument; to avoid this, the snares are lifted from the head when the drum is not in use.

TUNED IDIOPHONES

Many types of solid object emit a pitched sound when struck. This is the basis of the tuned percussion instruments, which consist of sets of solid vibrators selected or constructed so that their pitches form a musically useful sequence. The oldest known instrument of this type is made up of a set of ringing stones, excavated in China and dated earlier than 1000 BC (Blades 1984, p.90). In the modern orchestra, the most important instruments in the tuned percussion family are the xylophone, the marimba, the glockenspiel, the vibraphone and the tubular bells. In each of these instruments, the sound is generated by the transverse vibrations of an object whose length is much greater than its other dimensions. It is therefore useful to begin with a discussion of the normal modes and resonant frequencies of such an object: a long thin solid bar.

Transverse vibrations of a bar

If a bar of tempered steel is bent in the manner shown in Fig. 10.16 and then released, it springs back into its original shape. The forces which oppose the deformation of the bar arise from the inherent elasticity of the steel. Considering a small segment at the centre of the bar (ABCD in Fig.

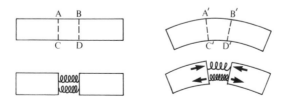

Fig. 10.16. The distortion produced by bending a bar. The compressed part between C' and D' acts like a compressed spring, pushing outwards; the extended part between A' and B' acts like an extended spring, pulling inwards.

10.16), we see that the bending motion stretches the top of the segment from its original length AB to a greater length A'B'. The upper part of the segment thus acts like a stretched spring, pulling the parts of the bar on either side together again. The bottom of the segment, in contrast, is compressed from CD to C'D'; the lower part acts like a compressed spring, pushing the adjacent parts of the bar away from each other. Similar sets of forces act all along the bar, their net effect being to straighten out the bend.

When a bar is struck by a hammer, it is bent into a more complicated shape than the simple curve shown in Fig. 10.16. The details of the shape in which the bar is left immediately after the hammer blow depend on the point at which the hammer strikes, the nature of the hammer head, the method by which the bar is supported and the force of striking. As in the analogous case of a struck string, the subsequent motion of the bar can be treated as a set of simultaneously vibrating normal modes, the relative strengths of the modes depending on the initial shape.

The bars in the instruments discussed in the present section are supported in such a way that both ends are free to vibrate. These free ends are therefore displacement antinodes, or points of maximum vibration. The lowest frequency bending mode which has an antinode at each end is illustrated in Fig. 10.17 (a); it has a third antinode at the centre of the bar, and two nodes approximately halfway between the centre and each end. When the middle of the bar rises, the two ends fall, and conversely. The vibration patterns of the next three modes are shown in Fig. 10.17 (b), (c) and (d); each successive mode has one additional node, and one additional antinode.

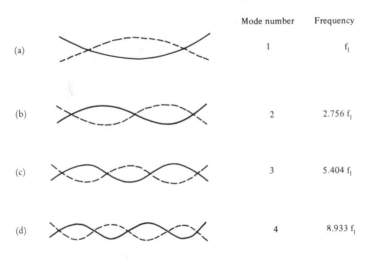

	Mode number	Frequency
(a)	1	f_1
(b)	2	2.756 f_1
(c)	3	5.404 f_1
(d)	4	8.933 f_1

Fig. 10.17. The first four transverse normal modes of a bar.

Normal mode frequencies of a rectangular bar

For a bar of rectangular cross-section, with length L, width W and thickness T (Fig. 10.18), the frequency of the first mode of vibration is given by

$$f_1 = 1.03 \, (Y/\varrho)^{1/2} t/L^2$$

(Kinsler et al. 1982, p.75).

In this formula Y is a quantity called 'Young's modulus', which is a measure of the rigidity of the material of which the bar is constructed, and ϱ is the density of the material. Typical values of Y and ϱ for some common materials are shown in Table 10.1. It is worth noting that, although the rigidity of a steel bar is more than three times that of an aluminium bar, the density of steel exceeds that of aluminium by almost the same factor; the quantity $(Y/\varrho)^{1/2}$ is therefore nearly equal for these two materials. Thus although a steel bar weighs about three times as much as an aluminium bar of the same size and shape, the two bars give almost the same note.

TABLE 10.1
Typical properties of some materials used in tuned percussion instruments

Material	Young's modulus (Y) $(/10^{10} \, Nm^{-2})$	(Density ϱ) $(/10^3 \, Kg \, m^{-3})$	$(Y/\varrho)^{1/2}$ $(/10^3 \, ms^{-1})$
[1]Mahogany (tangential to grain)	0.06	0.5	1.1
[1]Mahogany (along grain)	1.2	0.5	4.9
[2]Aluminium alloy	7.2	2.7	5.2
[2]Steel	20	7.8	5.1

[1]Kaye and Laby (1966), p.34.
[2]Gray (1972), pp.2-24, 25, 62, 68.

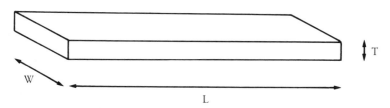

Fig. 10.18. Labelling of the dimensions of a rectangular bar.

In Table 10.1 two values are quoted for the hardwood mahogany sometimes used in xylophone bars. The resistance to beinding of a wooden bar depends greatly on whether the axis of bending lies along or transverse to the grain of the wood. In a xylophone bar, the wood grain is parallel to the long axis of the bar; the corresponding value of $(Y/\varrho)^{1/2}$ is comparable with that of aluminium alloy and steel. If a bar of the same dimensions were cut with the tangent to the wood grain lying along the long axis, the value of Young's Modulus would be reduced by a factor of 20. The pitch of the bar would drop by more than two octaves; internal damping would also increase considerably.

Using the values in Table 10.1, we can calculate the first mode frequency for a bar of known dimensions. For example, an aluminium alloy bar 100 mm long and 2 mm thick will have $f_1 = 1064$ Hz (pitch just above C_6). It should be borne in mind that the exact value of $(Y/\varrho)^{1/2}$, and hence f_1, will depend on the details of the composition and treatment of the material. Since the formula for f_1 does not contain W, the pitch of the first mode is unaffected by the width of the bar.

The dependence of f_1 on the thickness of the bar is straightforward: doubling T doubles f_1, raising the pitch of the first mode by an octave. On the other hand, the first mode frequency is inversely proportional to the *square* of the length of the bar: when L is doubled, the first mode pitch falls by two octaves. The variation of bar length with pitch on a glockenspiel or xylophone is thus much more gradual than the corresponding variation of tube length in a rank of organ pipes, since in the latter case the first mode frequency of the air column is proportional to its length (see Fig. 10.19). The frequency ratio corresponding to an equally tempered semitone is 1.0595, so that two organ pipes a semitone apart in pitch have their lengths (including end corrections) in a ratio of 1: 1.0595; the corresponding ratio for two glockenspiel bars a semitone apart is 1: $(1.0595)^{1/2} = 1.0293$.

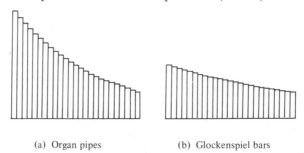

(a) Organ pipes   (b) Glockenspiel bars

Fig. 10.19. Illustrating the length ratios of a two octave set of (a) organ pipes; (b) glockenspiel bars.

The frequencies of the different transverse vibration modes of a long thin bar are not harmonically related. Although the vibration patterns shown in Fig. 10.17 bear a superficial similarity to those of a vibrating string, the elastic forces generated by the bending of a bar give rise to a more complicated behaviour than does the simple tension force on an ideal string. (The inharmonicity in real strings occurs because even a nylon string behaves to a small extent as though it were a bent rod.) Although the patterns of Fig. 10.17 are caused by transverse waves travelling in both directions along the bar, the speed with which these waves travel is not the same for each mode, as it is in the case of a stretched string. The transverse wave speed increases with the mode number, which has the effect of increasing the frequency spacing of the modes. The frequency of the nth mode is given to a very good approximation by the formula

$$f_n = \frac{(2n + 1)^2}{9.067} f_1$$

(Kinsler et al. 1982, p.75).

Table 10.2 gives the values of f_n/f_1 for the first four modes of a bar, and also shows the positions of the nodes for each mode. Fig. 10.20 illustrates the pitches of the first eight modes. If a bar is supported and struck in such a way that each of these modes is excited, the radiated sound will thus be a mixture of widely spaced and inharmonically related pure tones. We would not expect the ear to recognise such a sound as a musical note of definite pitch; at first sight, the vibrating bar looks unpromising as the basis of a tuned percussion instrument. Why is it that a glockenspiel bar produces such a clear, unambiguously pitched note?

TABLE 10.2

Modes of vibration of a rectangular bar of length L

Mode no.	Frequency ratio f_n/f_1	Nodal positions
1	1	0.224L 0.776L
2	2.756	0.132L 0.5L 0.868L
3	5.404	0.094L 0.356L 0.644L 0.906L
4	8.933	0.073L 0.277L 0.5L 0.723L 0.927L

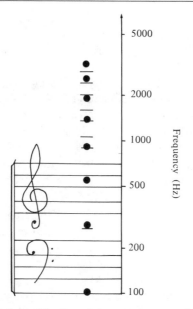

Fig. 10.20. Pitches of the first eight transverse modes of a rectangular bar.

The glockenspiel

The glockenspiel is the simplest of the tuned percussion instruments, consisting of a set of rectangular cross-section metal bars supported horizontally on a frame. The secret of the glockenspiel lies in the method by which the bar is supported: it rests on two narrow strips of felt or other damping material, which touch it only very close to the nodal points of the first mode of vibration (Fig. 10.21). From Table 10.2, it can be seen that these points should theoretically be 22.4% of the length of the bar from each end; for a real glockenspiel bar, non-uniformities introduced by the drilling of holes for the locating pins and by filing of the bar during tuning may shift the nodal positions slightly.

Fig. 10.21. The glockenspiel bar is supported under the nodal lines of the first transverse mode of vibration.

The first mode is not seriously damped by the supports, since the amplitude of vibration is zero at the nodal positions. On the other hand, the second and third modes have large vibration amplitudes at the points of support, and are therefore quickly damped out. The fourth mode has a

434

node 27.7% of the way along the bar, and is less effectively damped; however, the fourth mode (like the second) has a node at the centre of the bar, and will not be excited by the normal stroke at this point. Since the fourth mode pitch is already more than three octaves above that of the first, higher modes need not be considered. The method of support and striking thus gives rise to the strong excitation of only the first mode of the bar, and after the initial rapidly decaying transient the radiated sound is practically a pure tone.

It is clearly important that the supports should lie exactly under the nodes of the first mode; otherwise, it too will be damped. The nodal positions can be checked in practice by sprinkling a fine powder such as salt or dry sand on the top of the bar, and then striking it at the centre. The powder is displaced from the vibrating areas, and collects along the nodal lines perpendicular to the length of the bar (Fig. 10.22). These lines should lie exactly above the supporting strips.

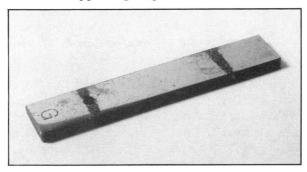

Fig. 10.22. Fine powder sprinkled on a glockenspiel bar collects on the nodal lines. In the case illustrated the bar was correctly supported below the nodal lines of the first mode, and struck at the centre.

The tuning of a glockenspiel bar uses two principles. To raise the pitch, the length of the bar is reduced slightly by filing the ends, making use of the fact that f_1 is inversely proportional to L^2. To lower the pitch, material is filed from the underside of the bar. Since f_1 is proportional to t, a uniform reduction of the thickness of the bar by 1% would lower its pitch by 17 cents. In practice, it is much more efficient to file only at the centre of the bar; since this is the point of maximum bending for the first mode, a small reduction in thickness gives a relatively large reduction in the springiness of the bar, and hence a relatively large drop in pitch (see Benade 1976, pp. 139–140).

Because the ringing sound of the glockenspiel is almost a pure tone, the instrument is most effective in the region above C_5, where the sensitivity of the ear to pure tones is high. The normal compass of the orchestral glockenspiel is from G_5 to C_8 (written two octaves lower). The famous passage in 'The Magic Flute' in which the sound of Papageno's bells is supplied by an offstage glockenspiel (Fig. 10.23) was almost certainly intended for a *keyboard glockenspiel*, in which bars (or tubes, or miniature bells) are struck by hammers operated by a piano-like mechanism. Although composers as late as Messiaen have written specifically for the keyboard instrument, modern conductors and performers distrust its notoriously unreliable action, preferring the parts to be played on the hand hammered instrument whenever possible (Del Mar 1983, pp.406–407).

Fig. 10.23. Excerpt from the part for keyed glockenspiel in Mozart's opera 'The Magic Flute'.

Dulcitone and celesta

Two instruments closely related to the keyboard glockenspiel should be mentioned here, although they are not technically part of the percussion section of an orchestra. The *dulcitone*, invented by either Victor Mustel or his son Auguste around 1860, contains a chromatic set of tuning forks. Each fork can be struck by a felt covered hammer operated by a piano style keyboard mechanism. The softness of the hammer (in contrast to the hard glockenspiel hammer) heavily damps the upper modes of the fork, so that the sharp initial percussive transient characteristic of the glockenspiel is almost completely absent. The sound is gentle, and surprisingly seductive.

Although Blades (1984, p.311) notes one orchestral score by d'Indy calling for dulcitone, the volume produced by the instrument is inadequate for general orchestral use. In the *celesta*, invented by Auguste Mustel in 1886, a box shaped resonator amplifies the sound output of each bar shaped vibrator. As with the dulcitone, the striking mechanism is a piano style keyboard with felt hammers. The celesta has established its place in the orchestra; its most famous solo is still probably one of its earliest (Fig. 10.24).

The xylophone and marimba

As its name (literally 'sounding wood') implies, the *xylophone* originated as a tuned percussion instrument based on the resonances of wooden bars. In the modern instrument, the bars are frequently made from a synthetic material. The crucial feature distinguishing the xylophone from the

Fig. 10.24. Excerpt from the celesta part in the 'Dance of the Sugar-Plum Fairy', from Tchaikovsky's 'Casse-Noisette' Suite.

glockenspiel is that the xylophone bar loses energy through internal friction much more rapidly than does the metal glockenspiel bar. As a consequence, even the first mode of the xylophone bar decays rapidly, giving the instrument the characteristic dry rattling sound exploited so effectively by Saint-Saëns in his 'Danse Macabre', and in the 'Fossils' section of 'Carnival of the Animals' (Fig. 10.25).

Fig. 10.25. Excerpt from the xylophone part in Saint-Saëns's 'Carnival of the Animals'.

This solo was written for the standard 19th century xylophone, with bars of uniform thickness and without resonators. A problem with this instrument was that on the lower notes the upper inharmonic modes sounded more loudly than the fundamental, and the sense of a definite pitch was lost (Del Mar 1983, p.410). Various modifications have been made to the xylophone in order to improve this and other aspects of its performance.

Present day xylophones are almost invariably equipped with *resonators*. Under each bar hangs a vertical tube, closed at the lower end, and of such a length that the lowest resonant frequency of the air column coincides with that of the bar. The vibration of the bar in its first mode therefore sets up a strong standing wave in the tube. It is important to realise that the resonator does not generate sound energy: it merely improves the efficiency with which the energy given to the bar by the hammer stroke is radiated as sound. As a consequence, the decay time of a resonated bar is shorter than that of the same bar with the resonator removed.

A modern xylophone bar does not usually have a uniform thickness; instead, the underside is cut away at the centre to form a shallow arch (Fig.

437

10.26). The reduction in stiffness at the centre lowers the frequency of the first mode of vibration much more than it does the second mode. The reason for this difference can be seen in the mode patterns in Fig. 10.17: the flexing of the bar corresponds to a maximum change of curvature at the centre in the first mode, whereas in the second mode the region of the bar near the centre remains almost straight (although its angle to the horizontal changes). Thus the sensitivity of vibration frequency to centre stiffness is very high in the first mode, and very low in the second mode.

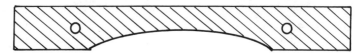

Fig. 10.26. Longitudinal cross-section of a modern undercut xylophone bar.

It is sometimes stated that the xylophone bar is undercut in such a way that the ratio of second mode frequency to first mode frequency is increased from 2.76 (the value for a bar of constant thickness) to 3.00 (Rossing 1976; Hall 1980; Pierce 1983). This ratio is advantageous on two grounds. The second mode of the bar is by no means completely damped by the method of support; if it contributes an apparent third harmonic to the radiated sound, the sense of pitch will be reinforced. In addition, since the resonator beneath each bar is a cylindrical tube closed at the lower end, the second mode of the air column has a resonant frequency three times that of the first mode. A suitably chosen tube can therefore supply resonant amplification for both first and second modes of the bar.

However, not all xylophones have bars undercut in the uniform way implied above. Measurements by one of the authors on a four octave orchestral xylophone have shown a rather more complicated pattern. For the lowest note on the instrument, C_4, the ratio of second to first mode frequency was found to be almost exactly 4: the second mode was thus two octaves above the first, rather than the twelfth suggested by the foregoing discussion. For the note C_5, the ratio was 3.8, giving an interval between the first two modes about a semitone less than two octaves. It was visually obvious that the undercutting was less significant for the higher pitched bars. By C_6, the mode ratio was reduced to 3.1. For the highest pitched bar tested, C_7, the mode ratio was 2.5, which is actually less than the theoretical value for a uniform bar. By this stage, however, the length of the bar was comparable with its other dimensions, and a more elaborate theory would be necessary to give accurate predictions of resonance frequencies.

Why should the degree of undercutting vary with the pitch of the bar? The explanation probably lies in the relative insensitivity of the ear to low pitched pure tones (see Chapter 3). If the C_4 bar had a second mode at G_5

(three times the first mode frequency), the G_5 component, amplified by the second mode of the resonator, might be so much louder than the C_4 component that the pitch of the bar would be identified as G rather than C. Instead, the second mode gives a component of pitch C_6, reinforcing the tone chroma of C.

This argument becomes less compelling as the fundamental pitch rises. At C_6, the first mode frequency is in the region of maximum sensitivity of the ear, and is unlikely to be dominated by the higher modes, which decay very rapidly at such high frequencies. The strength and brightness of the sound can then safely be reinforced by bringing the frequency of the second mode of the bar down to match the second mode of the resonator, a twelfth above the fundamental. For the highest pitches on the instrument, the upper modes decay so rapidly that it is hardly worth while attempting to tune them.

The compass of the instrument described above, from C_4 to C_8, is typical of a modern orchestral xylophone. The *marimba* is a similar instrument built on a larger scale, with a typical compass from C_3 to G_6. There is general agreement that most of the bars of the marimba are undercut to give a two octave interval between the first two modes, as would be expected from the discussion of the xylophone. The strength of the higher modes is also reduced by the use of softer mallets than those commonly employed on the xylophone. Modern composers frequently call for an instrument with a compass of five octaves or more; such an instrument combines features of xylophone and marimba, and is therefore known as the *xylorimba* or *marimba-xylophone*.

The vibraphone

The metallophone family consists of scaled-up glockenspiels with resonators. We have already met a member of this family in the celesta. The most important metallophone is the *vibraphone*, which has been extensively used by modern composers and jazz musicians. Its compass normally extends from F_2 to F_6. Even with the resonator draining energy, the metal bar has a decay time of several seconds, and a damper operated by a foot pedal is used to curtail the length of notes. Exponents of the vibraphone have developed a four hammer technique for playing chords, each hand using two sticks simultaneously.

The unique feature which gives the vibraphone its name is the provision of a rotating vane in the open end of the resonating tube just below each bar (Fig. 10.27). When the vane is vertical (Fig. 10.28 (a)), the resonator is fully effective; when the vane is horizontal (Fig. 10.28 (b)), it shuts off the resonator, decreasing the volume of radiated sound. The vane can be rotated by an electric motor to give a periodic fluctuation in volume; the speed of rotation determines the frequency of the fluctuation. The opening and closing of the vane has a negligible influence on the vibration frequency of the bar, so that the fluctuation in loudness is not accompanied by any change in pitch. The effect is thus quite different from the vibrato normally used on string and wind instruments, which is principally a periodic variation of pitch with a subsidiary fluctuation in volume. In fact, the rotating vanes generate a *tremolo* rather than a vibrato (see p.510). It is too late now, however, to suggest that the vibraphone would be more accurately named the 'tremolophone'!

Fig. 10.27. End view of a vibraphone by Premier, with the vanes partially closing the resonators. The damper (the central felt strip) is shown in its raised position, damping the bars. Note also the undercutting of the bars.

The relatively low pitch range of the vibraphone, together with the light internal damping of its metal bars, makes it imperative to alter or suppress inharmonic upper modes which would otherwise confuse the brain's pitch processor. Undercutting of the bars (Fig. 10.27) places the second mode two octaves above the first, as in the marimba. Suppression of other modes is achieved by a careful choice of mallet covering and striking position. Since the centre of the bar is a node for all even numbered modes (see Fig. 10.17), striking here eliminates many undesirable components. Occasionally, in very rapid chromatic passages, the bars are struck at the ends lying above the damping bar (see Fig. 10:27); since the end of a bar is an antinode for all modes, a number of inharmonic components of high pitch are then audible along with the fundamental pure tone.

The mallet head is usually a rubber core with a wound wool covering. Gradations of timbre are achieved by a range of thicknesses of covering. A bright sound requires a thin covering, which does not damp out the second mode (the 'fourth harmonic'). Mallets with very thin coverings cannot be used successfully on the lowest octave, since the inharmonic third and higher modes contribute too strongly to the sound.

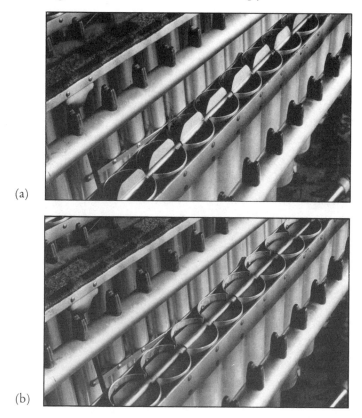

(a)

(b)

Fig. 10.28. The bars are removed from the vibraphone, showing the vanes (a) fully open, and (b) fully closed.

Bells

In all of the tuned percussion instruments so far discussed, the normal method of supporting and striking the bar emphasises the first mode frequency while damping the higher modes. The ear has no difficulty in assigning a pitch to the sound, since after the first few hundred milliseconds the fundamental component has a larger amplitude than any components generated by higher modes.

The *tubular bells* consist of a set of hollow metal tubes, graduated in length. The transverse vibration modes of a tube are similar to those of a rectangular bar, and the relative pitches of the modes are close to those shown in Table 10.2 and Fig. 10.20. In the usual orchestral set of bells, the tube is suspended vertically in a frame by a thin wire or rod passing

441

through holes drilled near the top of the tube; this method of support does not seriously dampen any of the modes of vibration. The tube is sounded by a transverse blow with a mallet against the upper end, which is an antinode for all the modes. As a result, the sound produced is a rich mixture of pure tone components which are not harmonically related.

How does the ear respond to such a mixture? We saw in Chapter 3 that the brain appears to determine the pitch of a sound by finding the harmonic series which best fits the set of components received by the ear; in the matching process, most weight is given to components lying in the 'dominant' pitch region, roughly from C_5 to C_7.

These principles can be used to explain the sometimes ambiguous sense of pitch aroused by the sound of a tubular bell. Let us take a practical example: a steel tube 1300 mm long, with an outside diameter of 50 mm and a wall thickness of 3 mm. This tube was formerly part of a set of orchestral bells, in which it was assigned the pitch $B^{\flat}_4$.

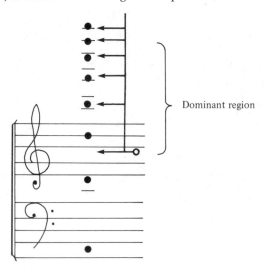

Fig. 10.29. The measured pitches of the first eight modes of a tubular bell are shown by the black notes. The ear finds an acceptable harmonic match based on $B^{\flat}_4$ (white note).

The measured frequencies of the first eight modes of this bell are given in Table 10.3, and the corresponding pitches are shown in Fig. 10.29. The pitches of the first few modes of the bell can be checked by ear, using a method similar to that employed by string players to produce harmonics (see p.214). If the bell is removed from its normal support, and held by the left hand at a distance from the end equal to 22.4% of the total length of the tube, all modes except the first are damped. When the bar is struck at the centre (Fig. 10.30 (a)), only the low pitch corresponding to the first mode can be heard ringing on after the initial rapid decay. Moving the supporting hand to a new position 13.2% of the way along the tube damps all modes except the second. The elimination of the first mode can be assured by striking the bar 22.4% of the way along, at the node of the first mode (Fig. 10.30 (b)); since this is near an antinode of the second mode, the pitch of the latter should ring out clearly. The third and fourth modes can be sounded individually in a similar way, by supporting the tube at one of the appropriate points listed in Table 10.2.

TABLE 10.3

Modes of vibration of a B♭ tubular bell

Mode no. (n)	Frequency (f_n)	Frequency ratio (f_n/f_1)
1	111	1
2	302	2.73
3	578	5.23
4	930	8.42
5	1342	12.14
6	1810	16.38
7	2295	20.77
8	2856	25.85

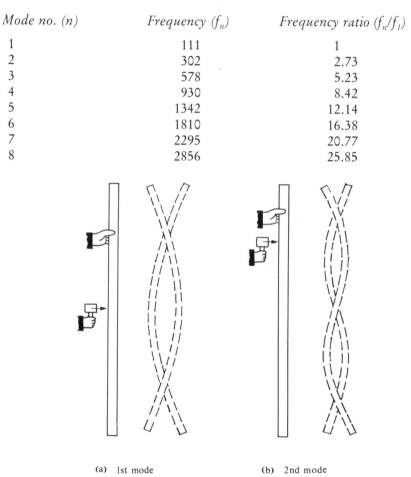

(a) 1st mode   (b) 2nd mode

Fig. 10.30. Method of selecting the first two modes of a tubular bell.

443

A comparison of the frequency ratios in Tables 10.2 and 10.3 reveals that the resonant pitches of the tubular bell are not quite as widely separated as those of an ideal rectangular bar. At least part of the discrepancy is due to the solid cap which reinforces the struck end of the tubular bell (see Fig. 10.31).

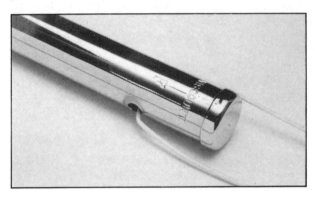

Fig. 10.31. The upper end of an orchestral tubular bell by Viscount, showing the cord used to suspend it in its frame, and the reinforcing end cap.

Searching for a harmonic pattern in the spectrum of components radiated by the bell, the brain finds a partial correspondence with a harmonic series whose fundamental is $B^\flat_4$ (Fig. 10.29). The 4th, 5th, 6th, 7th and 8th modes of the bell have pitches reasonably close to the 2nd, 3rd, 4th, 5th and 6th harmonics respectively of $B^\flat_4$. The fundamental pitch itself is not present, but we have seen previously that a missing fundamental is no barrier to a clear sensation of pitch. More of a problem is the existence of the tones radiated by the first three modes, which do not fit into the pattern. These tones contribute the dissonance and pitch uncertainty which is an essential part of the tone quality of a bell.

It is natural to suppose that if a tubular bell is shortened, the pitch will rise. This is not necessarily the case. Cutting 18% off the length of the $B^\flat_4$ bell raises the pitch of each mode by a fifth (Fig. 10.32). The pitch matching procedure previously described would then identify the overall pitch of the bell as F_5 (Fig. 10.32 (a)). However, most of the components used in this identification now lie above the dominant region for pitch perception. An alternative match (Fig. 10.32 (b)), in which the second mode is identified as the fundamental of the harmonic series, may be preferred by the brain: according to this match, shortening the tube has *lowered* the pitch slightly.

The ambiguity in pitch matching limits the upper range of the tubular bells; the highest pitch in an orchestral set is usually F_5. A similar problem occurs at the lower end of the range. Composers and conductors have frequently complained about the difficulty of finding bells that will sound at pitches below C_4. Norman Del Mar recounts that on one occasion the London Symphony Orchestra obtained a special tubular bell so long that the player had to mount a large stepladder to reach the striking point. Unfortunately, when the bell was struck it was found that its sounding pitch was no lower than that obtainable from the standard set (Del Mar 1983, p.402). Lengthening the bell merely moves a different set of inharmonic components into the dominant region for pitch matching: there is no guarantee that the ear will be able to find an acceptable match to a harmonic series among these components, or that the fundamental of any such series will be at a low pitch. A clearer understanding of the acoustical reasons for these problems may lead to improvements in the design of orchestral bells.

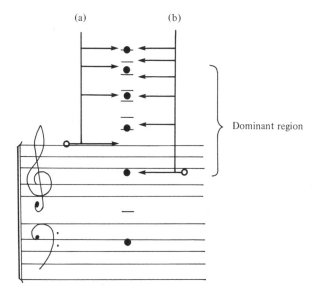

Fig. 10.32. The pitches of the first six modes of a short tubular bell, shown by black notes. The pitch may be identified as F_5 (white note and harmonic series (a)) or as a slightly flat B_4 (white note and harmonic series (b)).

TRIANGLE, CYMBAL AND GONG

The triangle

The triangle is one of the simplest of orchestral instruments. In its standard form, it is a steel rod bent into the shape of an equilateral triangle, with a small gap separating the two free ends. It is struck by a thin beater, usually also of steel.

The triangle is classed as an idiophone of indeterminate pitch: in other words, it does not produce a recognisable note. Even in such an exposed and delicately scored passage as the opening of Mahler's 'Lieder eines fahrenden Gesellen' (Fig. 10.33), the composer has not felt it necessary to specify a pitch for the triangle. Yet a straight rod generates a set of components similar to those of a tubular bell, and we have been that the ear can find an acceptable harmonic match (and hence a pitch) in such a set. Why is it that bending the rod into a triangular shape destroys the pitch of the sound?

Fig. 10.33. The opening bars of Mahler's 'Lieder eines fahrenden Gesellen'.

Some recent measurements and calculations by J.I. Dunlop of the University of New South Wales, Australia, have supplied an answer to this question (Dunlop 1984). The standing wave patterns corresponding to the normal modes of vibration of a straight rod arise because transverse waves are travelling simultaneously in both directions along the rod. When the rod is bent, these travelling waves are slowed down at the corners. As a consequence, the pattern of nodes and antinodes in the standing wave is distorted: the nodes near the corners move closer together, while those on the straight sections move further apart. This effect is illustrated in Fig. 10.34, for the fifth normal mode.

The frequencies of the normal modes are also modified by the bending of the bar. Usually, the mode frequency is lowered, but the magnitude of the change varies widely from mode to mode, and depends on the final shape of the triangle. The mode frequencies of a triangle of equilateral shape with side length 150 mm (a typical orchestral instrument) are shown in Fig. 10.35 (b). The mode frequencies which would be obtained from the same rod straightened out are shown for comparison in Fig. 10.35 (a). The ear would probably identify a pitch of $E\flat_5$ in the sound of the straight rod; however, the regularity of the mode frequencies is so disrupted when

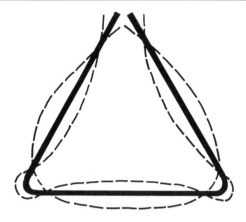

Fig. 10.34. The vibration pattern for the fifth mode of a triangle. Based on Dunlop (1984), p.251, Fig.1.

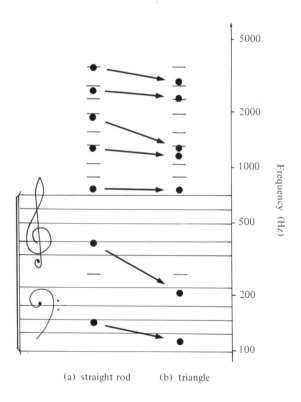

(a) straight rod   (b) triangle

Fig. 10.35. Pitches of the first seven modes of (a) a long thin rod; (b) the same rod bent into a triangle. Based on Dunlop (1984).

447

the rod is bent into its triangular shape that the brain's pitch processor is unable to find any semblance of a harmonic pattern.

The skill of the triangle maker lies in choosing a shape which generates a clear set of ringing components without any accidental pitch clues. The mode frequencies depend strongly on the radius of curvature of the corners. Deviations from the straight rod frequencies are sometimes accentuated by tapering the sides of the triangle. From a given triangle the player can produce a variety of tone colours by selecting the place of striking. Striking at the centre of a side tends to emphasise modes of lower pitch, such as that illustrated in Fig. 10.34. The normal striking position is near to a corner, exciting many high pitched modes and giving the instrument its characteristic 'silvery' sound.

Cymbals

The clash of the cymbals punctuates the climactic passages of most romantic symphonic works (see, for example, bar 4 of Fig. 2.9). Like the triangle and bass drum the cymbals are notated on a single line of stave. The standard modern orchestral cymbal is a thin brass plate with a slightly conical profile and a raised central dome (Fig. 10.36). It is held by a strap passing through a hole in the dome.

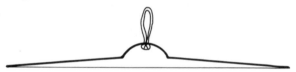

Fig. 10.36. Cross-section of an orchestral cymbal.

The frequency spectrum of the sound radiated by a 12" diameter cymbal immediately after it had been struck near the edge by a hard drumstick is shown in Fig. 10.37. A large number of closely spaced normal modes of vibration contribute to the sound, with frequencies predominantly in the region between 500 Hz and 6000 Hz (Rossing 1982 (b)). The mode frequencies are not harmonically related, so there is no sense of pitch associated with the sound.

The concentration of sound energy in the high frequency range gives a characteristic shimmer or 'splash' to the sound of the cymbal. The high frequency components are present in strength immediately after the striking of a thin jazz cymbal (Fig. 10.37). In contrast, a heavy symphonic cymbal, strongly struck, radiates initally from modes of relatively low frequency (Fig. 10.38 (a)). Over the course of several seconds, vibration energy is transferred into high frequency modes, until most of the sound output is in the high pitch shimmer (Fig. 10.38 (b)). The word 'clash' is in fact an onomatopoeic description of this effect (although to do justice to a symphonic cymbal it must be pronounced very slowly).

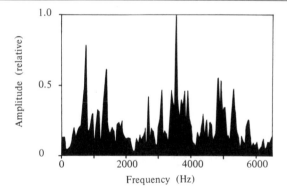

Fig. 10.37. Frequency spectrum of the sound radiated by a thin 12″ jazz cymbal (Avedis Zildjian) immediately after being struck near the edge by a hard stick (ff). The spectrum was measured in a moderately reverberant laboratory.

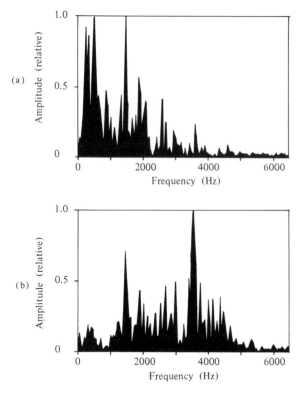

Fig. 10.38. Frequency spectra of the sound radiated by a heavy 15″ symphonic cymbal (A. Zildjian) struck near the edge by a hard stick (ff): (a) immediately after striking; (b) one second after striking.

As in the case of a drumskin free to radiate from both sides (see Fig. 10.9), a cymbal radiates little sound energy in the plane containing the rim. When the sound is allowed to ring on after two cymbals are clashed together, it is customary to turn the plates outwards to face the audience. This visually dramatic action also serves an acoustical purpose by beaming the high frequency radiation from the upper modes of vibration more effectively into the auditorium.

A single *suspended cymbal*, lying in the horizontal plane and struck by a stick or wire brush, is a crucial element in the kit of the dance band drummer, and is frequently demanded in modern orchestral scores. Striking with a triangle beater or hard stick excites predominantly modes of high frequency, while a soft felt covered stick gives more power to the low frequency modes. Occasionally a cello or double bass bow is used on the edge of a suspended cymbal (Fig. 10.39). It is possible in this way to produce a powerful sustained sound from the excitation of a single vibration mode of the cymbal.

Fig. 10.39. Excerpt from the cymbal part from Schoenberg's 'Five Pieces for Orchestra' Op. 16.

Gong and tam-tam

Some confusion surrounds the nomenclature of the gong family. The word *gong* is used in English as a generic term describing any sizeable circular metal plate, not necessarily flat, suspended vertically and struck by a beater. The type of gong usually required in Western orchestral scores is a flat or slightly convex bronze disc with a narrow rim (Fig. 10.40 (a)) producing a sound of indeterminate pitch. Some writers insist that this instrument should be described as a *tam-tam*, the term gong being reserved for an instrument producing a sound of definite pitch. Although this distinction is by no means universally observed, we shall make use of it in the following discussion.

The diameter of an orchestral tam-tam ranges typically from 700 mm to 1000 mm. The normal stroke, halfway between centre and edge, excites many modes closely spaced in frequency; beating between these components gives the characteristic shimmering sound. The principal difference between the symphonic cymbal and the tam-tam in this respect is that both the initially excited modes and those which give rise to the gradually developing shimmer are in a much lower pitch range than the corresponding modes of a cymbal. The difference is evident in comparing Figs 10.38 (a) and 10.41 (noting the different frequency scales).

An instrument with quite different musical properties is the *tuned gong*. This usually has a deep cylindrical rim, which effectively prevents the edge of the disc from vibrating; the raised central boss on Javanese and Burmese gongs (Fig. 10.40 (b)) further modifies the modal patterns. The sound radiated by such a gong contains sufficiently powerful discrete frequency components to allow the brain's pitch processor to find an approximate harmonic match. The pitch is particularly clear when the gong is struck on the central boss, since only a few modes are excited (Fig. 10.42). Sets of tuned gongs are major components of the Javanese gamelan orchestra. They were scored for by Puccini in 'Turandot', and have been increasingly adopted by modern composers interested in exotic percussion effects. (Blades 1984, Ch. 16; Del Mar 1983, p.400).

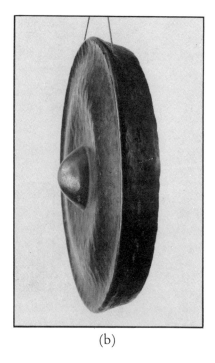

(a)   (b)

Fig. 10.40. (a) Chinese tam-tam. (b) Burmese gong.

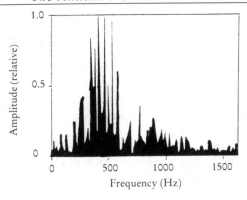

Fig. 10.41 Frequency spectrum of the sound radiated by the Chinese tam-tam shown in Fig. 10.40 (a), immediately after being struck halfway between centre and edge (ff).

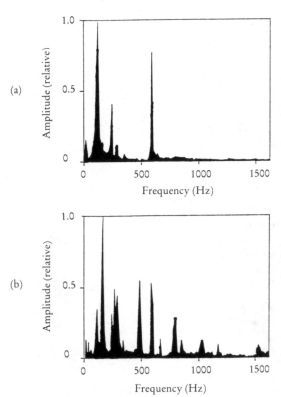

Fig. 10.42 Frequency spectrum of the sound radiated by the Burmese gong shown in Fig. 10.40 (b), immediately after being struck (mf) with a soft mallet: (a) on the central boss; (b) halfway between the boss and the outer rim.

452

11

Organs

In this chapter we shall be concerned with the traditional pipe organ, or church organ as it is sometimes called, and also a group of instruments which can loosely be classed as reed organs. This covers the regal, harmonium, American organ, accordion, concertina and harmonica. The acoustic principles on which these operate are in the main the same as for the woodwind instruments and these have already been described in Chapter 8. Despite the similarities, however, there are many special features which will need to be discussed as they arise.

PIPE ORGANS

For power and grandeur of tone the pipe organ is unrivalled by any other instrument. The magnificent range of timbres which can be produced on the modern instrument has resulted from centuries of development by dedicated craftsmen drawing on empirical data obtained from earlier designs. The invention of the organ is attributed to the Alexandrian engineer Ktesibios in 246 BC. His instrument had a row of reed pipes and used a hydraulic system for generating the air flow. During the next two centuries hand blown bellows and open and stopped flue pipes were all introduced. The great development of the organ, however, took place in Europe from the 9th century onwards, most of this being associated with the church. The great Winchester cathedral organ was built in about 950 and had a compass of 40 notes with 10 ranks of pipes. It apparently required two players and 70 men to operate the 26 sets of bellows. Most of the features of the modern organ had been invented by about 1500 and by the end of the 17th century the instrument was essentially in the form that we know it today, apart, of course, from electronic devices.

The organ may be considered as having three main components, the keyboards, the action and the pipes. Our primary concern is with the pipes, since this is where the sound is actually generated. We shall deal with these first and briefly discuss the keyboards and action later. There are two distinct types of pipes which are used, *flue pipes* and *reed pipes.*

Flue pipes

The flue pipes on an organ are the ones which give it its characteristic sound (Fletcher 1976). Their sound generation mechanism is essentially the same as on the flute or recorder, except for the fact that there is only one pipe per note. In this respect they are somewhat akin to a set of mechanically blown pan pipes. Fig. 11.1 shows cross-sectional drawings of a flue pipe from the front and the side. Air enters through the toe of the pipe and is formed into a narrow jet as it passes a deflecting plate, known as the *languid.* This is in line with the *lower lip* of the oblong opening to the outside, referred to as the *mouth.* Having passed across the mouth, the jet impinges on the *upper lip.*

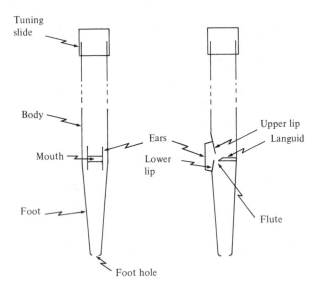

Fig. 11.1 An organ flue pipe: (a) front view; (b) side view.

The relationship of the air jet movements to the pressure fluctuations within the tube has already been described in Chapter 8 in relation to the flute. It will be worth reiterating some of the main points, especially as most of the research on the lip reed mechanism has actually been conducted on organ pipes (Coltman 1976 (a); Fletcher and Douglas 1980; Fletcher 1974 (b)). These are easier to deal with in the laboratory than the flute, since the jet characteristics are fixed by the manufacturers. Also there is only one note to deal with for any particular pipe and the blowing pressure is known. Thus the number of variable parameters is relatively small.

The basic principle of the oscillating jet imparting energy to maintain the standing wave within the tube has been known for over a century. Both Helmholtz and Lord Rayleigh wrote about this subject, although at that time experimental techniques did not exist for testing their theories in detail. Although their interpretations were similar, they disagreed about the phase relationship between the jet flow into the mouth and the pressure within the tube. Helmholtz thought that the maximum jet flow into the tube should occur when the pressure inside was greatest, as illustrated in Fig. 8.17. Rayleigh's interpretion, on the other hand, assumed that maximum excitation would occur when the acoustic flow and the jet flow were in step, i.e. the jet pulses should occur a quarter of a cycle earlier than predicted by Helmholtz.

The problem can probably be best understood by a mechanical analogy. Suppose that you produce a miniature swing and drive it by blowing it with a puff of air once every cycle. To achieve the highest swing with the least amount of driving energy, should you produce the puffs of air when the swing is stationary at its highest point or when it is moving fastest at its lowest point? The first of these corresponds to the Helmholtz interpretation and the second to Rayleigh's. In recent years detailed experiments have been conducted to quantify the magnitude of the phase lag (Fletcher and Thwaites 1983). The experiments use a blown organ pipe fitted with absorbing wedges at its open end in order to stop it from speaking. A loudspeaker directs sound waves down the tube from the open end and produces a standing wave which is recorded with a microphone inside. Both the blowing pressure and the loudspeaker frequency can be varied and the microphone can measure the wave amplitude either with or without the jet. In this way one can see whether the jet is adding or subtracting energy from the reflected wave at the mouth. The results show that the phase lag which imparts most energy to the oscillation depends both on the blowing pressure and on the frequency. The Helmholtz interpretation is more correct for most practical organ pipes.

Footage notation is used for specifying the pitch of organ pipes. On an 8' stop all notes sound at the written pitch, the length of an open pipe for the lowest note C_2 of a normal keyboard rank being 8'. With a 4' stop the notes sound an octave above written pitch, with a 2' stop, two octaves above written pitch and so on. Similarly a 16' rank sounds an octave below written pitch. A twelfth above written pitch is designated by $2^2/_3$' since the pipe lengths are one third of those used on the 8' stop. A $1^1/_3$' will similarly sound a nineteenth (two octaves plus a fifth) above written pitch. This notation has carried over to the harpsichord (see p.236) and also the modern electronic organ. Alternatively the sounding intervals above written pitch may be specified directly, e.g. a 2' stop may be designated 'fifteenth'. The 2⅔' and 1⅓' stops are referred to as *quints*, since they sound one or two octaves plus a fifth above the written note. Intervals which are neither octaves or quints are also used, the *tierce* being the most common. This lies at an interval of a seventeenth above written pitch, i.e. two octaves plus a major third. Since this is the fifth harmonic, the footage notation is 1⅗'. Stops which introduce pipes sounding at some interval other than the octave relative to the fundamental are sometimes referred to as *mutation stops*. *Mixture stops* bring together a combination of different intervals, e.g. the cornet generally sounds 8', 4', 2⅔', 2' and 1⅗' ranks simultaneously.

Timbre of flue pipes

A major factor affecting the tone quality of a flue pipe is the ratio of its diameter (D) to its length (L) (Mercer 1953). If D/L is small, then the sound is bright and rich in upper harmonics with a weak fundamental. If the ratio is large, then the sound is much more pure with strong fundamental and few overtones. Small D/L ratios are used for *string* stops such as viols and large ratios for the *flutes*. The *diapasons* which are the main organ tones lie somewhere between these two. In a clarinet, flute or other woodwind instrument the effective tube length is varied by opening or closing holes and the higher pitched notes are produced by overblowing. A tube diameter must then be chosen which produces an acceptable sound over the entire playing range, in effect a compromise between the diameters which would give the best sound in the low and the high registers. In the case of the organ, however, no such compromise is required since a single pipe is only required to sound one note. Up until the Middle Ages organs had a range of only two octaves or less and the pipe diameter was kept constant, normally at between 25 mm and 30 mm with D/L about ⅛ for the longest pipe. As the range increased it was found that the bass pipes were relatively too narrow, giving a string-like quality; in an extreme case the pipe would overblow to the next mode. Similarly the pipes in the treble became too wide and lacked brightness. To overcome this, scaling the pipe diameters was introduced around the 13th century. Initially this involved halving the pipe diameter with each rise of an octave. In other words, if the longest pipe had a diameter D_0 and sounded a frequency f_0, then the diameter (D) of a pipe sounding frequency f would be (Fletcher 1977 (b)).

$$D = D_0(f_0/f).$$

The logic behind this was quite simple. It was known that the pipe length should be halved for each octave rise in pitch (this of course is only true if end effects are ignored), so the scaling gave a constant value for D/L. It was found by experience that over a wide range this scaling made the bass pipes excessively broad and dull and the treble pipes too narrow. This was rectified by organ builders of the 17th and 18th centuries using the modified relationship

$$D = D_0(f_0/f)^s$$

where S is a constant correction factor. Nowadays it is more usual to use the power law scaling rule

$$D = D_0(f_0/f)^x$$

where x is a constant less than unity, generally taken to be about 0.75. It has been found that this gives a good balance for all the flue pipes through the range of strings, diapasons and flutes. As an example the diameter of a middle C open diapason (650 mm long) is typically 57 mm, giving a D/L ratio of just less than 0.1. String pipes of the same frequency, however, could have a D/L ratio equal to half of this or even less.

The majority of organ pipes are cylindrical in shape, either open or stopped, the cylindrical open diapasons being the basic organ sound. Open pipes, like the flute, give a complete set of harmonics and are half a wavelength long. Stopped pipes are only a quarter of a wavelength long and produce predominantly odd numbered harmonics, like the clarinet. This gives them a more hollow sound. Other shapes are also used, the most common being the rectangular wooden pipe and the conical bore, tapered down towards the open end. Stopped conical pipes are also encountered. Sometimes the stopper may be fitted with an open chimney in order to encourage the formation of stronger even harmonics, the Rohrflöte being a well-known example. One of the characteristics of this tone is its pronounced initial transient. Very occasionally an open pipe may be overblown to the octave with assistance from a small hole drilled halfway along its length to encourage the formation of a pressure node at that point.

Effects of pipe material on timbre

As with the woodwinds, the material of construction has only a minor effect on a pipe's tone quality, although the way in which it can be worked by a craftsman is of extreme importance. In the case of organ pipes it has been possible to conduct quite simple experiments to quantify the effect of wall vibrations. In a series of tests carried out by Backus and Hundley (1966) pipes were surrounded by a jacket with a space between which could be filled with water to damp the vibrations. These tests showed that wall vibrations radiated a negligible amount of sound and also that they had an insignificant effect on the formation of standing waves within the tube. The only exception was the case of a rectangular pipe constructed from metal. However, organ builders do not generally construct rectangular metal pipes as their tone quality is thought to be unstable, probably for this reason. Thick wooden walls with greater rigidity are preferred. The wood must be thoroughly seasoned, otherwise movement is possible and tuning problems will result. All kinds of metal have been used for constructing pipes at one time or other and many other materials have been tried, including clay, glass, plastic, paper and cement. However, the metal generally accepted for the majority of pipes is an alloy of tin and lead, referred to as *organ metal*. The usual proportions are about 30% tin to 70% lead, although these may vary widely. One or two percent of antimony may be added to harden an alloy with a low tin content. High tin alloys may be referred to as 'spotted' because of the crystalline structure which appears on their surface. Tin is extremely expensive and for this reason alternative metals may be used, copper being the preferred choice because it is malleable enough to work, yet sufficiently rigid to form into a pipe. Zinc is widely used for pipes longer than one metre. It is relatively cheap but difficult to work.

Voicing

The mouth dimensions and the orientation of the jet in relation to the upper lip are important. It is general practice to use a wide mouth for a bold toned pipe and a narrow mouth for a softer pipe. The width is expressed as a fraction of the pipe circumference, typically ¼ for a diapason. The height of the mouth is termed the *cut-up*. The wider the mouth, the smaller the cut-up needs to be, a typical ratio of cut-up to mouth width being 1:4. Too large a cut-up leads to a dull tone. The shape of the jet is influenced by the height of the languid and the shape of its tip together with the shape of the lower lip. Up to the beginning of the 19th century most pipes used a blunt end to the languid and a straight lower lip to give their characteristic fluty sound. For the bolder tones required by the romantic organ the end of the languid is sharper and normally bevelled on the downstream side, and the lower lip is curved inwards at its top. *Nicking* the ends of the languid or the lower lip involves cutting fine notches along the edge. This has been common practice for about three centuries. It stabilises the jet by ensuring that it is always fully turbulent and this leads to an improvement both in the starting transient and the quality of the sustained note. Unnicked pipes have a tendency to 'whistle' or scrape and to be slow in producing their steady note. The idea is somewhat similar to that of placing roughening elements on a tall chimney in order to inhibit the formation of periodic eddy patterns which lead to low frequency oscillations.

Although the oscillations of the jet are close to sinusoidal, the flow rate into the pipe will have a more complex shape, containing many upper harmonics which excite the higher resonance modes of the tube. There are two reasons for this. Firstly, near the end of its travel on either side a point will be reached when the jet is directed completely inside or outside the tube, so that further deflection will not produce any change in flow rate. This makes the flow rate profile flatter in shape than a sinusoid. Secondly, the upper lip is normally set such that the jet stream is divided asymmetrically. The exact position of this division greatly influences the speed at which the pipe speaks as well as the steady state tone quality. Fine adjustments to the positions of the languid and the two lips are made by the builder in a process known as *voicing* (Mercer 1954).

Reed pipes

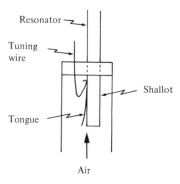

Fig. 11.2. Reed organ pipe.

The reed in an organ is generally of the single type made from a thin strip of metal, referred to as the *tongue* (Fig. 11.2). This vibrates over a cavity, termed the *shallot*, which is the equivalent of the mouthpiece on a clarinet or saxophone. The resonator may be either a full length pipe or a short length cavity, sometimes just in the form of a perforated box. In the latter case the stop is referred to as a *regal*, examples of these being the krummhorn and the trichter. Reed pipes are generally conical in shape, although the clarinet uses a cylindrical resonator. Commonly used reed pipe stops are the oboe (8′ pitch), the bassoon (16′ pitch), the trumpet (8′ and 4′ pitch) and the trombone (16′ pitch).

We have seen that with the woodwinds the reed is of the inward striking type and its resonant frequency is always above that of the resonating tube. In this case the reed and resonator form a stable coupled system which resonates at a frequency determined by the effective pipe length, a single reed covering the entire playing range of the instrument. Organ reeds are much more massive and have a resonant frequency below that of the resonator (Fletcher et al. 1982). The pitch is then essentially that of the tongue itself. The pitch of the note can be altered by adjusting the position of a stiff tuning wire which presses on the tongue and determines its effective vibration length. Shortening this length raises the pitch and lengthening lowers it. The free end of the wire runs outside the resonating chamber for easy access.

As the reed vibrates against the shallot it may produce a complete stoppage of the air flow on each cycle, giving rise to a tone rich in upper harmonics. Frequently reeds are given a smooth curvature (a process known as *voicing*) which allows them to roll over the aperture and cut off the airstream gradually. This has the effect of reducing the number of upper harmonics. The extent to which these are amplified will depend on how closely their frequencies coincide with the peaks on the impendance curve of the resonator. If a mode frequency coincides exactly with an impedance peak, then it will be strongly amplified. The application of impedance curves in determining the tonal structure of notes has been discussed in chapters 8 and 9.

Mechanism

Fig. 11.3 is a schematic diagram showing the way in which the mechanism of a pipe organ is laid out. In essence the instrument comprises a number of ranks of pipes, each having a different shape and tone character. Six ranks have been illustrated. Each of these ranks is made up of a set of pipes having different size and pitch. Seven different pitches are illustrated, corresponding to the notes F to B. The connections form a matrix so that air is channelled to a given pipe only when both its tone channel and its stop channel have been activated (Fletcher and Thwaites 1983). A tone channel is activated by depressing one of the keys such as the note G shown in the diagram. The stop channels are activated by pulling the drawstops. In Fig. 11.3 the third and the fifth stops from the front are shown drawn, so only the two pipes on the matrix corresponding to the circles will sound. In practice the situation is slightly more complicated than shown since some drawstops, known as mixture stops, activate a number of ranks simultaneously. An example is the cornet stop, which generally activates five ranks simultaneously (see p.456). This is used, amongst other things, for the playing of 'cornet voluntaries', much favoured in England in the 18th century. For the top notes on the keyboard the mechanism is so arranged that the higher component pitches of the combination 'break back' to a lower octave in order to keep the pipe frequencies within a manageable range. The pipes are fixed on top of a box known as a *wind chest*, which is supplied with air from a blower and has a system of valves to open and close the connections to the pipes in accordance with the matrix scheme shown in Fig. 11.3.

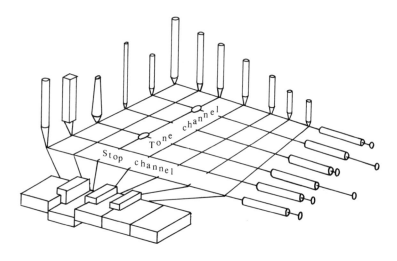

Fig. 11.3. Schematic representation of the pipe organ mechanism.

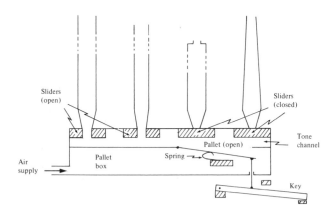

Fig. 11.4. The slider chest mechanism on a pipe organ.

Early organs were entirely mechanical and mostly used a traditional design of wind chest known as a *slider chest*. Fig. 11.4 shows the way in which this works. Air is supplied to a large pressurised box known as the *pallet box*. When a key is depressed, a pallet valve is opened and emits air into the *tone channel*. This is in the form of a narrow duct, as shown in Fig. 11.4. Here the pallet valve is connected directly to the key, although there is frequently a more complicated form of linkage mechanism consisting of *trackers* and *rollerboards*. Each channel supplies air to all the pipes of a

461

given pitch. Whether air enters a given pipe or not depends on the position of the *slider valve* located under the foot hole of the pipe. A slider valve is simply a long strip of material, usually wood, with holes drilled at spacings corresponding to the distances between the pipes of a given rank. Each valve is operated by a *drawstop*. When a drawstop is withdrawn, the holes of the slider valve lie just beneath the foot hole of each pipe, so all the pipes of a given rank with their pallet valve open will sound. When the drawstop is returned to its closed position, the slider cuts off all the airways of that rank. In other words a slider corresponds to a stop channel in Fig. 11.3.

There are two other forms of wind chest in common use, the *spring chest* and the *cone valve chest*. The layout of the spring chest is similar to that of the slider, the essential difference being that each pipe has a small pallet valve beneath its foot hole to replace the slider. Each set of valves for a particular rank is connected to a bar which is operated by a drawstop. When the drawstop is withdrawn these valves are opened and the effect is the same as moving a slider to the open position. The spring chest has the advantage that it does not suffer from the effects of warping of the wood which can cause leaks in a slider chest. On the other hand it is more complicated and expensive to make. Most Italian built organs up to the 19th century used the spring chest design. In the cone valve design, which appeared at the end of the 18th century, each pipe is served by a separate cone shaped valve. The valves for each pipe of a given pitch are attached to a roller which is operated by a key on the console. Each rank has a longitudinal duct which becomes pressurised when the appropriate draw-stop is withdrawn. Thus the stop channels in Fig. 11.3 are now the air ducts rather than the tone channels as with the traditional slider and spring chest designs.

During the 19th century all manner of electromechanical and electro-pneumatic mechanisms were invented for operating the valves, allowing huge organs to be played without the use of excessive key pressure. With a *pneumatic* system each valve is normally sprung in the open position, but its connecting rod is attached to small bellows which force the valve closed when supplied with air. Activation of an appropriate key or stop cuts off the air supply to the bellows which then collapses and opens the valve. With an *electrical action* the valves are opened by electromagnets. Modern organ builders have tended to return to the mechanical system for the keys and pedals because the directness of action gives the player a greater degree of control. The slider chest arrangement is now the most commonly used. Generally an electrical system is used for the stops, sometimes under the control of a microprocessor to allow the storage of complicated combination settings. With some organs, for example the giant instrument in Sydney Opera House which has 10,500 pipes operated by five keyboards and a pedal board, the mechanical operations are recorded digitally. The resulting tape can then be replayed at a later time to operate the organ and hence reconstruct the original performance.

The drawstops on an organ are shared out amongst a number of manuals, up to five on the largest instruments, together with a pedal board. Since these operate essentially as independent instruments they are given their own names. The most important manual having many of the louder stops is called the *great organ*. The next most important is the *swell organ*, so-called because it is contained in a box with shutters which can be opened or closed by a pedal to produce crescendo and diminuendo effects. This principle may be used on other manuals. It is also a feature of many of the *theatre organs* which were built in the earlier part of this century. In a two manual organ there will just be a Great and a Swell, the Great being the lower keyboard nearer the player. A third manual is normally called the *choir organ*. This has many softer stops and is useful for accompaniment purposes. Next comes the *solo organ* and then the fifth manual termed the *echo organ*, which contains delicate stops for distant sounding effects. The complete assemblage of keyboards and stops is referred to as the *console*. Finally there is the *pedal organ*, whose chief stops are pitched at 16' to give the instrument depth. *Couplers* are used for connecting the separate manuals and pedal board. By using an appropriate coupler it is possible to play two or more sections of the organ simultaneously, either on a single manual or on the pedal board.

On the traditional church organ each drawstop operates a separate rank of pipes. This is inefficient in the sense that many of the pipes are duplicated. Flute stops of 8', 4' and 2', for example, could all use a single rank of pipes of extended range and likewise for the mutation stops. Mechanically, this can only be implemented with a very elaborate linkage mechanism, but with modern electrical systems this is no great problem. The idea was developed by companies such as Compton mainly for theatre organs and subsequently has been used for electronic instruments. The term *unit organ* is sometimes used in this context. Although the scheme brings about a considerable saving in space and cost, there are fundamental problems which have inhibited its wider usage in more sophisticated instruments. Firstly it is difficult to obtain the correct balance between different pitches, e.g. 8' and 2', because the pipes have not been appropriately scaled and voiced. Secondly, the mutation stops do not generate frequencies which are precise multiples of the fundamental since they are selecting notes from a tempered scale. A third disadvantage is that in contrapuntal playing it is possible to have an overlap of notes. This causes problems because with a unit organ it is not possible to sound a note afresh if the pipe has already been activated.

In modern organs the blowing mechanism is an electrically driven fan. The air from this passes into *schwimmers*, which are small wind chambers with one end on springs. The expansion or contraction of the spring compensates for small changes in air pressure. With this arrangement it is possible to achieve an almost completely steady flow and if necessary a division of pressures between different parts of the organ using a single blower. Air pressures in an organ are reckoned in terms of the height of water column they can support. Early organs, especially those in Spain and Italy, tend to work on very low pressures, of around 50 mm. This gives them a gentle quality, ideal for cantabile playing. The more powerful organs built during the 19th and 20th centuries use higher pressures (sometimes above 1 m) to obtain their greater volume. The pressures used for the reeds are typically twice as great as those for the flue pipes.

REED ORGANS

By reed organs we mean all those instruments which rely purely on reeds for their sound production and which use a separate reed for each note. Two distinct types of reed are encountered, the so-called *beating reed* and the *free reed*. Reeds which vibrate against an air slot such as those used in the pipe organ are termed beating reeds. The only reed organ which utilises beating reeds is the ancient regal. All the others, the harmonium, American organ, accordion, concertina and harmonica, have free reeds. With a free reed the tongue vibrates over an aperture and is cut to exactly the same size so that it can move to and fro through the opening without being stopped by its edges. The typical form of free reed as used on a harmonica or harmonium is shown in Fig. 11.5. This will vibrate only when air is passed through from the side on which the tongue is fixed, i.e. from top to bottom in the diagram. This type of reed is inward striking and the mechanics of its operation are virtually the same as for the pipe organ reed, the main difference being that the vibration of the tongue is not stopped discontinuously at the end of its travel. If air flows from the other side, i.e. from beneath in Fig. 11.5, then the tongue is simply bent away from the base plate and no vibration occurs. With all of the reed organs the pitch of any note is determined by the natural frequency of the tongue.

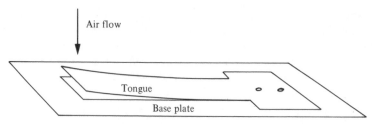

Fig.11.5. Free reed as used in a harmonica or harmonium.

Regal

The regal has the appearance of a small one manual portable organ. Each note has a short pipe and a beating reed similar to the ones found on a pipe organ. The pipes here have the purpose of controlling the sound quality but do not determine the pitch. The regal was introduced in the 15th century. At that time pipe organs only had flue pipes. The advent of the regal eventually led to the introduction of stops of this name on the pipe organ. In its later development flue pipes were sometimes added to a regal, making it in effect a small pipe organ. The instrument fell into disuse after the 17th century.

Harmonium

The harmonium is a reed organ about the size of an upright piano. It was mainly developed in Paris around 1840 and remained in production until about the 1930s. Although it was originally developed as a domestic instrument, it has found its greatest application in small churches, where it takes the place of a pipe organ.

The reeds are of the free type, the tongues consisting of strips of brass of various lengths fixed rigidly at one end to a metal plate. Underneath the plate is a wind chest and beneath this a reservoir supplied with air from two feeders connected by levers to the pedals, which are operated alternately by the player. The reservoir expands in bellows fashion, resisted by a strong spring in order to sustain the required blowing pressure. Above the reeds is a wooden board with channels of graded depth and the apertures are closed by pallet valves connected by levers to the notes of the keyboard. When a key is depressed the corresponding pallet valve is opened and air under pressure in the wind chest is forced through the reed. The wind channels leading to the different ranks of reeds are of various sizes in order that a range of blowing pressures and corresponding tone qualities can be obtained.

The majority of stops on a harmonium only operate over half of the keyboard, so that two must be drawn in order to play treble and bass simultaneously. Many of the modern electronic organs have a similar facility for splitting treble and bass. One rather useful stop is termed *expression*. When this is drawn the air from the feeders bypasses the reservoir and passes directly to the wind chest. The stabilising effect of the reservoir on the air pressure is now no longer present and so every small movement of the player's foot tells immediately on the tone. This gives him considerable power of light and shade, although its effective operation requires a good deal of practice. Another interesting stop often found on a harmonium is the *percussion*. This brings into action a set of small hammers which strike the reeds when keys are depressed. This makes them speak more quickly and gives them a distinctly percussive starting transient.

Many prominent composers have written music for harmonium,

among them César Franck, Saint-Saëns, Dvořák and Rossini. The only keyboard music that Berlioz wrote was for harmonium ('Three Pieces for Harmonium', 1845).

American organ

The American organ is virtually the same as the harmonium, the only real difference being that the air is sucked through the reeds rather than blown. There is generally no expression stop, which makes it somewhat easier to play. Its tone is less pungent than that of the harmonium and in its time it was more favoured for domestic use, the harmonium being preferred for churches and halls. Frequently the case is very ornate, with shelves, mirrors and ornamental woodwork set high above the back of the keyboard.

Accordion

The accordion was invented in 1829 by one Cyril Damian living in Vienna. It utilises the free reed principle, is hand-held and is powered by bellows. The reeds are made of steel, although on very early instruments brass was used. The right hand has the melody notes and the left hand plays an accompaniment whilst also operating the bellows. Accordions can be either *single* or *double action*. The distinction is that with double action both the press (compression of the bellows) and the draw (expansion of the bellows) give the same note. Since a reed will only speak when blown from one direction, this requires two similar reeds for each note, aligned in opposite directions. With the single action different notes are sounded on the press and the draw, as with the harmonica, which is to be discussed later.

The simplest form of accordion is the *melodeon*, sometimes referred to as the German accordion. This is a single action instrument which in its most basic form has a single row of buttons (usually ten) for the melody in the right hand. These play the diatonic scale in one key, which is usually C, although melodeons in F, G, D and A are also common. Each button gives a single note on the press and another on the draw, the fingering being arranged so that all the notes on the press are from the tonic chord. In the left hand there are two keys which give the bass note and the chord, tonic on the press and dominant on the draw. More sophisticated instruments have two or even three rows of buttons for playing in different keys (e.g. C and F), with corresponding buttons for the left hand. The melodeon is used almost exclusively for dance music, where the rhythmic effects of the push-pull action are most effective.

The British chromatic accordion is a development of the melodeon in which the single row of buttons has been supplemented by an additional row pitched a semitone higher or lower. A C/C# accordion, for example,

466

has two rows, giving the diatonic scales in these keys with corresponding bass buttons. Three row models are also available, each row again pitched a semitone apart. The best-known exponent of this instrument is Jimmy Shand.

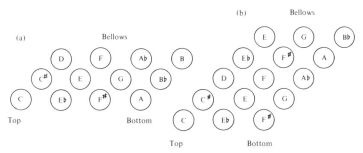

Fig. 11.6. A short section of the keyboard on the Continental chromatic accordion showing the layout of the buttons: (a) three row version; (b) full size version.

The Continental chromatic accordion, unlike its British counterpart, has a double action. The small version has three rows of buttons in the treble, adjacent notes in a row being a minor third apart. Moving diagonally across, the buttons in adjacent rows are a semitone apart. Fig. 11.6 (a) shows one octave of the keyboard. The full size version has five rows of twenty buttons each, the additional rows duplicating the outer two rows on the three row version, as shown in Fig. 11.6 (b). The bass has six rows of twenty buttons, the adjacent notes on any row being a perfect fifth apart. Moving outwards from the bellows, the rows are counter bass, fundamental bass, major chord, minor chord, dominant seventh and diminished seventh. The counter bass is a major third above the fundamental bass. Tone colour variations are obtained by using register tabs, which are found on both treble and bass sides of the instrument. These bring in further sets of reeds pitched at the octave relative to the fundamental, either above or below. By combining the octaves in different combinations and using tone chambers on selected sets of reeds, a wide variety of effects are obtained. Tremolo is obtained by having pairs of reeds tuned slightly differently so that they beat together.

The piano accordion is similar to the Continental chromatic accordion in that it is double action and uses the same layout for the bass. The treble buttons, however, are replaced by a conventional piano-style keyboard. Many people consider the Continental button layout to be more logical, although most accordionists find the keyboard easier to play.

One limitation of the piano and Continental chromatic accordions in their simplest form is that they are not well suited to the playing of bass melodies or contrapuntal accompaniments. This problem is overcome with the *free bass* models which have an extra manual of buttons for the left hand arranged chromatically in three rows as for the treble. Many models nowadays have a converter switch which, when depressed, changes buttons which are normally for chords into a free bass.

Concertina

The concertina is a bellows blown instrument similar to the accordion but much smaller and held between the hands, supported by straps. There are two distinct forms, the square shaped German model and the hexagonal British one. There is a set of buttons for each hand which are played with the four fingers, with the thumbs being used to support the instrument. All the buttons give single notes rather than chords. Like the accordion the concertina uses the free reed principle.

The German form is a single action instrument using two reeds per note tuned in unison or octaves but not in tremolo fashion. The fingering system is somewhat similar to the melodeon, with the higher notes in the scale being played with the right hand and the lower notes with the left. A *bandoneon* is a German-style concertina using a modified fingering pattern developed by one Heinrich Band. Three and four reed versions of this are now used a good deal in America. The British concertina is double action, with the notes of the scale played alternately with the right and left hands. It is not quite so effective for dance music as the single action concertina, where the bellows action gives a rhythmic drive, but it is very well suited to the playing of intricate melodies.

Harmonica

The harmonica, otherwise known as the mouth organ, is a small free reed instrument, hand held and blown by the mouth. The different length reeds are attached to two brass base plates having slots in them of the same size as the reed. A single reed is shown in Fig. 11.5. The plates are fixed on either side of a rectangular shaped base board which has slots cut in it to form the airways. Metal covers over the base plates act as tone chambers and also serve the purpose of protecting the reeds.

The basic instrument is the diatonic model, which can be bought pitched in different keys, commonly C or G. It has twenty reeds in all, ten fixed to each base plate. Both upper and lower plates have their reeds attached to the underside, so that for the upper plate they only speak on blowing and for the lower plate only on sucking. The arrangement of notes is similar to that used on the melodeon, all the notes in the blow being from the major triad. The instrument is blown in different positions along its length to sound the various notes and the tongue is used to cover notes which the player does not want to sound. The right hand is normally placed around the back of the tone chamber and its position is varied to produce different tonal effects. Tremolo can be obtained by vibrating the fingers.

For solo performance the more sophisticated chromatic harmonica is used. This may be likened to the British chromatic accordion in that it is really two diatonic systems set together, tuned a semitone apart, e.g. to C and C#. A spring loaded plate with holes in it passes in front of the air channels. This is operated by a button at the end which cuts off the airways for the C harmonica when pushed in. On release the C harmonica notes are brought back into operation. Chromatic harmonicas frequently use twelve rather than ten holes since this gives a complete three octave range without gaps. Many leading composers, including Milhaud, Vaughan Williams and Malcolm Arnold, have written works for the chromatic harmonica, inspired by virtuoso players such as Larry Adler.

As well as the standard diatonic and chromatic harmonicas, both bass and chord instruments are produced. These are designed specifically with the harmonica band in mind.

12

The human voice

Singing is the most natural and commonplace of all musical activities. Yet in many ways it is also the most remarkable. A professional singer is required not only to display the finest degree of pitch control, a wide range of tone colours and a volume sufficient to dominate a symphony orchestra, but also to render intelligible the words of the text being sung. In order to understand how singers cope with these sometimes conflicting demands, scientists have conducted many experiments using both professional and amateur performers. In particular, studies carried out at the Royal Institute of Technology in Stockholm by Johan Sundberg over the last fifteen years have contributed greatly to our understanding of the singing process. Although many aspects of this complex subject remain to be explored, it is now possible to provide an acoustical foundation for some of the principles of traditional voice training.

THE VOICE ORGAN

The section through the head and neck sketched in Fig. 12.1 shows the relationship between the principal parts of the voice organ. The acoustical behaviour of the organ is summarised by the schematic diagram in Fig. 12.2. Having filled the lungs with air, the singer compresses this volume, forcing an airstream upwards through the *trachea* (windpipe). At its upper end the trachea enters the *larynx*, which in turn opens through a short tube into the *pharynx* (the back of the throat). At the base of the larynx, the mucous membrane lining is folded inwards from each side, leaving a slit-like opening known as the *Gylottis* (Fig 12.3). These folts of membrane are commonly called the 'vocal cords', conjuring up a rather misleading image of stretched strings; the name *vocal folds* is now preferred.

471

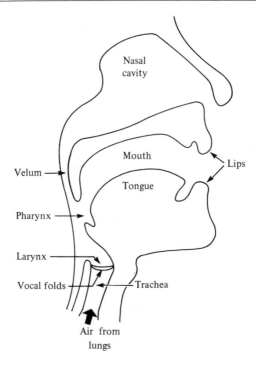

Fig. 12.1. The principal features of the voice organ.

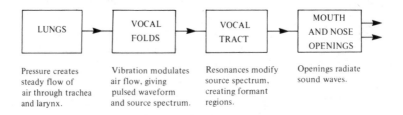

Fig. 12.2. Schematic diagram illustrating the operation of the voice organ.

The separation and tension of the vocal folds are controlled by muscles in the larynx. In normal breathing the folds are held apart to permit the free flow of air (Fig. 12.3 (a)). In singing or speaking the folds are brought close together and tensed (Fig. 12.3 (b)). The forcing of an airstream through the glottis in this state sets the vocal folds into vibration, alternately opening and closing the aperature at the base of the larynx. As

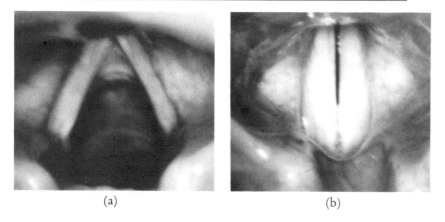

Fig. 12.3. The glottis photographed from above, showing the vocal folds
(a) separated, (b) pressed together.

a result, the flow of air from the lungs is modulated at the vibration
frequency of the vocal folds.

The sound wave generated in the larynx travels through the pharynx,
the mouth and the nasal cavity before finally emerging from the mouth
and nose apertures of the singer. These cavities constitute the vocal tract;
they have their own characteristic resonance frequencies, which play a
vital role in determining both quality and intelligibility in singing. Each
resonance of the vocal tract gives rise to a formant region in the spectrum
of the radiated sound. By adjusting the opening of the lips, the position of
the lower jaw, and the shape and position of the tongue, the singer (or
speaker) chooses a particular combination of formant frequencies.

In our discussion of the acoustics of the voice organ, we shall concentrate on the singing voice. Speech and singing clearly have much in common, and the modern understanding of speech production is well
surveyed by Fant (1970) and Flanagan (1972).

The pitch of a sung note is determined by the vibration frequency of the
vocal folds. The motion of the folds is almost completely independent of
the shape of the vocal tract (an exception in the case of male singers will be
discussed later in the chapter). On the other hand, the choice of a particular vowel sound is made by modifying the vocal tract to produce three or
four characteristic formants; the frequencies of the formants corresponding to a given vowel are very nearly the same regardless of the pitch at
which it is sung. It is therefore convenient to consider the acoustics of the
voice organ in more detail by concentrating first on the sound source (the
vocal folds), then on the vocal tract resonances. Finally we shall examine
some of the special techniques which distinguish the operatic soloist from
the bathroom tenor.

THE VOCAL SOUND SOURCE

Self-sustaining vibration of the vocal folds

The motion of the vocal folds in singing is similar in many ways to that of the lips of a trumpet player. The principal difference is that in a brass instrument the resonances of the tube exert a powerful influence on the motion of the lips, whereas the vocal tract resonances hardly affect the motion of the vocal folds. The analogy is closer if we remove the trumpeter's instrument, forcing him to play on the mouthpiece alone. We saw in Chapter 9 that in this case the motion of the lips is controlled by the combination of the tension forces exerted by the lip muscles and the Bernoulli force exerted by the air flow between the lips.

The motion of the vocal folds is similarly controlled. A build-up of pressure behind the closed vocal folds eventually forces them apart, allowing air to flow through. The Bernoulli force, which arises from the reduction in pressure due to the air flow, acts together with the tension forces on the folds to pull them together again. As they close, the air flow is cut off, the Bernoulli force disappears and a new cycle commences.

For the vocal fold vibration to give rise to a continuous sound, it must be self-sustaining. Since energy is lost through friction in the moving parts of the larynx and through radiation of sound, there must be a corresponding input of energy in order to keep the vibration going. The source of this energy is the Bernoulli force. A careful analysis of the problem shows that the air flow speed, and therefore the Bernoulli force, reaches its maximum value slightly *after* the vocal folds reach their maximum separation (Benade 1976, p.367). As a consequence, the average Bernoulli force during the half cycle when it is helping the vibration (when the folds are closing) is greater than that during the half cycles when it is hindering (when the folds are opening). This is the regeneration condition which allows the vibration to draw energy from the air flow supplied by the lungs.

The source spectrum

In loud singing the vocal folds close completely for a significant fraction of the vibration cycle. The resulting air flow has a waveform similar to that shown in Fig. 12.4 (a): a regular series of roughly triangular spikes. The fundamental repetition frequency of the waveform, which determines the pitch of the sung note, is controlled by the mass and tension of the vibrating areas of the vocal folds. In men the vocal folds are normally larger and more massive than in women; this is the primary reason for the characteristic difference in compass between male and female voices. At the low pitch end of a singer's register, the folds are relatively slack, and

474

almost the whole area vibrates. A rise in pitch is achieved by increasing the muscular tension on the folds, which become longer and thinner. At the upper end of the register only a small area near the edge of each fold is vibrating with large amplitude.

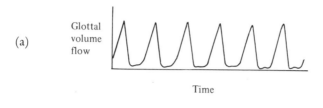

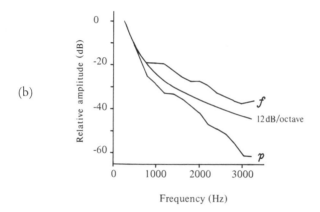

Fig. 12.4. (a) Glottal flow velocity waveform (Sondhi 1975, p.230, Fig. 3). (b) Mean source spectrum envelopes for a light bass voice singing at two dynamic levels, compared with a –12 dB/octave envelope. In each case the envelope is normalised to 0 dB at 250 Hz. Based on Sundberg (1973), p.81, Fig. 5.

Laryngoscopic studies of singers have shown that the motion of the vocal folds is not a simple vibration (Farnsworth 1940). On occasion, different parts of one vocal fold are seen to move in opposite directions at a given time. In fact, the vocal folds can vibrate in many different normal modes, in the same way as stretched strings or membranes (Titze and Strong 1975). Whether higher modes of vibration of the vocal folds significantly affect the production of the singing voice remains unclear. In general, our understanding of the mechanics of the larynx is in a much more primitive state than is the case for most musical instruments. The non-uniformity and variability in time of its component parts make a theoretical treatment formidably difficult – one leading researcher in this

475

field has feelingly described the larynx as being 'in the class of a plastic ukelele with rubber strings' (Titze 1983).

The frequency spectrum of the waveform shown in Fig. 12.4 (a) consists of a set of harmonic components whose amplitudes fall off fairly rapidly with increasing frequency. Measurements by Sundberg (1973) have shown that the source spectrum for a trained singer performing at the mezzoforte dynamic level has an envelope which falls at a rate of 12 dB/octave (Fig. 12.4 (b)). This means that the nth harmonic has an amplitude equal to $(1/n)^2$ times the amplitude of the fundamental. At the piano level, the envelope slopes more sharply: the larynx is generating less energy in the high harmonics. At the forte level, on the other hand, the envelope slopes more gently, implying that the high harmonics grow more rapidly than the fundamental as the loudness is increased.

Since the output of the sound source provides the raw material out of which the vocal tract resonances must fashion a desirable tone quality, it is important that there should be an adequate representation of upper harmonics in the source spectrum at all dynamic levels. The singer can control the spectrum envelope by adjustments of the muscles in the larynx which control the spacing and tension of the vocal folds. If the folds are too slack they do not close properly at any point in the vibration cycle; the resulting source waveform loses its spiky appearance and starts to resemble a sine curve. This gives rise to the 'breathy' sound characteristic of many untrained singers, especially when singing quietly. The spectrum envelope of a voice source operating in this way can fall off as rapidly as 18 dB per octave, leaving the vocal tract resonances with little to work on. It appears that vocal training gives a singer the ability to maintain a spiky source waveform, with the vocal folds pressed tightly together for a considerable fraction of each vibration cycle, over a much larger dynamic range than is possible for an untrained voice (Sundberg 1973; Troup 1981).

Efficiency of the vocal source

Breath control is one of the most important aspects of singing technique. Having filled the lungs, the singer naturally wishes to make the most economical use of the air supply in generating sound. It is also desirable that the method by which the sound is generated should involve the least possible strain on the muscles of the larynx, throat and chest. If the laryngeal muscles are too relaxed, not only will the source spectrum be deficient in upper harmonics, but the rate of air flow through the glottis will be increased, making it impossible to sustain long notes. On the other hand, if the vocal folds are too tight the air pressure required to push them apart will be increased, involving additional muscular effort both inside and outside the larynx.

In a remarkable series of experiments, Rubin, LeCover and Vennard

(1967) measured the relationship between the pressure below the larynx (the subglottic pressure) and the rate of air flow through the glottis during vocal performance. Two professional singers (a bass and a soprano) and a relatively untrained baritone were persuaded to allow a hypodermic needle to be inserted into the trachea just below the larynx. A tube connected the external end of the needle to a pressure measuring device. A closely fitting mask covered the nose and throat; air expelled through the larynx during singing passed through this mask and into a device which measured the rate of air flow. A microphone close to the mask registered the sound emitted (Fig. 12.5).

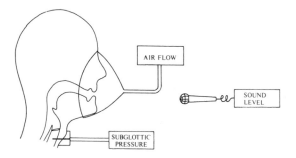

Fig. 12.5. The experimental arrangement of Rubin et al. (1967).

These could hardly be considered as normal singing conditions! Nevertheless, even with needles in their throats and masks on their faces the singers were able to perform a variety of vocal tasks, and some interesting results emerged. A rise in the pitch of the sung note was normally accompanied by an increase in subglottal pressure; this is understandable, since the vocal fold tension is increased in order to raise the vibration frequency. When the loudness of a note of constant pitch was increased, the pressure also rose. In each case the rate of air flow remained essentially constant. Thus the singers were able to increase the intensity of the sound source by increasing muscle tension, without using up more breath.

Fig. 12.6 (a) shows results obtained when one of the singers deliberately shifted from the normal, efficient type of voice production to an extremely breathy production. In order to keep the sound output constant, the pressure was slightly increased, and the air flowed through the glottis more than four times as rapidly as it did in the normal singing mode.

A more common type of inefficient voice production is illustrated by Fig. 12.6 (b). Here the singer deliberately increased the vocal fold tension above its optimum value, forcing an increase in the subglottal pressure. In this state the control of the air flow was poorer, resulting in a greater irregularity in the intensity of the sound output. A similar over-tightening of the laryngeal muscles was also observed when the singer was running out of breath near the end of a long note. These observations support the advice of singing teachers that good breath control and a relaxed throat are necessary for efficient voice production.

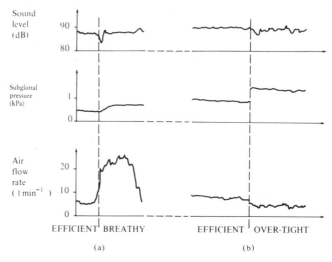

Fig. 12.6. Measurements by Rubin et al. of sound level, subglottal pressure and rate of air flow when a singer changes deliberately from efficient voice production to (a) breathy production; (b) over-tight production.

VOCAL TRACT RESONANCES

If the sound output from the vocal source were radiated directly, instead of passing through the vocal tract, it would have a rather harsh tone quality. We can get some idea of the nature of this raw sound by buzzing the lips against a circular ring, generating a series of puffs of air similar to that emitted by the larynx when the vocal folds are vibrating.

On its journey through the vocal tract, the sound is transformed. Components which lie close to one of the resonance frequencies of the tract are transmitted with high amplitude, while those which lie far from a resonance are suppressed. Much of the art of the singer lies in shaping the vocal tract in such a way that the crude source output is moulded into a sound of the desired volume and timbre (Sundberg 1977).

The vocal tract as a cylindrical tube

In the singing of most vowels, the velum or soft palate (see Fig. 12.1) is pressed against the back of the throat, closing the entrance to the nasal cavity. The vocal tract can then be thought of as a long thin tube with a cross-section which changes considerably through the larynx, pharynx and mouth (Fig. 12.7). The length of the tract is typically 175 mm in men and 150 mm in women, although considerable variations occur from individual to individual. From our earlier discussion of wind instruments we know that the resonance frequencies of such a tube will depend strongly on the bore profile. It is instructive to start by making a drastic simplifying approximation: we shall consider the vocal tract as a cylindrical tube of constant cross-section, closed at the larynx and open at the lips (Chiba and Kajiyama 1958; Fant 1970).

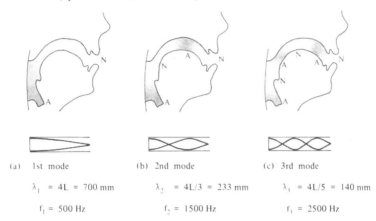

(a) 1st mode	(b) 2nd mode	(c) 3rd mode
λ_1 = 4L = 700 mm	λ_2 = 4L/3 = 233 mm	λ_3 = 4L/5 = 140 mm
f_1 = 500 Hz	f_2 = 1500 Hz	f_3 = 2500 Hz

Fig 12.7. The vocal tract behaves somewhat like a cylindrical tube closed at the larynx end. The diagram illustrates the first three standing wave patterns in the vocal tract, and the corresponding modes of a cylindrical tube of length L = 175 mm. The pressure amplitude is indicated by the depth of shading in the vocal tract, and by the separation of the curved lines in the cylindrical tube.

The resonances of such a tube were described in Chapter 4. In Fig. 12.7 the first three resonances are illustrated; each corresponds to a standing wave pattern with a pressure antinode (a velocity node) at the closed end, and a pressure node (velocity antinode) at the open end. Taking the length to be 175 mm, the wavelength of the first resonant mode is 4 × 175 = 700 mm. The speed of sound in the warm air of the vocal tract will be around 350 ms^{-1}, so that the first resonance frequency will be f_1 =350/0.7 = 500 Hz. Higher resonances will have frequencies which are odd integer multiples of f_1: f_2 = 3f_1 = 1500 Hz, and f_3 = 5f_1 = 2500 Hz.

Vocal formants

If the real vocal tract behaves at all like our simple cylindrical tube model, we should find that a singer's voice spectrum is characterised by a set of *formants*, each formant corresponding to one of the resonances of the tract. A resonance at 500 Hz, for example, would result in an emphasis on whichever harmonics of the source spectrum lay close to 500 Hz; a resonance at 1500 Hz would similarly accentuate the harmonics in that region of frequency.

Such formant regions do indeed exist, and were discussed briefly in Chapter 3 (p.154). When the jaw and tongue are moved in order to create a particular vowel sound, the vocal tract resonances are adjusted to give the pattern of formants characteristic of that vowel. The three lowest formants are most important in making the vowel recognisable. Measurements of vocal sound spectra show the first formant frequency ranging over a few hundred hertz on either side of 500 Hz; the second and third range similarly around 1500 Hz and 2500 Hz respectively (Fant 1970, p.109; Flanagan 1972, p.131). It is interesting that the central values of the formant frequencies are just those predicted by the cylindrical tube model.

Fig. 3.63 illustrated typical formant patterns for the two vowels 'ee' and 'oo' spoken by a man. A spectrum envelope with peaks around 300 Hz, 800 Hz and 2500 Hz in a male voice is perceived as an 'oo' vowel sound. The female vocal tract is on average around 17% shorter than the male, and the formant pattern is consequently transposed upwards by about three semitones when the same vowel sound is pronounced by a woman. In a child's voice the formant peaks are likely to be a further semitone higher (Fant 1970). It is thus not quite correct to say that a given vowel is associated with a fixed set of formants: the brain's vowel recognition process is able to make an allowance for variations corresponding to the normal range of sizes of the vocal organ.

The effect of transposing the formant patterns upwards can be explored by tape-recording a voice and replaying with the tape speed increased. Doubling the speed raises the entire sound spectrum by an octave, so that each formant peak is an octave above its original position. This is a much bigger transposition than the brain is used to dealing with, and the vowel sounds are altered beyond recognition (Benade 1976, p.378).

Speeding up the tape raises the fundamental repetition frequency as well as the formant frequencies, so that the pitch of the note also rises. An experiment which illustrates even more clearly the role played by formants in voice quality and intelligibility requires the singer to inhale a mixture of helium gas and oxygen instead of normal air, which consists of a mixture of nitrogen and oxygen. Because helium is much lighter than nitrogen, its density is lower. and the speed of sound in the helium-oxygen mixture is nearly twice as high as in normal air. The substitution has little effect on the frequency of vibration of the vocal folds, and the singer can therefore sing at normal pitch. However, the formant frequencies are raised in proportion to the change in the speed of sound in the vocal tract. In practice, some air remains in the lungs when the singer expires before breathing in the helium-oxygen mixture, and the speed of sound increases typically by about 25% (Sundberg 1981). The effect is most remarkable with a low voice male singer, since the typical bass source spectrum is then modified by a set of formants characteristic of a boy treble. This confuses the vowel recognition mechanism of a listener; it also plays havoc with the voice control mechanism of the singer, who adjusts his vocal tract to create one vowel sound and finds another emerging.

Shaping the vocal tract

The relationship between the shape of the vocal tract and the formant pattern is a complex one (Ladefoged et al. 1978). Altering the shape, for example by moving the tongue, affects each formant in a different way. We can get a rough idea of the effect of jaw opening and tongue shape on the first two formant frequencies by considering the pressure distributions for the corresponding standing waves in the vocal tract (Fig. 12.7). We also need to recall that when the diameter of a tube containing a resonating air column is reduced at a pressure antinode, the resonant frequency rises, whereas a reduction of the diameter at a pressure node makes the resonant frequency fall (see p.270).

The first formant corresponds to a vocal tract standing wave with a pressure antinode at the larynx and a node at the lips (Fig. 12.7 (a)). The body of the tongue lies in the region halfway between the antinode and the node; raising or lowering the tongue has thus relatively little effect on the first formant frequency. Lowering the jaw, on the other hand, opens up the vocal tract at the pressure node, which raises the resonance frequency considerably.

This effect is clearly evident in Fig. 12.8, which shows the results of measurements of the formant frequencies in the sound spectrum of a tenor singing the five vowel sounds [i], [e], [a], [o] and [u]. The vowel [i] (signifying here the 'ee' sound, as in 'Mimi') is produced with a high position of the lower jaw and a small mouth opening; the first formant frequency is correspondingly low (around 300 Hz). As the jaw is lowered and the mouth opened to give the [a] sound (as in 'Tosca'), the first formant frequency rises by an octave. With the raising of the jaw necessary to produce the [u] sound (as in 'Puccini'), the first formant falls again.

If the first formant is positioned mainly by the jaw movement, the second depends strongly on the shape of the body of the tongue. On the [i] sound the tongue is curved so that the central part approaches the roof of the mouth while the tip remains low. Since the second mode of the vocal tract has a pressure antinode above the tongue (Fig. 12.7 (b)), the constriction raises the frequency of the second formant. In Fig. 12.8 the second formant for the vowel [i] is around 2000 Hz, a perfect fourth higher than the value of 1500 Hz predicted by the simple cylinder model of the vocal tract. The opening of the jaw in going towards the vowel [a] tends to raise the second formant further, since the mouth opening is a pressure node in all the standing wave patterns. This rising tendency is, however, more than counteracted by the lowering of the tongue which accompanies the drop of the jaw, since this expands the tract at the pressure antinode. The net result is a fall in the second formant frequency. In changing to the vowel sound (u), the centre of the tongue is kept low as the jaw is raised; the back of the tongue is also moved closer to the roof of the mouth. Reference to Fig. 12.7 (b) shows that this shape corresponds to an expansion at an antinode and a constriction at two nodes, resulting in a further drop in the second formant frequency. In Fig. 12.8 the vowel [u] has a second formant below 700 Hz.

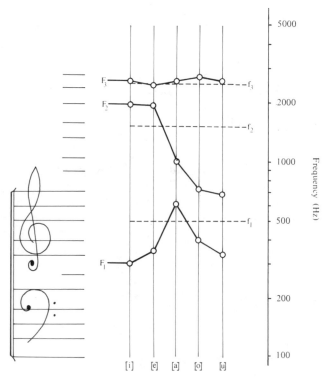

Fig. 12.8. Average frequencies of the first three formants (F_1, F_2 and F_3 for four tenor voices singing the vowel sounds [i], [e], [a],[o] and [u]. The pitches of the first three resonances of the cylindrical tube model of the vocal tract (f_1 f_2 and f_3) are shown for comparison. Based on measurements by Cleveland (1977).

It is possible to hear the dramatic fall of the second formant when a singer changes continuously from the vowel [a] to the vowel [u]. If a male voice sings the note C_3 with open mouth and lowered jaw and tongue, the vowel sound is [a]. The second formant, around 1000 Hz, emphasises the eighth harmonic of the source spectrum, which is C_6 (frequency 1046 Hz). Closing the jaw steadily lowers the second formant; when it has fallen to 915 Hz, the seventh harmonic (approximately $B_5^\flat$) is selected for emphasis. As the jaw continues to rise, the formant sweeps downwards through the harmonic spectrum of C_3, and each harmonic in turn is selected for special emphasis. By closing the mouth rather more than is usual when singing [u], it is possible to bring the second formant frequency down to 523 Hz, the frequency of the fourth harmonic of C_3. When the jaw is lowered to return to the [a] sound, the second formant can be heard sweeping back upwards through the harmonic spectrum. The notes to listen for when performing this experiment are shown in Fig. 12.9. An illustration of a musical exploitation of this technique is shown in Fig. 12.17.

Fig. 12.9. When the note C_3 (white note) is sung with the changing vowel sound indicated, the second formant emphasises in turn the harmonic components of the source spectrum shown by the black notes. The harmonic number of each component is shown above the corresponding note.

SPECIAL TECHNIQUES OF TRAINED SINGERS

The method of voice production and timbre control used by most untrained singers is very similar to that employed in normal speech. The ability to sustain a major operatic role is usually developed by an arduous course of training in which many special techniques are learned. Some of these techniques have recently been the subject of scientific study, and their acoustical basis is now fairly well understood (Sundberg 1977).

Covered tone

The vowel sounds produced in operatic singing are rather different from those in normal speech. Most of the discrepancies arise from measures taken to increase the vocal sound output. The obvious way to do this is to increase the area of the radiating aperture, and singing teachers frequently urge pupils to open their mouths more widely on vowels. Since the lips are a pressure node for all the vocal tract resonances, opening them tends to raise all the formant frequencies. The rise can be counteracted by widening the pharynx in the region just above the larynx, since this is a pressure antinode for all the resonances. In fact, the widening of the pharynx is often carried further than is necessary to compensate for the mouth opening, and the overall effect is to produce a formant pattern rather lower in pitch than that of normal speech (Lindblom and Sundberg 1971).

The drop in formant frequencies caused by opening up the back of the throat alters the vowel sounds significantly, giving the enunciation the slightly 'plummy' quality which is the most easily parodied feature of operatic singing. Natural pronunciation is sacrificed in the interests of a vocal timbre (often called a 'covered tone') which has the greater warmth associated with an increased emphasis on lower harmonics. Since tone quality and vowel intelligibility both depend on the shape of the spectrum envelope, the conflict is unavoidable, and the singer must judge how much vowel modification will be acceptable in a given set of circumstances.

The singing formant

The maximum sound power which the human voice can generate is of the order of one watt. Yet a soprano or tenor can be heard in a Wagnerian climax against an orchestra which is generating ten times as much sound power. Why is the voice not completely drowned by the orchestra?

The answer lies in a characteristic difference between the average spectrum envelope of orchestral sound and that of the operatic voice. An orchestra generates most of its sound energy in the frequency region around 500 Hz, reflecting the fact that many orchestral instruments have strong formants in that region. Above the treble clef the energy output of the orchestra drops off steadily with increasing frequency. This energy distribution is displayed clearly in the long-time-average-spectrum (see p. 154) of a piece of purely orchestral music shown by the dotted curve in Fig. 12.10.

When a similar analysis is performed on a piece of spoken dialogue, or on the voice of an untrained singer, the distribution of sound energy over the frequency spectrum is found to be almost identical to that for orchestral music. Thus the only way that a speaker or a singer using a 'natural' technique can avoid being masked by a loud orchestra is to use a microphone and amplifier to boost the power output of the voice to a level comparable with that of the orchestra.

The long-time-average-spectrum of an operatic tenor with loud orchestral accompaniment is shown by the solid curve in Fig. 12.10. Up to 2000 Hz the spectrum is similar to that of the orchestra alone. In the region around 2500 Hz, however, there is a striking divergence between the two curves: the contribution of the tenor has boosted the sound output in this frequency region by 15 dB. Thus although the total sound power radiated by the tenor is much less than that of the orchestra, in the critical band around 2500 Hz the tenor is able to generate considerably more sound energy than all the orchestral instruments combined. The harmonics of the tenor's voice spectrum which lie within this band are not masked by the orchestral sound, and their synchronised vibrato provides additional evidence to help the listener identify a vocal timbre in the total sound.

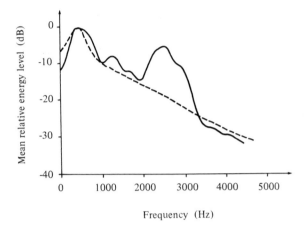

Fig. 12.10. Long-time-average-spectra of (a) a piece of orchestral music (dotted curve); (b) an operatic tenor with orchestral accompaniment (solid curve). From Sundberg (1977), p.21.

The main reason for the strength of the high frequency components in the spectra of male operatic singers is the existence of a strong additional formant between 2500 Hz and 3000 Hz (Bartholomew 1934). Unlike the formants discussed previously, which change frequency with each change of vowel, this additional formant remains at the same frequency regardless of the words being sung. Because it is a characteristic of the spectra of trained voices, it has become known as the *singing formant*.

The position of the larynx in singing

Since its pitch is independent of changes in the shape of the mouth opening and tongue, the singing formant cannot be a resonance of the vocal tract as a whole. Sundberg (1974) has demonstrated convincingly that it is in fact the lowest resonance of the short tube known as the *larynx tube*, which connects the larynx to the pharynx. Where the relatively narrow larynx tube opens out into the much wider pharynx, the impedance seen by the sound wave travelling upwards from the larynx changes. This results in the reflection of part of the sound energy back towards the larynx, and the consequent development of a standing wave in the larynx tube.

The strength of the larynx tube resonance depends on the magnitude of the reflection, which in turn is determined by the size and abruptness of the impedance change at the entrance to the pharynx. With the throat shape normally used by speakers and untrained singers, characterised by a fairly high position of the larynx, only a small fraction of the sound energy is reflected at the top of the larynx tube, whose resonance therefore contributes little to the vocal sound spectrum. When a trained singer switches from normal speech to the production of an 'operatic' voice, the larynx is usually lowered significantly (Shipp and Izdebski 1975); this has the effect of widening the lower part of the pharynx, so that the sound wave emerging from the larynx tube experiences a much more drastic change in vocal tract shape. Much more sound energy is then reflected at the junction, and a strong standing wave is set up at the lowest resonance frequency of the larynx tube, around 2800 Hz. This is the resonance responsible for the singing formant.

When an untrained singer performs an ascending scale, the larynx frequently rises as the pitch increases. It is possible that the upward stretching of the larynx helps to increase the tension on the vocal folds which is responsible for the rise in pitch. The opposite is observed in most professional singers; as the pitch of the note rises the position of the larynx, already low, falls even further. If the larynx were allowed to rise, the singing formant would be weakened. The upper end of the larynx tube usually widens as the pitch of the sung note increases; the lowering of the larynx provides a compensatory increase in the area of the pharynx, maintaining the impedance mismatch which is responsible for the strength of the singing formant.

It should be noted that Sundberg's linking of the lowered larynx to the production of the singing formant has recently been questioned by Wang (1983), who claimed that this type of 'bright voice' could be generated with a variety of larynx positions. Further study of this and other aspects of human voice production is clearly required.

The singing formant is usually associated with male professional singers, although Bloothooft and Plomp (1986) have shown that it is an even more prominent feature in the spectra of some alto voices. Sopranos, on the other hand, do not seem to make use of the technique. This is understandable, bearing in mind that the amplification of the high frequency components of the sound source spectrum corresponds to an increase in the brightness or 'sharpness' of the vocal timbre (see p. 154). The soprano voice range is typically about an octave higher than that of the tenor; the components lying in the frequency region around 3000 Hz are therefore already more powerful, since they are lower numbered harmonics in the source spectrum. Thus the female voice is inherently better adapted to penetrating the sound of the orchestra. The additional amplification of the high frequency components provided by the adoption of a singing formant would be liable to produce an unacceptably harsh timbre.

Although we have discussed the singing formant as a typical feature of professional singing, it should be emphasised that it is a weapon in the singer's armoury which must be used with discretion. It is clearly of most value in solo performance, when an individual voice has to project above a loud accompaniment. The vocal spectrum of choral singers, for whom blend is of paramount importance, shows a reduced singing formant and a greater emphasis on fundamental components (Rossing et al. 1986).

Distinguishability of vowels at high pitch

The difficulty of reconciling intelligibility with volume of sound output and beauty of tone is especially acute for a soprano in the upper part of her range. The listener recognises a particular vowel sound by perceiving peaks in the harmonic spectrum at the appropriate formant frequencies; the first and second formants are the most important clues for recognition. The first formant ranges in pitch from the bottom of the treble clef (for [i] and [u] vowels) to the top of the treble clef (for the [a] vowel). Thus when the soprano sings above F_5, even the fundamental component of her voice spectrum lies above the first formant for all normal vowel sounds. Clearly if there are no components near the formant frequency there cannot be a peak in the spectrum envelope at that point, and a crucial clue for vowel identification is absent.

Fig. 12.11. Excerpt from the duet between Pamina (soprano) and Tamino (tenor) in the finale of Mozart's opera 'The Magic Flute'.

As an example of this problem in a musical context, let us consider an excerpt from the finale of Mozart's opera 'The Magic Flute' (Fig. 12.11) in which the hero Tamino (tenor) and the heroine Pamina (soprano) rejoice in their reunion. On the first two notes of each entry, the singer is required to produce the vowel sound [a] followed by the vowel sound [i]. Looking first at the tenor entry, we see that these two vowels have to be enunciated at pitches of C_4 and F_4 respectively. In Fig. 12.12 the pitches of the harmonic components of these notes are shown, together with curves indicating the positions of the formant peaks for the two vowels. On the first syllable, the second harmonic of the tenor's source spectrum (C_5) is close to the first formant, while the fourth harmonic (C_6) is near the second formant. The output spectrum will therefore have strong second and fourth harmonics; the tenth and eleventh harmonics will also be emphasised, since they lie close to the third formant. All three formants

487

will be powerfully represented in the singer's output and the [a] sound will be clearly established.

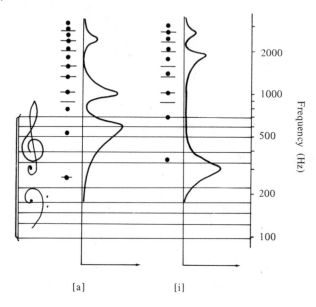

Fig. 12.12. Harmonic components and formants for the first two notes of the tenor entry in Fig. 12.11. The formants are qualitative curves based on data from Fant (1970) and Flanagan (1972).

In moving to the second syllable, the tenor raises the vibration frequency of the vocal folds to give a note with fundamental pitch F_4. He simultaneously adjusts the shape of the vocal tract to move the first formant down to about $E^\flat_4$ and the second formant up to about $B^\flat_6$, as required by the vowel sound [i]. The first harmonic of the sound source is now close to the first formant, while the fifth harmonic (A_6) is near the second formant. The strength of these two harmonics in the output spectrum will clearly mark the change of vowel from [a] to [i].

Consider now the first two notes of the soprano entry (Fig. 12.13). The first syllable requires the [a] vowel at the pitch C_5. The first, second and third formants are not too far from the first, second and fifth harmonics respectively, so that this vowel is fairly well characterised. In moving to the second syllable, however, the soprano raises the pitch to A_5. The normal formant pattern for the vowel [i] requires the first formant to be around $E^\flat_4$; a resonance at such a low pitch is useless in this case, since it has nothing to amplify, and can therefore contribute nothing to the output spectrum. The second and third formants will strengthen the second and third harmonics, but without the first formant much of the identity of the vowel sound will be lost.

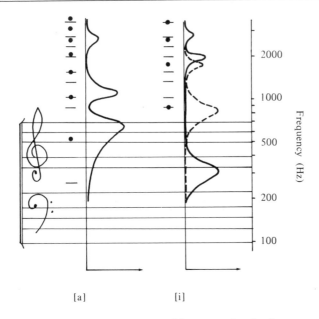

Fig. 12.13. Harmonic components and formants for the first two notes of the soprano entry in Fig. 12.11. For the vowel [i], the solid curve shows the normal placing of the formants, while the dashed curve illustrates the tuning of the first and second formants to match the first two harmonics of the source spectrum.

The deterioration in intelligibility due to the loss of the first formant clue is illustrated dramatically by the solid curve in Fig. 12.14, showing the result of a test in which a group of listeners had to identify four isolated vowel sounds sung at various pitches by a soprano. Up to C_5, the vowels were correctly identified more than half the time; above this pitch the identification rate fell sharply, until at A_5 only 4% of the vowels were recognised.

It might be concluded from our discussion so far that it is useless to set words at pitches above the treble clef, since they will be almost totally unintelligible. The picture is not quite as black as this, however. When the test was repeated, not with isolated vowels but with vowels sandwiched between consonants ('beed, bid, bed, bad') as they are usually in sung text, the identification was much more successful (dashed curve in Fig. 12.14). The reasons for this improvement in intelligibility are still not fully understood, but it seems likely that the brain of the listener is able to make use of additional information gathered from the rapid changes which occur in the vocal output spectrum as the vocal tract changes shape to generate successively the formants of the first consonant, the vowel and the second consonant. Thus the clear enunciation of consonants is particularly critical for intelligibility at high pitches.

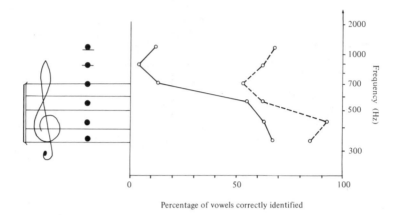

Fig. 12.14. Results of a measurement of vowel recognition accuracy. Solid curve: isolated vowel sounds. Dashed curve: each vowel preceded and followed by a consonant. Adapted from Smith and Scott (1980), p.1796, Fig.1.

Formant tuning

Vocal tract resonances are important, not only for intelligibility, but also for maximising the efficiency of voice production. Returning to Fig. 12.13, we see that the soprano can sing the vowel [a] at a given loudness with relatively little vocal effort, since all of the resonances corresponding to the formant peaks are being used to boost the output from the larynx. In contrast, the vowel [i], if sung with the normal formant pattern corresponding to the solid curve, would require a greater output from the larynx to achieve the same loudness, since the lowest vocal tract resonance would in effect be wasted.

Studies of the singing technique of operatic sopranos have shown that the normal formant pattern may be extensively modified as the pitch of the sung note rises (Sundberg 1975; Benade 1976, p.382). In particular, if the frequency of the first formant would normally lie below the fundamental, the formant may be raised to bring it into tune with the fundamental. The effect of such a change is shown by the dashed curve in Fig. 12.13: the fundamental will now be strongly amplified by the first formant and the loudness will be considerably enhanced. The sound will also have a weightier timbre, corresponding to the increased significance of the fundamental in the harmonic spectrum.

How does the singer achieve this tuning of the formant? We saw earlier that the first formant frequency could be raised by lowering the lower jaw and opening the mouth. Sundberg observed this action in a professional soprano. The singer was fitted with a helmet to which a bar was fastened; when her jaw opened, the bar bent, and a measuring device recorded the degree of movement. When the vowel [u] was sung at the pitch C$_4$, the jaw opening was 11 mm. As the pitch was raised to F$_5$, the jaw opening doubled (Fig. 12.15). The effect was to raise the formant frequency to keep it in tune with the fundamental of the sung note. A similar effect was noticed with the second formant, normally at a pitch around F$_5$ for this vowel. Once the second harmonic of the sung note reached this pitch, the second formant was moved upwards to follow it.

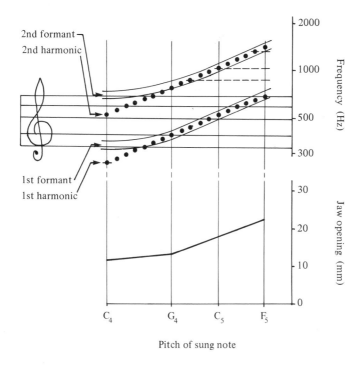

Fig 12.15. The relationship between formant tuning by a soprano and the opening of the jaw as the pitch of the vowel [u] rises. Based on Sundberg (1975), p.90, Fig.2, and p.94, Fig.6.

Stretching the mouth horizontally is an additional help in raising the formant frequencies, since it effectively shortens the vocal tract. This may lie behind the advice frequently given by singing teachers to 'smile' while singing high notes (Sundberg 1977).

Male singers probably also modify their vocal tract resonances in order to improve the volume and timbre of their sound output. However, if a male singer tries to tune his first formant accurately to the fundamental of the sung note, as a soprano does, he is liable to experience a shock – his larynx objects violently, and refuses to continue vibrating at that pitch (Ishizaka and Flanagan 1972; Sundberg 1981). The reason for this difference between male and female voices seems to be that there is more damping in the female vocal tract than in that of the male. As a result, the resonances of the male vocal tract are stronger and narrower (Fant 1972). When the vibration frequency of the vocal folds approaches one of these resonances, the large pressure variations in the standing wave exert a powerful influence on the vocal folds, disrupting their normal motion. The situation is then similar to that which produces a wolf note on a stringed instrument (p.212), and the consequences are equally unfortunate. Since the first formant pitch is normally in the treble clef region, this 'voice break' is most common among tenors.

It should in principle be possible for the vocal folds to interact with a set of strong and approximately harmonic vocal tract resonances in the same way that the lips of a trumpeter interact with the resonances of the instrument, setting up a co-operative regime of oscillation (see p.314). The resonances would then play a much more prominent part in determining the pitch of the note than in normal singing. It is possible that this mode of voice production is used by Tibetan monks who have developed the remarkable ability to accentuate certain harmonics of the source spectrum to such an extent that they become clearly audible as separate notes. The effect is that a single monk can apparently sing a chord (Crossley-Holland 1970).

Studies of this unusual singing technique have reported that the fundamental frequency of vocal fold vibration is typically around 70 Hz (near C_2) (Smith et al. 1967; Cogan 1984, pp.28–35). At such a low pitch the vocal folds are unusually relaxed, and therefore particularly susceptible to the pressures exerted by the vocal tract standing wave. In addition, vocal tract damping is particularly small for male voices at very low pitch (Fant 1972), so that the impedance of the vocal tract seen by the vocal folds at a formant peak will be unusually high. The coupling between voice source and vocal tract will therefore be much stronger than in normal singing.

In our discussion of brass instruments, we saw that the air column resonances of a trumpet were brought into an approximately harmonic relationship by appropriate shaping of the bore of the instrument. The vocal tract might be compared to a rubber trumpet, whose walls can be squeezed to alter the pitches of the formant resonances. In the Tibetan chanting technique, it appears that the vocal tract is shaped so that the first and second formants are exactly an octave apart. Smith et al. (1967) quote an example in which the first formant is pitched at $F^{\#}_4$, with the second at $F^{\#}_5$ (Fig. 12.16 (b)).

The vocal folds are vibrating in this case with a fundamental frequency of 75 Hz (D_2), which is a privileged tone of the vocal tract: although there is no resonance at the fundamental frequency, the fifth and tenth harmonics of the voice source coincide with the first and second formant resonances respectively. A co-operative regime of oscillation using these two resonances can thus stabilise the vibration of the vocal folds. From the source spectrum, containing all harmonics of D_2 (Fig. 12.16 (a)), the strong and narrow formants emphasise the components at pitches $F_4^{\#}$ and $F_5^{\#}$, which are dominant in the radiated vocal spectrum. The brain interprets these as first and second harmonics of a separate tone of pitch $F_4^{\#}$; the resulting sound is of the two note chord $D_2 F_4^{\#}$, (Fig. 12.16 (c)).

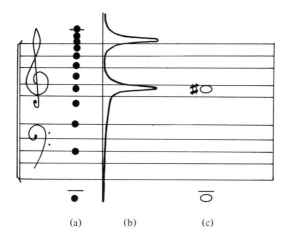

(a)   (b)   (c)

Fig. 12.16. (a) Harmonic components of the source spectrum at the pitch D_2.

(b) The first and second formants tuned to $F_4^{\#}$ and $F_5^{\#}$.

(c) The resulting impression of a two note chord.

This highly specialised singing technique, involving the simultaneous tuning of two formants and an unusual type of vocal fold vibration, has not so far found any application in Western music, and for male singers precise tuning of the first formant to a vocal source harmonic remains a danger to be avoided. Tuning of the second formant, however, is the basis of a novel vocal technique required by Stockhausen in his 'Stimmung' (1969) for six solo singers. Each singer is provided with a set of 'models', which include instructions on varying the timbre of a fixed pitch note. In an introductory explanation, Stockhausen makes it clear that what is required is an alteration of the vocal tract shape to emphasise particular components of the source spectrum. 'With enough practice', he comments, 'one can reach the point where the pitch one is singing is relatively soft and the dominating overtone relatively loud.' An example of a model for a male vocalist is shown in Fig. 12.17. The required timbre variation is indicated by phonetic vowel symbols. Above each symbol is a number representing the emphasised harmonic for a high pitched fundamental (around C_4). For a fundamental an octave or so lower, the harmonic emphasised by the same vocal tract shape will naturally have a higher number, shown below the vowel symbol. A comparison of Figs 12.9 and 12.17 (focusing on the lower set of numbers in Fig. 12.17) makes it clear that tuning of the second formant is the acoustical basis of the technique.

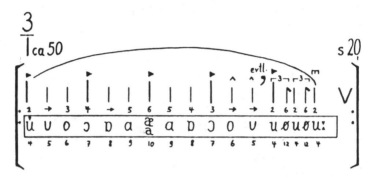

Fig. 12.17. One of the models from 'Stimmung' by Karlheinz Stockhausen (1969).

Head and chest resonances

Our discussion has concentrated on the resonances of the vocal tract formed by the larynx tube, the pharynx and the mouth. There are several other cavities within the head and chest which may play some role in modifying the timbre of the voice. The most important of these is the nasal cavity. In the production of the sung vowels which we have been discussing, the connecting passage between the throat and the nasal cavity is closed by the raising of the back of the soft palate. Opening this passage while singing these vowels produces the disagreeable sound usually described as 'singing through the nose'. The resonance of the nasal cavity is of great importance, however, in the production of the consonants 'm' and 'n', since for these sounds the mouth is closed and the primary radiators of sound are the nasal apertures (Flanagan 1972).

In the cheekbones, and in the part of the skull behind the forehead, are several additional hollow passages known collectively as the *sinuses*. Whether resonances of the sinuses have a significant effect on vocal timbre is a matter of continuing controversy (Troup 1981, p.385). Some singing teachers consider that the sinuses are responsible for a 'head resonance' which gives additional brilliance to the voice by strengthening the upper harmonics. On the other hand, singers who performed with the cheekbone sinuses half-filled with water and with the nasal passages stuffed with gauze to dampen their resonances were judged by a panel of experts to have unimpaired vocal quality (Vennard 1967). (The trials willingly undertaken by singers in the interests of science make those of Pamina and Tamino seem trivial in comparison!)

Although more study of this subject is required, it seems probable that the direct effect of sinus resonances on vocal timbre is small. The brilliance ascribed to the 'head resonance' is due to the combination of a sufficiently spiky voice source waveform and the resonances of the vocal tract that have already been described. Nevertheless, the sensation of a strong response in the sinuses of the singer when this type of sound is produced is undoubtedly a real one, and may well act as an important guide to the performer by providing an internal signal confirming that the correct adjustment of voice source and vocal tract has been achieved.

Another region in which a strong internal response is sensed by a singer is the chest. The opening and closing of the vocal folds generates variations of pressure below the larynx as well as above, and the pressure variations in the lungs pump the chest wall in and out. Measurements by Sundberg (1979) have shown that the amplitude of the chest wall vibration follows closely that of the fundamental of the voice source spectrum. The vibrations are strongest near the sternum (the breast bone), and Sundberg suggests that vibration sensitive corpuscles in the subcutaneous tissue covering the sternum can sense the tiny displacements involved (of the order of a thousandth of a millimetre). The sensitivity of these corpuscles is known to fall off quickly above 300 Hz, which agrees with the fact that chest vibrations can normally be sensed only for loud singing at pitches below about G_4.

Although the chest wall vibrations are probably too small to contribute directly to the sound output of the singer, they can provide another internal signal to assist in the control of the voice. In loud operatic singing the performer increases the fraction of each vibration cycle during which the vocal folds are closed, thereby increasing the relative strength of the upper harmonics in the source spectrum (see Fig. 12.6). If this 'pressed' type of singing is carried too far, the sound will become harsh and lacking in body. The amplitude of the fundamental will then be too low to generate detectable chest vibration, and the sense of chest resonance will disappear. A strongly felt chest vibration is thus a signal to the singer that the vocal folds are vibrating correctly.

13

Electronic instruments

There are two distinct ways in which electronics are used in the production of musical sounds (Ernst 1977; Crowhurst 1975). In the first of these the electronic circuits are used simply to amplify the signal from some form of pick-up or microphone which is placed on or near an instrument. In this case the musical tones are generated by a vibrating mechanical system or air mass rather than by electronic circuits. We shall deal with arrangements of this type only very briefly. In the second way, electronic circuits are used to generate and shape the waveforms themselves before they are passed to a power amplifier and ultimately to loudspeakers. These are the true electronic instruments and what we shall be primarily concerned with in this chapter.

The sounds produced by most early electronic instruments were generally considered by musicians to be simulations of acoustic instruments and rather poor simulations at that. This brought electronic music as a whole into disrepute as far as the more serious musicians and listeners were concerned. In more recent times, however, electronic instruments have been made capable of very much more realistic simulations. Also they have come to be more and more accepted in their own right and for the unique sound qualities which they can produce. The electronic organ, for example, is now included as one of the instruments for which students can sit the London College of Music grade examinations.

The two most important electronic instruments used today are the organ and the synthesizer and in the following sections we shall outline the principles of their operation. This will be without reference to any specific makers or models, since there is a bewildering variety of these and new versions come on the market almost weekly. Both the organ and the synthesizer use the keyboard as their primary control element, this being universally accepted as the simplest means of varying the pitch. Synthesizers which do not use a keyboard have been produced, but none have proved very successful, except for the drum synthesizer, which is now frequently used in place of the conventional drum kit in pop groups. Guitar synthesizers, which use strings and a fingerboard like the normal guitar, have been produced but are seen only quite rarely. These are effectively hybrid systems, using the vibrating string to produce the embryo signal and electronic circuits to change the waveforms by sophisticated signal processing.

ELECTRO-ACOUSTIC INSTRUMENTS

Microphones

The most straightforward way of increasing the sound level from an acoustic instrument is to place a microphone in close proximity and then pass the signal to loudspeakers via an amplifier. Most systems incorporate some means of filtering out signals in different frequency bands so that the response characteristics of the microphone, amplifier and speaker can all be matched to the room characteristics and microphone position. Virtually all amplifiers have treble and bass frequency attenuators, i.e. high and low pass filters, but these give only a rather limited degree of control. More sophisticated arrangements incorporate a graphic equaliser, which is a bank of narrow band filters covering the complete audio range. By setting the attenuation level of each filter individually, any required frequency response characteristic can be achieved.

When using a microphone to amplify acoustic instruments or the voice, the musician's main enemy is feedback, that ear piercing whistle which is often heard when an amateur is setting up the equipment. This occurs when sound issuing from the loudspeakers is picked up by the microphone. If the amplifier gain is high, then this sound is further amplified and comes out even louder from the speakers. An unstable loop is created in which even the tiniest of sounds quickly builds up beyond the overload point. Feedback is generally avoided by using a unidirectional microphone, i.e. one which is only sensitive to sounds from one direction. The directional characteristics of a microphone are generally specified by means of a polar diagram showing its sensitivity at different angles; this specification is an important consideration when making a purchase.

Three different types of microphones are commonly used for amplification purposes (the letters PA, standing for public address, are normally used). These are the *dynamic*, the *ribbon* and the *condenser* microphones. The dynamic type is the most popular, probably because of its robustness and relatively modest cost. The diaphragm is attached to a small coil of wire which is free to move between the poles of a magnet. When activated by sound waves, the coil vibrates and a small current is generated in its windings, giving rise to the alternative name, *moving coil* microphone. As it stands, this arrangement is omnidirectional, but a heart shaped or *cardioid* directional characteristic can be achieved by using a suitable casing and inserting acoustically absorbing pads at the rear.

Ribbon microphones tend to be less robust and often bulky in size, so they are more extensively used for studio recording purposes. They employ a very thin metal ribbon suspended between the poles of a magnet which generates a current when it vibrates. The output effectively registers the velocity of the air vibrations rather than the pressure; hence the term *velocity* microphone. Ribbon microphones are bidirectional, with a polar directionality diagram resembling a figure of eight, but they can be made effectively unidirectional by inserting acoustically absorbing pads on one side of the ribbon.

Condenser (or capacitor) microphones tend to be very expensive but are often of very high quality. The flexible diaphragm forms one plate of a capacitor, the other being a rigid backplate spaced a short distance away. The capacitance formed from the two plates, known as a capsule, is included as one element of an electrical circuit so that the diaphragm vibrations register as voltage changes. This means that a power supply is required to maintain the polarising voltage across the capsule. Because the sensitivity is extremely low, a pre-amplifier is generally included in the microphone housing. A range of directional characteristics can be achieved by changing the polarising voltage (Jenkins and Smith 1975). The fragility of the diaphragm and the need for a power supply make the condenser microphone most popular for studio and laboratory application. A variant which eliminates the need for a polarising supply voltage is the prepolarised condenser microphone frequently referred to as the *electret* microphone. An electret is a material which can permanently sustain an electric charge rather as a permanent magnet can retain its magnetism. The charge carrying electret must be placed between the two plates and in practice usually takes the form of a thin layer of material fixed to the backplate. Electret microphones are frequently very small in size and have their own battery operated pre-amplifier built into the casing (Freeman et al. 1973).

It is worth briefly mentioning two other types of microphone which are commonly encountered, the *carbon* and the *crystal*, although they have little application in the performance of music. Carbon microphones are used in telephones and have a very poor frequency response. Crystal microphones do not suffer this disadvantage but are omnidirectional, so their main application is limited to cheap tape recorders.

We have stressed the importance of arranging microphone positions so that they do not pick up sound from the loudspeakers, otherwise feedback will occur. This can easily be avoided by having the loudspeakers located close to the front of the stage and facing the audience, with the microphones located on the stage but facing in the opposite direction. This ensures that the polar directionality plots for the output of the loudspeakers do not overlap those for the microphone sensivity. An immediate problem then faces the performer. It is imperative that he should be able to hear the output from the loudspeakers clearly and without undue time lapse due to wall reflections, otherwise intonation, timing and balance will all be impaired. This problem is usually overcome by using monitor speakers which have the sole purpose of relaying a small proportion of the overall sound directly to the performer. If these are placed at the front of the stage facing the performer, then their sound is not picked up to any great extent by the microphones which are facing in the same direction, provided of course that the latter are of the unidirectional type.

Before leaving the topic of microphones, it should be mentioned that it is sometimes desirable to have one connected directly to a wind instrument. The most successful application here has been with flutes. The miniature microphone in this case is usually connected to the vibrating air column by means of a narrow tube which passes through a hole in the cork. In effect one is inserting a probe microphone into the headjoint. Similar arrangements have been used on the mouthpieces of saxophones, clarinets and even trombones but have not found much favour amongst players. A problem here is that the internal pressure vibrations do not precisely match those of the radiated sound and so the timbre is changed. The advantage of such a scheme is that it allows the player freedom of movement and also reduces feedback, since the amplifier gain need not be set as high. It also virtually eliminates the effects of background noise, a primary consideration if the performer wants to move about the stage, which he often does in pop music. Even if microphone stands have rubber feet, they tend to transmit floor vibrations to the microphone and every tap of the foot or footstep comes through the loudspeakers as an annoying thud.

Pickups

Transducers designed to register the mechanical vibrations of some part of an instrument, rather than the radiated sound waves, are usually referred to as pickups, by far the most common example being the magnetic guitar pickup. The single coil guitar pickup is the simplest in form and may be found, for example, on the Fender Telecaster. The coil is wound over a bobbin which has six holes in it to take the metal polepieces which are magnetised by a strong permanent magnet underneath. The polepieces are often threaded so that their heights may be adjusted and are positioned at about ½mm below each string. As a string vibrates above its polepiece it varies the magnetic field passing through the coil and generates an electrical signal. This passes to the output socket via volume and tone controls located on the guitar body. The principle of operation is similar to that used in early telephone receivers, the diaphragm simply being replaced by the strings. The positioning of the pickup along the length of the string is clearly of importance. When placed close to one end, it tends to accentuate higher modes, whereas a more central position gives stronger lower modes. Most electric guitars in fact have two or more pickups located in different positions along the strings, their outputs being combined in appropriate proportions using a mixing circuit. The standard pickup tends to be rather prone to electrical hum, a problem which is overcome in the more elaborate *humbucking pickup* used on Gibson guitars. This has two separate coils positioned adjacent to each other with the windings in reverse directions and connected in series. Each has a set of six polepieces which are magnetised with reverse polarities by a single magnet underneath. The arrangement has a noise cancelling effect which improves the overall sound quality, although the increased number of windings increases the electrical inductance, which has the effect of damping higher frequency components. A fundamental limitation of the magnetic pickups just described is that they can only be used with steel strings. Nylon or gut strings will not affect the magnetic field and hence no signal will be produced when they are plucked.

Another type of pickup which may be used is commonly referred to as a *bug* and is designed to make direct contact with some vibrating part of the instrument. This operates in a manner similar to the cartridge on a record player, generally being either magnetic or piezoelectric. Magnetic bugs are in effect miniaturised dynamic microphones, although it is possible to have the magnet, rather than the coil, as the vibrating element. The piezoelectric transducer uses a tiny crystal which generates an electrical signal when stressed by the movements of its support. The whole unit may be so tiny that it can be cemented into the bridge of say a violin by drilling a small hole. Generally, though, bugs are either glued or clamped on to the body of an instrument. They are most frequently seen on violins and nylon strung acoustic guitars, although they can in principle be used to amplify almost any instrument. They have, for example, been fitted to the soundboard of harps with some success. There are also bugs specifically designed to fix under the ligature of a saxophone or clarinet mouthpiece and respond to the reed vibrations. A major problem in the application of a bug is that the signal it generates is highly dependent on its exact position on the instrument. Depending on whether it is close to a node or an antinode, a particular frequency component will be suppressed or accentuated. In practice a good deal of experimentation is required to obtain a satisfactory overall sound. Another problem is that bugs are prone to feedback problems since when attached to the instrument they act just like microphones.

Many musicians and listeners alike are critical of the whole concept of amplification applied to musical instruments, mainly on the grounds that it is quality not volume that one is looking for. Certainly it is true that the finer subtleties of the sound from an acoustic instrument are lost when electrical amplification is used. However, probably the most important point about using amplification is that it gives the player the opportunity of modifying the sound by electronic signal processing units. All manner of processing units are now available on the market, including artificial reverberation, vibrato, tremolo and fuzz, (a deliberate clipping of the signal peaks to cause distortion). For further details refer to Jenkins and Smith (1975).

EARLY ELECTRONIC INSTRUMENTS

It was the invention of the wireless valve by Lee de Forest in 1906 that led to the possibility of producing music electronically. With his triode vacuum tube, electrical circuits could be built which amplified small signals, the amplifier being the basic component of any electronic system. However, it was not until twenty years after Lee de Forest's invention that the first real commercial electronic instrument appeared. This was the *etherophone*, invented by the Russian scientist Leon Theremin (Schrader 1982). It is now usually referred to as the *theremin* after its inventor. The theremin had two antennae, one in the form of a horizontal loop used for varying loudness, and the other a vertical rod, used for varying the pitch. These responded to the proximity of the left and right hands respectively of the thereminist, giving rise to a high frequency electrical signal of variable amplitude and frequency. This was mixed, or added, to a fixed frequency signal so as to produce a lower frequency beat which was in the audio range and could be fed to the loudspeaker. These instruments were sold on the market in a simplified form and in fact in the 1930s one could buy a combined theremin and electric gramophone. With this the user could play a melody on the instrument, accompanied by the gramophone. A major problem with the theremin was that playing it was extremely difficult, since the exact positions of the hands had to be found in mid-air, so to speak, without reference to a fingerboard such as one has on a guitar or violin. The theremin was a monophonic instrument, i.e. only one note could be played at a time, as opposed to the polyphonic instruments on which chords could be played. The player had immediate control over pitch and volume but only limited control over timbre. This was by means of a switch which filtered out certain harmonics, rather like the tone control on a radio. Despite its shortcomings, the theremin enjoyed a life of over thirty years.

Shortly after the theremin came a rather similar but more sophisticated instrument known as the *ondes musicales* (musical waves) or *ondes Mar-*

tenot. This was invented in France by Maurice Martenot and was first exhibited in 1928. The player wore a ring on the finger of the right hand and the position of this controlled the pitch, much as on the theremin. Other models were also introduced using either a dummy keyboard or a keyboard with notes which could be moved laterally to vary the pitch. The great advantage of the ondes Martenot was that the player could obtain a wide range of timbres. The quality of the sound from this instrument was such that it became accepted by leading composers of the time. Honegger, Milhaud, Koechlin and Messiaen all wrote works making use of this instrument.

In 1930 Dr F. Trautwein produced an instrument known as the *Trautonium* in Germany. This made use of a different idea for varying the pitch. A wire was stretched over a metal rail and when this was pressed down with the finger a note sounded whose pitch was determined by the position of contact. With this method it was possible to obtain a good degree of control and in fact the ribbon control used on some modern synthesizers is just a modification of this. A good range of timbres was also available and later models were duophonic, i.e. could produce two separate notes simultaneously. Hindemith himself played the trautonium and his compositions for the instrument include the Concerto for Solo Trautonium and String Orchestra.

ELECTRONIC ORGANS AND SYNTHESIZERS

The forerunner of the modern electronic organ was the Hammond organ introduced in America in 1935. This used a series of 91 rotating iron discs known as *tone wheels*, driven by a single synchronous motor. The periphery of each disc was cut rather like rounded off teeth on a cog wheel; as the disc rotated near a coil wound on a permanent magnet, it induced a sinusoidally fluctuating current in the coil. The wheels had different numbers of teeth so that tones of each pitch in the scale could be produced. These were then combined to form sounds of different timbre by adding appropriate components using a drawbar system.

Additive synthesis

The method of adding component sine waves to construct a complex wave of given spectral characteristics, which was employed on the early Hammond organs, is known as additive synthesis. Modern organs use the same idea, the only difference being that the component waves are produced by electronic oscillator circuits. Any periodic wave can be constructed from the sum of component sine waves having frequencies which are integer multiples of the fundamental f_0, i.e. f_0, $2f_0$, $3f_0$, etc. (see p.18). The greater the number of component frequencies, the closer one can get to any required complex waveform. The form of the complex wave depends on the relative phases of the components, although in practice varying the phase of any one component has an insignificant aural effect. For this reason it is only the component amplitudes which are controlled, normally with a bank of drawbars, the phase being arbitrary. Fig. 13.1 shows a typical layout for the drawbars and the pitches they will sound, assuming that the 8′ drawbar sounds C_3. Drawbars are labelled using the footage notation as used on a pipe organ. The 8′ register is considered to be the fundamental. Since the frequency of oscillation in a pipe is inversely proportional to its length, the footage markings on the upper harmonics are $^8/_2 = 4$, $^8/_3 = 2^2/_3$, $^8/_4 = 2$, $^8/_5 = 1^3/_5$, $^8/_6 = 1^1/_3$ and $^8/_8 = 1$. The seventh harmonic is normally left out since it is not in tune with a note on the equally tempered scale. Most organs have two additional drawbars, a 16′ subtone an octave below the fundamental and a $5^1/_3′$ tone which is the third harmonic of this subtone. In Fig. 13.1 drawbars 2, 4 and 7 are shown fully extended, indicating that the amplitudes of these tones is a maximum. The other drawbars are shown half extended, i.e. the amplitudes of these components is only half that of the fundamental. The frequencies of the different drawbar tones correspond to the pitches of the notes shown in Fig. 13.1 on the equally tempered scale, rather than to the frequencies of the true harmonics, although we shall refer to them as harmonics in accord with normal convention. This means that only one oscillator frequency is needed for each note in the scale, the drawbars being used simply to

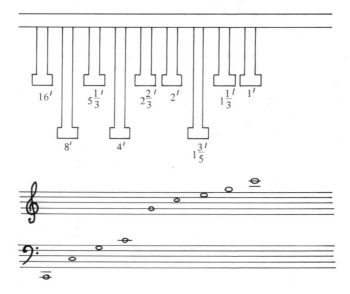

Fig. 13.1. Drawbars used on an electronic organ with the notes that they sound when the fundamental 8′ tone is C_3.

add them in different combinations. In practice only twelve oscillators need to be used, covering all the notes in the scale for the highest octave. The signals for notes in the lower octaves are obtained from these by an electronic process of frequency division. This not only reduces the number of components required but simplifies the process of tuning the oscillators and eliminates the problem of notes in different octaves being out of tune with each other.

In some organs wave shaping circuits are used to modify the sine waves coming from the different drawbars. This effectively introduces more upper harmonics and so limits the number of drawbars required, although at the expense of some loss of flexibility. Fig. 13.2 shows waveforms produced by a low cost organ which has only four drawbars on the upper manual, 16′, 8′, 5⅓′ and 4′. The note played is A_4, this being the middle A on the upper manual. Figure 13.2 (a) shows the waveform when only the 8′ drawbar is withdrawn. This is a wave of frequency 440 Hz, almost a pure sine wave but not exactly, indicating the presence of some upper harmonics. Figure 13.2 (b) shows the waveform for the same note when only the 5⅓′ drawbar is used. Since this gives the fifth above, its frequency is $440 \times \frac{3}{2} = 660$ Hz, i.e. for every two waves of the 8′ note there are three for the 5⅓′ note. Notice that for this note the waveform is more triangular in form than sinusoidal, showing strong components of upper harmonics. In Fig. 13.2 (c) the waveform is shown for the two drawbars withdrawn together. The combined wave is much more complex than before and the

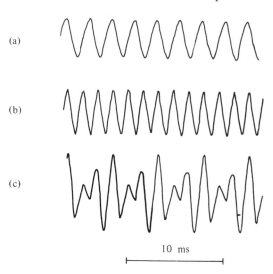

(a)

(b)

(c)

10 ms

Fig. 13.2. Waveforms produced by a low cost electronic organ playing A_4 with (a) the 8′ drawbar withdrawn, (b) the 5⅓′ drawbar withdrawn and (c) both the 8′ and 5⅓′ drawbars withdrawn together.

sound much fuller. Its frequency is now 220 Hz, i.e. half of the fundamental, so the note sounds an octave lower. This is because the 5⅓' drawbar gives a tone which is the third harmonic of the 16' subtone but is not a harmonic of the 8' fundamental. If the waveform of the tone from the 5⅓' drawbar is complex in form as in Fig. 13.2 (b), then each component frequency is a harmonic of the 16' subtone. In fact it might be more logical to refer to the 16' pitch as the fundamental and the 8' pitch as its second harmonic.

Transients

On an electronic organ there is normally a set of switches, referred to as tabs, which are marked as *percussion*. These are used to produce tones which have percussive characteristics, i.e. the tones have sharp starting transients. The word percussion here is not used to indicate that any percussion instrument such as a drum is being simulated. Most frequently there are two attack times, long and short, and two or three harmonics on which percussion sounds can be produced, e.g. 4' and 5⅓'. When added to the non-percussive tones from the drawbars or from other tabs representing specific musical instruments, these give the sounds more definition and bite. The percussion tones are one of the characteristic features of the Hammond organ. In addition to the percussion there are tabs labelled *sustain*. These operate in one of two different ways. Most frequently they sustain all the sounds for a short period after the key release so that they do not die instantaneously to zero. In this case there are generally two levels of sustain, either short or long. Alternatively they produce independent sounds which ring on after the key release and can be added to the tones from the other tabs and drawbars. Generally when playing the organ a certain amount of both percussion and sustain are used, as without these the sound tends to be lifeless. The exact amounts used depend not only on the musical context but also on the loudspeaker system and the room acoustics.

With the synthesizer, more sophisticated means of producing transients have been developed and these are available on some modern organs. If the sounds from actual musical instruments are to be realistically reproduced then it is essential that both the starting and finishing transients are faithfully simulated. The transient is produced by an envelope generator which modulates or varies the amplitude of the waveform according to the settings of a number of separate controls. Generally there are four independent controls for attack time, decay time, sustain level and release time, labelled A, D, S and R respectively. In this case one refers to an *ADSR envelope generator*. The function of the four controls is shown in Fig. 13.3. When the key is depressed an electrical signal referred to as a gating pulse is produced which starts the note sounding. The signal then takes a finite time A to reach its peak amplitude, A being referred to as the *attack time*. After this it falls gradually to a *sustain level* S, over a time D, known as the *decay time*. The amplitude of the signal is maintained constant at the sustain level until the key is released, at which point the gating pulse returns to its original level. On the release of the key the amplitude dies gradualliy to zero over a time R, referred to as the *release time*. By varying the four parameters it is possible to obtain a very wide variety of transient shapes and in practice one can normally match the amplitude contour relevant to any particular instrument closely enough to obtain an aurally realistic simulation.

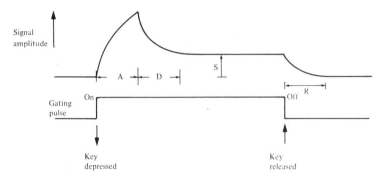

Fig. 13.3 The ADSR envelope generator.

The signal from the ADSR generator is used to vary the gain of a *voltage controlled amplifier* (VCA) whose input is the continuous waveform produced by the oscillators and other components associated with that particular note. If, for example, the input signal is a pure sine wave as shown in Fig. 13.4, then the output is a sine wave whose amplitude is varying according to the settings of the four parameters A, D, S and R. Notice that the ADSR pattern as shown in Fig. 13.3 must be mirrored about the baseline in order to obtain the outline shape of the final signal. This is because both the positive and negative parts of the sine wave are varied by the VCA. Since adjacent positive and negative peaks undergo different amounts of amplification at times when the transient is rising and falling sharply, the outline of the output waveforms may not appear completely symmetric. This gives rise to rather complex looking signals when the input is not a pure sine wave. Fig. 13.5 shows the output recorded from a synthesizer playing the note A_4, where the envelope generator parameters were set approximately to A = 80 ms, D = 100 ms, S = 280 mV and R = 70 ms. The sustain level is measured relative to the peak voltage, which can be varied simply by adjusting the gain of the output amplifier. In this case the peak voltage was set to 1V.

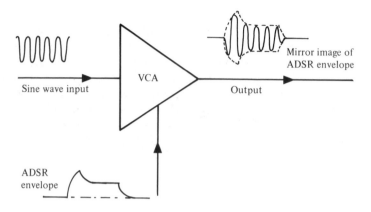

Fig. 13.4. Input and output from a VCA controlled by an ADSR envelope generator.

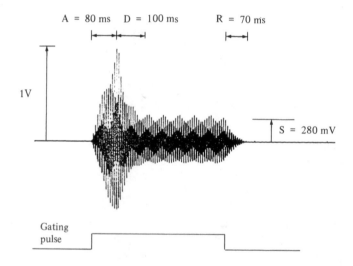

Fig. 13.5. Waveform from a synthesizer having an ADSR envelope generator showing the settings of the four variable transient parameters.

Although the ADSR type of generator is the most common, there are numerous variants which are used. Additional features often encountered are *delay* and *hold*. These simply alter the 'on' and 'off' times of the gating pulse (Fig. 13.3) in relation to the times at which the key is depressed and released. Generally the two facilities are not found together in the same module but either one or the other is found separately. Fig. 13.6 (a) shows how the gating pulse onset, which controls the envelope generator, starts later when a delay is incorporated. With the hold facility in operation (Fig. 13.6 (b)), the gating pulse is not switched off until some time after the key release. Sometimes the decay and sustain are not incorporated, in which case the generator is said to be of the AR type. Generators of this form are commonly used with a delay facility. Fig. 13.7 (a) shows the envelope waveform in this case. Another common alternative is the AD generator. Here the waveform rises to its maximum value over the attack time A (Fig. 13.7 (b)) and then immediately begins to fall back to the zero level. With an AD generator the signal is unaffected by the time of key release.

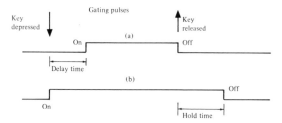

Fig. 13.6. Timing of the gating pulse 'on' and 'off' switching when (a) delay and (b) hold are incorporated.

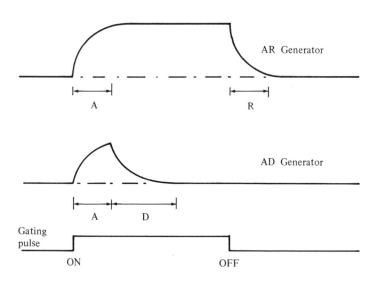

Fig. 13.7. Waveforms produced by envelope generators of the AR and AD type.

Vibrato

Even the very early electronic organs incorporated a vibrato facility, for without this the sound is very dead, unless a Leslie loudspeaker system is used, as described later in this chapter. Vibrato is introduced by modulating, i.e. periodically varying, the frequency of the oscillator signal (referred to as the carrier). The modulating frequency is normally a few cycles per second and can often be varied over a limited range. The effect on the signal is shown in Fig. 13.8 (a). For comparison, the rather similar effect generally referred to as *tremolo* is shown in Fig. 13.8 (b). Here it is the amplitude of the signal rather than the frequency which is periodically varied. The flexibility of the modern synthesizer allows for both vibrato and tremolo. Readers who are familiar with radio transmission will know these as FM (frequency modulation) and AM (amplitude modulation) respectively.

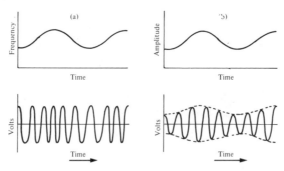

Fig. 13.8. Modulation of the oscillator signal: (a) frequency modulation (vibrato) and (b) amplitude modulation (tremolo).

Computer controlled systems

The advent of the microcomputer has now made it possible to build much more flexible systems based on the concept of additive synthesis, where the oscillators and transient wave shaping components are computer controlled. Fig. 13.9 shows the overall layout of such a scheme, referred to as hybrid since it is partly digital and partly analogue, i.e. it uses both a digital computer and components designed to give a continuously varying voltage output.

The main sound generators are a series of sine wave oscillators whose frequencies are set to correspond to notes covering the full audio range. The amplitudes of these oscillators are controlled by the microcomputer, which is programmed to give suitable combinations of fundamental and upper harmonics when a particular note is played on the keyboard. The operator uses a control unit to input information on harmonic structure. Sinusoidal signals from the oscillators pass through voltage controlled amplifiers which vary their amplitudes in order to produce transient effects, the final signal being the sum of the waveforms from all the VCAs.

The great advantage of the computer controlled system lies in its flexibility. Any number of harmonic components can be introduced and the transients can be of arbitrary shape. It is also possible to have different transient shapes for the various harmonics. This facility helps in the realistic simulation of some acoustic instruments, e.g. the piano, where it is known that the mid-range tones die less rapidly than the extreme low and high frequency components (see p.249).

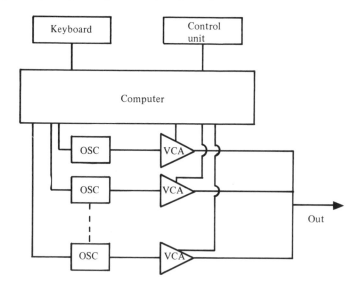

Fig. 13.9. Computer controlled system for additive synthesis.

Subtractive synthesis

The main drawback of the additive synthesis technique is that a large number of harmonic components may be required to produce waveforms of any given shape. In an electronic organ, where the component amplitudes are set by drawbars, it is not practical to have more than about ten components. Furthermore, these components are not in general all true harmonics of the notes being played, since the fundamental tones need to be set to a tempered scale and the drawbars effectively just add these tones in different combinations. This is also true of the computer controlled system. This problem is overcome in the method of subtractive synthesis which is used in most modern synthesizers (Graham 1980; Wells 1981; Strange 1972).

In subtractive synthesis one starts with complex waveforms which have

511

many spectral components which are not required. This method only requires one oscillator for each note and, since the signal from each oscillator is periodic, one is assured that the spectral components of the final wave will be true multiples of the fundamental frequency. The most commonly used source waveforms and their spectra are shown in Fig. 13.10. The simplest of these is the sine wave, which has a single peak in its spectrum at a frequency of 1/T Hz, where T is the period of the wave measured in seconds. This is assuming that the wave oscillates symmetrically about zero volts. If the mean value is not zero, then this shows

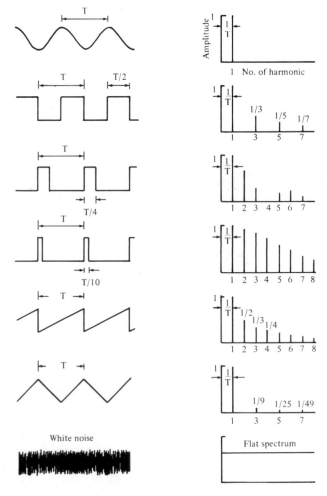

Fig. 13.10. The waveforms most commonly used on the synthesizer, together with their harmonic spectra. The period of each wave is T and the amplitudes of the spectral components are shown with the fundamental amplitude normalised to unity.

up as a peak at zero frequency on the spectrum. For practical purposes, however, this is of no great importance since all the circuits in a synthesizer are AC coupled, i.e. they only respond to voltage fluctuations. For this reason zero frequency components have been ignored in all of the spectra. The square wave has a much more complex spectrum, although in some ways it is easier to produce electronically since there are only two voltage levels for the signal.

A square wave can thus be produced by alternating a switch between the 'on' and 'off' positions. Form the spectrum it is seen that only the odd numbered harmonics are present. For comparing the amplitudes, it is usual to normalise the spectrum by making the amplitude of the fundamental equal to unity. The amplitude of the third harmonic is then $\frac{1}{3}$, of the fifth harmonic $\frac{1}{5}$, etc. With the pulse wave again there are only two voltage levels, the percentage time for which the signal is in the higher level being referred to as the *duty cycle*. For the two pulse waves shown, the duty cycles are 25% and 10%, i.e. the pulse widths are T/4 and T/10 respectively, where T is the period. The spectrum for a pulse wave has both odd and even harmonics, the strength of the upper harmonics being greater for waves with a shorter duty cycle. In the limit as the duty cycle approaches 0%, the harmonics will all have the same strength. The spectrum of the sawtooth wave again has both odd and even harmonics. In this case the amplitude of the nth harmonics is $1/n$. The triangular waveform is the one which most closely resembles the sine wave. It has only odd harmonics and the amplitudes of these are very much less than they are for the square wave. The third harmonic has amplitude $(\frac{1}{3})^2$, the fifth harmonic $(\frac{1}{5})^2$, etc. The final signal shown in Fig. 13.10 is white noise. This is not strictly speaking a wave, since there is no period of oscillation. It contains all frequencies within the range of the generator's response curve, so its spectrum is theoretically a straight line terminating at the upper limit of this response.

Filters

Four basic types of filters, low pass, high pass, band pass and band reject, are used for shaping the complex waveforms. The frequency characteristics of these are shown in Fig. 13.11, where the vertical axis represents the output power in dB measured with the input power as reference. Where the curves are at 0 dB the frequency components pass through without change in amplitude, but at other points they are attenuated. Filters on a synthesizer are normally voltage controlled, so for the low and high pass filters the cutoff points are continuously adjustable and in the case of the band pass and band reject filters both the centre frequency and the bandwidth may be varied. The rate at which the filter shape 'rolls off' from unity towards zero determines the sharpness of cutoff and depends on

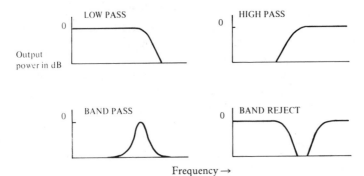

Fig. 13.11. The four basic filters used for shaping complex waveforms in a synthesizer.

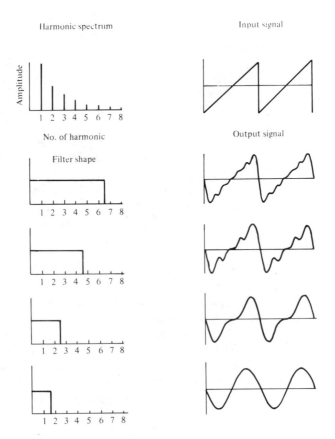

Fig. 13.12. A sawtooth waveform with different components eliminated by low pass filtering.

the precise details of the electrical circuit employed. The simplest filters have a roll-off of –6 dB per octave, meaning that a frequency change corresponding to one octave is associated with a halving of the wave amplitude in the region where the filter shape is a straight sloping line. Such a cutoff rate is considered too weak for many applications and most synthesizers employ filters which have either a –12 dB or –24 dB per octave roll-off.

As an example of how filtering alters the shape of a complex signal, Fig. 13.12 shows a sawtooth waveform after varying amounts of low pass filtering. For the purpose of illustration it has been assumed that the cut-off is very sharp, so that the harmonics are completely eliminated if they are outside the filter bandwidth. It will be seen that six harmonic components give a reasonable approximation to the sawtooth, although the sharp corners are rounded. With only two components the output bears little resemblance to the original input. The final stage of the filtering is when only the fundamental remains, in which case the output is a pure sine wave.

Analogue synthesizers

The term synthesizer is generally used to mean a complete instrument which operates on the subtractive synthesis principle. Early designs were monophonic, i.e. only one note could be played at a time, but most modern synthesizers are polyphonic, allowing a number of notes to be played simultaneously. The main signal generating unit in the synthesizer is referred to as the *voice module* (Crombie 1982 and 1984). This contains a number of voltage controlled modules, a typical arrangement being shown in Fig. 13.13. At the heart of the voice module are two *voltage controlled oscillators* (VCO 1 and VCO 2). These can be set to produce any of the periodic waveforms shown in Fig. 13.10. The signals from the two oscillators and the noise source are added together to produce a single waveform in the *mixer*. The two VCOs are not phase related and are generally set to give frequencies of a few Hertz difference. This leads to beating effects and results in more lively sounds than can be produced with a single oscillator. The frequencies of these oscillators are set by the control voltage from the keyboard, which is different for each note, a variation of 1V per octave being common. In addition to this, small variations in frequency can be introduced by using a *low frequency oscillator* (LFO) for vibrato effects. The complex signal from the mixer is shaped using the *voltage controlled filter* (VCF), which can be set to the various filter shapes shown in Fig. 13.11. The control voltage determines the cutoff or centre frequency and can be varied either using some form of adjustable potentiometer or by feeding in a voltage from the keyboard or one of the other modules. Finally the signal passes through the *voltage controlled amplifier* (VCA) for producing transient effects. The control voltage here is given by an envelope generator, e.g. one of the ADSR type as shown in Fig. 13.3.

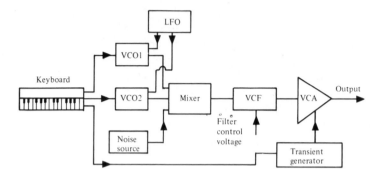

Fig. 13.13. A typical layout for a synthesizer voice module.

The use of separate voltage controlled modules gives the synthesizer a great deal of flexibility since there is generally a facility for connecting these in different ways. This is often done by a process of *patching*, which involves making cross-connections on a display panel using purpose designed connectors. In this way, for example, it would be possible to use the LFO to periodically vary the cutoff or centre frequency of the VCF or to introduce amplitude modulation using the VCA. One interesting effect is referred to as *cross-modulation*. In this, one of the VCOs is used to frequency modulate the other, the modulation rate being much greater than is produced by the more usual application of the LFO. This high frequency modulation produces additional frequencies known as side bands which are within the audible range but are not in general harmonics of the fundamental note. The effect is that of a clanging sound useful sometimes in the simulation of gongs and bells and for special effects.

Monophonic synthesizers have only one voice module, whereas polyphonic instruments have a number of separate modules, usually four to sixteen. Since there are generally more notes on the keyboard than voice modules, a priority scheme is used to determine which notes sound. Usually the note played last will have priority and will always sound, robbing one of the previously played notes of sound. On most instruments there is only one set of controls, so that each note produces the same tone quality. This is referred to as a homogeneous system. Some sophisticated modern instruments used a microcomputer to control the individual voice modules, which gives extreme flexibility and allows a single performer to generate sounds of almost orchestral dimensions.

516

Ring modulation

The primary function of the mixer is to add signals from the two oscilla-tors and the noise source. However, on some synthesizers the mixer can also be used for multiplying the two oscillator signals, a function known as *ring modulation*. Multiplying two signals results in sum and difference frequencies: e.g., if two sine waves of frequency 1 kHz and 100 Hz are multiplied together, the result is a wave which has two peaks in its spectrum at 900 Hz and 1100 Hz. In effect multiplying the 1 kHz wave by the lower frequency has produced an amplitude modulation which is the same as the beating effect when two waves of 900 Hz and 1100 Hz are summed. This is rather similar to cross-modulation, since components in the spectrum are produced which are not harmonically related to the fundamental note. The resulting sound is often described as 'metallic'.

Ring modulation may be used with any complex waveforms. Fig. 13.14 shows an example when a square wave of frequency 1760 Hz (A_6) has been ring modulated with a square wave of frequency approximately 200 Hz. The minimum value of the latter is zero, so that it behaves effectively as an on-off switch. The resulting waveform (Fig. 13.14 (a)) is a square wave of frequency 1760 Hz which stops and starts approximately every four and a half cycles. The resulting spectrum is shown in Fig. 13.14 (b). Notice that in addition to the peak at the fundamental frequency there are two strong peaks at 1760 + 200 = 1960 Hz and 1760 − 200 = 1560 Hz. There are also corresponding peaks for the third harmonic of A_6. A detailed analysis of the situation is a little complicated because sum and difference frequency components arise between all the harmonics of the two waves.

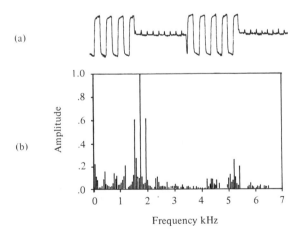

Fig. 13.14. The effect of ring modulating two square waves of frequency 1760 Hz (A_6) and 200 Hz: (a) the resulting waveform, (b) the frequency spectrum.

517

Digital synthesizers

In all the systems which have been described so far, the signal is produced by an analogue device, i.e. a circuit which gives a continuously varying electric current. With the modern high speed computer, complex waveforms can be produced digitally, i.e. as a series of numbers within the machine (Howe 1975; Manning 1985). These are then converted to a continuous signal by means of a digital-to-analogue (D to A) converter. This technique has the great advantage that waveforms of any desired shape can be produced at will and these can be stored in the memory for recall when required. Early attempts at using the computer for music production were hampered by the speed of the machines. In order to generate a minute or two of music, an hour or more of computer time might be required. This meant that the performer had to feed in a program and hear the result some time later, normally using some form of taped output. The problem here is that the essential interactive role of the performer is lost and in effect he becomes a computer programmer. This major drawback has now almost completely been overcome with the new generation of high speed microcomputers. These are so fast that they can operate in real time, i.e. the sounds are produced virtually instantaneously on a command from the performer (Roads and Strawn 1985). Also they are so small that they can form part of a complete portable instrument, e.g. a keyboard synthesizer. The digital technique offers the ultimate in flexibility and it appears that it will be used more and more widely in instruments of the future, although most digital instruments on the market are still rather expensive.

Digital machines represent waveforms as a series of binary numbers, i.e. numbers using only the two digits 0 and 1 rather than the ten digits 0 to 9 used in decimal, and these are finally output as voltages from the D to A converter. Since there is a finite number of digits which are available in the machine for representing any one number, the accuracy with which any required voltage can be reproduced is also limited. The noise level which this produces can be specified by a signal-to-noise ratio. Most machines use 16 binary digits for each number, which gives a signal-to-noise ratio of 98 dB. A digital system should be capable of producing waveforms with frequency components nominally covering the range 0–25 kHz, although in practice this is slightly narrowed down by the limitations of the D to A converter. Fig. 13.15 shows a typical signal and how it might be discretized by a series of numbers, represented here by the dots on the graph. As well as the fact that each voltage must be represented by a number having a sufficient number of digits, it is also clear that the time interval S between each point, known as the sample time, must be sufficiently short, otherwise detail associated with high frequency fluctuations will be lost. In fact the sampling frequency $1/s$ must be at least twice the maximum frequency of interest, i.e. there should be at least 50,000 samples per second.

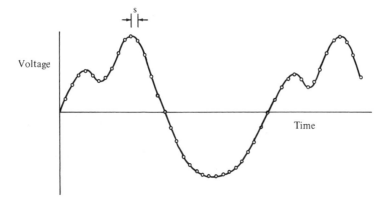

Fig. 13.15. Digital representation of a typical waveform. The discretized voltages are shown as circles, S being the sample time.

A major problem in applying a digital system is to produce a working scheme which allows the musician to specify his sounds in a relatively straightforward manner. In its very simplest mode of operation the computer can be used to store waveforms which are known to be representative of specific musical instruments or effects and be programmed to call on these when a specific tab is depressed on the console. A number of modern electronic organs use this system. Operation is similar to the present tone stops which are found on most organs of an earlier vintage. In its more sophisticated mode of operation the computer is used to generate its own waveforms through a program which is fed into it prior to a performance. Waveforms which are frequently used can be stored in the memory and recalled at will. Programs have been written for both additive and subtractive synthesis. These are compiled from a number of blocks called subroutines which in effect replace the individual electronic modules in the analogue synthesizer or electronic organ. Each of these subroutines has a number of inputs and an output; e.g., a subroutine for generating a triangular wave would require two separate inputs, one to specify the wave amplitude and the other its frequency.

An interesting scheme which has proved highly successful is referred to as digital frequency modulation synthesis. A sine wave is produced whose frequency is modulated by a second sine wave. The modulating frequency is generally set to be much higher than would be used in producing vibrato, so the effect is the same as cross-modulation in analogue synthesis. If the carrier frequency (f_c) is an integer multiple of the modulating frequency (f_m), then a wave is produced whose spectrum has a number of side bands grouped around a central peak at frequency f_c, all of these being harmonics of f_m. These are the essential spectral characteristics of the voice, where f_m represents the fundamental frequency of the note and f_c the centre of a formant peak associated with one of the vowel sounds. Quite realistic voice simulations can be obtained in this way. With the digital simulation technique it is fairly simple to arrange for f_c to be an exact multiple of f_m. The operator can change the sound by varying both the frequency of the carrier wave and the modulation index (m), which determines the depth of modulation. Transient parameters may also be input to vary f_c and m as functions of time in order to obtain dynamic effects. Interesting brassy sounds are obtained when the carrier and modulation frequencies are equal. An attractive feature of the FM technique is that a wide range of sounds can be produced with the input of just a few parameters. It thus lends itself readily to real time application in performance.

Computer generated music

The digital computer can be used not only to generate the waveforms for specific notes and sounds input by the performer but also to generate its own music (Greenhough 1984; Hammond 1983; Roads 1985). This may simply take the form of converting chords played on a keyboard into arpeggio passages or adding harmonic and rhythmic backing to a melody line. Many electronic organs have this type of facility. The computer, however, is capable of much more sophisticated operations and its full range of capabilities has not as yet been exploited (Maconie and Cunningham 1982). The primary ingredient for its extended use is the introduction of some element of chance (Watkins 1985). Programs which include random inputs, i.e. make decisions based on some statistical parameters, are referred to as *stochastic.*

Computer programs have been used to generate complete compositions using stochastic techniques, although it is debatable whether the results have any real musical content. The most successful applications to date have been either where the machine has been used simply as a way of automating the composition process, rather as a program is used to aid an architect or the designer of electronic circuits, or where it has been used in real time to generate musical fragments. In the latter case the operator takes the role of both composer and instrumentalist. On commands from a console the machine will generate various sounds and melodic passages and the operator has a certain degree of control over their outcome. A good deal of research has gone into the recognition of patterns in musical composition, particularly in the construction of melodies (Holtzman 1980). For the computer to generate a melody the chance element must be incorporated, but equally there must be certain restrictions imposed, for example in the range and the number of large intervals used. Music in the style of certain periods and schools lends itself more readily to computer aided generation. The serialist movement, for example, imposed well-defined rules on the generation and manipulation of musical structures which can readily be programmed into a computer.

LOUDSPEAKERS

In electronic music the loudspeaker system has a very significant effect on the sound. Most electronic organs and synthesizers have only one output channel, the signal being fed to a single power amplifier unit and the sound output through one or more loudspeakers attached to it. The effect of this is that the listener always hears the sound coming from a single direction and it therefore has a somewhat lifeless quality. This limitation can be disguised to some extent using either *echo* or *reverberation*. Echo can be introduced by using a continuous tape loop. This has a recording head and three or more pick-up heads located at different positions round the loop. When a sound is played into the echo unit the output consists of the original sounds plus a number of repetitions of diminishing amplitudes, similar to the echo effect produced in a large and very reverberant room. Many modern echo systems dispense with the magnetic tape and instead use a digital storage device for producing the delayed waveforms. Reverberation is similar to echo, except that the signal repetition is not so clearly defined. Normally an electrical transducer is used to convert the input signal into mechanical motion. This is attached to a spring along which the disturbance travels and on arrival at the other end a short time later the motion is converted back to electrical energy by another transducer. Various delays can be introduced by using a number of transducers and different spring lengths. The amount of echo or reverberation used will depend very much on the acoustics of the room or hall in which the music is being performed; it may not be required at all if the conditions are very resonant.

Full three-dimensional sound effects can only be produced by using a number of output channels and loudspeakers. The sound field at a point is defined by four parameters, the pressure and three velocity components in mutually perpendicular directions (e.g. up and down, forward and back and left to right). In theory any three-dimensional sound field can be produced at a point by using four loudspeakers located at the corners of a tetrahedron. However, this is not a very practical system, since the listener must sit in the centre of the tetrahedron and not move from a clearly defined spot. Also, determining the relative amplitudes and phases of the four loudspeaker signals for the production of different aural effects is extremely complicated. Rooms have been designed specially for the performance of electronic music in which a number of loudspeakers

521

located around and above the audience give a strong sense of three-dimensionality. In this case an electronic system is purpose built for the room. Most practical electronic instruments, however, are made for more general use and make no pretence at simulating full three dimensionality. Common configurations are stereophonic, using two loudspeakers in front of the listener, and quadrophonic, using four loudspeakers, two in front and two behind. With four speakers reverberation effects can be reproduced more realistically.

An interesting type of loudspeaker, used very extensively with electronic organs, is the *Leslie speaker* (Dobbins 1984). This uses mechanical moving parts to produce a type of three dimensionality and also imposes a vibrato by making use of the Doppler effect. This was discussed briefly in Chapter 1. Most Leslie speakers have a rotating horn and a bass speaker with a rotating baffle. These can operate at two speeds of rotation, slow (termed 'chorale') and fast (termed 'tremolo'). Fig. 13.16 indicates the motion of the horn speaker relative to the listener, the dotted line being a dumming horn used for mechanical balancing. Rotation is in the horizontal plane and clockwise in the diagram. In the position shown the bell of the horn, which acts as the sound source, is moving towards the listener with speed v_s. The crests of two sound waves are shown. The inner circle represents one which is just starting to radiate, whereas the outer one is a wave which started to radiate at a time $1/f$ seconds earlier, where f is the frequency of the wave input to the loudspeaker. The centre of this outer circle is displaced a distance v_s/f to the left in the diagram, since the bell was at this position when the wave started. If the horn had been stationary the distance between the wavefronts would have been c/f where c is the velocity of sound. Owing to the motion, though, the distance between wavefronts travelling towards the listener is contracted to $c/f - v_s/f = (c - v_s)/f$. This means that the frequency heard by the listener is raised to

$$\text{freq. heard} = \frac{c}{(c - v_s)/f} = f \cdot \frac{c}{(c - v_s)} \text{ Hz.}$$

When the horn has rotated by half a cycle, the bell will be moving away from the listener with the same speed so the frequency heard will be lowered to

$$\text{freq. heard} = f \cdot \frac{c}{(c + v_s)} \text{ Hz.}$$

As the horn rotates there is a gradual variation in frequency between these two extreme values, in effect a vibrato. The aural effect of this is enhanced by the amplitude modulation which is brought about by the changing direction of the sound radiation pattern, i.e. the Leslie speaker produces both vibrato and tremolo.

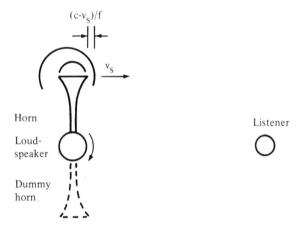

Fig. 13.16. Rotating horn on a Leslie speaker showing the crests of two sound waves as the bell of the horn is moving towards the listener.

The degree to which a Leslie speaker enriches the tone quality of an electronic organ is quite extraordinary, so much so that it is often considered to be of equal importance to the organ itself and will cost about the same. There have been a number of attempts at producing static speaker systems which simulate the Leslie but these have not proved highly successful, mainly because of the complexities involved. The static system is required to produce a rotating beam of sound waves and this can only be obtained by having an array of loudspeakers whose output amplitudes and phases are dynamically weighted. A further complication arises because, due to the mechanical system, the Leslie produces a gradual change in vibrato rate as the motor speed is altered. This effect is similar to the delayed onset of vibrato often used in violin playing and is considered an important feature by most organists. The simplest Leslie simulators using just a single static speaker tend to lack depth of tone. On the other hand, the more sophisticated ones using an array of speakers are frequently more complex and expensive than the mechanical system, so they offer little advantage.

One rather simple way in which virtually any three-dimensional sound can be produced is by using headphones. Unfortunately this is not a very practical solution for concerts. Apart from the fact that each listener requires an individual headphone set, he must remain seated motionless otherwise the sound will not appear to come from the desired direction.

14

The musical environment

The acoustics of the room or auditorium in which music is played greatly influence the sound which a listener hears and consequently his feeling of satisfaction or otherwise. The quality of musical performance can also be affected very significantly, so much so that there are many orchestras, bands and solo artists who will not play in certain auditoria which do not have acoustics to their liking. The acoustical characteristics considered to be most desirable are dependent to a great extent on the type of music being performed and also on the subjective assessment of different users. What may suit a rock band, for example, would possibly be quite unacceptable for a solo flautist. Up until the turn of this century concert hall designs were based solely on the experience gained from previous constructions. In the case of large auditoria the evolution process in design has not worked in the same way as with musical instruments, firstly because so few are built, and secondly because the architect does not have the possibility of building a prototype and then making adjustments to perfect the design before deciding on the final version, as a musical instrument maker can. Recent research, following the pioneering work of Wallace Sabine, has led to theories which can now be used to predict acoustical characteristics of buildings at the design stage; also measuring techniques have been developed which can be used to check these characteristics in a completed construction or in a laboratory model.

When a sound is initiated in an enclosure by an instrumentalist, it radiates in different directions, some of the sound travelling directly to the listener and some being reflected from the walls before it reaches his ear. A few of the possible paths for sound rays are indicated in Fig. 14.1. The shortest ray is the direct path (D), so this sound will reach the listener first. All the other paths involve reflections from the side walls and are longer.

In Fig. 14.1 the sound travelling along ray R_1 will reach the listener next, then R_2 and R_3. There is in fact an infinity of different paths along which sound waves can travel, but these gradually involve more and more reflections (see Fig. 3.57), so the sound intensity will die as the overall path length increases. The sound which passes to the listener without reflection is termed the *direct sound*, whereas the sound arriving by way of reflections is referred to as the *reverberant sound*. A knowledge of both of these is important in assessing the acoustical characteristics of an enclosure.

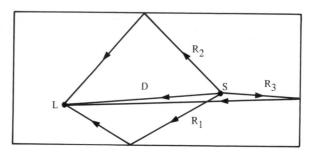

Fig. 14.1. Propagation of sound rays from a source S to a listener L. Four rays are shown, the direct sound D, the first reflection R_1 and the next longest rays R_2 and R_3.

Several different approaches can be applied to determine the spatial and temporal distribution of sound pressure in an enclosure. In concert halls and auditoria the distances between reflections are generally large compared with the wavelengths involved, and the formation of standing wave patterns is not a highly significant effect. Under these circumstances many of the important acoustical features can be determined by tracing ray paths. Since the number of rays which can be traced, even with the aid of a computer, is rather limited, it is complicated to use this technique to calculate parameters such as overall sound intensity or reverberation time. These can generally be determined, however, by using theoretical expressions which have been derived using a statistical approach. In small enclosures such as studios and practice rooms the distances between reflections may be of the same order as the wavelengths, in which case the resonances of the space become dominant. The problem must then be tackled using the wave approach.

BEHAVIOUR AT SURFACES

Reflection of sound

Sound waves incident on a hard flat surface wall are reflected such that the angle of reflection (r) is equal to the angle of incidence (i). The angle i is measured between the incident ray and a line perpendicular to the surface (the 'normal' to the surface) as shown in Fig. 14.2 (a). The angle r is similarly defined. The incident ray, the normal to the surface and the reflected ray all lie in the same plane. These laws of reflection can only be applied directly when the size of the surface elements are large compared with the wavelength, normally at least four wavelengths long. If the surface elements are less than four wavelengths in size, then the sound will be scattered in all directions as shown in Fig. 14.2 (b). This is termed *diffuse reflection*. At a right angled corner two reflections may occur, as shown in Fig. 14.2 (c). The reflected ray then travels along a path parallel to the incoming ray but is displaced laterally. When a source of sound is placed near to a flat surface, the incident rays strike at different angles, resulting in a spreading effect as shown in Fig. 14.3 (a). The reflected rays appear to come from a point on the other side of the wall, as indicated by the dashed lines.

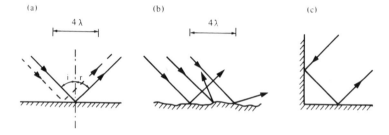

Fig. 14.2. Reflection at a plane surface: (a) when the surface is flat and large in area compared to four wavelengths, then the angle of incidence (i) is equal to the angle of reflection (r); (b) when the surface elements are small compared to four wavelengths, then diffuse reflection will occur; (c) at a right angled corner, the wave is reflected with a lateral displacement.

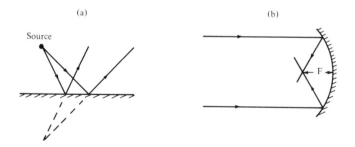

Fig. 14.3. (a) Rays from a point source striking a flat surface; (b) parallel rays being brought to a focus at a distance F from a concave surface.

At a curved surface the same laws of reflection apply, the normal now being the line at right angles to the plane which is tangential to the curved surface. If the curved surface is part of a sphere, then it will have a focal length (F) equal to half the radius of curvature, the same as a curved mirror. For a concave surface this means that parallel rays from a distant source will be brought to a focus at a distance F from the surface, as shown in Fig. 14.3 (b). Strictly speaking this is only true for rays, known as *paraxial rays*, which are close to the axis, although the paraxial approximation is good enough for most practical purposes. A parabolic surface will bring even parallel rays far from the axis to a point focus. Ray tracing is reversible; e.g., if a point source is placed at a distance F from a concave mirror, the reflected rays will be parallel, the reverse of the situation depicted in Fig. 14.3 (b). If the source is placed at a distance S from the concave surface and S is greater than F, then the reflected rays will be brought to a focus at a distance I from the surface where S and I are related by the reciprocal formula

$$1/S + 1/I = 1/F.$$

This situation is shown for S = 3F/2 in Fig. 14.4 (a). It can be seen that when S = 2F, the reflected rays are focused back to the point of the source. When S is less than F, then the rays are spread rather than focused, as shown in Fig. 14.4 (b). The reflected rays now appear to come from some point behind the reflecting surface. The reciprocal formula can be used to calculate the distance at which this apparent focus lies behind the reflector, the negative value of I obtained indicating that the focus is only an apparent one. For example, if the source is placed at a distance of F/2 from the reflecting surface, the value obtained for I is −F, indicating that the reflected rays appear to emerge from a point distant F behind the wall. distance F behind the wall.

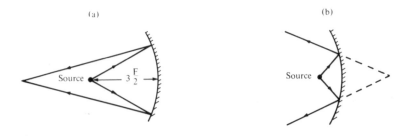

(a)

(b)

Source ← 3 $\frac{F}{2}$ →

Source

Fig. 14.4. Reflection of rays from a concave surface when a point source is placed (a) a distance 3F/2 from the surface and (b) a distance less than F from the surface, where the focal length F is equal to half the radius of curvature.

If the source of sound is off-axis, i.e. does not lie on the line of symmetry, then the point to which the sound is focused will also be displaced laterally, although its distance from the wall will not alter significantly. This is shown in Fig. 14.5 (a). Convex walls are occasionally encountered. These distribute the sound waves over a greater area than a flat wall does. When parallel rays from a distant source strike a convex wall, the reflected rays spread out as though they had come from a point on the other side, this point being half the radius of curvature from the wall (Fig. 14.5 (b)). The position of this apparent focus can be calculated in the same way as for a concave mirror using the reciprocal formula, but the focal length must now be taken as negative.

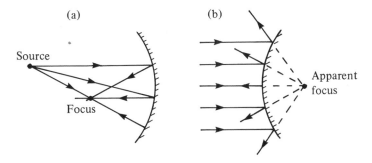

Fig. 14.5. Reflection from (a) a concave surface when the point source is positioned off-axis and (b) a convex mirror when the incoming rays are parallel.

It is essential in an auditorium that the sound should be evenly distributed. Focusing into certain regions of the audience is to be avoided. In addition to this, it is important that adequate intensity should be reflected back to the players so that each one can hear himself loudly enough in the overall sound, otherwise intonation will be impaired. Players must also receive enough sound from others in the ensemble, otherwise precision in timing will suffer. Furthermore, if there is a conductor, he must hear a balanced impression of the overall sound from all sections of the orchestra. All of these points can be checked by ray tracing.

Absorption

So far we have only considered the directions in which waves are reflected, not the wave amplitudes. When waves strike a surface, a certain amount of their energy is absorbed by the material and is ultimately converted into heat; the remainder is reflected according to the rules just described. Hard smooth surfaces reflect most of their sound energy, whilst soft porous surfaces absorb large percentages. The fraction of incident sound energy which is absorbed by a surface is known as the *absorption coefficient,* which we shall designate by the Greek letter α. The total amount of absorption (A) is proportional to the surface area (S) of a reflecting surface and by definition

$$A = \alpha\, S.$$

If S is measured in square metres, then A is in metric sabins. The absorption coefficient for a particular surface will lie in the range zero (representing total reflection) to unity (for total absorption). Very hard flat surfaces such as marble have absorption coefficients close to zero and an open window has an absorption coefficient of unity. An open window of cross-sectional area 2m², for example, would have a total absorption of 2 metric sabins.

Absorption coefficients vary with the frequency. Solid walls or floors which have a porous surface, for example, will reflect bass tones but absorb high pitch waves. These are known as *treble absorbers*. At the opposite end of the spectrum are surfaces such as wood panelling which act as *bass absorbers*. Massive panels in front of large cavities will absorb the lowest frequency components. Closed glass windows act as bass absorbers, thick plate glass windows being most efficient at the lowest frequencies. Surfaces which absorb predominantly in the centre of the spectrum, such as thin perforated wood panels and breeze blocks, are termed *middle absorbers*. Concrete blocks with slotted cavities are some-times used to give mid-range absorption. These act as Helmholtz resona-tors and absorb only over a narrow bandwidth. Audience-filled seating areas are middle absorbers, although the dominant absorption band tends to be towards the higher end of the spectrum.

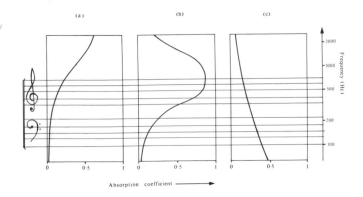

Fig. 14.6. Typical variation of absorption coefficient with pitch for (a) treble absorbers, (b) middle absorbers and (c) bass absorbers.

530

Fig. 14.6 shows the way in which the coefficient varies with pitch for three surfaces: (a) a heavy carpet on concrete (treble absorber); (b) a perforated hardboard panel backed by glass wool (middle absorber); and (c) a glass window (bass absorber). Table 14.1 give absorption coefficients at six different frequencies for a selection of surfaces commonly encountered.

Table 14.1

Absorption coefficient (α)

Surface	Frequency (Hz)					
	125	250	500	1000	2000	4000
Occupied audience area	0.45	0.65	0.84	0.95	0.92	0.84
Cloth-covered seats without audience	0.44	0.60	0.76	0.87	0.80	0.70
Heavy curtains	0.14	0.36	0.57	0.72	0.70	0.62
Wooden floor	0.14	0.12	0.09	0.08	0.06	0.07
Wooden platform with air space below	0.39	0.29	0.22	0.17	0.16	0.20
Plaster on brick	0.01	0.01	0.01	0.02	0.04	0.06
Plaster on lath	0.30	0.18	0.09	0.05	0.05	0.05
Acoustic tile	0.08	0.25	0.55	0.68	0.72	0.70
Heavy carpet on concrete	0.02	0.06	0.16	0.37	0.59	0.64
Glass window	0.34	0.25	0.18	0.12	0.08	0.04
Heavy plate glass window	0.18	0.07	0.04	0.02	0.02	0.02
Marble or glazed tile	0.01	0.01	0.01	0.01	0.02	0.02
Plywood on studs (5mm)	0.60	0.30	0.10	0.09	0.09	0.09
Glass wool (25 mm) behind perforated hardboard	0.10	0.35	0.85	0.85	0.35	0.09

The total absorption for an enclosure is determined by summing the absorptions of the individual surfaces, i.e.

$$A = \alpha_1 S_1 + \alpha_2 S_2 + \alpha_3 S_3 \text{ etc.}$$

As an example, consider the room shown in Fig. 14.7. The floor is concrete covered by heavy carpet with an area of 10 m × 15 m and the ceiling is covered with acoustic tiles and has a height of 4 m. The walls are brick covered with plaster. For the purpose of this example, doors, windows and the like have been ignored. The ceiling and floors both have area 150 m² and the wall area is 50 × 4 = 200 m². Taking a representative mid-range frequency of 1000 Hz, the absorption coefficients for the floor, ceiling and walls are 0.37, 0.68 and 0.02 respectively, so the total absorption becomes

$$A = 150 \times 0.37 + 150 \times 0.68 + 200 \times 0.02$$
$$= 162 \text{ metric sabins.}$$

Even if all of the surfaces of an enclosure were perfectly reflecting, a sound once initiated would gradually die because of the absorption of the air. The effect of air absorption increases rapidly with frequency, so that although it can safely be ignored at frequencies below 1 kHz its effect may be quite significant at the high frequency end of the spectrum in a large auditorium. At 1 kHz the absorption of air per 1000 m³ is approximately 3, the corresponding values at 2 kHz and 4 kHz being 7 and 20. These values are dependent on the humidity, being generally smaller at high relative humidities. In the example calculation of absorption, the room volume is 600 m³, so the air increases the absorption by 600 × 3/1000 = 1.8. This is almost negligible compared with the 162 metric sabins contributed by the reflecting surfaces. Air absorption becomes most significant in very large resonant buildings such as churches and cathedrals. For example, the volume of St Mary's Church, Lübeck, is 100,000 m³ and the absorption of the surfaces is approximately 2500 metric sabins (Meyer 1978). At 1kHz the contained air will increase this by 300 metric sabins, quite a significance component. At 4kHz the air absorption is of the same order of magnitude as the surface absorption.

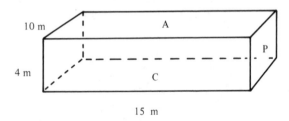

Fig. 14.7. An example room with reflecting surfaces of different materials. A = acoustic tiles; C = concrete covered with heavy carpet; P = plaster on brick.

REVERBERATION TIME

When an instrumentalist begins to play a note in a concert hall, the listener first hears a sudden increase in intensity as the direct sound reaches his ear. This is indicated by D in Fig. 14.8 (a). After a short instant of time the first reflection R_1 arrives so the sound level increases. Then the second reflection R_2 further increases the level and so on, the successive reflections being of smaller and smaller amplitude and arriving at progressively shorter time intervals. For a steady note a time is eventually reached when the rate of sound energy production by the instrumentalist just balances the rate of dissipation by absorption. The intensity is then at its maximum value. The reverse situation occurs once the sound is terminated. First the direct sound is lost, then reflection R_1 etc., until eventually the intensity the listener hears has fallen below the noise level in the room. When plotted in terms of the intensity level in decibels, the fall-off curve is approximately a straight line, as shown in Fig. 14.8 (b). The slope of this is the most important acoustical parameter associated with a concert hall. It is defined by the *reverberation time*, which is the time for the sound to die by 60 dB, i.e. for the intensity to fall to one millionth of its value.

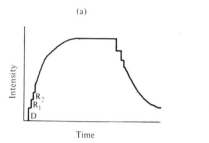
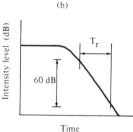

Fig. 14.8. (a) The intensity heard by a listener in an enclosure when a note begins and is then cut off. D is the direct sound, R_1 the first reflection, and R_2 the second reflection. (b) The decay curve plotted as intensity level in dB. The reverberation time T_r is the time for the sound intensity to fall by 60 dB.

Sabine arrived at an empirical relationship for the reverberation time in terms of room volume and absorption, and since then many more sophisticated statistical models have been developed, all giving similar results. Neglecting air absorption, which is usually of secondary importance, it can be seen that the reverberation time must be proportional to the volume V of the enclosure. This may be deduced by considering what happens when we vary V and A independently. Doubling the volume, for instance, but keeping the sound intensity (and A) the same, will double the stored sound energy and this will take twice as long to be absorbed. On the other hand, if A is doubled, the time required for the sound to be absorbed will be halved. Thus

$$T_r \text{ is proportional to } V/A.$$

Detailed statistical calculation shows that

$$T_r = 0.16 \, V/A$$

where V is the volume in cubic metres, A is the total absorption in metric sabins and T_r is the reverberation time in seconds. This equation is known as *Sabine's formula*. Like absorption, the reverberation time varies with frequency and may vary considerably over different parts of the spectrum.

It is conventional to determine it at the six different frequencies 125, 250, 500, 1000, 2000 and 4000 Hz. Nowadays, when the term 'reverberation time' is used without reference to frequency it is the 500 Hz band which is implied. This results from the importance attached to the early measurements of Sabine which were all conducted at 512 Hz.

As an example of how to apply the formula, consider the room shown in Fig. 14.7. At 1 kHz the absorption of the surfaces was calculated as 162 metric sabins, or 164 metric sabins including the air absorption. The volume is 600 m³, so

$$T_r = 0.16 \times 600/164 = 0.59 \text{ s.}$$

When the average absorption coefficient of the surfaces ($\bar{\alpha}$) is large, then Sabine's formula leads to an error in the calculation of reverberation time, the average absorption coefficient here being defined as $\bar{\alpha} = A/S$, where A is the total absorption of the surfaces and S their total area. A more precise relationship, which does not suffer from this defect, is known as *Eyring's formula*. This is

$$T_r = 0.16V/(A_a - S\ln(1-\bar{\alpha}))$$

where A_a is the absorption of the air and ln denotes natural logarithm (to the base e). Most calculators have a facility for computing natural logarithms as well as logarithms to the base 10. In the case when $\bar{\alpha}$ is small compared to unity, $\ln(1-\bar{\alpha})$ is approximately equal to $-\bar{\alpha}$ so the Eyring and Sabine formulae are identical. In the example calculation A = 162 and S = 500 m² giving $\bar{\alpha} = 0.324$. Application of Eyring's formula then gives $T_r = 0.49$ s instead of the value of 0.59 s predicted by Sabine. In this case the difference is seen to be quite significant. The Eyring formula should preferably be used whenever $\bar{\alpha}$ is greater than 0.2.

A crude estimate of reverberation time can be obtained by clapping hands in the room and listening for the time it takes for the sound to die away completely. Although this is a subjective measurement, quite consistent results can be obtained with a little practice, especially if a stop watch is used for measuring the time. Far more accurate results can be obtained if a gun shot is used and the reverberant sound is recorded on tape. This can then be played back through a level recorder having a logarithmic potentiometer to give a plot of sound level in dB. Fig. 14.9 shows such a record obtained in the Reid Concert Hall, Edinburgh. The interior is approximately rectangular in shape, with floor dimensions 11.5 m × 28 m and height 12 m. It is seen that in this case the decay is almost a straight line, although there are small periodic fluctuations superimposed on this which are due to flutter echo, to be discussed later. Even though the line falls below the noise level before it has dropped 60 dB, the reverberation time can be found from the slope. The time to drop 30 dB is 0.92 s, so that $T_r = 2 \times 0.92 = 1.84$ s.

The method just described gives an overall reverberation time effectively averaged over the entire spectral range, since the frequency spectrum of an impulsive sound is flat. This gives one a good measure of the rapidity with which percussive sounds in the orchestra will fade and hence the degree of clarity which can be obtained. However, it may well be that sounds from a high instrument such as a piccolo die more rapidly than those from a low instrument such as a double bass. This effect can only be quantified by measuring reverberation times for a range of different frequencies. A frequency analysis is essential if the overall decay curve is not a straight line, since this indicates wide variations in reverberation time over the spectral range (Smith 1971; Russell and Nelson 1975). For frequency analysis, narrow band filtered white noise is the best sound source, although warble tones produced by a beat frequency oscillator have been used in many studies (Furrer and Lauber 1953). The noise is preferable to a pure sine wave since this might by chance coincide with a particular resonant mode of the room. When the tape has been started the sound is suddenly cut off and the reverberant sound recorded. The tape is then played back through a narrow band filter, used to reduce background noise, and a level recorder plots the decay curve. If a narrow band noise source is not available, then a gun shot recording can be frequency analysed using a narrow band filter. The main problem here is that the sound source contains many unwanted spectral components, which increases the background noise level. In the case of the Reid Hall a frequency analysis showed that each reverberation curve had essentially the same slope, so that in this case the reverberation time is more or less independent of frequency.

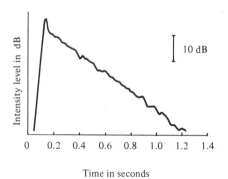

Fig. 14.9. Reverberation of a gun shot in the Reid Hall, Edinburgh.

The optimal reverberation time for a particular enclosure is to a certain extent a matter of personal taste and depends on the type of music being performed. A solo flautist, for example, may like a very reverberant room

535

since it increases the sound level (p.539). Pop bands using electronic amplification, on the other hand, often like a very dead room. It is generally accepted that for speech and singing, relatively short reverberation times are desirable in order that intelligibility may not be impaired. Concert halls require longer reverberation times to give the fullness of sound and even longer values are considered desirable for romantic organ music. Suggested optimal reverberation times at 500 to 1000 Hz for different purposes are

Theatre	1 s
Chamber music	1.4 s
Opera	1.3–1.6 s
Concert halls	1.7–2.0 s
Organ music	2.5 s

although these values cannot be taken in any way as being definitive (Tzekakis 1979). The optimal values vary with the volume (V) of the hall and the total floor area (A_T) occupied by audience, orchestra and chorus. It appears that the optimum reverberation time increases almost in direct proportion to the ratio V/A_T. Other factors must be considered, however, particularly the date of construction and the preferences held by audiences and musicians in that period. A hall which was considered to be excellent on construction may not appeal to the general taste today. For example, shortly after the Second World War there was a tendency towards short

Table 14.2

Reverberation times for well-known concert halls in the mid-frequency range 500-1000 Hz with the seats occupied

Hall	Volume (m³)	Date of construction	Reverberation time (s)
New Philharmonic, Berlin	26,000	1963	1.9
Royal Festival, London	22,000	1951	1.45
Symphony Hall, Boston	18,740	1900	1.8
Concertgebouw, Amsterdam	18,700	1887	2.0
Liederhalle, Stuttgart	16,000	1956	1.65
Beethovenhalle, Bonn	15,700	1959	1.7
Large Musikvereinsaal, Vienna	14,600	1870	2.05
Konzerthus, Gothenburg	11,900	1935	1.7

reverberation times, but this has been reversed in recent times. Table 14.2 shows reverberation times for well-known concert halls (Meyer 1978).

All musicians will be familiar with the fact that reverberation times can be dramatically reduced when an empty hall becomes filled by an audience. This effect is particularly apparent in halls where the seats are not padded, and after a successful rehearsal in the empty hall the conductor or instrumentalist can sometimes be in for a rude awakening on the night of the performance. To minimise this effect, many halls use padded seats with absorptive backs, which absorb similar amounts of sound energy when not in use as when occupied. Fig. 14.10 shows reverberation times as a function of frequency for two halls in the occupied and unoccupied condition. In the case of the Vienna Musikvereinsaal the seats are wooden and at 1000 Hz (B_5) the reverberation time comes down from 3.5 s to 2 s on occupation by an audience (Meyer 1978). In the New Philharmonic, Berlin, the effect is very much less marked because it has absorptive seats.

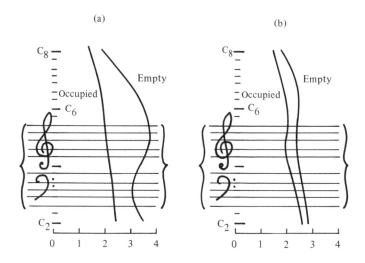

Reverberation time in seconds

Fig. 14.10. Reverberation times in (a) the large Vienna Musikvereinsaal and (b) the New Philharmonic, Berlin.

The manner in which reverberation time varies with frequency is important. For music of the 19th century and later, it is considered desirable to have the reverberation decreasing as the pitch rises, a satisfactory variation being shown in Fig. 14.11. It can be seen that both the halls depicted in Fig. 14.10 have good characteristics for this type of music. For baroque music, on the other hand, it is better for the reverberation time to be virtually constant throughout the frequency range. The ratio between the low frequency and mid-frequency reverberation times is sometimes referred to as the *warmth* of an enclosure.

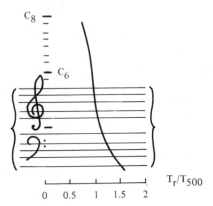

Fig. 14.11. Variation with frequency of the reverberation time T_r as a fraction of the mid-frequency value T_{500} for a satisfactory room; adapted from Kinsler et al. (1982).

DIRECT AND REVERBERANT SOUND

The sound which a listener hears in an auditorium is a combination of the direct sound and the reverberant sound. In the open air there is no reverberant sound and the intensity I falls off in inverse proportion to the square of the distance from the source, i.e.

$$I = P/4\pi r^2$$

where P is the power of the source (see p.105). In an enclosure the listener hears this intensity together with the reverberant sound. The latter has approximately the same intensity at all positions in the enclosure since it is the result of numerous reflections from all directions (Plomp and Steeneken 1973). The intensity of the reverberant field depends on the total absorption A and can be shown equal to 4P/A, so the total intensity becomes

$$I = P(1/4\pi r^2 + 4/A)$$

In this expression the intensity is the acoustic energy flowing per unit time through unit area perpendicular to the direction of propagation of the direct sound, in one direction only (Hassall and Zaveri 1979; Kinsler et al. 1982). To illustrate how these two components vary in a hall, the intensity has been plotted as a function of distance from the source, taking the absorption appropriate for the Edinburgh Reid Hall. This is shown in Fig. 14.12. The sound intensities are shown in decibels relative to the constant

538

level of the reverberant sound. At positions very close to the source the direct sound dominates, whereas at large distances the intensity is almost wholly due to the reverberant field. The distance (R) from the source at which the direct and reverberant fields have the same intensity is known as the *room radius*. Using Sabine's equation, R can be expressed directly in terms of the reverberation time, i.e.

$$R = (A/16\pi)^{1/2} = 0.056 \, (V/T_r)^{1/2}$$

This formula implies that the source radiates equally in all directions. If this is not the case, the radius will be larger in the direction of preferred radiation and less in other directions. A *directivity ratio* is sometimes included in the formula to take account of this. The room radius for the Reid Hall, Edinburgh, is 2.6 m, a typical value for larger halls being 5 m.

It can be seen that at large distances from the source the intensity is almost entirely due to reverberation and that this varies approximately in direct proportion to the reverberation time:

$$I \simeq 4P/A \simeq 25P. \, T_r/V.$$

It is important then that in larger halls the reverberation time is sufficiently large, otherwise quiet instruments will not be heard clearly, except very close to the stage. On the other hand the reverberant sound field tends to mask the recognition of new sounds, so excessively long reverberation times lead to lack of clarity.

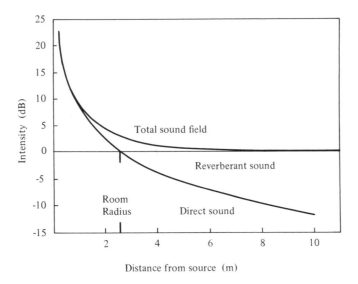

Distance from source (m)

Fig. 14.12. Variation of direct, reverberant and total sound intensities with distance from the source for the Reid Hall, assuming a non-directional radiation pattern.

539

In outdoor auditoria there is no reverberant sound field, although the direct sound is usually supplemented by reflections from the back walls and floor. Classical examples are the Greek amphitheatres, which are renowned for their excellent acoustical qualities (Knudsen 1963). These were generally built into a hillside and had steeply sloping circular rows of seats arranged so that each person in the audience had an unobstructed view of the stage. They often seated well over ten thousand people, so it is quite surprising that each member of the audience could receive adequate sound energy to hear the performance. However, it must be remembered that in these surroundings the background noise levels are very low. A feature of outdoor auditoria of this type is the clarity of the sound due to the lack of extended reverberation. However, sound levels are extremely low compared to concert halls.

Time delay

It is important that the sound from the first reflections should be heard very shortly after the arrival of the direct sound (Ando and Gottlob 1979). The delay of the first reflection should not be greater than about 20 ms, corresponding to a path length of $0.02 \times 340 \simeq 7$ m. Thus in Fig. 14.1 the difference in lengths between rays D and R_1 should not be greater than 7 m. Small values of this delay factor give the audience a sense of *intimacy*, whereas large values lead to a feeling of being in a cavernous chamber. After the first reflection has arrived, the others should follow in rapid succession and with relatively even spacing in order to blend together to form a smooth reverberation. It is desirable that the first reflections arrive from the side walls rather than from above or from the rear wall. Path lengths for the different reflections can be obtained by drawing ray diagrams for selected instrument and audience positions.

ROOM MODES

Just as the air inside a clarinet or flute will resonate at certain discrete frequencies, so the air inside a room or concert hall will be excited to resonance at certain normal mode frequencies. A knowledge of these modes is important if a complete acoustical analysis is to be carried out for any enclosure, although in practical terms they are most important in smaller rooms and halls (Morse and Bolt 1944). Determination of the standing wave patterns in the general case is extremely complicated because of the three-dimensional nature of the problem, but fortunately the vast majority of halls can be approximated by a rectangular enclosure for which theoretical patterns have been derived (Meyer and Neumann 1972). In this case, standing waves can be set up between both pairs of facing end walls and between floor and ceiling, the possible frequencies being given by

$$f = c[(n_x/l_x)^2 + (n_y/l_y)^2 + (n_z/l_z)^2]^{1/2}/2$$

where ℓ_x, ℓ_y and ℓ_z are the length, width and height of the enclosure, c is the speed of sound and n_x, n_y and n_z are integer numbers greater than or equal to zero representing the mode numbers in the three directions. The standing wave pattern has three sets of nodal pressure planes parallel to the three perpendicular sides. The spacing of these planes along the x-axis for example is $\lambda/2$ such that

$$n_x \lambda/2 = \ell_x$$

and there are similar planes perpendicular to the y and z axes. If a listener is seated or a microphone placed at one of these nodal positions, then the sound detected at that particular reson·nt frequency is very small.

If a note is played at a certain location in a room and the listener moves to different positions, the intensity of the sound he hears will be dependent on whether he is close to a node or an antinode, the maximum intensity occurring at a pressure antinode. Similarly the position of the instrument in relation to the standing wave patterns is important, maximum excitation occurring when a particular mode is excited at a pressure antinode. If, for example, a note is played at the centre of a rectangular room, then only those modes having even numbers simultaneously for n_x, n_y and n_z will be excited, i.e. about one mode in ten. The pressure amplitudes for all standing wave patterns are maximised in the corners, where all the resonant modes will be excited or heard. For this reason absorbing material used for damping normal modes is most effective when placed in the corners of a room.

When an instrument is played in a room frequencies which are close to one of the normal modes will be emphasised. These modes are widely spaced at low frequencies and distort the natural characteristics of the instrument. At higher frequencies, they become closer and overlap to produce a smooth response. It can be shown that the number of normal modes N having frequencies in a band width Δf centered on f is approximately

$$N = \Delta f.f^2 4\pi V/c^3$$

where V is the volume of the room and c the speed of sound. Note that the number of modes increases with the volume. As an example, in a large assembly hall of volume 75,000 m^3 there will be approximately 60,000 modes just within the bandwidth 500 to 510 Hz. This very large number indicates that the spectral response in this region will be almost completely smooth. This is not the case, however, in small practice rooms. For a room 3 m × 3 m × 3 m the equivalent number is just 22.

When a continuous sound is started in a room, e.g. when a clarinettist tongues the beginning of a note, steady state waves are set up and in addition the transient effect initiates damped vibrations at the normal mode frequencies of the room. Each of these dies out at its own rate, eventually leaving the steady state standing wave. A similar effect occurs when a sound terminates, the collection of all the decaying normals modes being the reverberant sound field.

REMEDIAL MEASURES

We have seen that the four most important criteria for good acoustics in a hall are that (a) the sound level should be adequate in all parts of the room, (b) the sound should be evenly distributed both in the audience and on stage, (c) the reverberation should be suitable for the particular application, and (d) the first reflections should not be excessively delayed. These factors should all be accounted for in the original design, although unfortunately, even with present day knowledge, the final result is not always exactly as predicted. Remedial measures are then the only course of action. These are also frequently required in older halls which were built at a time when acoustical design principles were not developed or in cases where the purpose of a building has been changed. The Queen's Hall in Edinburgh, for example, was originally a church and has subsequently been converted for concert use.

A problem frequently encountered in older halls is that of *flutter echo*. This normally occurs when there are two parallel walls having rather low absorption. Sounds produced at some position between the walls then traverse backwards and forwards, giving a repeated echo effect rather than a smooth reverberation. This is disturbing to both player and listener, especially in staccato or percussive passages. In the Edinburgh Reid Hall there is a pronounced flutter echo between the two parellel side walls. When a sound is generated near the centre of the hall the path length to the side wall and back is approximately 11.5 m, giving a time lapse of 11.5/340 s = 34 ms. Flutter echoes can be avoided at the design stage by not having large parallel surfaces. Once present they can usually be reduced by covering one or both of the surfaces with absorbing material.

One of the simplest and most flexible means of increasing absorption is to use curtains. The network of interlocking pores in the fabric acts primarily as a treble absorber in the same way as a carpet, although by mounting the curtains some way from a wall their range of absorption can be extended into the lower frequencies. The effective lower limit of absorption is reached when the distance d_c between the curtains and the wall is equal to one quarter of a wavelength, corresponding to the lowest mode of resonance in a pipe closed at one end. The curtains will then absorb frequencies down to a limit of $f = 340/(4d_c) = 85/d_c$ Hz. The absorption properties of curtains are best when they are made of heavy fabric and are hung in pleats.

Reflectors can often be used to increase sound levels in different parts of a hall and to reduce the delay times of the first reflections. In auditoria with very high ceilings these are frequently suspended above the orchestra area and because of their appearance are referred to as clouds. They can also be effective in reducing flutter echoes between ceiling and floor, particularly in dome shaped structures. An example of their use is in the Royal Albert Hall, London. The most important point about reflectors is that they are only effective at wavelengths which are considerably smaller than their own dimensions and their effectiveness in coping with low frequency reflections diminishes as their distance from the source and the listener is increased. By suitably angling the reflectors, rays can be directed towards different regions of the audience. Generally reflectors directed towards the back of a hall are made larger in size to compensate for the reduction in low frequency response caused by the increased distance. When reflectors are set at an angle to the wavefronts, their effective area is reduced and so consequently is their low frequency response. One useful feature of hanging reflectors is that they allow the possibility of adjustment to suit specific situations. For example, they might be set in a relatively low position for a concert of classical music requiring the clarity of sound associated with few delayed reflections and raised for a concert of romantic music.

In the design of a room or hall it is important that unwanted noise should be reduced to a minimum, otherwise this will mask the musical sounds. Internal noises can arise from such things as air conditioning systems or water pipes used for central heating, so acceptable levels should be specified when these are installed. External noise is generally airborne and is transmitted through an external wall which is set into motion by the pressure variations outside and then radiates noise inside the enclosure. High absorption inside the enclosure has the effect of minimising ambient noise levels, although the reverberant sound field from the source will be likewise reduced.

Where reverberation times are excessive, remedial measures usually take the form of adding absorbent material to one or more of the surfaces or occasionally altering the effective volume by introducing an artificial ceiling. Reverberation times which are too short are often more difficult to correct. A method sometimes used is to introduce electronically produced reverberation, referred to as *assisted resonance*. Many varied schemes have been used. We saw in Chapter 13 how reverberation is introduced in electronic music using a spring fitted with transducers. This method can be used more generally for any type of instrument if its sound is picked up by a microphone. Reverberation is added to the microphone signal and then this is amplified and radiated through one or, more often, a pair of loudspeakers. This method is the one generally used by pop groups, although a magnetic tape or digitally operated echo unit may be used in place of the reverberation spring. Pop groups frequently prefer a very dead room to which they add their own electronic reverberation. This is not satisfactory, however, for classical music. Here, much more elaborate systems using a large number of permanently installed microphones and loudspeakers are required to give a realistic spatial distribution of sound. Digital computer techniques may be used to repeat the signals picked up by the microphones, with up to 1000 repetitions per second being used. Various other methods have been used with differing degrees of success. In one of these a large brass plate is driven by a speaker mechanism: signals are picked up at a number of different positions on the plate and added to the original sound. Another method employs a small hard-walled reverberation room fitted with a loudspeaker and several microphones to detect the reverberant field. A system employed at the Royal Festival Hall, London (Parkin et al. 1953; Parkin and Morgan 1970), has separate electrical circuits for different regions of the frequency spectrum. Each circuit is fed with the signal from a microphone housed in either a Helmholtz resonator or a quarter wavelength tube, the latter being used at the higher frequencies. This gives them a narrow band frequency response. These are located in the ceiling at pressure antinode positions in order to maximise their response. The circuits drive loudspeakers also located at antinodal positions in the ceiling, one speaker being used for each circuit where possible. In total there are 172 channels covering the frequency range 58–700 Hz, the frequency spacing between adjacent channels being smaller at the low end of the spectrum. The reverberation time achieved at any particular frequency depends on the gain of the amplifier in that particular channel and each one of these needs to be

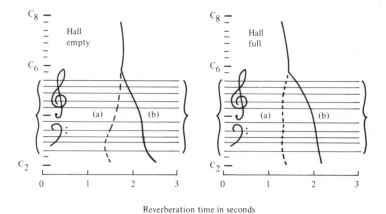

Reverberation time in seconds

Fig. 14.13. Reverberation times at different pitches measured in the Royal Festival Hall, London, (a) without assisted resonance and (b) with assisted resonance.

544

properly adjusted to give the desired effect. This can be a major problem with this type of system. The advantage is that the reverberation times within different frequency bands can be varied separately to achieve the optimal variation over the frequency range. Fig. 14.13 shows the reverberation times in the Royal Festival Hall with and without assisted resonance.

LABORATORY ENVIRONMENTS

Two types of rooms which are used extensively for laboratory testing deserve a special mention: they are the *anechoic chamber* and the *reverberation room*. These are the primary facilities of most acoustics laboratories and the concepts behind them may be helpful in understanding the acoustics of normal rooms used for musical performance.

Suppose, for example, that one wants to measure the directional characteristics of an instrument, say a clarinet. To do this the instrument is blown, either mechanically or by a player, and the resulting sound intensity is measured by placing a microphone at numerous different positions around the instrument. If a frequency analysis is required, then the microphone signal is passed through a narrow band filter before its signal power is measured. The result of this type of measurement, however, depends on the room in which the instrument is played. In other words, one is really measuring the combined resonance characteristics of the instrument and the room. If, for example, the microphone happens to be at a nodal pressure position for a particular mode, then the signal will be small. Repeating the experiments in another room would change the positions of nodes and antinodes and hence the microphone output. This problem is overcome by taking the measurements in an anechoic chamber. This is a room in which the walls are designed to give as near to total absorption as possible. Fig. 14.14 (a) shows the anechoic chamber in the Physics Department, Edinburgh University. The walls, ceiling and base are all lined with foam rubber wedges designed to give optimum absorption over the complete frequency spectrum. The floor on which you walk is made from a metal grid supported some distance above the foam wedges below, so that all flat surfaces which would cause reflection are avoided. The door also is lined with foam and where possible measuring apparatus and users are located outside with the door closed when an experiment is being conducted. In this way wall reflections and the resulting standing waves are almost entirely eliminated and only the direct sound is measured.

In complete contrast to the anechoic chamber is the reverberation room. Here the walls are smooth plastered on hard surfaces to maximise their reflection properties. The walls and ceiling are designed so that no two facing surfaces are parallel, in order to eliminate discrete standing waves and ensure that the sound field is diffuse. This can be seen in Fig. 14.14 (b), which shows the reverberation room in the Physics Department at Edinburgh University. The reverberation time in such a room is extremely long because of the low absorption.

A reverberation room can be used for many different types of experiment, e.g. the measurement of loudness curves (see p.211). It can also be used to measure the acoustic power (P) of a source. The sound intensity measured at any position in the room is equal to $4P/A$ (p.539), provided that one does not take the measurements too close to the source. The only unknown factor is the absorption A, which can easily be measured from the reverberation time. Another important use of reverberation rooms is in the measurement of absorption coefficients. A measurement of the reverberation time (say T_1) is first recorded with the room empty and from Sabin's formula the absorption coefficient (α) of the wall surface is calculated, i.e. $T_1 = 0.16 \, V/(\alpha S)$, where V is the room volume and S the total wall surface area. One of the walls is then covered with the material whose absorption coefficient (α_a) is required, and a new reverberation time T_2 is measured. If the area of this covered wall area is S_a then

(a)

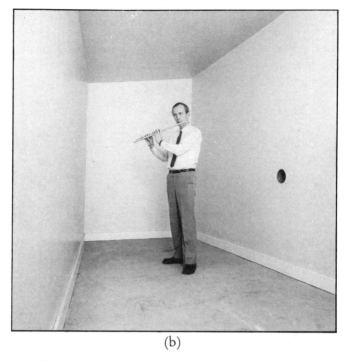

(b)

Fig. 14.14. Two enclosures used for acoustical experiments in the Physics Department at Edinburgh University: (a) the anechoic chamber and (b) the reverberation room.

$$T_2 = 0.16V/((S-S_a) \alpha + S_a \alpha_a)$$

and, since α is known, α_a can be determined.

A technique sometimes used by architects to predict acoustical characteristics of a new structure is that of model building (Taylor 1976). An exact scale model of the interior of the hall is made. Let us suppose for the sake of argument that it is 1:8 scale. Typical musical sounds from instruments are then recorded in an anechoic chamber so that they are free from reverberation effects. They are then played through a loudspeaker on the stage position in the model at eight times normal speed. In this way the spatial pattern of standing waves in the model will be exactly as in the final hall, since time scales in exact proportion to length, the speed of sound being a constant. The sound in any particular position can then be recorded using a microphone and finally the tape is played back at one eighth speed to reconstruct what a listener in the hall would actually hear. Frequency spectra, reverberation times and other acoustical parameters can be obtained from the tape recording. One difficulty with the tech-

547

nique is that absorption coefficients must also be scaled, so different construction materials must be used in model and prototype. The great advantage is that alterations can be made quite cheaply to the model and their effect observed almost immediately.

References

Note: In the list which follows, the *Journal of the Acoustical Society of America* has been abbreviated to JASA, while the *Journal of Sound and Vibration* has been abbreviated to JSV. Other abbreviations are standard.

Abraham, O. (1901) "Das absolute Tonbewusststein". Sammelbde. International Musikges. *3*, 1–86.

Aebi, W. (1971) "Die innere Akustik des Waldhornes". Proc. 7th International Congress on Acoustics, Budapest, *3*, 589-592, 605-608.

Aebi, W. (1976) "Stopped horn". Horn Call *b* (2), 47-49.

Ancell, J.E. (1960) "Sound pressure spectra of a muted cornet". JASA *32*, 1101-1104.

Ando, Y. and Gottlob, D. (1979) "Effects of early multiple reflections on subjective preference judgements of music sound fields". JASA *65*, 524–527.

Bachem, A. (1950) "Tone height and tone chroma as two different pitch qualities". Acta Psychologica *7*, 80–88.

Backus, J. (1963) "Small vibration theory of the clarinet". JASA *35*, 305–313.

Backus, J. (1974) "Input impedance curves for the reed woodwind instruments". JASA *56*, 1266–1279.

Backus, J. (1976) "Input impedance curves for the brass instruments". JASA *60*, 470–480.

Backus, J. (1977) "The Acoustical Foundations of Music". 2nd ed. New York: Norton.

Backus, J. (1985) "The effect of the player's vocal tract on woodwind instrument tone". JASA *78*, 17-20.

Backus, J. and Hundley, T.C. (1966) "Wall vibrations in flue organ pipes and their effect on tone". JASA *39*, 936–945.

Backus, J. and Hundley, T.C. (1971) "Harmonic generation in the trumpet". JASA *49*, 509–519.

Baines, A. (1976) "Brass Instruments, their history and development". London: Faber and Faber.

Bak, N. (1969) "Pitch, temperature and blowing-pressure in recorder-playing. Study of treble recorders". Acustica *22*, 295–299.

Balzano, G.J. (1984) "Absolute pitch and pure tone identification". JASA *75*, 623–625.

Barbour, J.M. (1953) "Tuning and Temperament". Michigan State College Press.

Barkhausen, H. (1926) "Ein neuer Schallmesser für die Praxis". Z. Tech. Phys. *7*, 599–601.

Barnes, J. (1979) "Bach's keyboard temperament". Early Music *7*, 236–249.

Bartholomew, W.T. (1934) "A physical definition of 'good voice quality' in the male voice". JASA *23*, 25–33.

Bate, P. (1966) "The Trumpet and Trombone". London: Ernest Benn.

Bate, P. (1969) "The Flute". London: Ernest Benn.

Batteau, D.W. (1967) "The role of the pinna in human localization". Proc. Roy. Soc. *168B*, 158–180.

Békésy, G. von (1960) "Experiments in Hearing". New York: McGraw Hill.

Bell, A.J. and Firth, I. (1984) "Vibrations of the concert harp soundboard and soundbox". Proc. Inst. of Acoustics. Acoustics '84 Swansea, 65–72.

Benade, A.H. (1959) "On woodwind instrument bores". JASA *31*, 137–146. *Repr. (with corrections) in* Kent (1977)

Benade, A.H. (1960(a)) "The physics of woodwinds". Scientific American, October, 144–152. *Repr. in* Hutchins (1978).

Benade, A.H. (1960(b)) "On the mathematical theory of woodwind finger holes". JASA *32*, 1591–1608.

Benade, A.H. (1960(c)) "Horns, Strings and Harmony". New York: Doubleday.

Benade, A.H. (1973) "The physics of brasses". Scientific American, July, 24–35. *Repr. in* Kent (1977) *and* Hutchins (1978).

Benade, A.H. (1976) "Fundamentals of Musical Acoustics". New York: Oxford.

Benade, A.H. and French, J.W. (1965) "Analysis of the flute head joint". JASA *37*, 679–691.

Benade, A.H. and Gans, D.J. (1968) "Sound production in wind instruments". Annals of the N.Y. Academy of Sciences *155*, 247–263. *Repr. in* Kent (1977).

Benade, A.H. and Hoekje, P.L. (1982) "Vocal tract effects in wind instrument regeneration". JASA *71*, S91.

Benade, A.H., Greenberg, P.S., Hoekje, P.L. and Suttle, R.M. (1977) "Wind instrument very-nearfield and room-average spectra". JASA *61* S35.

Benade, A.H. and Jansson, E.V. (1974) "On plane and spherical waves in horns with nonuniform flare. I. Theory of radiation, resonance frequencies, and mode conversion". Acustica *31*, 80–98. *Repr. in* Kent (1977).

Beranek, L. (1949) "Acoustic Measurements". New York: Wiley.

Berger, K.W. (1964) "Some factors in the recognition of timbre". JASA *36*, 1888–1891.

Berlioz, H. (1844) "Instrumentation". Paris: Lemoine.

Bilhuber, P.H. and Johnson, C.A. (1940) "The influence of the soundboard on piano tone quality". JASA *11*, 311–320.

Bilsen, F.A. (1973) "On the influence of the number and phase of harmonics on the perceptibility of the pitch of complex signals". Acustica *28*, 60–65.

Bismarck, G. von (1974(a)) "Timbre of steady sounds: a factorial investigation of its verbal attributes". Acustica *30*, 146–159.

Bismarck, G. von (1974(b)) "Sharpness as an attribute of the timbre of steady sounds". Acustica *30*, 159–172.

Blackham, E.D. (1965) "The physics of the piano". Scientific American, December, 88–98. *Repr. in* Hutchins (1978).

Blades, J. (1984) "Percussion Instruments and their History". Rev. ed. London: Faber and Faber.

Blandford, W.F.H. (1922) "Wagner and the horn parts of Lohengrin". Musical Times *63*, 693–697.

Bloothooft, G. and Plomp, R. (1986) "The sound level of the singer's formant in professional singing". JASA *79*, 2028–2033.

Boehm, T. (1964) "The Flute and Flute Playing". New York: Dover.

Boer, E. de (1956) "Pitch of inharmonic signals". Nature *178*, 535–536.

Boer, E. de (1976) "On the 'residue' and auditory pitch perception". In *"Handbook of Sensory Physiology", ed. W.D. Keidel and W.D. Neff, Vol. V/3, Chap. 13. Berlin: Springer.*

Boer, E. de (1980) "Auditory physics. Physical principles in hearing theory. I". Physics Reports *62*, 87–174.

Bouasse, H. (1929(a)) "Instruments à Vent". Paris: Librairie Delagrave.

Bouasse, H. (1929(b)) "Tuyaux et Résonateurs". Paris: Librairie Delagrave.

Bouhuys, A. (1965) "Sound power production in wind instruments". JASA *37*, 453–456.

Bowsher, J.M. and Watkinson, P.S. (1982) "Manufacturers' opinions about brass instruments". Brass Bulletin *38*, 25–30.

Brady, P.T.(1970) "Fixed-scale mechanism of absolute pitch". JASA *48*, 883–887.

Brindley, G. (1969) "A method of analysing woodwind cross-fingerings". Galpin Soc. J. *22*, 40–46.

Brindley, G. (1971) "The standing wave-patterns of the flute". Galpin Soc. J. *24*, 5–15.

Brink, G. van den (1975) "The relation between binaural diplacusis for pure tones and for complex sounds under normal conditions and with induced monaural pitch shift". Acustica *32*, 159–165.

Bruijn, A. de (1978) "Timbre-classification of complex tones". Acustica *40*, 108-114.

Burney, C. (1803) "The horn". In Rees' Cyclopaedia, London.

Burns, E.M. (1982) "Pure tone pitch anomalies. I. Pitch-intensity effects and diplacusis in normal ears". JASA *72*, 1394–1402.

Burns, W. and Robinson, D.W. (1970) "Hearing and Noise in Industry". London: HMSO.

Butler, R.A. (1975) "The influence of the external and middle ear on auditory discriminations". *In* "Handbook of Sensory Physiology", *ed.* W.D. Keidel and W.D. Neff, Vol. V/2, Ch. 6. Berlin: Springer.

Campbell, D.M., Greated, C.A. and Lucey, E.C.A. (1984) "Sound generation mechanism in the flute". Proc. Inst. of Acoustics. Acoustics '84 Swansea, 29–36.

Cardwell, W.T. Jnr (1970) "Cup-mouthpiece wind instruments". U.S. Patent No. 3,507,181 (April 21, 1970). *Repr. in* Kent (1977).

Carroll, J.B. (1975) "Speed and accuracy of absolute pitch judgements: some latter-day results". Educ. Test. Serv. Bull. RB-75-35, Princeton, New Jersey.

Carruthers, A.R. (1977) "Sound radiation characteristics of the Highland bagpipe in open air". Acustica *38*, 153–156.

Carruthers, A.R. (1978) "Pitch changes in the sound of the Highland bagpipe". Acustica *41*, 46–50.

Carterette, E.C. (1978) "Historical notes on research in hearing". *In* "Handbook of Perception", *ed.* E.C. Carterette and M.P. Friedman, Vol. IV, Ch. 1. New York: Academic.

Caussé, R., Kergomard, J. and Lurton, X. (1984) "Input impedance of brass musical instruments". JASA *75*, 241–254.

Caussé, R. and Sluchin, B. (1982) "Mutes of brass instruments". JASA *71*, S91-S92.

Chiba, T. and Kajiyama, M. (1958) "The Vowel, its Nature and Structure". Tokyo: Phonetic Society of Japan.

Chladni, E.F.F. (1787) "Entdeckungen über die Theorie des Klanges". Leipzig: Breitkopf and Härtel.

Chocholle, R. and Greenbaum, H.B. (1966) "La sonie de sons purs partiellement masqués". Journal de Psychologie 4, 385–414.

Christian, R.S., Davis, R.E., Tubis, A., Anderson, C.A., Mills, R.I. and Rossing, T.D. (1984) "Effects of air loading on timpani membrane vibrations". JASA *76*, 1336–1345.

Clack, T.D., Edreich, J. and Knighton, R.W. (1972) "Aural harmonics: the monaural phase effects at 1500 Hz, 2000 Hz and 2500 Hz observed in tone-on-tone masking when f_1 = 1000 Hz". JASA *52*, 536–541.

Clark, M. Jnr and Luce, D. (1965) "Intensities of orchestral instrument scales played at prescribed dynamic markings". J. Audio Eng. Soc. *13*, 151–157.

Clebsch, R.F.A. (1862) "Theorie der Elasticität fester Körper". Leipzig: Teubner.

Cleveland, T.F. (1977) "Acoustic properties of voice timbre types and their influence on voice classification". JASA *61*, 1622–1629.

Clinch, P.G., Troup, G.J. and Harris, L. (1982) "The importance of vocal tract resonance in clarinet and saxophone performance; a preliminary account". Acustica *50*, 280–282.

Cogan, R. (1984) "New Images of Musical Sound". Cambridge, Mass.: Harvard University Press.

Collins, P. (1976) "How to Play the Guitar". Sydney: Summit Books.

Coltman, J.W. (1966) "Resonance and sounding frequencies of the flute". JASA *40*, 99–107.

Coltman, J.W. (1968(a)) "Acoustics of the flute". Physics Today *21*, 25–32.

Coltman, J.W. (1968(b)) "Sounding mechanism of the flute and organ pipe". JASA *44*, 983–992.

Coltman, J.W. (1971) "Effect of material on flute tone quality". JASA *52*, 520–523.

Coltman, J.W. (1973) "Mouth resonance effects in the flute". JASA *54*, 417–420.

Coltman, J.W. (1976(a)) "Jet drive mechanisms in edge tones and organ pipes". JASA *60*, 725 - 733.

Coltman, J.W. (1976(b)) "Flute scales, pitch and intonation". The Instrumentalist, May issue, 1–4.

Coltman, J.W. (1979) "Acoustical analysis of the Boehm flute". JASA *65* 499–506.

Cooke, D. (1959) "The Language of Music". London: Oxford University Press.

Cooper, A. (1980) "The Flute". EB Reproductions, 368 Ladbroke Grove, London W10 4SS.

Copp, E.F. (1916) "Musical ability". Journal of Heredity *7*, 297–305.

Cremer, L. (1981) "The Physics of the Violin". Cambridge, Mass.: M.I.T. Press.

Crombie, D. (1982) "The Complete Synthesizer". London: Omnibus Press.

Crombie, D. (1984) "The Synthesizer and Electronic Keyboard Handbook". London: Dorling Kindersley.

Crossley-Holland (1970) "The music of the Tantric Rituals of Gyume and Gyoto". *In* Notes to the recording, "The Music of Tibet: The Tantric Rituals", Anthology AST–4005. New York: Anthology.

Crowhurst, N. (1975) "Electronic Musical Instruments". Slough, Bucks., U.K.: Foulsham-Tab Ltd.

Cuddy, L.L. (1971) "Absolute judgement of musically related pure tones". Can. J. Psychology *25*, 42–55.

Del Mar, N. (1983) "Anatomy of the Orchestra". Rev. ed. London: Faber and Faber.

Deutsch, D. (1982) "Grouping mechanisms in music". *In* "The Psychology of Music", *ed*. D. Deutsch, Ch. 4. New York: Academic.

Dick, R. (1978) "The Other Flute" Vol. 1. U.S.A.: Edu-tainment Publishing Co.

Dobbins, P.F. (1984) "A new approach to simulating the Leslie speaker". Proc. Inst. of Acoustics. Acoustics '84 Swansea, 129–135.

Donington, R. (1970) "The Instruments of Music". 3rd ed. Edinburgh: Constable.

Downey, P. (1984) "The Renaissance slide trumpet: fact or fiction?". Early Music *12*, 26–33.

Drobish, M.W. (1855) "Über musikalische Tonbestimmung und Temperatur". Abhandl.Math. Phys. Kl. Konigl. Sachs, Gess. Wiss. *4*, 1–120.

Dunlop, J.I. (1984) "Flexural vibrations of the triangle". Acustica *55*, 250–253.

Egan, J.P. and Hake, H.W. (1950) "On the masking pattern of a simple auditory stimulus". JASA *22*, 622-630. *Repr. in* Schubert (1979).

Elliott, S.J. (1979) "Non-linear regeneration mechanisms in wind instruments". Journal de Physique *40* (C8), 341–345.

Elliott, S.J. and Bowsher, J.M. (1982) "Regeneration in brass wind instruments". JSV *83*, 181–217.

Elliott, S.J., Bowsher, J.M. and Watkinson, P. (1982) "Input and transfer response of brass wind instruments". JASA *72*, 1747–1760.

Ernst, D. (1977) "The Evolution of Electronic Music". New York: Schirmer.

Evans, E.F. (1975) "Cochlear nerve and cochlear nucleus". *In* "Handbook of Sensory Physiology", *ed.* W.D. Keidel and W.D. Neff, Vol. V/2, Ch. 1. Berlin: Springer.

Fairley, A. (1982) "Flutes, Flautists and Makers". London: Pan Educational Music.

Fant, G. (1970) "Acoustic Theory of Speech Production". The Hague: Mouton.

Fant, G. (1972) "Vocal tract wall effects, losses, and resonance bandwidths". STL-QPSR 2-3/1972 (KTH Stockholm) pp. 28–52.

Farnsworth, D.W. (1940) "High speed motion pictures of the human vocal cords". Bell Lab. Rev. *18*(7), 203–208.

Fearn, R.W. (1975(a)) "Level limits on pop music". JSV *38*, 501–502.

Fearn, R.W. (1975(b)) "Level measurements of music". JSV *43*, 588–591.

Firth, I.M. (1976(a)) "A method of adjusting the pitch of top and back plates of the cello". Acustica *36*, 307–312.

Firth, I.M. (1976(b)) "Mechanical admittance measurements on the sound post of the violin, and its action". Acustica *36*, 332–339.

Firth, I.M. (1977(a)) "Physics of the guitar at the Helmholtz and first top plate resonances". JASA *61*, 588–593.

Firth, I.M. (1977(b)) "On the acoustics of the harp". Acustica *37*, 148–154.

Firth, I.M. (1978) "Action of the cello at the wolf note". Acustica *39*, 252–263.

Firth, I.M. (1984) "Acoustics of the harp". Proc. Inst. of Acoustics. Acoustics '84 Swansea, 55–64.

Firth, I.M. and Sillitto, H.G. (1978) "Acoustics of the Highland bagpipe". Acustica *40*, 310–315.

Fischer, H.G. (1984) "The Renaissance Sackbut and its Use Today". New York: Metropolitan Museum of Art.

Fisher, J. (1975) "Piano Tuning: a simple and accurate method for amateurs". New York: Dover Publications.

Flanagan, J.L. (1972) "Speech Analysis, Synthesis and Perception". 2nd ed. New York: Springer.

Fletcher, H. (1924) "The physical criterion for determining the pitch of a musical tone". Phys. Rev. *23*, 427–437. *Repr. in* Schubert (1979).

Fletcher, H. (1930) "A space time pattern theory of hearing". JASA *1*, 311–343.

Fletcher, H. (1940) "Auditory patterns". Rev. Mod. Phys. *12*, 47–65. *Repr. in* Schubert (1979).

Fletcher, H. (1953) "Speech and Hearing in Communication". New York: Van Nostrand.

Fletcher, H. (1964) "Normal vibration frequencies of a stiff piano string". JASA *36*, 203–209.

Fletcher, H. and Basset, I.G. (1978) "Some experiments with the bass drum". JASA *64*, 1570–1576.

Fletcher, H. and Munson, W.A. (1933) "Loudness, its definition, measurement and calculation". JASA *5*, 82–108.

Fletcher, H. and Munson, W.A. (1937) "Relation between loudness and masking". JASA *9*, 1–10.

Fletcher, H. and Sanders, L.C. (1967) "Quality of violin vibrato tones". JASA *41*, 1534–1544.

Fletcher, N.H. (1974(a)) "Some acoustical principles of flute technique". The Instrumentalist Vol. *28(7)*, 57–61.

Fletcher, N.H. (1974(b)) "Nonlinear interactions in organ flue pipes". JASA *56*, 645–652.

Fletcher, N.H. (1975) "Acoustical correlates of flute performance technique". JASA *57*, 233–237.

Fletcher, N.H. (1976) "Sound production by organ flue pipes". JASA *60*, 926–936.

Fletcher, N.H. (1977(a)) "Analysis of the design and performance of harpsichords". Acustica *37*, 139–147.

Fletcher, N.H. (1977(b)) "Scaling rules for organ flue pipe ranks". Acustica *37*, 131–138.

Fletcher, N.H. (1978) "Mode locking in nonlinearly excited inharmonic musical oscillators". JASA *64*, 1566–1569.

Fletcher, N.H. (1979) "Excitation mechanisms in woodwind and brass instruments". Acustica *43*, 63–72.

Fletcher, N.H. and Douglas, L.M. (1980) "Harmonic generation in organ pipes, recorders, and flutes". JASA *68*, 767–771.

Fletcher, N.H., Silk, R.K. and Douglas, L.M. (1982) "Acoustic admittance of air-driven reed generators". Acustica *50*, 155–159.

Fletcher, N.H. and Thwaites, S. (1979) "Wave propagation on an acoustically perturbed jet". Acustica *42*, 323–334.

Fletcher, N.H. and Thwaites, S. (1983) "The physics of organ pipes". Scientific American, January, 84–93.

Flugrath, J.M. (1969) "Modern-day rock-and-roll music and damage-risk criteria". JASA *45*, 704–711.

Freeman, W.F., Murphy, P.V. and Ferran, R.J. (1973) "Electrets in miniature microphones". JASA *53*, 1601–1608.

French, A.P. (1971) "Vibrations and Waves". New York: Norton.

Furrer, W. and Lauber, A. (1953) "The accuracy of reverberation time measurements with warble tones and white noise". JASA *25*, 90–91.

Gabrielssohn, A. and Jansson, E.V. (1979) "Long-time-average-spectra and rated qualities of twenty-two violins". Acustica *42*, 47–55.

Galambos, R. and Davis, H. (1943) "The response of single auditory-nerve fibres to acoustic stimulation". J. Neurophysiology *6*, 39–57.

Galpin, F.W. (1906) "The sackbut, its evolution and history". Proceedings of the Musical Association, *33*, 1–25.

George, W.H. (1954) "A sound reversal technique applied to the study of tone quality". Acustica *4*, 224–225.

Giacomo, P. (1983) "The new definition of the metre". Eur. J. Phys. *4*, 190–197.

Goldstein, J.L. (1973) "An optimum processor theory for the central formation of the pitch of complex tones". JASA *54*, 1496–1516.

Gouch, E. (1922) "The effects of practice on judgments of absolute pitch". Archives of Psychology *7*, No. 47, 93.

Graham, B. (1980) "Music and the Synthesizer". Watford, Herts., U.K.: Angus Books.

Gray, D.E. (*ed.*) (1972) "American Institute of Physics Handbook". 3rd ed. New York: McGraw Hill.

Green, D.M. and Swets, J.A. (1966) "Signal Detection Theory and Psychophysics". New York: Wiley.

Greenhough, M. (1984) "A real-time stochastic melody generating system". Proc. Inst. of Acoustics. Acoustics '84 Swansea, 47–53.

Greenwood, D.D. (1971) "Aural combination tones and auditory masking". JASA *50*, 502–543.

Grey, J.M. (1977) "Multidimensional perceptual scaling of musical timbres". JASA *61*, 1270–1277.

Grey, J.M. and Moorer, J.A. (1977) "Perceptual evaluation of synthesized musical instrument tones". JASA *62*, 454–462.

Hacklinger, M. (1978) "Violin timbre and bridge frequency response". Acustica *39*, 323–330.

Hall, D.E. (1980) "Musical Acoustics, an introduction". Belmont: Wadsworth.

Hall, J.C. (1955) "Effect of the oral and pharyngeal cavities on trumpet tone quality". JASA *27, 996*.

Hammond, R. (1983) "The Musician and the Micro". Poole, Dorset, U.K.: Blandford Press.

Harris, C. (1979) "Handbook of Noise Control". 2nd ed. New York: McGraw Hill.

Hassall, J.R. and Zaveri, K. (1979) "Acoustic Noise Measurements". 4th ed. Naerum, Denmark: Bruel and Kjaer.

Helmholtz, H.L.F. von (1863) "Die Lehre von den Tonempfindungen als Physiologische Grundlage für die Theorie der Musik". Braunschweig: Vieweg. *Transl.* Ellis, A.J. (1885), "On the Sensations of Tone as a Physiological Basis for the Theory of Music", *repr.* New York: Dover (1954).

Holtzman, S.R. (1980) "Generative grammars and the computer-aided composition of music". Ph.D. thesis, University of Edinburgh.

Houtgast, T. (1974) "Lateral suppression in hearing". Doctoral dissertation, Free University of Amsterdam.

Houtgast, T. (1976) "Subharmonic pitches of a pure tone at low S/N ratio". JASA *60*, 405–409.

Houtsma, A.J.M. and Goldstein, J.L. (1972) "The central origin of the pitch of complex tones: evidence from musical interval recognition". JASA *51*, 520–529.

Howe, H.S. (1975) "Electronic Music Synthesis". New York: Norton; London: Dent.

Hundley, T.C., Benioff, H. and Martin, D.W. (1978) "Factors contributing to the multiple rate of piano tone decay". JASA *64*, 1303–1309.

Hutchins, C.M. (1962) "The physics of violins". Scientific American, November, 78–93. *Repr. in* Hutchins (1978).

Hutchins, C.M. (*ed.*) (1975) "Benchmark Papers in Acoustics. Vol. 5: Musical Acoustics, Part I: Violin Family Components". Stroudsburg, Pennsylvania: Dowden, Hutchinson and Ross.

Hutchins, C.M. (*ed.*) (1976) "Benchmark Papers in Acoustics. Vol. 6: Musical Acoustics, Part II: Violin Family Functions". Stroudsburg, Pennsylvania: Dowden, Hutchinson and Ross.

Hutchins, C.M. (*ed.*) (1978) "The Physics of Music: readings from Scientific American". San Francisco: Freeman.

Hutchins, C.M., Hopping, A.S. and Saunders, F.A. (1960) "Subharmonics of plate tap tones in violin acoustics". JASA *32*, 1443–1449.

Hutchins, C.M. and Stetson, K.A. (1971) "Hologram interferometry applied to violin plates and compared with an acoustical test method". Proc. 7th International Congress on Acoustics, Budapest, *3*, 601–604.

Ishizaka, K. and Flanagan, J.L. (1972) "Synthesis of voiced sounds from a two-mass model of the vocal cords". Bell System Tech. J. *51*, 1233–1268.

Itokawa, H. and Kumagai, C. (1952) "On the study of violin and its making". Report of the Institute of Industrial Science, Univ. of Tokyo, *3*(1), 5–19. *Transl. in* Hutchins (1975).

Jansson, E.V. (1976) "Long-time-average-spectra applied to analysis of music. Part III: A simple method for surveyable analysis of complex sound sources by means of a reverberation chamber". Acustica *34*, 275–280.

Jansson, E.V. (1977) "Acoustical properties of complex cavities. Prediction and measurements of resonance properties of violin-shaped and guitar-shaped cavities". Acustica *37*, 211–221.

Jansson, E.V. and Benade, A.H. (1974) "On plane and spherical waves in horns with non-uniform flare. II. Prediction and measurements of resonance frequencies and radiation losses". Acustica *31*, 185–202. *Repr. in* Kent (1977).

Jansson, E.V. and Sundberg, J. (1975) "Long-time-average-spectra applied to analysis of music. Part I: Method and general applications". Acustica *34*, 15–19.

Jeans, J. (1938) "Science and Music". Cambridge University Press.

Jeffress, L.A. (1975) "Localization of sound". *In* "Handbook of Sensory Physiology", *ed.* W.D. Keidel and W.D. Neff, Vol. V/2, Ch. 10. Berlin: Springer.

Jenkins, J. and Smith, J. (1975) "Electronic Music, a practical manual for musicians". London: David and Charles.

Jesteadt, W., Wier, C.C. and Green, D.M. (1977) "Intensity discrimination as a function of frequency and sensation level". JASA *61*, 169–177.

Johnstone, B.M. and Boyle, A.J.F. (1967) "Basilar membrane vibration examined with the Mössbauer technique". Science *158*, 389–390.

Kagel, M. (1962) "Sexteto de cuerdos". London: Universal.

Kaye, G.W.C. and Laby, T.H. (1966) "Tables of Physical and Chemical Constants". 13th ed. London: Longmans.

Kuriyawaga, M. and Kameoka, A. (1966) "P.S.E. tracing method for subjective harmonics measurement and monaural phase effect on timbre". JASA *39*, 1263.

Keefe, D.H. and Benade, A.H. (1983) "Wave propagation in strongly curved ducts". JASA *74*, 320–332.

Kellner, H.A. (1980) "The tuning of my harpsichord". Frankfurt am Main: Verlag Das Musikinstrument.

Kent, E.L. (1961) "Wind instrument of the cup-mouthpiece type". U.S. Patent No. 2,987,950 (June 13th 1961). *Repr. in* Kent (1977).

Kent, E.L. (1965) "Influence of irregular patterns in the inharmonicity of piano tone partials upon tuning practice". Dokumentation Europiano Kongress Berlin. *Repr. in* Kent (1977).

Kent, E.L. (*ed.*) (1977) "Benchmark Papers in Acoustics. Vol. 9: Musical Acoustics: Piano and Wind Instruments". Stroudsburg, Pennsylvania: Dowden, Hutchinson and Ross.

Kiang, N.Y.S., Watanabe, T., Thomas, E.C. and Clark, L.F. (1965) "Discharge Patterns of Single Fibres in the Cat's Auditory Nerve". Cambridge, Mass.: MIT Press.

Kinsler, L.E., Frey, A.R., Coppens, A.B. and Sanders, J.V. (1982) "Fundamentals of Acoustics". 3rd ed. New York: Wiley.

Kirby, P.R. (1930) "The Kettle-drums". Oxford.

Kirk, R.E. (1959) "Tuning preferences for piano unison groups". JASA *31*, 1644–1648.

Knaus, H.D. and Yeager, W.J. "Vibrations of the walls of a cornett". JASA *13*, 160–162.

Knudsen, V.O. (1963) "Architectural acoustics". Scientific American, November, 78–95. *Repr. in* Hutchins (1978).

Krell, J. (1973) "Kincaidiana. A flute player's notebook". New York: Anderson, Ritchie and Simon.

Kryter, K.D. (1973) "Impairment to hearing from exposure to noise" (and following critiques). JASA *53*, 1211–1252.

Ladefoged, P., Harshman, R., Goldstein, L. and Rice, L. (1978) "Generating vocal tract shapes from formant frequencies". JASA *64*, 1027–1035.

Lawergren, B. (1983) "Harmonics of S motion of bowed strings". JASA *73*, 2174–2179.

Lawson, B. and Lawson, W. (1985) "Acoustical characteristics of annealed French horn bell flares". JASA *77*, 1913–1916.

Lee, A.R. and Rafferty, M.P. (1983) "Longitudinal vibrations in violin strings". JASA *74*, 1361–1365.

Leguy, J. (1979) "Some reflections on the acoustics of the cornett". Cornett and Sackbut *1*, 42–49.

Lenihan, J.M.A. and McNeil, S. (1954) "An acoustical study of the Highland bagpipe". Acustica *4*, 231–232.

Leppington, F.G. (1982) "On the theory of woodwind finger holes". JSV *83*, 521–532.

Lewis, D. and Cowan, M. (1936) "Influence of intensity on the pitch of violin and cello tones". JASA *8*, 20–22.

Licklider, J.C.R. (1951) "Basic correlates of the auditory stimulus". *In* "Handbook of Experimental Psychology", ed. S.S. Stevens. New York: Wiley.

Licklider, J.C.R. (1954) "'Periodicity pitch' and 'place pitch'". JASA *26*, 945(A).

Lindblom, B.E.F. and Sundberg, J. (1971) "Acoustical consequences of lip, tongue, jaw and larynx movement". JASA *50*, 1166–1179.

Løkberg, O.L. and Ledang, O.K. (1984) "Vibration of flutes studied by electronic speckle pattern interferometry". Applied Optics *23*, 3052–3056.

Lurton, X. (1981) "Étude analytique de l'impédance d'entrée des instruments à embouchure". Acustica *49*, 142–151.

Maconie, R. and Cunningham, C. (1982) "Computers unveil the shape of melody". New Scientist, *94*, 206–209.

Mangeot, A. (1953) "Violin Technique". London: Dobson.

Manning, P. (1985) "Electronic and Computer Music". Oxford: Clarendon Press.

Martin, D.W. (1942) "Lip vibrations in a cornet mouthpiece". JASA *13*, 305–308. *Repr. in* Kent (1977).

Martin, D.W. (1947) "Decay rates of piano tones". JASA *19*, 535–541.

Mayer, A.M. (1876) "Researches in acoustics". Phil. Mag. *2*, 500–507. *Repr. in* Schubert (1979).

McGee, J., Walsh, E.J. and Javel, E. "Intensity coding in the auditory nerve". JASA *76*, S4.

McIntyre, M.E. and Woodhouse, J. (1984) "A parametric study of the bowed string: the violinist's menagerie". Proc. Inst. of Acoustics. Acoustics '84 Swansea, 115–121.

Mercer, D.M.A. (1953) "The physics of organ flue pipes". Am. J. Phys. *21*, 376–386.

Mercer, D.M.A. (1954) "The effect of voicing adjustments on the tone quality of organ flue pipes". Acustica *4*, 237–239.

Meyer, E. and Neumann, E.G. (1972) "Physical and Applied Acoustics". New York: Academic.

Meyer, J. (1978) "Acoustics and the Performance of Music". Frankfurt am Main: Verlag Das Musikinstrument.

Meyer, M. (1899) "Is the memory of absolute pitch capable of development by training?" Psychol. Rev. *6*, 514–516.

Miller, J.D. (1974) "Effects of noise on people". JASA *56*, 729–764. *Repr. in* "Handbook of Perception", *ed.* E.C. Carterette and M.P. Friedman, Vol. IV. Chs. 14–16. New York: Academic.

Møller, A.R. (1974) "The acoustic middle ear muscle reflex". *In* "Handbook of Sensory Physiology", *ed.* W.D. Keidel and W.D. Neff, Vol. V/1 Ch. 16. Berlin: Springer.

Moore, G. (1962) "Am I too Loud? Memoirs of an accompanist". London: Hamilton.

Morgan, D.E. and Dirks, D.D. (1975) "Influence of middle ear contraction on pure-tone suprathreshold loudness judgements". JASA *57*, 411–420.

Morley, T. (1599) "First Book of Consort Lessons", *ed.* S. Beck. London: Peters (1959).

Morley-Pegge, R. (1960) "The French Horn". London: Ernest Benn.

Morse, P.M. (1948) "Vibration and Sound". 2nd Ed. New York: McGraw-Hill.

Morse, P.M. and Bolt, R.H. (1944) "Sound waves in rooms". Rev. Mod. Phys. *16*, 69–150.

Munrow, D. (1976) "Instruments of the Middle Ages and Renaissance". London: Oxford University Press.

Nederveen, C.J. (1967) "Hole calculations for an oboe". Acustica *18*, 47–57.

Nederveen, C.J. (1969) "Acoustical Aspects of Woodwind Instruments". Amsterdam: Knuf.

Nelson, D.A., Stanton, M.E. and Freyman, R.L. (1983) "A general equation describing frequency discrimination as a function of frequency and sensation level". JASA *73*, 2117–2123.

New Oxford Companion to Music (1983). Oxford University Press.

Nordmark, J.O. (1978) "Frequency and periodicity analysis". *In* "Handbook of Perception", *ed.* E.C. Carterette and M.P. Friedman, Vol. IV Ch. 7. New York: Academic.

Ohgushi, K. (1983) "The origin of tonality and a possible explanation of the octave enlargement phenomenon". JASA *73*, 1694–1700.

Olson, H.F. (1967) "Music, Physics and Engineering". 2nd ed. New York: Dover.

Padgham, C. (1986) "The scaling of the timbre of the pipe organ" Acustica *60*, 189–204.

Parkin, P.H. (1965) "On the accuracy of simple weighting networks for loudness estimates of some urban noises". JSV 2, 86–88.

Parkin, P.H., Allen, W.A., Purkis, H.J. and Scholes, W.E. (1953) "The acoustics of the Royal Festival Hall, London". JASA *25*, 246–259.

Parkin, P.H. and Morgan, K. (1970) "Assisted resonance in the Royal Festival Hall, London". JASA *48*, 1025–1035.

Patterson, B. (1974) "Musical dynamics". Scientific American, November, 78–95.

Patterson, R.D. (1969) "Noise masking of a change in residue pitch". JASA *45*, 1520–1524.

Pierce, J.R. (1983) "The Science of Musical Sound". New York: Freeman.

Plomp, R. (1964) "The ear as a frequency analyser". JASA *36*, 1628–1636.

Plomp, R. (1967) "Pitch of complex tones". JASA *41*, 1526–1533.

Plomp, R. (1970) "Timbre as a multidimensional attribute of complex tones". *In* "Frequency Analysis and Periodicity Detection in Hearing", *ed.* R. Plomp and G.F. Smoorenburg, pp. 397–414. Leiden: Sijthoff.

Plomp, R. (1976) "Aspects of Tone Sensation". London: Academic.

Plomp, R. and Steeneken, H.J.M. (1973) "Place dependence of timbre in reverberant sound fields". Acustica *28*, 50–59.

Pollard, H.F. and Jansson, E.V. (1982(a)) "A tristimulus method for the specification of musical timbre". Acustica *51*, 162–171.

Pollard, H.F. and Jansson, E.V. (1982(b)) "Analysis and assessment of musical starting transients". Acustica *51*, 250–262.

Praetorius, M. (1619) "Syntagma Musicum". Wolfenbüttel. *Transl.* H. Blumenfeld, 2nd ed. New York: Bärenreiter (1962).

Preis, A. (1984) "An attempt to describe the parameter determining the timbre of steady-state harmonic complex tones". Acustica *55*, 1–13.

Pyle, R.W., Jnr. (1975) "Effective length of horns". JASA *57*, 1309–1317.

Pyle, R.W., Jnr. (1981) "The effect of lacquer and silver plating on horn tone". Horn Call *11(2)*, 26–29.

Rasch, R.A. and Plomp, R. (1982) "The perception of musical tones". *In* "The Psychology of Music", *ed.* D. Deutsch, Ch. 1. New York: Academic.

Rayleigh, J.W.S. (1879) "Acoustical Observations". Phil. Mag. (5th Series) *7*, 149–162.

Rayleigh, J.W.S. (1894) "The Theory of Sound". 2nd ed. *Repr.* New York: Dover (1945).

Reinicke, W. and Cremer, L. (1970) "Application of holographic interferometry to vibrations of the bodies of string instruments". JASA *48*, 988–992.

Rensch, R. (1969) "The Harp". London: Duckworth.

Revesz, G. (1954) "Introduction to the Psychology of Music". Norman, Oklahoma: Univ. of Oklahoma.

Rhode, W.S. (1971) "Observations of the vibration of the basilar membrane in squirrel monkeys using the Mössbauer technique". JASA *49*, 1218–1231.

Rhode W.S. (1978) "Some observations on cochlear mechanics". JASA *64*, 158–176.

Richardson, B.E. (1983) "The influence of strutting on the top-plate modes of a guitar". Catgut Acoustical Society Newsletter, No. 40, 13–17.

Richardson, B.E. (1984) "Investigations of mode coupling in the guitar". Proc. Inst. of Acoustics. Acoustics '84 Swansea, 65–72.

Richardson, B.E. and Taylor, C. (1983) "Resonance placement in guitars". Proc. 11th International Congress on Acoustics, Paris, *4*, 381–384.

Richardson, E.G. (1929) "The Acoustics of Orchestral Instruments and of the Organ". London: Arnold.

Rigden, J.S. (1977) "Physics and the Sound of Music". New York: Wiley.

Rintelman, W.F., Lindberg, R.F. and Smitley, E.K. (1972) "Temporary threshold shift and recovery patterns from two types of rock and roll music presentation". JASA *51*, 1249–1255.

Risset, J.C. and Mathews, M.V. (1969) "Analysis of musical instrument tones". Physics Today *22*(2), 23–30.

Risset, J.C. and Wessel, D.L. (1982) "Exploration of timbre by analysis and synthesis". *In* "The Psychology of Music", ed. D. Deutsch, Ch.2. New York: Academic.

Ritsma, R.J. (1967) "Frequencies dominant in the perception of the pitch of complex sounds". JASA *42*, 191–198.

Roads, C. (1985) "Composers and the Computer". Los Altos, California: William Kaufmann Inc.

Roads, C. and Strawn, J. (*eds.*) (1985) "Foundations of Computer Music". Cambridge, Mass.: MIT Press.

Roberts, B.L. (1976) "Some comments on the physics of the horn and right-hand technique". Horn Call *6*(2), 41–45.

Robinson, D.W. and Dadson, R.S. (1956) "A re-determination of the equal-loudness relations for pure tones". Brit. J. Appl. Phys. *7*, 166–181.

Roederer, J.G. (1975) "The Physics and Psychophysics of Music". 2nd ed. Berlin: Springer.

Rose, A.S. (1894) "Talks with Bandsmen: a popular handbook for brass instrumentalists". London: William Rider and Son.

Rose, J.E., Brugge, J.F., Anderson, D.J. and Hind, J.E. (1967) "Phase-locked response to low frequency tones in single auditory nerve fibres of the squirrel monkey". J. Neurophysiology *30*, 769–793.

Rossing, T.D. (1976) "Acoustics of percussion instruments – Part I." Physics Teacher *14*, 546-556.

Rossing, T.D. (1977) "Acoustics of percussion instruments – Part II." Physics Teacher *15*, 278-288.

Rossing, T.D. (1982 (a)) "The physics of kettledrums". Scientific American, November, 147–152.

Rossing, T.D. (1982 (b)) "Chladni's law for vibrating plates". Am. J. Phys. *50*, 271–274.

Rossing, T.D., Sundberg, J. and Ternström, S. (1986) "Acoustic comparison of voice use in solo and choir singing". JASA *79*, 1975–1981.

Rubin, H.J., LeCover, M. and Vennard, W. (1967) "Vocal intensity, subglottic pressure and air flow relationships in singers". Folia Phoniat. *19*, 393–413.

Russell, G.A. and Nelson, D.L. (1975) "Reverberation index measurements using a lock-in amplifier". JASA *58*, 1339–1341.

Russell, I.J. and Sellick, P.M. (1977) "The tuning properties of cochlear hair cells". *In* "Psychophysics and Physiology of Hearing", *ed.* E.F. Evans and J.P. Wilson. London: Academic.

Sachs, C. (1940) "A History of Musical Instruments". New York: Norton; London: Dent.

Sachs, C. (1950) "Chromatic trumpets in the Renaissance". Musical Quarterly *36*, 62–66.

Saldanha, E.L. and Corso, J.F. (1964) "Timbre cues and the identification of musical instruments". JASA *36*, 2021–2026.

Saunders, F.A. (1937) "The mechanical action of violins". JASA *9*, 81-98. *Repr. in* Hutchins (1975).

Scharf, B. (1978) "Loudness". *In* "Handbook of Perception", *ed.* E.C. Carterette and M.P. Friedman, Vol. IV, Ch. 6. New York: Academic.

Schelleng, J.C. (1974) "The physics of the bowed string". Scientific American, January, 87–95.

Schouten, J.F. (1938) "The perception of subjective tones". K. ned. Akad. Wet. Proc. *41*, 1086–1093. *Repr. in* Schubert (1979).

Schrader, B. (1982) "Introduction to Electro-Acoustic Music". New Jersey: Prentice-Hall.

Schroeder, M.R. (1974) "Recent advances in hearing research: non-linear mechanics and neural transduction". *In* "Acoustics 1974", *ed.* R.W.B. Stephens. London: Chapman and Hall.

Schroeder, M.R. (1975) "Models of hearing". Proc. IEEE *63*, 1332–1350.

Schubert, E.D. (*ed.*) (1979) "Benchmark Papers in Acoustics. Vol. 13: Psychological Acoustics". Stroudsburg, Pennsylvania: Dowden, Hutchinson and Ross.

Schuck, O.H. and Young, R.W. (1943) "Observations on the vibrations of piano strings". JASA *15*, 1–11.

Sear, W. (1972) "A Guide to Electronic Music and Synthesisers". London: Omnibus.

Seashore, C.E. (1938) "Psychology of Music". New York: McGraw-Hill. *Repr.* New York: Dover (1967).

Sellick, P.M., Patuzzi, R. and Johnstone, B.M. (1982) "Measurement of basilar membrane motion in the guinea pig using the Mössbauer technique". JASA *72*, 131–141.

Shankland, R.S. and Coltman, J.W. (1939) "The departure of the overtones of a vibrating wire from a true harmonic series". JASA *10*, 161–166.

Shepard, R.N. (1982) "Structural representations of musical pitch". *In* "The Psychology of Music", *ed.* D. Deutsch, Ch. 11. New York: Academic.

Shipp, T. and Izdebski, K. (1975) "Vocal frequency and vertical larynx positioning by singers and non-singers". JASA *58*, 1104–1106.

Shivas, A. (1957) "The Art of Tympanist and Drummer". London: Dobson.

Sirker, U. (1974) "Strukturelle Gesetzmässigkeiten in den Spektren von Blasinstrumentenklängen". Acustica *30*, 49–59.

Sivian, L.J., Dunn, H.K. and White, S.D. (1931) "Absolute amplitudes and spectra of certain musical instruments and orchestras". JASA *2*, 330–371.

Sivian, L.J. and White, S.D. (1933) "On minimum audible sound fields". JASA *4*, 288–321. *Repr. (part) in* Schubert (1979).

Small, A.M. (1937) "An objective analysis of violin performance". Univ. of Iowa Studies in the Psychology of Music *4*, 172–231. *Repr. (part) in* Seashore (1938).

Smith, B.J. (1971) "Acoustics". Harlow: Longman.

Smith, H., Stevens, K.N. and Tomlinson, R.S. (1967) "On an unusual mode of chanting by certain Tibetan lamas". JASA *41*, 1262–1264.

Smith, L.A. and Scott, B.L. (1980) "Increasing the intelligibility of sung vowels". JASA *67*, 1795–1797.

Smith, R.A. (1978) "Recent developments in brass design". International Trumpet Guild Journal *3*, 27–29.

Smith, R.A. (1981) "Material vibration and its influence on performance of wind instruments". Proc. Inst. of Acoustics. Paper 4E1, 317–319.

Smith, R.A. (1986) "The effect of material in brass instruments; a review". Proc. Inst. of Acoustics *18*, 91–96.

Smith, R.A. and Daniell, G.J. (1976) "Systematic approach to the correction of intonation in wind instruments". Nature *262*, 761–765.

Smith, R.A. and Mercer, D.M.A. (1974) "Possible causes of woodwind tone colour". JSV *32*, 347–358.

Smithers, D. (1973) "The Music and History of the Baroque Trumpet before 1721". London: Dent.

Smithers, D., Wogram, K. and Bowsher, J. (1986) "Playing the Baroque trumpet". Scientific American, April, 104–111.

Smoorenburg, G.F. (1970) "Pitch perception of two-frequency stimuli". JASA *48*, 924–942.

Snow, W.B. (1936) "Changes of pitch with loudness at low frequencies". JASA *8*, 14–19.

Sondhi, M.M. (1975) "Measurement of the glottal waveform". JASA *57*, 228–232.

Sorge, G.A. (1745) "Vorgemach der Musikalischen Composition". Lobenstein: Verlag des Autoris.

Stevens, S.S. (1935) "The relation of pitch to intensity". JASA *6*, 150–154.

Stevens, S.S. (1936) "A scale for the measurement of a psychological magnitude: loudness". Psychol. Rev. *43*, 405–416. *Repr. in* Schubert (1979).

Stevens, S.S. (1955) "The measurement of loudness". JASA *27*, 815–829.

Stevens, S.S. (1972) "Perceived level of noise by mark VII and decibels (E)". JASA *51*, 575–601.

Stevens, S.S. and Davis, H. (1938) "Hearing – It's Psychology and Physiology". New York: Wiley.

Stevens, S.S., Volkmann, J. and Newman, E.B. (1937) "A scale for the measurement of the psychological magnitude pitch". JASA *8*, 185–190. *Repr. in* Schubert (1979).

Strange, A. (1972) "Electronic Music". Dubuque: Brown Company.

Stumpf, C. (1883) "Tonpsychologie". Leipzig: Herzel.

Stumpf, C. (1926) "Die Sprachlaute". Berlin: Springer.

Sundberg. J. (1973) "The source spectrum in professional singing". Folia Phoniat. *25*, 71–90.

Sundberg, J. (1974) "Articulatory interpretation of the 'singing formant'". JASA *55*, 838–844.

Sundberg, J. (1975) "Formant technique in a professional female singer". Acustica *32*, 89–96.

Sundberg, J. (1977) "The acoustics of the singing voice". Scientific American, March, 82–91.

Sundberg, J. (1979) "Chest vibrations in singers". STL–QPSR 1/1979, pp. 49–64.

Sundberg. J. (1981) "Formants and fundamental frequency control in singing. An experimental study of coupling between vocal tract and voice source". Acustica *49*, 47–54.

Sundberg, J. and Jansson, E.V. (1976) "Long-time-average-spectra applied to analysis of music. Part II: An analysis of organ stops". Acustica *34*, 269–274.

Swindale, O. (1962) "Polyphonic Composition". Oxford University Press.

Tartini, G. (1754) "Trattato di Musica Secondo la Vera Scienza dell' Armonia". Padua: Manfré.

Tasaki, I. (1954) "Nerve impulses in individual auditory nerve fibres of guinea pig". J. Neurophysiology *17*, 97–122.

Taylor, C.A. (1966) "The Physics of Musical Sounds". English Universities Press.

Taylor, C.A. (1976) "Sounds of Music". London: British Broadcasting Corporation.

Taylor, H.W. (1964) "Art and Science of the Timpani". London: Baker.

Taylor, R. (1979) "Noise". 3rd ed. Harmondsworth: Penguin.

Terhardt, E. (1971 (a)) "Die Tonhöhe harmonischer Klänge und das Octavinterval". Acustica 24, 126–136.

Terhardt, E. (1971 (b)) "Pitch shifts of harmonics. An explanation of the octave enlargement phenomenon". Proc, 7th International Congress on Acoustics, Budapest, 3, 621–624.

Terhardt, E. (1974 (a)) "On the perception of periodic sound fluctuations (roughness)". Acustica 30, 201–213.

Terhardt, E. (1974 (b)) "Pitch, consonance and harmony". JASA 55, 1061–1069.

Terhardt, E. and Fastl, H. (1971) "Zum Einfluss von Störtönen und Störgeräuschen auf die Tonhöhe von Sinustönen. Acustica 25, 53–61.

Terhardt, E. and Ward, W.D. (1982) "Recognition of musical key: Exploratory study". JASA 72, 26–33.

Titze, I.R. (1983) "The Vocal instrument viewed from a materials science point of view". JASA 73, S72.

Titze, I.R. and Strong, W.J. (1975) "Normal modes in vocal cord tissues". JASA 57, 736–744.

Troup, G.J. (1981) "The physics of the singing voice". Physics Reports 74, 379–401.

Tzekakis, E. (1979) "Data on the acoustics of Byzantine churches of Thessaloniki". Acustica 43, 275–279.

U.S.A. Standards Institute (1960) "American Standard Acoustical Terminology, S1.1–1960". New York: USA Standards Institute.

Vennard, W. (1967) "Singing – the Mechanism and the Technic". New York: Fischer.

Vernon, P.E. (1977) "Absolute pitch: A case study". Br. J. Psychol. 68, 485–489.

Vitruvius (1960) "The Ten Books on Architecture". Transl. M.H. Morgan. New York: Dover.

Walliser, K. (1969 (a)) "Über die Abhängigkeiten der Tonhöhenempfindung von Sinustönen vom Schallpegel, von überlagertem drosselndem Störschall und von der Darbietungsdauer". Acustica *21*, 211–221.

Walliser, K. (1969 (b)) "Zusammenhänge zwischen dem Schallreiz und der Periodentonhöhe". Acustica *21*, 319–329.

Walliser, K. (1969 (c)) "Zur Unterschiedsschwelle der Periodentonhöhe". Acustica *21*, 329–336.

Wang, Shi–Gian (1983) "The relationship between bright timbre, acoustic features, and larynx position: a comparison of different singing voices". JASA *73*, S73.

Ward, W.D. (1954) "Subjective musical pitch". JASA *26*, 369–380.

Ward, W.D. (1963) "Absolute pitch". Sound *2*, 14–21; 33–41.

Ward, W.D. (1970) "Musical perception". *In* "Foundations of Modern Auditory Theory", *ed.* J. Tobias. New York: Academic.

Ward, W.D. and Burns, E.M. (1982) "Absolute pitch". *In* "The Psychology of Music", *ed.* D. Deutsch, Ch. 14, pp. 431–451. New York: Academic.

Warren, R.M. (1977) "Subjective loudness and its physical correlate". Acustica *37*, 334–346.

Watkins, A.J. (1985) "Perceptual aspects of synthesized approximations to melody". JASA *78*, 1177–1186.

Watkinson, P.S. and Bowsher, J.M. (1982) "Vibration characteristics of brass instrument bells". JSV *85*, 1–17.

Weast, R. (*ed.*) (1974) "Handbook of Chemistry and Physics". 55th ed. Cleveland: CRC.

Wegel, R.L. and Lane, C.E. (1924) "The auditory masking of one pure tone by another and its probable relation to the dynamics of the inner ear". Phys. Rev. *23*, 266–276. *Repr. in* Schubert (1979).

Weinreich, G. (1977) "Coupled piano strings". JASA *62*, 1474–1483.

Weinreich, G. (1979) "The coupled motions of piano strings". Scientific American, January, 118–127.

Wells, T. (1981) "The Technique of Electronic Music". New York: Schirmer.

Wever, E.G. (1949) "Theory of Hearing". New York: Wiley.

Whitfield, I.C. (1978) "The neural code". *In* "Handbook of Perception", *ed.* E.C. Carterette and M.P. Friedman, Vol. IV, Ch. 5. New York: Academic.

Whittle, L.S. and Robinson, D.W. (1974) "Discotheques and pop music as a source of noise-induced hearing loss. A review and bibliography". NPL Acoustics Report Ac66.

Wick, D. (1984) "Trombone Technique". 2nd ed. Oxford Univerity Press.

Wightman, F.L. (1973) "The pattern-transformation model of pitch". JASA *54*, 407–416.

Winckel, F. (1962) "Optimum acoustic criteria of concert halls for the performance of classical music". JASA *34*, 81–86.

Winckel, F. (1967) "Music, Sound and Sensation". New York: Dover.

Wogram, K. (1979) Paper presented at International Horn Workshop, University of Southern California, Los Angeles (unpublished).

Wood, A. (1962) "The Physics of Music". 6th ed. *rev.* J.M. Bowsher. London: Methuen.

Wood, W.S. and Lipscomb, D.M. (1972) "Maximum available sound pressure levels from stereo components". JASA *52*, 484–487.

Wordsworth, W. (1847) "The Solitary Reaper". *In* "The Poetical Works of Wm. Wordsworth". London: Moxon.

Worman, W.E. (1971) "Self-sustained monlinear oscillations of medium amplitude in clarinet-like systems". Ph.D. Dissertation, Case Western Reserve University, Ann Arbor. University Microfilms (ref. 71-22869).

Wye, T. (1982) "Practice Book for the Flute", Vol. 4. Sevenoaks, U.K.: Novello.

Young, R.W. (1939) "Terminology for logarithmic frequency units". JASA *11*, 134–139.

Young, R.W. (1967) "Optimum lengths of valve tubes for brass wind instruments". JASA *42*, 224–235.

Young, R.W. and Peterson, A. (1969) "On estimating noisiness of aircraft sounds". JASA *45*, 834–838.

Zwicker, E. (1975) "Scaling". *In* "Handbook of Sensory Physiology", *ed.* W.D. Keidel and W.D. Neff, Vol. V/2, Ch. 9. Berlin: Springer.

Zwicker, E., Flottorp, G. and Stevens, S.S. (1957) "Critical bandwidth in loudness summation". JASA *29*, 548–557. *Repr. in* Schubert (1979).

Zwicker, E. and Jaroszewski, A. (1982) "Inverse frequency dependence of simultaneous tone-on-tone masking patterns at low levels". JASA *71*, 1508–1512.

Zwicker, E. and Scharf, B. (1965) "A model of loudness summation". Psychol. Rev. *72*, 3–26.

Zwislocki, J.J. (1978) "Masking: experimental and theoretical aspects of simultaneous, forward, backward and central masking". *In* "Handbook of Perception", *ed.* E.C. Carterette and M.P. Friedman, Vol. IV, Ch. 8. New York: Academic.

Suggestions for further reading

For the reader wishing to pursue the study of musical acoustics in greater depth, we offer here brief comments on a selection of books and collections of papers. Full bibliographical details of the selected works will be found in the list of references.

Backus, J. (1977): *The Acoustical Foundations of Music.*
John Backus is one of the leading researchers in musical acoustics, making this a most authoritative text. Nearly all aspects of the subject are covered, with the emphasis more on the physical understanding of phenomena than on their musical implications.

Benade, A.H. (1976): *Fundamentals of Musical Acoustics.*
Arthur Benade has worked on the acoustics of wind instruments for more than thirty years, and his contributions to the advance of the subject can hardly be overestimated. In this book Benade leads the reader step by step through various branches of musical acoustics, offering many fresh insights along the way. Although little mathematics is used, a fairly serious commitment from the reader is assumed.

Benchmark Papers in Acoustics:
This is the title of a series of volumes containing collections of seminal papers on different aspects of acoustics. Many of these papers are not otherwise readily accessible, and the series is an invaluable source for the serious student of the subject. The volumes relevant to musical acoustics are:
Vol. 5: Hutchins, C.M. (1975): *Violin Family Components.*
Vol. 6: Hutchins, C.M. (1976): *Violin Family Functions.*

Vol. 9: Kent, E.L. (1977): *Piano and Wind Instruments.*
Vol. 13: Schubert, E.D. (1979): *Psychological Acoustics.*

Donington, R. (1970): *The Instruments of Music.*
This widely respected book surveys the whole range of musical instruments from the player's point of view. Only the most elementary acoustical aspects are covered, but the book is very valuable to the reader with a scientific background who wishes to expand his general knowledge of musical instruments.

Hall, D.E. (1980): *Musical Acoustics.*
A relatively up-to-date textbook covering the subject at an elementary level, with many stimulating suggestions for exercises and projects.

Helmholtz, H.L.F. von (1863): *On the Sensations of Tone as a Physiological Basis for the Theory of Music.*
This is one of the classic texts which must not be overlooked by anyone wishing to study the subject seriously. It is quite easy to read, and full of detailed points relating to the perception of musical sounds.

Hutchins, C.M. (1978): *The Physics of Music: Readings from Scientific American.*
Articles in *Scientific American* are aimed at the reader with only a limited scientific background. They are generally written by leading workers in the field, and frequently contain new and important results. Carleen Hutchins has collected in this volume articles on musical topics originally published between 1948 and 1977.

Jeans, J. (1938): *Science and Music.*
A classic textbook of musical acoustics which makes easy and interesting reading. It must, however, be read with caution, since many of the author's early findings, which are described in the book, have more recently been shown to be incorrect.

Meyer, J. (1978): *Acoustics and the Performance of Music.*
This book comprehensively covers the tonal characteristics of the main orchestral instruments, as well as the acoustics of concert halls. It is written with the advanced student in mind, and contains the results of many experiments conducted by the author.

Morse, P.M. (1948): *Vibration and Sound.*
A standard scientific text, written at a fairly advanced level. A good basic knowledge of physics and mathematics is required in order to understand the detailed arguments.

Plomp, R. (1976): *Aspects of Tone Sensation*.
This is useful reading for anyone wishing to delve more deeply into the field of psychoacoustics. It is written by one of the leading researchers in this field, and is pitched at a fairly high academic level.

Rayleigh, J.W.S. (1894): *The Theory of Sound*.
Lord Rayleigh developed much of the basic theory of the radiation of sound from vibrating bodies, and many of his original derivations are lucidly explained in this book.

Sachs, C. (1940): *A History of Musical Instruments*.
One of the best books covering the history and classification of musical instruments from the anthropologist's point of view. It is easy to read, and copiously illustrated.

Taylor, C.A. (1976): *Sounds of Music*.
A useful book written at a very elementary level by an authority on musical acoustics. It has many photographs and little mathematics. The bias is towards physics rather than music.

Index